Conserving
American
Resources

Conserving American Resources

SECOND EDITION

RUBEN L. PARSON

Resource Geographer
Northern Illinois University

Prentice-Hall, Inc.
Englewood Cliffs, N.J.

Library of Congress
Catalog Card No.: 64-10843

PRENTICE-HALL INTERNATIONAL, INC., *London*
PRENTICE-HALL OF AUSTRALIA, PTY., *Sydney*
PRENTICE-HALL OF CANADA, LTD., *Toronto*
PRENTICE-HALL FRANCE, S.A.R.L., *Paris*
PRENTICE-HALL OF INDIA (PRIVATE) LIMITED, *New Delhi*
PRENTICE-HALL OF JAPAN, INC., *Tokyo*
PRENTICE-HALL DE MEXICO, S.A., *Mexico City*

PRINTED IN THE UNITED STATES
OF AMERICA
C-16768

*To all those who have toiled
on my grandfather's homestead,
and especially to Lillian,
this book is dedicated.*

Preface

The gratifying reception of my initial work has warranted publication of this revised volume. Those who deemed the first edition acceptable did, indeed, thereby afford me the privilege of compiling this second edition; and, as token recompense, I tried diligently to honor their suggestions for improving the book. Consensus favored some expansion of content and several changes in topical sequence, but also enjoined against any alteration of style or compromise of philosophy.

In compliance, many sections have been strengthened with new material, relevant statistics, and pertinent illustrations. The chapters have been rearranged so that treatment of each resource category is uninterrupted, and a new chapter dealing with mineral reserves and primary production has been added. The appendix listing sources of current literature has been improved.

A lighter, livelier treatment of a usually serious subject is sometimes justified, especially if it can thereby attract a wider audience without sacrificing its inherent truths and objectives. This seems to apply to conservation and its problems; more busy Americans can and should become interested in the story of our national resources and the ways they can be conserved. For a simple, readable statement of those fundamentals of conservation pertinent to America's major natural resources, all citizens, whether they be laymen, teachers, or novices, are invited to participate in the following discussion.

In our great American democracy the citizen governs; if he would govern well, he must be well informed on issues involving his entire nation, as well as those limited in effect to his own state, county, or community. With these goals in mind, he will find herein a broad survey of his resource heritage by categories, and some ideas for improvement through intelligent conservation. That he may be informed without boredom, and stimulated without misrepresentation, is my purpose and hope.

Acknowledgments

Hundreds of persons contributed to this book in one way or another, and although many must remain anonymous, I am to each profoundly grateful. Especially gratifying was the kindness of those public servants who responded conscientiously to my inquiries.

My work was greatly facilitated by the patronage of Dr. Loren T. Caldwell, Chairman of the Earth Science Department, Northern Illinois University, who reduced my teaching load and accorded me full access to departmental facilities. I owe him a debt of gratitude. It was on Dr. Caldwell's endorsement of my petition that the University executives— the President, Dr. Leslie A. Holmes, and the Provost, Dr. Francis R. Geigle, granted me sabbatical leave during which to conclude this work and muster courage for another. I trust that this volume may be an acceptable token of my appreciation.

For cartographic changes and additions I engaged the talents of three graduate students—John H. Ross, Ronald R. Dilamarter, and Robert L. Weaver. Mr. Ross constructed several special maps.

Mr. Leonard J. Kouba, Graduate Assistant, corrected the addresses in the appendix. Mrs. Carroll Hardy compiled the film sources. Mrs. Judy Barton typed all textual changes and assembled the entire manuscript. For her meticulous work I am especially grateful. I am obliged to several of my cohorts for reading proofs.

My archival sources came largely from the Swen Parson Library, Northern Illinois University, through the kindness of Miss Bernadine C. Hanby, Librarian, Mrs. Margaret Quensel, Secretary to the Librarian, Miss Esther Park, Reference Librarian, Miss Sarah M. Davis, Reserve Librarian, Mr. William Harold Johnson, Documents Librarian, and his secretary, Mrs. Barbara Noon. Since I drew heavily from public records, the help of

Mr. Johnson and Mrs. Noon was most essential, and I am commensurately appreciative.

To my sponsors and deductions—Mary Louise, Ronal, Charles, and Luanne—I owe the confidence, reliance, and encouragement I needed to persist and complete the work. Perhaps Luanne's doting interruptions alleviated tedium and brightened the composition. So I, paternally, would believe!

Ruben L. Parson
De Kalb, Illinois

Contents

1   *The Conservation Idea*   1

2   *Natural Environment and Resources*   14

3   *Water on the Land*   27

4   *Water Conservation*   51

5   *Our Soils and Their Depreciation*   85

6   *Soil Conservation*   121

7   *Spoliation and Restoration of Our Dry Grasslands*   150

8   *Our Forests and Their Exploitation*   174

9   *Forest Conservation*   195

10   *Conservation Patterns on the Land*   234

11 *Wildlife: Functions and Abuses*   271

12 *Wildlife Conservation*   291

13 *Resources for Recreation, Inspiration, and Instruction*   316

14 *Resources of Our Bordering Seas*   352

15 *Mineral Fuels and Major Metals*   393

16 *Mineral Conservation*   428

17 *Prospect and Responsibility*   458

    Teaching Aids   476

    Notes   493

    Index   509

Conserving
American
Resources

1

The
Conservation
Idea

our material culture derives from natural wealth

Conservation is an old theme that has been played many times before, but usually in a somber and depressing key. The present discussion is an optimistic variation on this theme, attempting to transpose from B minor to F major a subject so important to America and Americans that each of us should have a "whistling knowledge" of it. We will not play a dirge to mourn lost possessions, nor concoct a recipe for allaying any imaginary pangs of hunger in a full stomach. We will find no threat of impending poverty and starvation, because America is far removed from both. The arrangement presented here will be neither technical nor exhaustive and will require no special background or training on the part of the reader.

An optimistic viewpoint

What follows is largely an attempt to acquaint thinking Americans with the broad categories of natural wealth upon which their well-being depends. The treatment of each category includes a brief statement of its usefulness, a quick glance at its past history, and several suggestions for getting greater benefit from it in the future. The entire discussion is a development of concepts rather than a recitation of facts; an exhortation to think and participate rather than an exposition on statistics and techniques.

1

Every American owes it to himself to be informed on resources and their conservation. That is our premise. If this volume generates sufficient interest in conservation to prompt further inquiry and action, it will have justified itself. If it arouses real curiosity about their stock interest in the problem among our citizens, especially those quite detached from any kind of primary production, it will have served its main purpose. Only when enough Americans become conversant with the subject of conservation can the democratic process operate to ensure desirable application.

Anyone who reads carefully should acquire enough ideas here to discuss the subject of conservation intelligently. He can then serve himself and his country by imparting that knowledge to others. In so doing, he can become an American "conservator,"

the hero of our story. *Conservationists* are those persons who prescribe, administer, or supervise the various conservation techniques and programs. They are the technical, professional, and practical experts who actually plan and organize the work. The *conservators* mentioned so frequently in this book are the laymen who practice conservation themselves and accept a personal responsibility for improving our use of resources as an obligation of citizenship. They are the informed citizens who awaken a favorable public opinion. They are the voters who support good policies and programs and appropriate the funds necessary to implement them. In a manner of speaking, the conservator, representing the public, employs or sponsors the conservationist by authorizing and financing his work. The conservator "sweeps his own doorstep" as an example for others. He is the decisive factor in determining how well we shall manage our natural wealth. We need many more confirmed conservators, and this discussion is therefore addressed primarily to prospective converts.

The natural resources with which we shall concern ourselves are the basic earth materials—water, soil, plants, animals, and

minerals—that we employ or convert to sustain our material culture. They supply food, clothing, and shelter; fuel for heating, cooking, and lighting; power and raw materials for industry; vehicles and carriers for trade and travel; luxuries and conveniences; machines and medicines; weapons and munitions for national defense; protective coatings and containers; fish lines, shotguns, and baseball bats. They serve us every day of our lives in almost everything we do. They are essential to our existence, and our continued prosperity depends upon the wisdom with which we use them. There is much room for improvement, as we shall see.

Resources differ as to how they are used—and as to what happens to them in the process of consumption. Water comes to the land again and again no matter how badly it is abused each time around. Plants and animals will reproduce and maintain their numbers unless they are very badly treated. Soils can be maintained, and even improved, under productive use. But minerals extracted from the earth serve us only once, although certain metals can be salvaged and re-used before they are spent. Thus, the conservator deals with two great groups of resources, one renewable or *perpetual,* and the other nonrenewable or *fugitive.*

Some resources are perpetual; others serve only once

Minerals, the "one time" servants, have attained pre-eminence in this, the age of technology; but they will surely lose that position as one after another becomes exhausted. As minerals grow scarce, we will gradually lean more and more heavily upon the renewables. Our eventual dependence must be upon those resources which can be used without destroying them. Being consumed by use, minerals are conservable only by more thorough exploitation and more efficient employment.

Our emphasis is on renewable resources, and the book is so organized that they come in logical order. This natural unity is discussed in Chapter 2, and succeeding chapters present the separate categories according to their logical places. Water comes first because it is essential to all the others, including normally developed soil. Secondly come the soils in which the plants grow. Then come the plants (forests and grasslands) that support the animals. And, finally, come the animals (wildlife) that climax the whole progression. Thus the arrangement of our investigation coincides with the natural scheme of things. The discussions in the previous chapters hinge on Chapter 10, wherein the major land resources treated reappear as components in certain patterns of integration. The patterns also incorporate resources considered later on, in Chapters 11 through 16, of which some play secondary roles (wildlife and recreation) and others (minerals) have localized distribution. Chapter 17, which concludes the book, charges the citizen-conservator with a patriotic responsibility by means of which he may envisage for himself, for his children, and for his country, a bright and prosperous future.

Subjects presented in this book follow a natural sequence

Conservation of natural resources means the fullest possible use of them without abusing the ones exploited, without destroying any needlessly, and without neglecting any that can be used. It is not necessarily "conservative" in the ordinary sense of the word. It means thrift, but not denial; frugality, but not privation; efficiency, but not austerity. Nor does "exploitation" as used here mean piracy; exploitation and conservation are not opposites.

Conservation means employment, not idleness, of a resource

Conservation involves exploiting our natural gifts so that they serve us better and longer than they would otherwise. It does not mean hoarding or storing anything for possible use in the future if we can make constructive use of it in the present. It is not a daydreamer's vision for the distant future, but rather the means of immediate and progressive improvement. Conservation concerns us here and now, and its dividends come at once, or within the predictable future. Its application is well advanced; its proceeds already substantial.

We conserve a resource when we make the best use of it, not when we let it be idle. We conserve renewable resources when we use and re-use them without destroying them or overtaxing their regenerative powers. Soils are conserved when they are so tilled that they produce good crops and yet retain their fertility. Forests are conserved when they are so managed that they produce one generation of useful trees after another. Coal is conserved when we burn it in efficient furnaces; not when we leave it in the ground. We conserve the "fugitive" resources by making them do as much work as possible before they expire.

Maximum use and maximum benefit from resources are the objectives of conservation. Frozen assets are of little interest in conservation. Neglect can be quite as wasteful as abuse. In conservation, as in life, there are sins of omission as well as of commission.

Preservation conserves our natural treasures

Preservation has a place in conservation, but only in exceptional phases of it. We conserve natural *treasures,* such as wilderness, geologic wonders, and rare animal species, by restricting their use and protecting them against damage or injury. Aesthetic resources are like prized antiques and heirlooms: displayed with pride, but not used for profit. Their worth is lost, or impaired, unless they be retained in their original state. Thus, conservation excludes them from productive exploitation for material gain. The lofty purpose of conserving wilds and wonders, as discussed in Chapter 13, concerns intangible benefits derived from natural wealth. That is the only chapter in which we shall stress *preservation* as a necessary form of conservation.

Practice versus theory

Sentiment and theory have fostered the conservation movement, but the real test comes with practical application. Many conservation enthusiasts are like new converts to a religion, eager to spread the gospel; but in their enthusiasm they often overlook the practical aspects of a problem. They intone splendid pledges to posterity, committing us to deliver all nature, as a sacred trust, from generation to generation. Sometimes they seem to forget that one generation becomes the ancestor of another, that ances-

tral initiative and progress may be a richer legacy than undeveloped resources. Pity the woodsman who sees in a tree only
board feet and the huntsman who sees in it only a home for
squirrels—but pity also him who sees in it only poetry. We would
not ridicule sentiment, but we would temper it with realism. We
can have board feet and squirrels today and still have trees tomorrow.

Theoretically we might wish that all our streams were so clean
and pure that we might safely drink out of them, but practically
streams cannot be so while people occupy and use the lands they
drain. In this and many other facets of conservation we must
strike a compromise between a theoretical ideal and its practical
feasibility. We could save all our soils by retiring them from use,
but as long as we wish to eat we must conserve soil while employing it to produce food.

For the most part, conservation must pay its own way and show
return on investment. If they must do it at a loss, the miner cannot conserve minerals, the farmer cannot conserve soils, and the
lumberman cannot conserve forests year after year. Conservation
practices that require additional application of work or money
must also bring additional compensation to the operator in a
reasonable time. Those that bring no reward might almost as
well be ignored, because they can have little more than theoretical
value. Conservation must be consistent with economics.

Exploitation of resources produces our wealth and builds our
prosperity, and the profit motive keeps the exploiter going. The
farmer, the logger, the miner, or the fisherman is pleased to
conserve the resource he works, unless thereby he narrows his
margin of profit. If he appears at times to be wasteful and slovenly, it may be because more meticulous practices would increase
his production costs and reduce his income. One cannot pay
wages for the salvage of waste unless that waste can be marketed
profitably. Here, once again, conservation becomes involved with
economics.

*The conservator must distinguish between "material" waste
and "economic" waste,* particularly when he votes for a regulatory measure or chooses a policy. Compulsory salvage of material
waste could easily place such a burden on an operator that he
would change to another pursuit, and leave entirely unexploited
the very resource that the mandate was intended to conserve.
Better that some part of an exploitable resource be wasted than
that all of it be abandoned. It may be better conservation to cut
and sell one log length from a tree and leave the rest of it in the
woods than to abandon the whole tree; better to pump oil from

Exploitation for profit versus salvage of waste

a pool than to leave it in the ground, even though its taking entails the loss of natural gas that cannot be piped to a market profitably. When the branches of the tree and the gas from the oil well can pay their way to a consumer and still are not utilized they become *economic* waste; this is the kind of waste that a conservator need not condone. The methods and arrangements whereby material waste can be converted into economic goods constitute, in fact, a significant problem of conservation. Until we find all the solutions to that problem, we must tolerate many forms of waste incidental to our exploitation and use of natural resources.

Government has a unique responsibility as coordinator and supervisor of conservation programs and policies, but the actual application of conservation practices devolves largely upon private enterprise. Since resources pertain to property, and most of our American property is privately owned, it follows that private citizens and private capital must do a major share of the work.

Especially effective conservators are some of the large corporations so conspicuous in the American scene. The well-organized company, efficiently operated to succeed in open competition, is often our greatest exponent of conservation. Corporate organization implies continuity beyond the life of any individual stockholder. The company can look far ahead and pursue a program that no individual could attempt. There is no time limit on dividends, and the longevity of the company depends upon the endurance of the resource it works.

Where does government come in? Government must be the moderator among competing users, the protector of public interests that conflict with selfish pursuits, and the sponsor of projects that exceed private means. Government is the "benevolent despot" of conservation, and no one else can play that important role. None but the national government could adequately preserve our aesthetic resources. Only government can prescribe and finance conservation of such scope as flood prevention, forest-fire protection, and range restoration. Only government can establish and enforce regulations for cleansing our streams and purifying the air we breathe. Indeed, the function of government in conservation is attested by public conservation agencies at every administrative level—county, city, state, and national. Our progress to date has come largely through publicly constituted agencies. It is our duty as citizens to see that such agencies are properly organized, adequately financed, and headed in the right direction: politics is one of the tools of the conservator.

In conservation as in any worthwhile endeavor, accomplishment becomes commensurate with the planning that precedes the action. The great planning movement that emerged from economic depression in the 1930's gave tremendous impetus to conservation. In 1934 the National Resources Board published an inventory of our natural wealth and a comprehensive set of recommendations based upon the inventory. Those facts and findings are a milepost to both the planners and conservators of today. Economic depression, aggravated by haphazard exploitation, recalled to mind the continuing urgency of conservation, and we determined to plan our future course more carefully than ever before.

Planning sets the course

Planning brought system and direction to conservation and the two ideas often became intimately associated, as they should be. Certainly the planner should be a conservator, and the conservator who would be effective must also be a good planner. Conservation without planning would be like traveling without a map. In Chapter 10 we shall consider the importance of planning to the development and use of land resources.

Ignorance and apathy are the greatest obstacles to conservation. Much waste and abuse of resources stems from inadequate understanding of their nature and importance and from the innocent behavior of well-meaning fools. Many a present-day voter sees no connection between last year's forest fire and this year's flood. Too few New Yorkers appreciate fully how dust storms in Texas can raise the price of steaks in Manhattan or how the draining of marshes can ruin their duck-shooting. This situation can become intolerable in a democracy, where voters are the policy makers.

Our people must be informed

Our people must be informed. Until they are, education will remain a most important conservation activity. The individual American must be shown the advantages accruing to him, personally, before he can be expected to take a real interest in conservation. He must be made to see the light. Where laws and penalties often fail despite rigid enforcement, a genuine appreciation of their purposes might render them quite effective, if not altogether unnecessary. When understanding replaces compulsion, conservation may become a reality.

Since national security is one major objective of conservation, it assumes great importance to the conservator. Conservation bolsters the material means necessary for waging war, and neglect of conservation is usually a price paid for victory. Renewable resources carefully developed during peace for long-range benefits have often become casualties of war. Planned schedules for the best exploitation of minerals have been abandoned when

Our nation must be defended

wars intervened. War disrupts conservation, yet conservation remains a first line of defense.

War is a paradox of terrible destruction and accelerated progress. Its consequences are not entirely negative; on the contrary, war also brings its benefits. The extremes and strains of war compel us to conserve by means we might never adopt except under stress. During an emergency we outdo ourselves in the conservation of scarce materials, and at war's end certain substitutions and other innovations developed to win the war become established peacetime practices. Thus, war, the most wasteful destroyer of resources, helps conserve those it does not consume.

The mention of defense and national security turns our attention to the geographic compass of this book—the United States. Isolationism is neither intended nor implied in the limitation of our subject, but the focus is strictly on America and Americans. We acknowledge that no nation can prosper on our shrunken globe except as a participating member of the international family. We insist that the American member shall be strong at home, and being strong, shall remain helpful and influential abroad. We assert that American wealth, integrity, and vigor are so important in the world that American conservation concerns all freedom-loving peoples everywhere.

National conservation influences international relations

It is not with malice toward our neighbors that we would live well and keep our own house in order; it is simply that we have a good home, and we wish to enjoy it as long as possible. The remainder of this chapter sketches the basic floor plan of our "house" and intimates that the "furnishings" need better care than we have given them.

Our part of the earth was well endowed by nature

That part of the earth which is now the continental United States of America was well endowed by nature. Its middle-latitude location gives much of it a moderate climate, with seasonal rhythm conducive to vigorous human activity. Its massive size imparts to its occupants broad horizons and grand visions. Set betwixt the two great northern oceans, the Atlantic and Pacific, with a warm sea, the Gulf of Mexico, at the south, and a chain of Great Lakes at the north, the main area is readily accessible to world commerce. Within its boundaries is contained a rich variety of landscapes, each with its unique contribution to the whole—high, rugged mountain ranges and broad, lowland plains; subtropical desert and temperate rain forest; windswept grasslands and steaming swamps; quiet lakes, bubbling brooks, and mighty, rolling rivers. The entire federated territory extends poleward beyond the Arctic Circle and southward, in mid-Pacific, to the Tropic of Capricorn—from permafrost to perpetual florescence.

The conservator should be familiar with the physical arrangement and peculiarities of the various regions of the country: geologic; physiographic; climatic; biotic; cultural. He might begin with the "floor-plan" shown in Figs. 1.1, 1.2, and 1.3. Most of the area is sufficiently watered to be highly productive of cultivated plants; availability of sunshine and length of growing season permit a wide choice of crops. Generously dispersed, rich and varied mineral deposits are available for conversion into tools and implements with which to occupy and develop the good land as a home for enlightened people.

To this wonderland of the New World came European seekers of freedom and fortune who, only a few centuries ago, laid the foundation for our great nation of today. Based on incomparable natural wealth and projected by democratic principles, there arose from that foundation the proud nation we now jealously guard, acknowledged by many as the richest, most powerful country on earth.

Fig. 1.1 *Our Alaskan frontier invites modern pioneering. Daily duration of summer sunlight lengthens the short growing season. (After U.S.G.S. map.)*

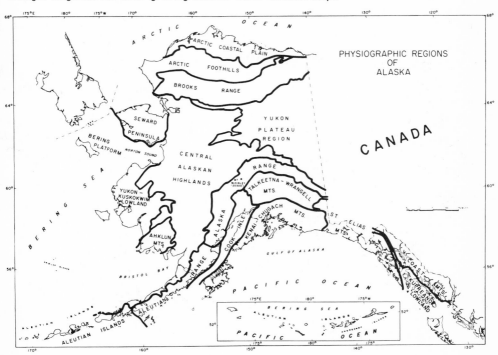

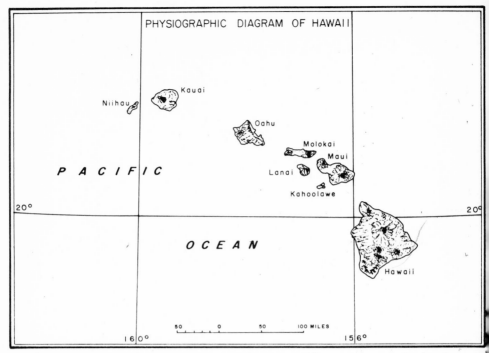

Fig. 1.2 *Our Island State, Hawaii: tropical, marine, and cosmopolitan. Rains drench its windward slopes, but often fail its sheltered valleys.*

Fig. 1.3 *Note the floor plan of our main estate. National planning and conservation must be correlated with regional geography. (After U.S.G.S.)*

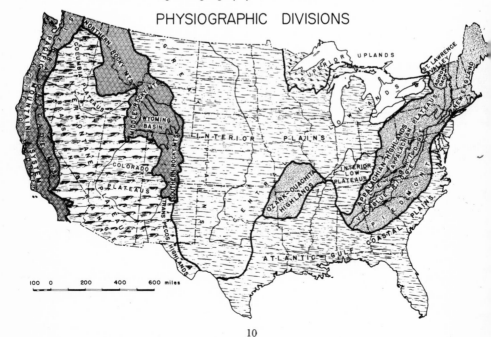

In infancy the nation was immeasurably rich in natural resources appropriate to the traditions and skills of the colonials.
Forests, fish, and game seemed utterly inexhaustible. Fish, furs,
timbers, and naval stores—pitch, turpentine, and so on—were
early American contributions to world trade. The market was
strong, reserves were virtually unlimited, and the commodities
went out as fast as the short manpower and crude methods could
deliver them. Only the best was desirable, and the best was taken
without regard for any destruction incidental to its taking.

Trees, birds, and animals were regarded as natural obstacles
to the white man's advancing dominion; so, he destroyed them
with all means at his command. One wonders whether there
might be a United States of America today had our founding
fathers brought tractors, chain saws, Tommy guns, and steam
trawlers with them. However, their destructive behavior was not
wasteful except as later viewed in retrospect. At the time, circumstances made it expedient and productive. Unfortunately, the
idea outlived its necessity.

Westward expansion of our young, vigorous nation brought
with it a waste of natural wealth no less stupendous than the
historic movement itself. Ax, musket, and plow forced the frontier westward. After organized Indian resistance was broken,
settlement surged across the interior valleys and plains in a few
decades. Killing, clearing, and burning tamed the wilderness and
transformed it into farms, ranches, and towns. In the South the
notorious row crops marched inland under a sort of scorched-
earth policy, leaving mutilated lands in their wake. In New
England the thin upland fields, once laboriously cleared of trees
and stones, reverted to nature when the richer Western lands
sent grain and meat to the Yankee markets. Crumbled stone
walls attest the apparent waste of resources and human energy
which attended their building. When better farm lands in the
Old West changed the use capability of poor fields in New England, those fields reverted to pasture and forest. Economics dictated the adjustment, just as it dictates many of our resource
activities at present.

Should one consider as waste the prodigious expenditure of
natural wealth which accompanied the feverish development of
our country, or should he count the destruction an inevitable
price of precocious national strength? Are not recklessness and
wastefulness normal releases for growing pains? Is the energetic,
ambitious young man also cautious and conservative? Who will
assert that our pioneers were truly wasteful, that they should have

In infancy
our nation
was
immeasurably
rich

Rank waste
salved our
growing pains

bridled their greed and spared the means to quick riches—and postponed our rise to national greatness?

Nations, like people, grow more deliberate and moderate with age. Maturity tempers the rash impetuousness of youth and applies sober judgment to the correction of foolish mistakes. After little more than a hundred years of independence, its expansion and growth unequalled in history, the United States had secured the continent from coast to coast and settled the major areas most suitable for human occupance. The nation had come of age geographically and politically at a fabulous price in natural resources.

With geographic maturity came moderation of extravagance, and a critical examination of depreciated assets. There was no more new land to appropriate as the old wore out. Good trees for lumber were fewer and farther between, streams flowed with less regularity—waters were less transparent—and men could no longer escape the environment they had defaced. The geographic frontier had attained coincidence with geographic boundary. Their spacial limits fixed, Americans turned to new frontiers, more challenging, more rewarding, and infinitely more expansive than any known to the pioneer—the modern frontiers of conservation. The exploration and development of these frontiers will continue to determine the strength and endurance of our nation.

The conservator becomes our contemporary pioneer whose far horizons are the limits of his own imagination. He is not the rugged individualist who blunders about among his fellows; he is the social being who works with his group or community for the common benefit of all its members. He is the kind of leader who advances his society by behaving intelligently himself and by cooperating actively to promote the best group interests.

Conservation becomes part of our social philosophy and is, in turn, fostered by a stronger social consciousness. The two have often developed together, and their closer union will strengthen both in the future. Better use of resources elevates both the individual and the group, both the private citizen and the general public. It must therefore be a collective endeavor, each participant helping his nation while helping himself.

Conservation is not a punitive campaign to regiment the individual. Instead, it is his challenge and opportunity, his hope for a bright future. Every American can be a conservator, and without straining himself unduly. He can acquire the art easily and practice it with distinction. He can begin by using sidewalks to conserve the grass. He can use caution with matches and ciga-

Geographic maturity brought us new frontiers

Individualism yields to society

The practicing conservator

rettes in the woods. He can refrain from throwing trash on the roadsides. He can join an organization that practices or sponsors conservation. He can patronize businessmen who are conservators. He can buy the products of manufacturers who practice conservation. He can turn off a water faucet left running and switch off the light in an empty room. He can vote for men who will promote conservation through public office. He can read and discuss the writings of conservationists and conservators. He can teach others conservation by example—the best possible form of instruction. He can take greater pride in our achievements to date and have even greater confidence in our prospect for the future. He is our hope. We must have faith in him. He is becoming more numerous and more optimistic. Perhaps he will be set on his path by the discussions that follow.

2

Natural Environment and Resources

unity of natural environment and resources demands a unified approach to conservation

Natural resources are essentially parts of the environment to which man adapts himself, often neither wisely nor well, and from which he derives his worldly goods. As his intellect grows and his numbers multiply, his needs become ever greater, and he must of necessity adjust his activities more carefully to accord with natural conditions in order to utilize more efficiently the natural resources available to him. He can achieve such adjustment and utilization only when he comprehends his environment as a whole and recognizes the intricate relationships among its parts. As conservator, he must interpret the relationship and unity of place attributes (qualities of an area, including natural resources) and strive to manipulate them so that each will render optimum service without adverse influence upon another.

As a framework for understanding the unity and interdependence of natural resources, one might best employ the catalog of factors ordinarily taken by earth scientists to compose the natural environment. These basic factors include climate, rock materials and structures, water and drainage, topography, soils, natural vegetation, and native animal life. All are mutually interdependent, though some are qualities and others, resources. The character of one influences the character of the others. A change in one produces, more or less, the modification of all. Therefore the con-

14

servator should understand the concept of composite environment, lest he condone the development of one resource to the detriment of another or fail to enlist the natural interactions at his service. Without that concept his thinking will be piecemeal, and he might be likened to a carpenter who constructs roofs, walls, and floors, and never builds a house.

Among the attributes of place, climate holds high rank; but, it cannot be regarded a natural resource in the ordinary sense, being essentially neither mutable nor destructible. To date, man has wrought no real change in it, nor has he consumed any quantity of it. Yet he cannot escape its influence and he cannot prosper without heeding its dictates as to the accumulation or growth of other types of resources.

Climate: prime attribute of place

Amounts, ratios, and variations of heat and moisture *condition* the disintegration and decomposition of rocks, the formation and development of soils, the shape and arrangement of land forms, the quality, quantity, and availability of water, and the kinds and numbers of plants and animals.

Whereas a favorable combination of sunshine and rain is fundamental to good environment, deficiency of one or the other imposes distinct environmental limitations—cold and drought. Where cold or drought prevails, it reduces or excludes vegetation and causes a desert. It restricts the development of renewable resources and complicates the utilization of the nonrenewable ones, which may exist because of, or despite, climatic adversity. Consider the accumulation of water-soluble minerals in desiccated regions, e.g., the borax in Death Valley. If there were enough rain to grow grass the borax would be washed away.

Neither abundance nor poverty, generation nor exhaustion, conservation nor waste of natural resources can be interpreted intelligently without constant regard for the inevitable, persistent influences of climate.

From the rocks of the earth come our basic raw materials—the elements and their compounds. The rocks are both foundation and source for our surface existence. From the rocks we loosen and raise our minerals and expend them in surface development.

Rocks yield the fundamental raw materials

Under the impacts of sun, wind, and water and the activity of organisms, exposed rock disintegrates into grains and fragments, and decomposes into sand, silt, and clay—parent materials of soil. Soils as we know them could not develop except upon a mineral base, be it solid bedrock or loose gravel.

Rock structures may be regarded as the skeletons of landscape, the foundation of topography. When uplifted, their etching is accomplished by wind and water, agents that are generated by gravity and that reduce high places while filling in low ones. We term the removal of materials etched away *erosion;* the filling of low areas is called *deposition.* Removal, transportation, and deposition are parts of the endless geologic process shaping the earth. Deep in the earth, rock structures confine nature's mineral assets, and by their disposition, determine the ease with which oil pools, ore bodies, and coal seams may be extracted. By their permeability and solubility, rocks contribute to the composition and behavior of both surface and ground waters.

Soils unite the organic with the mineral

Where soil has developed naturally and remains undisturbed, it reflects the whole composite of environmental properties. It combines air and water with mineral and organic materials and forms an entity which helps to sustain life. It has been called the *zone of life,* or *biosphere,* because all life on earth depends upon it, directly or indirectly. Within it and contributing to it are a host of organisms, plant and animal, living and dead. From it spring the higher plants which feed the higher animals; and in due course all these add their substance to it. In youth it resembles its parent rock material; in maturity it conforms to its climatic and topographic situation. Indeed, soils epitomize the entire gamut of environmental factors and functions.

Water is nature's bloodstream

Water permeates every segment of surface environment and influences the character of each. In liquid, solid, or gaseous state it performs unique and vital functions. Streams and glaciers are prime movers among the agents that shape the earth's surface. Another agent, wind, bears water to the stream or glacier but paradoxically loses its own erosive power in proportion to the water delivered. Freezing water helps rend rocks asunder and prepare them for transport from high to low places.

Percolating water is essential in the normal development of soil, and within certain limits soil fertility depends upon moisture content. Plants take their nourishment in solution and starve to death in the absence of water. Water, charged with nutrients dissolved from the soil it helped to form, delivers those foods to the assimilating plant parts. Vegetable tissue thus produced cannot sustain animal life and build animal tissue without the aid of water. Water operates a wholesale "pick-up and delivery" service upon which life depends—it is the bloodstream of nature. The quick, often spectacular, verdure of a desert after rain demonstrates the vital role of water.

Surface configuration of the land—topography—lends variety and design to the composite scheme. Forces deep in the earth construct the major framework of mountains, plains, and plateaus, while surface forces carve and shape the more intricate

Rising air is cooled and condensation takes place

Descending air is warmed and picks up available moisture

WINDWARD SLOPE
VERDANT

LEEWARD SLOPE
BARREN

Fig. 2.1 *The single topographic element, exposure, can be a critical environmental factor.*

details. Most proficient among the surface sculptors is running water; as if in gratitude for the height that gives it strength, water works most diligently in the high, steep places, and as if in indignation casts its debris upon the low places that frustrate and weaken it.

Topography includes relief and drainage, slope, elevation, and exposure. It is at once both product of and contributor to environmental factors. Windward slopes receive more rain than leeward ones because they deflect the air upward, causing it to cool by expansion and to condense its water vapor (Fig. 2.1). The intercepted moisture promotes plant growth and normal soil development. The vegetative cover, itself a product of rain and soil, protects the soil against erosion and enriches it with humus, which increases its water-storing capacity. Water storage reduces soil injury by leaching. Let this suffice to indicate the profound peculiarities and exchange of environmental factors instituted by a single topographic element—exposure to winds. A score of other situations might be similarly attributed, the more significant when one considers that exposure remains the least tangible aspect of topography. Each of its partners operates with equal,

Topography designs the environmental composite

17

or even greater, potency in the variegation and arrangement of the environmental composite. Every one contributes to the development and distribution of natural resources; yet none holds resource status in its own right. Like climate, they are properties, not materials. But those properties, especially as they delimit spacial units and contrive certain zonations of renewable resources, must be recognized and respected by the conservator.

Plants and animals comprise our *living* natural resources; and, being alive, they respond readily to conservation. They are endowed with a degree of mobility enabling them to discriminate in their choice of habitat. Unrestrained, they invade and occupy those sites which best suit them, or sites so favorable to them that they can compete for the space successfully. Nor do they lack organization and system in their migration and occupance: they live in elaborate, cooperative associations, and move in ordered sequence, each form or species breaking trail for another until the entire group becomes established. In the vanguard stand the flora, providing food and shelter for the fauna.

Natural vegetation reflects in its form, density, and variety the gradations of quality in the environment. Being fixed in place, every tree, bush, grass, and forb must be adapted to the situation or die, yielding its place to another better adapted or more capable of adaptation. Furthermore, by the slow process of seed dispersal, growth, and reproduction, vegetation conforms to environmental changes, advancing and retreating in response to mutation of site factors. So accurately do certain plant species evince particular climatic or soil conditions that the conservator seeks acquaintance with these recognized *plant indicators.*

An intimate reciprocity operates between vegetation and soils. Soil sustains the growth with its substance; the growth in turn protects the soil and enriches it with humus that aids in water storage. Without soil there can be only scant vegetation, but without vegetation there can be no true soil.

There exists also a notable exchange between vegetation and climate. Climatic conditions, obviously, exert a direct influence over vegetation distribution, and in varying degree vegetation moderates light and temperature, reduces wind velocity, promotes water absorption and storage, and impedes run-off. Here, as between and among all the environmental constituents, there is a real and vital *mutuality.* That is the latchstring to nature's storehouse. The vegetation map (Fig. 2.2) merits careful study because it portrays the culmination of several natural environmental attributes.

Lest the discussion of environment appear to neglect the "birds

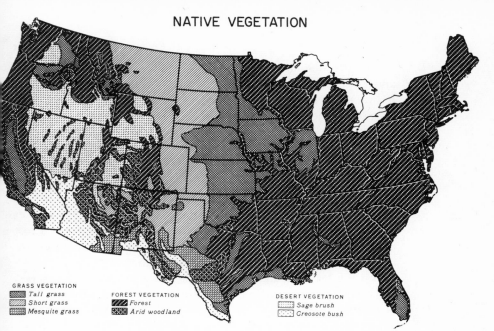

NATIVE VEGETATION

GRASS VEGETATION
▨ *Tall grass*
▥ *Short grass*
▦ *Mesquite grass*

FOREST VEGETATION
▰ *Forest*
▩ *Arid woodland*

DESERT VEGETATION
▨ *Sage brush*
▨ *Creosote bush*

Fig. 2.2 *Vegetation reflects the relative quality and spatial arrangement of other environmental attributes. (U.S.D.A. map.)*

and bees" and admit a common error, be it asserted that plant-animal relationships involve a nice reciprocity. As if in payment for their food, birds and rodents disperse the seeds, berries, and nuts they feed upon. As reward for her nectar the bee fertilizes the flower. All the exchanges are not beneficial; there is both cooperation and competition. And plants are not solely the benefactors. The arrangement is not entirely one-sided. Animals, large and small, contribute infinitely more to total environment than is generally understood.

To this wonderful composition man fell heir, with a strict charge—as the Bible says—to "multiply and fill the earth." Multiplication he has achieved admirably, numbering more than three billion, but he has "filled" only a few places to date, many of them ill-suited to his kind. Many spaces suitable for human habitation remain only partially occupied—neglected portions of the grand legacy. Man has behaved like a playboy who inherits more than he can squander and has neither the incentive nor the wisdom to appraise and employ his unearned wealth. Man has until now demonstrated neither the competence nor the vision commensurate with his endowment.

Man presumes ownership of all

Despite his superior intellect and mobility, man has during his brief domination frequently devastated occupied areas by misappropriation and waste. Just as often, seemingly restrained by something akin to brute instinct, he has lingered and rotted in his own desolation; thus, by so mean a process have nations and cultures vanished from the earth. From time to time man has ventured forth into unspoiled areas to replenish his exhausted stores at home; but only rarely has he attached himself to a new area without the compulsion of hunger, expulsion by force, or threat of destruction. Driven rather than drawn, fleeing rather than pursuing, he has shown little wisdom in his dispersal. Until he has better fitted his occupance pattern to his earth environment, until he has occupied and developed all the good places now empty, let him blame himself for his regional poverty. Let him correct his inequitable distribution before he mourns a lost estate. Meanwhile, the nobler objectives of conservation are twofold: better distribution and wiser occupance.

Landscape portrays an intricate complex logically arranged

Shifting his focus from the general to the specific, the conservator becomes concerned with landscape, the spacial combination of natural features and works of man. The whole complex, and its arrangement, must be considered in resource conservation. From the landscape one takes the pulse of the community before proceeding to a more careful diagnosis. Well-kept buildings, clean roadsides, living fences, green fields, and wooded slopes are as symptomatic for the community as are rosy cheeks for the barefoot boy.

Simple, discerning interpretation of landscape is a prerequisite to planning and conservation. Roads and homesteads conform to land use. Land use conforms to drainage and relief. A sawmill means timber and logging; a quarry, solid country rock. And the entire, intricate complex hangs together. Figure 2.3 indicates several criteria by which a good, functional landscape may be judged.

Undisturbed, nature maintains a nice balance

Where nature operates without interference she maintains a nicely balanced organization. Organisms live together both cooperatively and competitively. Similar species eat together at a common table. Those with the best boarding-house reach grow fat and numerous until they have consumed their favorite menu; then another group with different tastes takes its turn at the table. The stronger crowd out the weaker until hunger finally curbs even the hardiest. (The cottontail rabbit will eat himself right out of house and home unless checked by his natural enemies.) Food supply controls the numbers of all animals, whether herbivorous, carnivorous, or omnivorous. Among the carnivores each falls prey to another until the fiercest predator, finding little to kill, becomes weak and improvident. Ultimately, he succumbs, his young starve, and the proud family lies as carrion—food for scavengers.

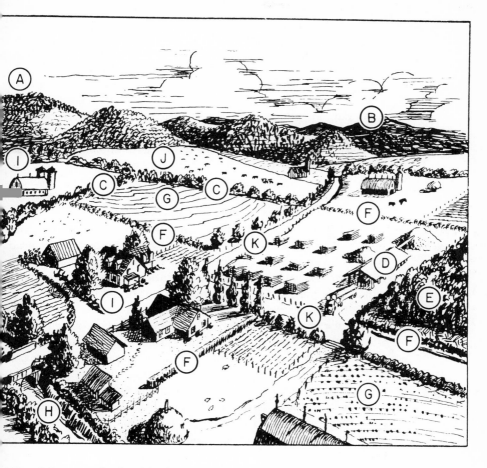

Fig. 2.3 A good cultural landscape fits harmoniously into its natural setting.

A. Tree farming on steep slopes.

B. Protected watershed.

C. Wooded strips for wildlife cover and windbreak.

D. A sawmill utilizes the timber crop.

E. Well-kept woods serve for water storage, wind break, and wildlife habitat.

F. Living fences restrain domesticated animals and provide homes for wild ones.

G. Contoured slopes conserve soil and water for crops.

H. A clean, perennial stream reflects community health.

I. Good homes are the product of good adjustment to the environment.

J. Permanent meadow: slopes suitable for grazing, but subject to erosion if plowed.

K. Roads for convenient access, their sides clean and unscarred.

Plants, as well as animals, live in balanced communities. Tall plants shade the short ones, and those at the bottom develop the ability to utilize partial light. Under a dense forest canopy the green ones that live by photosynthesis give way to parasites and saprophytes that rely on ready-made food. Differing in their food requirements, many species live harmoniously together without disturbing the balance of soil elements. Loss of a single member species disrupts the entire cooperative society. A single intruder can precipitate group disaster. In a rich habitat plants stand close together; in a poor one they space themselves according to the availability of nutrients. In the natural scheme of things plants and animals maintain a certain balance between associated species, and a distribution precisely fixed by food supply.

It behooves the conservator to comprehend the natural cycles in which environmental factors move. The regular round of day and night assumes significance in terms of daily temperature ranges and duration of life-giving sunlight. The annual round of seasons takes on vital realism when transposed into vegetation cycle, temperature variation, and rainfall regimen, every one of which influences conservation practices. Profoundly important to the conservator are the long-range climatic cycles which bring alternate excess and deficiency of moisture, peculiarly characteristic of marginal moisture belts such as the steppe lands. Periodic and recurring changes influence all the resources we are concerned with.

Nature moves in finite cycles

Lest one attempt to stop everything, let him ponder the magnificent revolution operative in the cycle of erosion. Rocks break into fragments; gravity causes them to fall or slide into a stream; the stream tumbles them and rounds them and reduces them to grains of sand. At its mouth, the river deposits the grains in layers under the sea, sorted by their density. Compressed and cemented together, the sorted grains become rock once more; and when in due course the rock emerges from the sea, the cycle begins anew. With this cycle the conservator does not presume to interfere; he seeks only to stem its acceleration by man, wherever this is harmful.

Processes of soil formation evince a certain cyclic character. While, in effect, they bring up into the soil from the bottom the parent mineral materials, they release from the surface a residue of those same materials which have passed upward through the soil section during its downward development. If the statement seems involved, it suits the case. But its implications are simpler —the sterile residue needs removal, for its retention may be detrimental, unduly impeding renewal of the soil by burying it under debris.

If careless observation seems to show that water only runs downhill, even common sense tells us that what comes down must have gone up. Water is no exception, and its endless changes of state and position are described as the *hydrologic cycle*. Air over the ocean takes up water vapor; winds carry the moist air onto the land; and the processes of condensation and precipitation deposit it upon the surface. Thence, both by overland flow and subsurface percolation, it moves back to its source, the sea. In its circuit it becomes alternately salty and fresh, clear and polluted, gas, solid, and liquid, servant and menace, solvent and precipitator—and through all these retains its basic characteristics and potentialities. Here is a wonder of nature that no one should view casually, least of all the conservator.

The organisms, plants and animals, respond to environment in ordered circuits and sequences; many of them are so apparent and simple that man has detected their modes with little trouble. Many invite his attention; a few command his respect. An established, balanced plant association may not occupy the site indefinitely, for when its dominant growth form matures and dies another form previously subdued takes advantage of the situation and attains prominence. When that one expires another gains supremacy—then another and another—until a long line of pretenders have held temporary sway. Finally, a new generation of the original royal family, like heirs apparent, re-establish their sovereignty—*vegetation climax*. Such is the natural rotation in which the noble oaks yield to aspens and wait their turn to rise again in proper company.

Animals attain social prominence according to available food supply and their ability to compete for it. Squirrels cannot be social climbers without oaks or other nut trees. They bow to the beaver when aspens succeed the oaks. There is a close parallel between plant and animal cycles.

Animal rotation serves as a safety valve for the natural balance of life already mentioned. When conditions favor the increase of field mice, owls flourish until they decimate the mouse population. By that time unwisely numerous, the owls decrease while the mice regain momentum. Nature survives her economic cycles without opposing the law of supply and demand.

Be mindful that all life on earth follows the inevitable "dust to dust" cycle. Every organism in some way takes its substance from the earth and reverts to it. Nature would perpetuate her own fertility!

Ever since his career began man has flagrantly violated the laws of nature; the daughters of Eve are surely accessories before the fact. More intelligent than his fellow creatures, he has none-theless often shown dubious superiority in the use of his environ-ment. In fact, he appears to be the worst misfit of the lot, doing more damage than all the others together. He was gifted with enough intelligence to mutilate and destroy efficiently; but ap-parently not with enough to appraise the destruction and foresee its consequences. Man's technology too often exceeds his wisdom.

Man violates the laws of nature

Failing to comprehend the error of his doing, man has often curtailed the very resource he prized most highly and injured the very one he sought to develop. He has drained swamps and marshes where his idea of surface utilization was not nearly so good as the natural condition of swamp or marsh that provided the vital moisture relations for large adjacent areas. By irrigating dry lands he has sometimes precipitated salts in toxic concentra-tions, rendering the desert more forbidding than it was before he meddled. In other places he has expended water for irrigation of crops adequately produced in areas nearby, creating by waste a problem of surplus.

He has killed trees to clear land utterly unsuited to anything more productive than forest. He has broken the sod and sown crops where native grasses were his best resource. He has exposed the soil to wind and wash where natural cover was its only de-fense against their ravage. He has opened festering sores on the land and spurned nature's aids for their healing.

He has exterminated several animal species desirable to him and unwittingly propagated others in his disservice. He has killed one predator and thereby encouraged another more predacious. In many ways he has upset the balance in nature and obstructed natural processes that would regain it.

Nature instructs both gently and severely

Gently yet firmly nature instructs her "problem child." When he errs she corrects with infinite patience; when he rejects her suggestion she disciplines severely. Where he clears a wooded slope he is warned by a hurried run-off; where, impudently, he strips a watershed, he is chastened by death and destruction in the valley.

Like an indulgent mother, nature spoils man by generosity, but like a strict father she teaches him industry and frugality through denial. She molds character and inspires faith more with im-providence than with abundance. Consider how both civilization and religion have evolved and flourished in desert environments. In resource conservation one must beware lest human quality decline in the face of plenty. The greater man's material wealth, the less may be his inclination to guard it; easy living tends to beget indolence.

Had man better attended nature's instruction he might have attained a higher state of well-being without impairment of the source. Were he to mend his ways and learn her lessons she would even now help him repair the damage wrought and ensure his future prosperity without further shrinkage of its base. The good conservator has great respect for tolerant, deliberate nature.

Yet, man cannot prosper and progress under abject servitude to nature. As the elite animal, it is his privilege, indeed his obligation, to modify the natural scheme of things in any manner he can devise to suit his own purposes. Civilization has progressed—not by holding inviolate the pristine attributes of natural environment but by modifying and even destroying them to accommodate society. Natural balance has been largely displaced by artificial manipulation, and population growth accelerates the process. By this procedure Anglo-America now affords some 200 million people the highest living standards in the world where once only 1 million savages, quite in harmony with nature, survived precariously. Rather than bemoaning our loss of natural balance and presuming to regain it generally, American conservators should concern themselves with the improvement of *cultural balance* in their total environment.

Natural balance yields to cultural balance

A few conspicuous, even spectacular, adjustments to his natural environment have made man so confident and conceited that he boasts of *controlling* nature. He has accomplished no such thing! The same advancement in knowledge and technology which has magnified his destructive exploitation has merely advanced, also, his constructive adaptation. His so-called "controls" are simply the more tangible responses to environment. Many less apparent responses are actually much more considerable and enduring. Man *adapts* continually and progressively; but he *controls* neither nature nor her rewards.

Man's arrogant "controls" are really feeble adaptations

At least since the Tower of Babel man has presumed upon nature's omnipotence. His command has never been more than misinterpretation. He develops an economic community in a valley shaped by nature. Nature provides the footing for a bridge with which he spans the river. But there has been no change in the valley or in the river that built it. There has come a new element of human adaptation—a bridge. And when nature finally asserts her dominance, she topples the steel-and-concrete adaptation into the river, which eventually dumps every fragment of the monumental structure into the sea. A comparable misconception attends man's "control" of surface waters with a dam. The effective life of the structure is extremely limited—a few decades or centuries, depending upon the natural arrangement of rainfall and slope. In any case, the adaptation is temporary. Its more profound resistance of natural forces stems from the incidental interruption of stream profile and consequent delay of valley development.

Man seeds a cloud and makes rain, cracks the atom and makes a terrible bomb. In both cases he merely employs natural functions previously unknown to him. In the first his vaunted "control" fails when the winds bring insufficient moisture; in the second, nature may save him from self-destruction—perhaps only by withholding the necessary supply of fissionable materials. Even atomic energy represents a human adaptation to environmental factors, not control over them. Man might well be less arrogant about controls and more humbly grateful for the privilege of adaptation.

Every mode of resource conservation represents a refinement of man's adjustment to his earth environment. When he leaves a steep, rocky slope forested, when he leaves dry grassland unbroken, when he plows along the contour and rotates his crops, when he keeps the waters clear, when he levels and plants the gigantic furrows of strip mining, when he reserves a little space for wild creatures, and when he repairs a dripping faucet, man improves his adaptation to the natural environment.

Technology lends refinement

When we apply in conservation the most advanced technologies at our command, whether to fertilize the soil, to concentrate metallic ores, to control noxious pests and diseases, or to magnify the worth of resources in any fashion whatever, we thereby refine our environmental adjustment.

The conservator must look to his environment

It devolves upon resource conservation to make human culture more compatible with its natural setting. Conservation can serve its full purpose only when it employs the interactions of environmental factors. The conservator will multiply his services and progressively extend their yields when he fits each endeavor into nature's scheme of things. His frustrations to date have come from a failure to see how things hang together. Let him, henceforth, be sure he understands the *unity of environment* before he works the least change in any of the components. Let him study first the influences of environment, and then the techniques for conserving natural resources. Let him always consider prevailing economic and social forces in planning his work. The American conservator should know the *whole American landscape* and its regional attributes and traditions before he meddles with any part of it, anywhere.

3

Water
on the
Land

*water, lifeblood of the earth,
circulates through many forms
and moods*

Oceans and seas cover almost three-quarters of the earth's surface, to an average depth of almost 2.5 miles. A maximum depth of more than 6 miles has been sounded.[1] Mount Everest would disappear if it were dropped into the deepest part of the Pacific. Of all the water on earth, estimated at some 340 million cubic miles, the oceans and seas contain about 97 per cent, with prodigious quantities of minerals in solution or suspension. At any given time, about 1 per cent of all the earth's water is solid, frozen in snows and glaciers. Only about 2 per cent of the total volume constitutes the fresh, liquid water in rivers, lakes, and sloughs on the land surface; in soils and rocks underground, most of it also fresh. A minute fraction of 1 per cent (perhaps 1/2,000 per cent) floats in the atmosphere, much of it as invisible vapor. In the upper portion of the earth's crust the quantity of water is three times that of all other substances together.[2] Plants and animals are literally full of water. About 70 per cent of the living human body is water.

With all this water, why be concerned about water shortage and conservation? Because there is a significant distinction between water and *useful* water. Time, place, and quality lend it resource value.[3] Sufficient clear, clean water on the land is an asset anywhere. It is more useful in summer than in winter, more

**Much
of the earth
is water**

valuable in metropolitan areas than in sparsely populated rural areas where it is easily obtainable. Many places are handicapped by a dearth of good water.

Life stops in the absence of water. Plants and animals can survive hunger much longer than thirst, and water can revive them when food fails. Without water they starve amid plenty.

The distribution of plants and animals tends to accord with the availability of useable water. Where water is abundant life flourishes and multiplies; where it is limited life shrinks accordingly. Seasonal moisture promotes seasonal growth and reproduction. By either deficiency or excess water expels, excludes, and selects species, restricts and modifies growth form, and narrows the margin of health and survival. Only where favorable water conditions prevail will the habitat sustain a full, vigorous community.

Water resembles an itinerant peddler in its transient character, and it outdoes the peddler at changing mood, appearance, behavior, and quality in the course of its regular circuit. From sea to air, to land, and back to sea again goes the endless round of water movement. It is perhaps the most significant cycle in all nature; the fundamental medium and facility for conserving our renewable resources. It is the ordered rotation of water, called the *hydrologic cycle,* which is traced pictorially in Fig. 3.1.

Fig. 3.1   *The Hydrologic Cycle. Lesser cycles operate within the main one.*

Given time to do so, air over the ocean takes up water in vapor form until it is full—saturated. Given less time, it becomes more or less charged with water vapor. With onshore wind the moisture-laden air moves onto the land, and there, its moisture capacity reduced by cooling—mainly by ascent and expansion—the water vapor condenses into visible cloud form. Accretion of water particles causes precipitation of cloud moisture as rain, snow, hail, or sleet—*meteoric water*—its form and arrival on the land surface related to temperature and other variable atmospheric properties. To the conservator the form, intensity, and volume of precipitation have tremendous significance. Liquid water in large drops causes "splash" erosion when it strikes bare soil. Rain runs off as it falls, while snow contributes no run-off until it melts. Snow stores moisture for future use. Many valleys owe their verdure to mountain snows that melt in summer.

The hydrologic cycle never falters

Water precipitated upon the land begins its journey back to the sea by devious and circuitous routes. Some runs off surface slopes into brooks and rivers, hurrying toward the ocean. Some soaks into the ground, moistening the soil as it percolates through, filling rock crevices and pores as it seeps deeper into the earth. Such water in transition between the surface and the zone of saturation underneath is called *vadose* water. Its true character is lost where seepage enters open channels and flows seaward in subterranean streams. It falls short of its mission when it fails to replenish the ground-water supply, being dissipated before it penetrates to the water table. Such failure means that water pumped from a well in the area comes from rain that fell elsewhere.

Much of the water that falls upon the land takes a short cut by evaporating directly back into the air, postponing its long journey to the sea. Some prolongs its sojourn on the land as capillary water in soil and as body fluid in plants and animals. Plants release their portion to the air by transpiration; animals expel their share by various means. Whatever the detour or delay, all water travels back to its origin, the sea; thence to rise again as vapor, to fall again as rain, and to return again, eventually.

The earth's waters are everywhere transient. To intercept and detain them where they are beneficial, to restrain them where they would be violent, to quicken them where they would stagnate, contributes to water conservation.

The distribution of precipitation—regional, seasonal, and quantitative—affects every kind of resource conservation, but more especially that of water. The *amount* of precipitation that falls in a certain place has obvious implications for conservation,

Distribution of rainfall implies both time and place

but its *time* and *manner* of arrival may be quite as important as
quantity. Nor may one disregard the geographic location, the
topographic position, or any other attribute of the place itself
when he examines its rainfall. Winter precipitation on dormant
vegetation may do little good. Unless the soil be frozen or otherwise protected against erosion, winter rain may be extremely destructive. A 20-inch rainfall well distributed during the growing
season can develop a good stand of wheat; but 20 inches of rain
in as many days might ruin the crop and injure the field. If the
field were in the northern United States, the seasonal 20-inch
rainfall would better mature a crop than it could in the South
where greater evaporation steals more moisture. If it fell on a
steep slope, the twenty-day rain might erode the soil; if on a low
flat, it might waterlog and inundate. Many more situations might
be cited to illustrate the extreme variability of precipitation efficiency incidental to time and place factors.

Climatic diversity in the United States poses many different
water problems attendant upon the vagaries of precipitation.
Averages of rainfall have only limited value for conservation—

Fig. 3.2 *Although only a general index, average annual precipitation is a fairly good
clue to regional land capabilities and attendant conservation problems. (Adapted from
Climate and Man, U.S.D.A.)*

AVERAGE ANNUAL PRECIPITATION

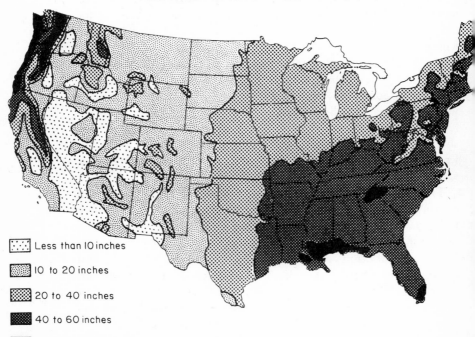

Less than 10 inches

10 to 20 inches

20 to 40 inches

40 to 60 inches

More than 60 inches

mainly as a general frame of reference. Locally it may be most significant that certain mountain slopes get 100 inches or more annually and that sheltered valleys below get their total supply from those slopes. Wet slopes and dry valleys afford obvious opportunities for utilizing water, but deviation from normal expectancy creates problems. Even more challenging to the conservator are the erratic fluctuations of rainfall in areas moderately supplied. Drought in moist regions and flood in dry regions, heavy rain in the "dry season" and dryness during the "wet season"— every deviation from normal expectancy tests the conservator's mettle.

Hyetal (rainfall) maps incorporate data indispensable to water conservation, but they require cautious interpretation. Their application must be no more specific or detailed than their representation. They must be viewed in the light of several other environmental factors, such as slope, soil, vegetation, and evaporation. They constitute an essential frame of reference for any discussion of renewable resources (Fig. 3.2).

Rain that falls on the ground and cannot soak in becomes surface run-off—water with a return ticket to the ocean by the fastest route. In their downhill hurry, rivulets merge into brooks and brooks join to form rivers. Every merger, or confluence, augments and accelerates the flow. Every pool, pond, and lake retards and equalizes it by interrupting the gradient down which it speeds. Unhampered, little rills on high slopes can grow into torrents before they reach the valley. Heavy, sudden rain on bare, steep slopes produces the most excessive run-off, which, gathering force as it goes, displays its unbridled power in the damage done by rampant streams and flash floods. Throughout its journey from land to sea, from initial diffusion to ultimate aggregation, run-off harms and hinders man where it moves too rapidly and serves him best where its movement is leisurely and regular. It is the phase of the hydrologic cycle with which we are most concerned, because its behavior and manipulation influence all aspects of resource conservation. The map (Fig. 3.3) shows the approximate amount of run-off in each part of contiguous United States during a normal year.

Rapid run-off presents problems

Whereas it would be neither possible nor desirable to stop run-off, it behooves man to counter the acceleration his work has caused and avail himself more fully of the benefits proffered by run-off. Perhaps nowhere else in his environment are there problems more momentous and more neglected, yet more amenable to solution. Therein lies one of man's most conspicuous failures as well as a most urgent opportunity for conserving the regen-

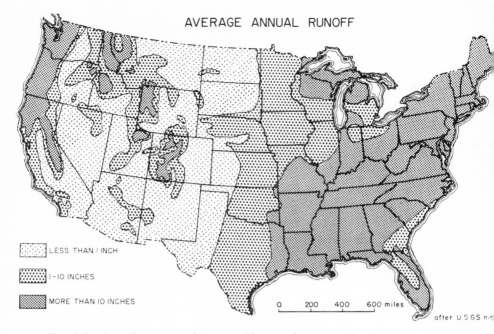

LESS THAN I INCH

I-IO INCHES

MORE THAN IO INCHES

0   200   400   600 miles

after U.S.G.S. map

Fig. 3.3 *Run-off presents obvious problems and opportunities in water conservation. Note the regional disparity between the maps shown in Fig. 3.2 and Fig. 3.3 and consider why their patterns do not coincide. (After U.S.G.S. map.)*

erative natural resources. Therein lies a unique prospect of succeeding by beginning at the top.[4]

Whether composed of direct run-off or ground water reissued through springs and seepage zones, surface waters are most readily available to man and affect his occupance of land through a multiplicity of means. Surface waters fall into two general categories: *running* water in streams and *standing* water in lakes, sloughs, swamps, and marshes. The latter may be subdivided into at least two major classes: that which is open, such as in a deep, clear lake, and that which is choked with vegetation more or less submerged, such as in a marsh or swamp. Each form has its individual characteristics and its peculiar functions. Each serves man according to the intelligence with which he manages it. When he views each water state and form as a link in an endless chain, he has acquired the basic idea in hydrology and water conservation.

Regular stream flow and moderate fluctuation of water level indicate a desirable, healthy state of surface waters, and obviate many needs for conservation. Unfortunately, many streams flow irregularly, even intermittently, and many lake levels fluctuate widely in consequence of natural variations in precipitation, evaporation, freezing, and thawing. Some have become extremely erratic after man invaded the drainage basin and occupied the

Surface waters have various forms and functions

32

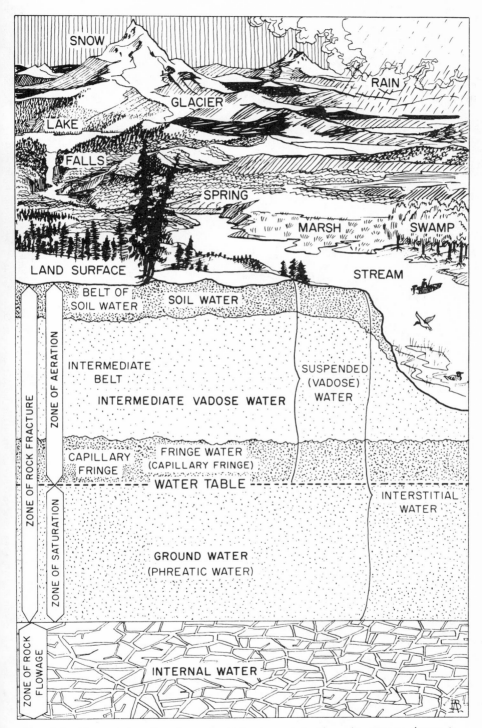

Fig. 3.4 *The water section from clouds to deep rock. The subterranean detour is slower than the overland route.*

GROUND-WATER AREAS IN THE UNITED STATES

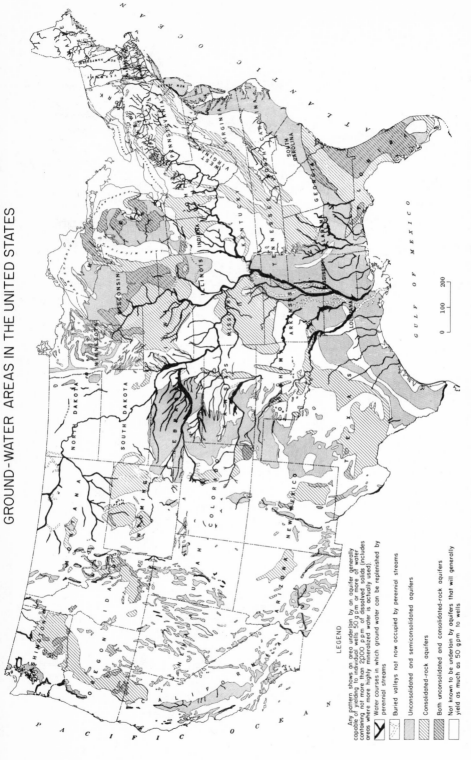

LEGEND

Any pattern shows an area underlain by an aquifer generally capable of yielding to individual wells 50 g p m or more of water containing not more than 2,000 p p m of dissolved solids (includes areas where more highly mineralized water is actually used)

Water courses in which ground water can be replenished by perennial streams

Buried valleys not now occupied by perennial streams

Unconsolidated and semiconsolidated aquifers

Consolidated-rock aquifers

Both unconsolidated and consolidated-rock aquifers

Not known to be underlain by aquifers that will generally yield as much as 50 g p m to wells

GULF OF MEXICO

0   100   200

Fig. 3.5 *Availability of water from underground storage has been a prominent factor in regional resource development, but in many places ground water has been withdrawn faster than nature can recharge the reservoirs. (Map from The Conservation of Ground Water, by Harold E. Thomas.*

34

watershed. The first objective toward conservation of surface waters is to equalize flow and to stabilize level to a degree of constancy as good as, or better than, that which obtained before human intrusion.

At varying depths below the surface lies a zone of permanent saturation, where water-filled crevices and interstices comprise a natural storage reservoir for moisture. Water thus held against quick release to the sea and protected against evaporation is called *ground water,* which, because it is most reliable but least understood, constitutes a critical phase in water use and conservation. Its magnitude and accessibility vary greatly from place to place, but it is probably present everywhere, extending in places to depths of several thousand feet.[5] See Figs. 3.4 and 3.5.

Ground water constitutes the critical phase

Notwithstanding the tremendous quantities of ground water in the earth, it is *not unlimited;* neither is it everywhere available economically. The water-filled spaces and cavities in earth and soil can store a fixed volume, and no more. Since the stores derive almost entirely from rainfall, they must shrink whenever drain exceeds replenishment from surface sources. Far from being separate, independent entities, surface and ground waters are mutually complementary. In a manner of speaking, ground water provides "defense in depth" for our water resources and fights a "delaying action" against wholesale plundering of the total supply.

The top of the zone saturated with ground water has become known as the *water table,* a term that requires liberal interpretation. The water table is neither flat nor horizontal, as a table should be; it has neither standard dimensions nor conventional design. The level at which water that is free—contained among earth particles rather than confined between rock layers—stands in a hole dug into the ground marks the water table. That level conforms more or less to surface topography, being most nearly accordant during the wet season and receding from the higher places toward a lower, less undulating surface during drought, since ground water moves both vertically and horizontally. Unless replenishment equals removal, the water table fluctuates. It rises during rainy weather and sinks during dry weather. The fluctuation amounts to several feet where precipitation is erratic and abundant (Figs. 3.6 and 3.7).

The water table fluctuates with supply

Normal water-table conditions exist only where moisture is adequate and the earth materials are pervious to water. Unless there is sufficient moisture and unless it can penetrate, there can be no water table in the ordinary sense. An impervious surface prohibits the absorption by which ground water accumulates. An

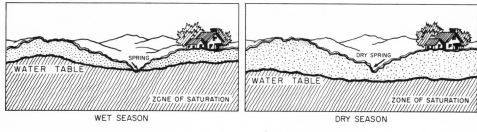

WET SEASON   DRY SEASON

Fig. 3.6 *The water table rises during a rainy period and falls during dry weather.*

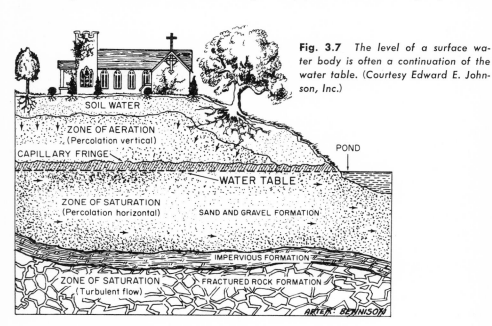

SOIL WATER

ZONE OF AERATION
(Percolation vertical)

CAPILLARY FRINGE

WATER TABLE

POND

ZONE OF SATURATION
(Percolation horizontal)   SAND AND GRAVEL FORMATION

IMPERVIOUS FORMATION

ZONE OF SATURATION   FRACTURED ROCK FORMATION
(Turbulent flow)

AFTER: BENNISON

Fig. 3.7 *The level of a surface water body is often a continuation of the water table. (Courtesy Edward E. Johnson, Inc.)*

Fig. 3.8 *A perched water table can be as deceptive as a false bottom in a box. (After Bennison and W.S.P. 494.)*

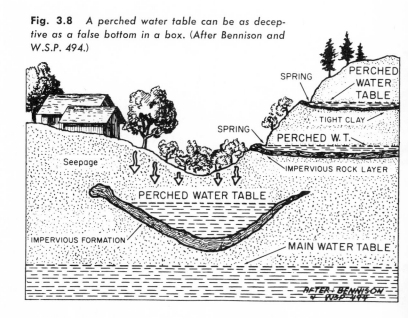

SPRING   PERCHED WATER TABLE

TIGHT CLAY

SPRING   PERCHED W.T.

IMPERVIOUS ROCK LAYER

Seepage

PERCHED WATER TABLE

IMPERVIOUS FORMATION

MAIN WATER TABLE

AFTER BENNISON
& WSP 494

impervious layer below the surface causes an abnormality called a *perched* water table (Fig. 3.8). Where ground water moves in open subterranean channels, as under solution topography (karst), the top of the stream may simulate a water table.

Porous rock strata between dense, impervious layers above and below them carry confined ground water under appropriate conditions of exposure. With sufficient moisture where they crop out and moderate inclination downward from an extensive catchment area, they become charged with water. Water from such strata—called *aquifers*—has several desirable characteristics.

Aquifers carry naturally filtered water

Confined water in an aquifer becomes naturally filtered as it passes through the rock formation; it is generally purer and clearer than free water under an ordinary water table. As it fills, an aquifer builds up hydrostatic pressure, which is comparable with "head" in surface water, and resembles a standpipe installed in an attitude more nearly horizontal than vertical. Much the same as with the man-made contrivance, any puncture of the natural standpipe by drilling a well brings water up to a level approximating the water line. If the top of the well be lower than the head, water flows out upon the surface. Rock fissures or fractures similarly disposed give rise to all-weather springs. Whether it gushes forth from an opening or merely rises above the water table, water under hydrostatic pressure in an aquifer becomes artesian water, the ultimate in ground-water supply. Cooled deep in the earth, its temperature lends special values. Derived from a colossal reservoir, it has uniform quality and reliable quantity. Translated horizontally long distances from its intake, it can supply areas otherwise deficient in moisture. Artesian waters have given life and verdure to deserts, creating garden spots where all was barren waste before they were tapped. In many places such water is, however, so heavily charged with minerals in solution that its usefulness is impaired.

The multiple personality of water magnifies the scope of its conservation and complicates the procedures by which optimum conservation may be achieved. Many streams become raging torrents in one season and dwindle to mere trickles at other times. Floods that destroy crops and buildings may also deposit fertile silt in which succeeding crops can flourish and defray the costs of reconstruction; but, the silt itself represents grand larceny of upland soils. Although water is essential to our existence, it is also a dangerous medium of infection. Most epidemics of intestinal diseases are spread by water. Shoal waters that stand at a constant level are generally most productive of fish and other

Water has a multiple personality

desirable life forms, but they also breed the biggest swarms of mosquitos.

The contradictory, impetuous nature of water imposes upon its conservator the momentous responsibility of adjudicator between good and evil: shall he try to prevent floods, or shall he encourage them to enrich the valleys over which they spread? He must discover the natural tolerance beyond which he dare not preside: how much waste can a stream carry without becoming more detrimental than beneficial? Where can he drain, and where irrigate, without regretting it later?

Water, more than stone or bronze or iron or any other substance, has molded human cultures and set the course of civilization. Water procurement has sharpened man's wit and strengthened his society. By water navigation man has expanded his geographic and scientific horizons. Water courses have directed human migration and patterned human settlement, precipitated wars for their control, and served as boundary between the aspiring nations. In several great religions water symbolizes divine cleansing and purity.

Agrarian Indian folk live intimately with water. Their typical village clusters about a common source of water, be it a stream, spring, lake, well, or reservoir, and that single source furnishes water for their simple requirements—drinking, bathing, cooking, cleansing, and watering of animals. Crocks, pots, and buckets are standard household utensils in huts otherwise almost devoid of furnishings. Water stands first among family provisions.

Agrarian folk live intimately with water

The life of a rice farmer in India is so closely associated with water that he is virtually amphibious. He encloses his paddies with handmade mud dikes, floods them with crude, hand-operated lifts, plants them wading knee-deep in muddy water, then daubs mud and sloshes more water to keep them inundated until the rice matures. And all his sodden drudgery comes to naught if his paddies lie the least bit high and the monsoon shortchanges him. The rice turns yellow and the farmer faces hunger.

The Indian jheel, or tank, outdoes all that the immortal Kipling ascribed to it. In it the villagers bathe themselves and their bullocks, wash their clothes and worship their gods, cleanse their mouths and catch their fish, and fill their brass or earthen vessels after scouring them. Little wonder that the overworked water, taxed by many pot-bearing women and rapid evaporation, shrinks to a green, stinking slime as the dry season wears on. Little wonder the Hindu worships those waters that serve his needs without stagnating—the holy, tawny rivers which at last carry away the ashes of his mortal remains. For centuries past his ancestors have lived and worked with water, died of diseases carried by it, and been consigned to it upon death.

Space forbids our tracing hydraulic engineering from Babylonian or Roman aqueducts to its elaborate development and complex employment in an advanced society such as ours, but it must be asserted that new demands on water have accompanied the progress of civilization and that these increasing water requirements compel improvement of water conservation. The Indian woman who dips "natural" water from a jheel knows little of water qualities other than wetness; but the twentieth-century American rates the *quality* of water by several criteria: chemical hardness; sediment; bacteria count; aeration; taste; precipitate.[6] The degree or proportion of a single one may determine the value of the water for a specific purpose. Hard water, with calcium and magnesium carbonates dissolved in it, refuses to associate with ordinary soap in a washtub and fouls up indoor plumbing. Steam engineers avoid it because it chokes the boiler tubes with scale. Water with a high bacteria count may be dangerous to drink. Water with sulphur in it, however harmless, disgusts both smell and taste. Water charged too highly with salts may not be used for irrigation because it poisons the very land it should make productive.

Our sophisticated industrial society imposes new demands

For the most important modern uses, water needs to be clear, pure, and soft. To correct deficiencies, natural or induced, modern technology applies specific treatments. Some are simple, like softening, filtering, or chlorinating; others are so complex and costly that they strain the tax budget or often exceed practical feasibility. Nor are quality and quantity enough to satisfy modern water demands; storage, pressure, transport, and distribution are also ordinary requisites. Good water conservation means optimum provision of water for all special purposes without undue expenditure for artificial treatment.

Whether a squalid, straw-thatched Indian village or an American skyscraper metropolis, every community arises where there is water to drink—*potable* water; and none can grow beyond the available supply, although we must remember that in the modern community availability is a matter of cost, not of distance, depth, or anything else. If the supply diminishes, the community shrinks accordingly. If the supply fails, the community moves away or dies. The minimum water supply available at any given time fixes the ultimate size to which a permanent agglomeration of people can grow. Fortunately, the minimum asserts itself in higher costs, restrictions, or other inconveniences before its absolute limits are reached, and the population becomes static

Potable water supply limits population density

before it thirsts. Our daily use of water in the United States, taking each withdrawal at face value whether or not the same water is used more than once, exceeds 1,500 gallons per person, of which less than 400 gallons are consumed.[7]

The entire population of the country drinks perhaps less than 100 million gallons of water daily; a mere trickle compared with other uses. But that little trickle receives more attention than all the rest; in any circumstance of limited supply, it holds top priority.

Domestic tranquility runs from a faucet

Running water, hot and cold, has become so nearly universal in American homes that the "modern conveniences" once proudly exhibited are now taken for granted. Sinks, showers, and lavatories have all but displaced dishpans, washdishes, water pitchers, and tubs. The ever-empty water pail and family dipper that once menaced both health and connubial bliss gave way to the domestic tranquility that should run from a faucet—unless it drips. Every added convenience and facility has increased the use—and waste—of domestic water. When grandpa drew the water by hand and fetched it in a bucket, grandma used it sparingly, to save the man if not the well. The Monday wash and the Saturday-night bath were sizeable undertakings and expended several tubfulls; but the privy did not flush and the lawn shifted for itself between rains. The average household of the water-pail era used less water in a week than the modern family uses in a day. However, the total water used for domestic purposes still remains less than that for any other major-use category. Least in quantity, it holds first rank in both quality and importance. A good supply guards its users against infection and their property against fire. It promotes health, hygiene, and sanitation—personal well-being.

Certain industries use vast volumes of water

Few people realize how much modern industry depends upon water—not only as a source of power or raw material, but infinitely more as a conditioning agent and processing medium. In canneries, breweries, distilleries, and other food plants, water does four-way duty. It cleans ingredients and containers; it cools the coils or boils the brew, as the case may be; it becomes part of the product; finally, it washes away the wastes. (At best they are so distinctively scented that one wonders how a fish cannery or a slaughter house would smell were they not constantly washed with water.) As steam, water remains the medium whereby fuels turn power shafts. In many factories water is used to prevent overheating of certain machine parts, while in others it is used to heat essential parts of the machinery. High-speed cutting tools need cooling; drying rolls in a paper machine need

Table 1

Typical Water Use in Manufacturing

Product	Unit	Water Use (in gals.)
Rayon yarn	Ton	250,000-400,000*
Cotton cloth	Ton	10,000-16,000
Woolen cloth	1000 yds	340,000-510,000
Soap	Ton	500-4,500
Steam generation	1000 kw-hr	80,000-170,000
Cane sugar	Ton	4,000-27,900
Fluid milk	1 cwt	.063-2.07
Canned vegetables	100 cases	3,500-16,000
Paperboard	Ton	7,700-90,000
Oil refining	1000 bbls	770,000
Refined petroleum products	1000 bbls	151,000-15,000,000
Rolled steels	Ton	6,000-110,000

* The figures given here represent water usage by various companies and under differing processes. The gallonage figures are typical of the water requirements for the manufacture of the products listed.

Source: *Battelle Technical Review*, VI, No. 11 (November 1957), 6.

heating. The bulk of industrial water goes for power and cooling;[8] fortunately, cooling may be done with low-quality water and it may be recycled for use several times.

A considerable volume of water in manufacturing serves as a medium for dissolving, mixing, precipitating, cleansing, or otherwise changing the materials being processed. Paper is literally made in water. Certain synthetics require tremendous quantities of process water. In these and other manufactures, water serves also as transporter of materials through various stages of fabrication. About 30 gallons of water were employed to convert from wood the paper in this book. A ton of steel may represent the use of 65,000 gallons of water in its manufacture. One ton of rayon yarn may involve the use of 400,000 gallons or more. It takes 500 gallons of water to make a ton of soap; 160 gallons to make a pound of aluminum.[9] The table above shows the comparative requirement of water in various industrial applications.

Obviously, industrial water supply is a real factor in plant location, and in the geographic distribution of manufactures.[10] Water is essential to the production, exploitation, and utilization of many other resources, be they vegetable, animal, or mineral.

Hydraulic mining has long been a water user, and more recently the flotation process of separating or concentrating minerals from low-grade ores has greatly increased the use of water in the mining industry. Many minerals laid down by water—potash, salt, placer gold—are now recovered by the same agent that deposited them. Many, previously worthless, are extracted profitably by flotation or leaching with water as described in a later chapter.

Water and gravity are a natural team of workhorses, which, when properly harnessed, can do a prodigious amount of work. Water and fire make another team, which, being easier to hitch and handle, does more work at present despite its ravenous appetite for coal or other fuel and its tremendous consumption of water.

The water-gravity team requires rather elaborate "stabling" in the form of dams and reservoirs, but it consumes neither "feed" nor water and affects thereby a magnificent economy of resources.

Hydroelectric power will outlive the mineral fuels

Early American manufacturing depended upon direct water-power developed with wooden (crib) or masonry dams, open flumes, and water wheels. There was neither the need nor the know-how for damming full-fledged rivers. The choice dam sites were on small streams, and there was little necessity for impounding a great water reserve against seasons of slack flow; the streams were more dependable then than now. On such sites sprang up the gristmills, sawmills, and hammer mills, which were the magnetic nuclei of many historic villages. Industry was confined to stream banks, and other community appurtenances often gravitated to industry. Onto this scene strode the giant of industrial energy, coal, and released industry from its stream-side bondage. Steam-driven factories arose where transport facilities and other advantages of location favored them. Auxiliary steam plants kept industry going during periods of low water and flash floods. The availability of fuel—coal or wood, not running water—became the decisive factor in plant location, and coal traveled farther and farther as improvements in transportation, among others, asserted themselves.

With the application of the water turbine to generate transmissible energy, the water-gravity team surged to prominence again in the form of hydroelectric power; the United States leads the world in hydroelectric production. Water generates about one-fifth of our nation's electricity.[11] Transmission losses restrict the economical use of electricity to a radius of about 200 miles from its source at present, but increased efficiency of distribution may be anticipated. Though perpetual as the rain from whence it derives, the ultimate potential of water power cannot exceed that portion of precipitation that runs off; this amount affords us only a small fraction of our total energy requirements.

Indestructible as water itself, water power will probably serve us after all mineral fuels have been consumed. It affords a unique opportunity for conservation, with many attendant benefits co-incident. Though treated here as a singular service of water, hydroelectric power becomes only one among divers gains from unified water management and may, indeed, have less importance than others.

The generation of hydroelectric power in the U.S. increased more than eightfold during the period 1920-1960.[12] Hydroelectric installations, public and private, produced, as of January 1, 1961, an annual average of 172 billion kilowatthours of electrical energy. Installed capacity approximated 33 million kilowatts, which is less than one-fourth of what we might have if all potential power sites were developed.[13]

Nationally, the relative importance of hydropower is declining steadily. It generated 40 per cent of our electricity in 1920, but little more than half that percentage in 1955. (In 1960 coal generated some 53 per cent, oil more than 6 per cent, and gas almost 20 per cent.[14])

The practice of applying water artificially to land inadequately supplied with atmospheric precipitation began when ancient desert-dwelling peoples developed sedentary agriculture in their limited environment. Water for crops ranked second only to water for men and animals to drink. Irrigation was born of necessity, and its achievement stretched man's wits before it filled his stomach. It did much to advance ancient civilization, and it has never ceased to challenge human ingenuity. Today its compatibility with good water conservation becomes less apparent but increasingly urgent. Not everywhere does the rich productivity of irrigation justify its extravagant expenditure of water. Irrigation is our greatest consumer of water. Many communities in our dry West are entirely dependent upon irrigation, and it is a prominent factor in the regional economy. Cash crops predominate, but in many places, as in parts of Colorado, irrigated forage crops also lend stability to the range livestock industry.

Irrigation consumes water extravagantly

Irrigation exploits adversity, risking heavy capital outlay against a broad margin of profit. Its dividends come from natural paradox. Soils too dry to sustain plant growth do not suffer much leaching by rain water and are therefore generally rich in plant nutrients. Many desert soils are indeed so full of certain soluble salts that water renders them toxic to plants.[15] Such soils are not suitable for irrigation because the alkaline substances in them tend to be floated out by water and precipitated at the surface in poisonous concentration. Thus water *can* render desert soil even more sterile than it was before water was introduced.

But in many places desert soils need only suitable water to make them abundantly productive. Deficient rainfall means fewer clouds to obstruct sunlight and consequently the receipt of a higher percentage of possible sunshine. In effect, desert crops under irrigation receive sun and rain simultaneously—an ideal arrangement. The combination of rich soil, full sun, and regulated water promotes luxurious plant growth, high yield of forage or fruit, and uniform, early ripening of a superior product. The warm sunshine which imparts quality to the crop also takes by vaporization much of the water in reservoirs and open irrigation systems, raising water costs by extravagant wastage. A warm, dry location means lower water efficiency because of a higher evaporation rate.

In our humid areas, irrigation attains increasing importance in the production of certain crop specialties and as seasonal supplement to rainfall,[16] but in the arid regions it sustains crop agriculture and thriving communities where the land lay barren without it. West of the hundredth meridian there are only limited areas capable of safe and profitable cultivation without artificial

Fig. 3.9 *Lettuce under irrigation in California. Good crisp salad may be worth the price, unless its production entails water consumption exceeding replenishment. (S.C.S. photo.)*

watering. In the vast, dry intermontane region, irrigation has converted many a parched valley into a veritable garden spot. Man-made oases produce many of our choice fruits and vegetables (Fig. 3.9), and a variety of such common field crops as cotton, alfalfa, barley, and sugar beets. Hawaiians began irrigating sugar cane in 1856. In 1960 irrigation took about 75 per cent of all water used in the state, mainly for sugar cane but also for pineapples, alfalfa, and truck crops.

In 1889 less than 4 million acres were irrigated in the entire United States, and expansion was slow.[17] In 1902 Congress passed the Reclamation Act, putting the Federal government into the irrigation business. By 1959 we had extended irrigation to more than 33 million acres,[18] about 7 per cent of our total cultivated acreage. Almost 92 per cent of our irrigated land was in the seventeen Western states, in which more than one-fifth of the irrigation water came from federal projects. Relatively small in area, our irrigated lands contribute, acre for acre, much more than their proportionate share toward our high living standard. Under certain conditions irrigation is certainly consistent with good water conservation; but let us hasten to say that even verdure may be bought overdear. Remember Tam O'Shanter's mare.

Water has carried man and his worldly goods from place to place since the dim dawn of civilization. Boats and rafts served our species long before Noah built the Ark and were bearing important commerce when Archimedes shouted "Eureka." The story of mankind might be read in the evolution of floating carriers, from inflated animal skins and hollowed-out logs to tankers, barges, and refrigerated, steam-powered liners.

Water provides our cheapest transport medium

The United States was discovered, explored, settled, and developed largely by water. The deep estuaries of the Atlantic Coast, the greatest chain of inland lakes in the world, a broad, warm sea—the Gulf of Mexico—and one of the largest rivers—the Mississippi—were the framework for initial strength and progressive westward expansion halfway across the continent. Water courses were the highways by which our young nation reached greatness. With few exceptions, our greatest cities began as water terminals of one sort or another.

During the formative period of our nation, we were so reliant upon water to carry our growing commerce that inland waterway improvements, such as canals and locks, were promoted both privately and publicly. But the fabulous steamboats of Mark Twain's day were no match for locomotives on iron tracks; and engineers turned to bridging rivers instead of dredging them.

Fig. 3.10 *Two large tows meet on the Intra-coastal Waterway near Houma, Louisiana. Water transport is economical where nature provides the highway without expensive artificial adjuncts. (Corps of Engineers, U.S. Army photo.)*

Modernization of overland transportation so facilitated traffic that many canals fell into disuse.

In terms of ton-miles, water carried 17 per cent of our domestic freight in 1960. At 22 per cent, motor carriers were a very poor second to the railroads' 43 per cent. Oil pipe lines moved a tonnage equal to that water-borne. Air freight was less than 0.06 per cent of the total.[19]

Under favorable conditions such bulk commodities as coal, iron ore, grain, and oil can be shipped by water at a ton-mile rate a fraction as high as by railroad, but water carriers are too slow to compete for cargo with high insurance rates in transit. We have more than 20,000 miles of commercial waterway (exclusive of the Great Lakes system). Almost two-thirds of the mileage has a depth of 9 feet or more and can accommodate heavy barge traffic.[20]

The scenic Intracoastal Waterway extends the length of the Atlantic and Gulf Coasts. It is popular for pleasure cruises and carries much freight as well (Fig. 3.10). It is neither "inland" nor "ocean," but a cross between the two. Only a few stretches of it remain uncompleted.

Excepting the Great Lakes, whose importance was greatly magnified by completion of the St. Lawrence Seaway, our inland waterways have yielded their former pre-eminence to faster modes of transport. As incidental adjuncts to well-planned water development, certain segments will be extended or improved, but there may be few water projects that will merit execution for the sole purpose of transportation.[21] Better water connection of the Great Lakes and the Mississippi system will probably materialize. We may anticipate improvement of the present Illinois traverse as well as new canal construction in both Indiana and Ohio to link Lakes Michigan and Erie with the Ohio River. Completion of the St. Lawrence Seaway has revived canal schemes that were abandoned long ago when railway construction rendered their execution impractical.

The use of water as vehicle for transporting pulverized coal and ores by pipe line, which has practical merit in certain situations, commends itself especially to the conservator because, once laid in the ground, the pipe imposes no obstruction to surface-land utilization except that its trace must be accessible for periodic inspection and maintenance.

Far from being outmoded by mechanical and chemical innovations, ice continues its time-worn service as refrigerant. Where "moist cold" is required there is no satisfactory substitute for ice. It protects many perishable foods in storage and transit and renders many more palatable on our tables. Thanks to ice, lettuce from irrigated valleys in the West reaches Eastern city markets fresh and crisp. By the aid of ice one may enjoy fresh shrimp cocktail or oysters on the half-shell anywhere in the country— products of salt water delivered in frozen fresh water. In many other ways ice enriches our diet and contributes to good American living.

Water refrigerates and air-conditions

Not so long ago our refrigeration came from an annual ice harvest on northern lakes and ponds. Huge cakes, perhaps 18 inches thick and twice that long, were shipped considerable distances by rail, laid up tier upon tier in storage sheds, and covered with sawdust to insulate them against summer heat. By promptly replacing the sawdust after each removal of ice, a calculated supply was made to last out the summer. Many railroads, creameries, packing houses, and other ice-using concerns had their own ice storage, and many a farmer laid up his private supply.

However, most of our ice today comes from ice-manufacturing plants using water of high quality. Ice-making machines are standard equipment in food-service establishments and in other

ice-using institutions. Many commercial establishments make ice
for sale to the public. These utilities took ice off the luxury list
even during summertime in Dixie and multiplied our use of
water in solid form.

As solid or liquid, water is virtually indispensable to modern
air-conditioning. Actually most air conditioning is accomplished
with naturally cooled water pumped from wells, though it can
be done by costlier artificial means. So considerable has become
the use of water for cooling large buildings in summer that it
creates a very special water problem in certain metropolitan
areas. During one hot day in July, 1952, 60.5 million gallons of
Potomac water were pumped through the Pentagon to keep that
colossal building cool.[22]

Engineers were not content to use water for cooling alone, so
they developed a "heat pump," which cools in summer and heats
in winter by simply reversing refrigeration processes. It uses
naturally tempered well water throughout the year and may
thereby aggravate the problem of ground-water shortage already
acute in some places. The recharging well by which water is
pumped back into the earth after being used for air conditioning
has become a special water-conserving device. It appears likely
that the use of water in air conditioning will continue as the
need for decontaminating air becomes more pressing; however,
air is supplanting, or supplementing water as a coolant for many
purposes, notably for removing "thermal pollution" of water.[23]

Water governs the abundance of fish and wildlife

Water governs the abundance of fish and wildlife even more
precisely than it governs the pattern of human population. The
conservator must not overlook the fact that all wildlife—upland
birds and animals as well as water fowl—need water to live, that
species can range only a limited distance from water, and that
most of them tend to gravitate toward it. Furthermore, wild
creatures discriminate in their choice of water. Some prefer it
cold; others, warm. Some prefer it running; others, quiet. Most
of them thrive best where the water is clean and shallow and
plant life flourishes. Shore areas are the epitome of habitat; but,
unfortunately, they are often affected negatively, even to the
point of destruction, by water developments considered by men
to be more desirable. Wildlife suffers whenever a marsh is drained
off or flooded by a dam.

Water affords wholesome recreation

Water affords us many of our most popular and wholesome
forms of recreation. Lakes and streams amuse, refresh, and inspire both young and old from all walks of life. Beside them we
build parks and camps for public enjoyment, lodges and homes
for pleasant living. People travel long distances to enjoy them

during a brief vacation. They are the arenas for many favorite outdoor sports, winter and summer—swimming, boating, sailing, water skiing, skin diving, fishing, hunting, and skating. Surface waters provide much of the fun and relaxation essential to health and efficiency under the stress and strain of our accelerated culture.

For recreation, as for most other purposes, we have increased both our use and our expenditure of water. In the old swimming hole we used water naturally available, untreated, unmetered, and free. We swam in the nude and carried away no water in wet bathing suits. We were, unwittingly, conservative. But the swimming hole lost its magnetism to the private pool and the public natatorium. Swimming became expensive business, especially in terms of water. A well-patronized public pool requires frequent changes of water to meet acceptable health standards, and one refilling may take hundreds of thousands of gallons of high-quality water. The total United States water bill for swimming pools alone is charged with billions of gallons annually.

It is also old-fashioned to skate on natural outdoor ice on lakes and ponds. Nor do we wait for wintertime to enjoy our ice sports. Winter or summer we flood and freeze indoor rinks, using large quantities of high-quality water. Midsummer "Ice Capades" illustrate the greater enjoyment and greater expenditure of water that parallels our technological progress.

As if determined to be the complete servant of mankind, water voluntarily removes the grime and filth which would otherwise so befoul his habitat as to render it ultimately untenable. "Refreshing rain" and "purifying streams" are much more than poetic phrases; they are the faithful janitors in our environment. Anyone who has seen the accumulation of dirt during drought, or breathed the acrid air of a tropical desert city, appreciates the cleansing power of rain and run-off. If water did not remove wastes and spent materials from the land and deliver them to the sea, there would be eventually neither marine nor terrestrial life. A fundamental natural cycle would break.

Water carries away our noxious wastes

Man, the ingrate, while pleased and profited by the manifold services of water, consigns to it his refuse and offal for disposal. Mindful only of its readiness, and ignorant of its limitations, he is inclined to overwork the good servant and jeopardize his own well-being. He has exaggerated the capacity of the greatest solvent.

In the United States we have increased enormously our employment of water for industrial production, domestic comfort and convenience, and other desirable applications; but, we have apparently failed to acknowledge that our expanded productivity and elevated living standards, to say nothing of our growing population, expel an increasing volume of wastes that must be removed. By greater expenditure for high-priority uses, we have curtailed the water available for waste removal while constantly augmenting the load of waste cast into it. In effect, we have used so much water about the house that there is not quite enough left for swabbing the back porch.

Much of our domestic water, of potable quality before soiling, serves only to carry sewage. In 1962 some 22 billion gallons of water carried sewage from American municipalities every day and dumped 25 per cent of it untreated into natural surface waters.[24] Septic tanks or cesspools and dispersal lines serving rural homes also expend temporarily the confined water used, but without the prodigious water wastage caused by sewerage lines. But sewerage is one of our expanding public facilities; garbage disposals and detergents have greatly increased the burden of household refuse. Continuing industrialization, and especially the emphasis on synthetics, places additional strain on water as a waste bearer. In many places over our fair land streams overloaded with wastes are blighting the landscape. When overworked by all the tasks we would set it, water balks first and most violently against its meanest function, waste removal. Unless water be treated with due respect, it becomes an agent of contamination rather than purification. We are delinquent in attending to that obvious threat. Here, as in all too many cases, our abuse of one resource does violence to several others. A polluted stream can injure every resource it touches and befoul the entire landscape through which it flows.

Water influences every activity everywhere, and concerns every one of us. For the country as a whole, we receive about 30 inches of rainfall annually, of which approximately 70 per cent returns to the air by evapotranspiration. We get each year an average replenishment of 8.5 cubic inches to every square inch of area.[25] That is our limit of fresh-water supply for manipulation from both surface and underground sources. If we consume more than that, we deplete our stored reserves. If we conserve those 8.5 inches carefully, they will satisfy our growing water requirements for a long time to come. The choice is ours.

4

Water Conservation

water conservation intercepts the rain that falls upon the land, regulates its movement, and gains maximum benefit from it within the limits of replenishment

Water on the land, above and underground, must be adjudged the phase of the hydrologic cycle most useful to man—without discounting the role of the sea, the source of all water. In other words, the water of real service to us is that which, having fallen upon the land, either soaks in or runs off the surface; it is the segment of the water cycle that begins with precipitation and terminates in the sea.

Since our most *useable* water is always on its way to the sea, it should be possible to magnify its usefulness by delaying its escape—thereby in effect increasing its volume. Nature demonstrates this fundamental principle of water conservation with the snows accumulated on mountains in winter and released through life giving streams during summer. Many a valley oasis owes its verdure to such natural detention of water on the land. Freezing stores it up when it would otherwise be wasted. Warmth converts it into useable form and draws it off when it may do the most good. Exactly so can the practical conservator-engineer (i.e., the user of the land) store up water by detaining it with dams, or terraces, or duff, or sod, or other barrier to obstruct its seaward course and gain from it much greater service.

However it is accomplished, whether in the ground or upon it, storage increases the total water resource, and by rendering the

Crux of the problem: slower return to the sea

51

Figs. 4.1 and 4.2 *Structures such as contour ridges (Fig. 4.1) and ponds (Fig. 4.2) conserve water by detaining run-off at its source and inducing it to soak in. The new pond should have its banks protected against erosion. It should be fenced against cattle, and the water piped to a tank from which the animals might drink. (S.C.S. photos.)*

supply more constant increases its efficiency. Storage derives from slower return to the sea and that is the crux of the problem. Its solution is best assured by enlisting the same tactics as those employed by an infantry commander: attack the enemy before he can assemble his forces, engage him at several points simultaneously, and neutralize his dispersed units before they can mass for concerted action. Intercepted and absorbed where they fall, raindrops cannot join forces in a rivulet, rivulets interrupted and dispersed cannot produce vigorous tributaries, and tributaries curbed with dams and other detainers cannot compose a violent river. If the engineer stands idly by until the waters combine their force—as in a river—his mission is doomed to failure and he should be relieved of his command. Water management must commence where the rain falls, as shown in Figs. 4.1 and 4.2.

Water conservation begins with the raindrop. If the drop is induced to soak into the ground instead of running off, it escapes evaporation, joins the less fugitive ground-water supply, and moistens the soil without eroding it. If the drop be shed into surface waters, it steals a little soil and silts the storage areas. Likely as not, it evaporates before it can reach the sea. All in all, it is short-lived and limited in service. An open body of surface water may lose several inches by evaporation during a summer month.[1] Surface water storage is makeshift compared with an aquifer.

Rain that soaks in does the most good

Land receptive to rain can absorb it and hold it like a blotter. Loose, deep soil, mulch or litter, grass sod, and best of all a broadleaved forest with a deep floor covering of duff and leaves are good absorbers (Fig. 4.3). Healthy forests are storage reservoirs more efficient than those we build of concrete. They capture the raindrop the very moment it begins the useful phase of its life cycle, thus getting maximum work out of water.[2] Furthermore, they are immune to sedimentation. It goes without saying that exposed sand or gravel beds may absorb all the water that falls upon them. They are natural manipulators of water

Fig. 4.3 *Good vegetal cover on the land impedes run-off, promotes infiltration, and dissipates the erosive force of water. Forest and sod are about equally effective except as the forest accumulates more snow and causes it to melt less rapidly. Forest curbs the wind and reduces evaporation, but wastes prodigious quantities of water to the atmosphere by transpiration. (After Journal of American Water Works Association.)*

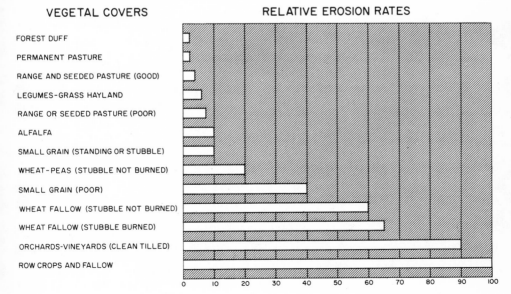

VEGETAL COVERS   RELATIVE EROSION RATES

FOREST DUFF

PERMANENT PASTURE

RANGE AND SEEDED PASTURE (GOOD)

LEGUMES-GRASS HAYLAND

RANGE OR SEEDED PASTURE (POOR)

ALFALFA

SMALL GRAIN (STANDING OR STUBBLE)

WHEAT-PEAS (STUBBLE NOT BURNED)

SMALL GRAIN (POOR)

WHEAT FALLOW (STUBBLE NOT BURNED)

WHEAT FALLOW (STUBBLE BURNED)

ORCHARDS-VINEYARDS (CLEAN TILLED)

ROW CROPS AND FALLOW

0   10   20   30   40   50   60   70   80   90   100

much as mountain snow reserves, but whether they store the water or merely drain it off, the conservator can do little more than estimate the consequences and make the most of them. Some gravel beds feed rich aquifers;[3] some are useful as media for artificial recharge of ground-water supplies.

Raindrop reception and absorption initiate water conservation; penetration improves water storage with depth. Detention of run-off helps maintain ground-water level by inducing soakage, besides performing the more obvious functions of surface water. But none of these operations equals the all important retention of moisture in the soil, without which rains pass through it too quickly to do much good. Without adequate soil moisture neither wild nor cultivated plants can flourish. Desirable as is the percolation of water to replenish underground reservoirs, the storage of soil water is of more immediate and more general importance to resource conservation. It is a primary soil factor, and the basic promoter of all other renewable resources. It exemplifies the complementary relationships that pervade the whole field of conservation.

Humus in the soil acts as a sponge

Plant and animal remains—organic materials—in various stages of decomposition, constitute the sponge that holds soil water. Collectively they are called *humus,* a most significant single word, and material, in conservation. By its capacity for holding water, humus renders plant nutrients more easily and constantly available to growing plants and resists the loss of those nutrients to erosion or leaching. Humus contributes even more toward soil quality than toward water quantity, and we shall consider it again in connection with soil conservation. That it conserves water cannot be doubted by anyone who has seen nursery stock shipped in sphagnum moss or felt the wetness under an old pile of leaves. Soils rich in humus retain moisture and dissolved minerals, releasing them to nourish growing plants. Humus in the soil holds in reserve the surplus moisture of a wet period as defense against seasonal drought and crop-water shortage. In contrast, soil devoid of humus either resists penetration or releases the water as through a sieve, becoming droughty almost before rain stops falling. Such soil sheds water so rapidly that little can soak into the earth, and the bulk rushes off the land too fast for effective surface use. Soil conditions are potent elements in water conservation.[4]

Supplies of ground water are limited

Ground water deserves emphasis in water conservation because it is by nature "conservative." It moves less rapidly, suffers less loss to natural forces, and maintains uniformly high qualities. Certain rock basins and deep aquifers may be almost leakproof, but most ground-water reservoirs release water through springs, streams, or seepage areas; so, their storage is not absolutely permanent. Unless they be replenished they would ultimately be empty. Their total capacity is fixed. If all the earth cavities and interstices were filled with water, there would be a certain quantity, and no more. Contrary to popular notions, *ground-water supplies are limited*. The only way to maintain them is to take out no more than goes in. Unless we do this, we will eventually pump the land so dry underneath that we shall be forced to change our whole scheme of water supply, becoming increasingly dependent upon elaborate and costly surface storage. About one-third of our metropolitan water supply comes from wells; in virtually all the metropolitan areas supplied by wells, the draft of ground water is excessive.[5] Many cities have already constructed surface reservoirs to supplement a ground-water supply once adequate, and many others may be compelled to make similar provision. How many acre-feet of surface water would our cities require if all their wells went dry (1 acre of water 1-foot deep is an acre-foot)? Could we devote all that space to water supply at the expense of other land uses? If they are pumped faster than rain can soak into the catchment areas, the wells will go dry!

What are the warnings against overdrawing our subterranean accounts? Can we audit and balance them or must we gamble on credit? Thus far we have spent recklessly from reserves grossly overestimated; but now we have need and knowledge to regain our credit rating. We have been warned by flowing wells that stopped flowing, by pumped wells that had to be drilled deeper, by deep wells that began to yield salty water. In each case it was a blunt notification that withdrawals exceeded deposits.

Hydrologists and well-drillers speak in terms of *draw-down, cone of depression,* and *ground-water flow* when they wish to determine the safe pumping capacity of a well for continuous use.[6] Draw-down results from pumping out the water faster than the flow will replace it, a normal well condition. However, if draw-down be so excessive that the resultant cone of depression reaches the bottom of the casing, the well goes dry, at least until natural flow can begin to refill the cone (Fig. 4.4). A steep cone of depression indicates that pumping exceeds the maximum sustained capacity of the well, which depends directly upon the rate of ground-water flow. The rate of flow depends, in the main, upon the thickness and the permeability of the water-bearing stratum. It is not unusual for large water users to make several borings in proximity to secure a combined flow adequate for

The lowering water table

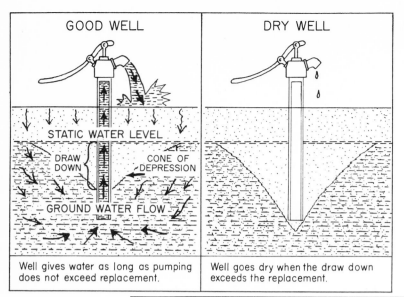

GOOD WELL	DRY WELL
STATIC WATER LEVEL — DRAW DOWN — CONE OF DEPRESSION — GROUND WATER FLOW	
Well gives water as long as pumping does not exceed replacement.	Well goes dry when the draw down exceeds the replacement.

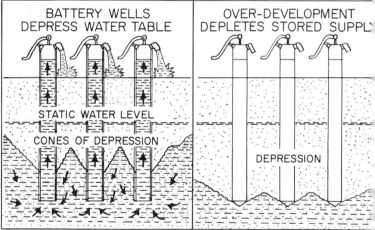

BATTERY WELLS DEPRESS WATER TABLE — STATIC WATER LEVEL — CONES OF DEPRESSION

OVER-DEVELOPMENT DEPLETES STORED SUPPLY — DEPRESSION

Figs. 4.4 and 4.5 *Overdevelopment of ground water invites regional calamity when depression of the water level becomes extreme. When too much water is pumped from too many wells, the general ground-water level falls lower and lower until the depth makes further drilling and pumping prohibitively expensive, if not physically impossible.*

their purposes. If they pump the battery of wells so heavily that the general ground-water level under the area sinks deeper and deeper, they have committed the hydrological sin called *over-development*. They have drained the underground reservoir beyond a safe margin of recovery and they have lowered the water table as shown graphically in Fig. 4.5.

Most regions of our country were naturally well endowed with ground water, particularly the extensive Coastal and Interior

Plains with their excellent artesian structures. However, in some of the more richly blessed areas water users have so radically overdeveloped the supply as to lower the water table several feet in a few years. It is estimated, for example, that under portions of the High Plains the water table fell as much as 40 feet in only a few years.[7] Such depression foreshadows regional calamity. The wealth of water under portions of the Gulf Coastal Plain remains a major factor in the industrial development of the South, but even this great wealth may be subjected to overdevelopment.

Be it understood that a lowering water table results from reduced intake as well as from excessive output, though the latter may be more apparent and its consequences usually more immediate. Clearing of forest, breaking of sod, draining of swamps and marshes, and abusive cropping or grazing of the land can reduce absorption materially. Buildings, hard roads, and other cultural features constrict the absorbing area. Whatever its cause —other than normal fluctuation with rainfall—a lowering water table indicates urgent need for appropriate conservation measures to prevent exhaustion of ground-water supply. Restriction of established uses imposes hardship and cannot be recommended except as a last resort. Closure of a factory to save water would be too costly a method of conservation unless it were necessary in order to have enough drinking water for the community. Owners and workers cannot forfeit their earnings in anticipation of water shortage. But they can be acquainted with the gravity of the situation and encouraged to use the dwindling supply more sparingly. New users can be excluded from critical areas, and no additional water development permitted. Timely warnings and recommendations given by the Federal Geological Survey or appropriate state agencies should be heeded automatically, but legal controls need application in more places than one likes to contemplate.[8] Overuse cannot exceed recharge indefinitely. The control of flowing wells to prevent waste, the development of recharge areas and recharge wells,[9] the re-use of water when feasible, and other direct water-saving practices have checked much foolish wastage of subterranean waters, but not nearly enough.

Forests are the effectual regulators and conservers of water by natural means, virtually prohibiting run-off. A dense canopy of leaves can intercept a light rain so completely that the ground underneath gets none at all. Trees in foliage draw back up much of the water they admit to the ground and give it off by transpiration. From a vigorous forest, evaporation and transpiration dispose of 15 to 20 or more inches of water a year.[10] How then do

Forests regulate water

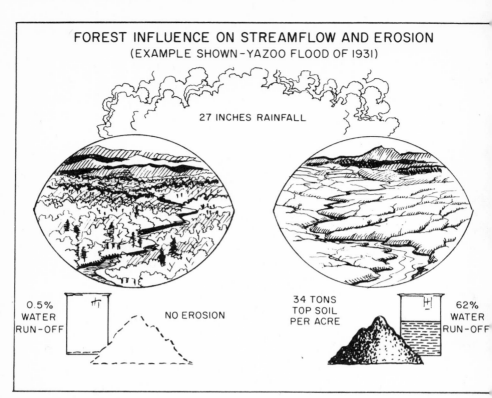

FOREST INFLUENCE ON STREAMFLOW AND EROSION
(EXAMPLE SHOWN–YAZOO FLOOD OF 1931)

27 INCHES RAINFALL

0.5% WATER RUN-OFF

NO EROSION

34 TONS TOP SOIL PER ACRE

62% WATER RUN-OFF

Fig. 4.6 *This comparative diagram represents an actual case of forest influence on run-off and erosion. The barren watershed became even more denuded. (After U.S. Forest Service photo.)*

forests conserve water? That portion of the rainfall which reaches the forest floor is absorbed by leaves, litter, and humus, whence much of it passes into the ground to emerge elsewhere later on in springs and streams. Some of it passes all the way down to deep ground-water reservoirs. Forests stow away water which comes in heavy, erratic rains and release it gradually over an extended period of time.[11] An actual measurement of this forest function is illustrated in Fig. 4.6. By reducing wind velocities, by breaking the raindrops, by checking evaporation from the floor with shade and natural mulch, by loosening and deepening the soil mantle with roots, forests perform a unique service. Themselves a major renewable resource, they help conserve all the others. Perhaps no other resource better demonstrates the interdependence of all than do forests; we will have occasion to consider their function many times in this book.

So proficient are forests in the regulation of water that the water wheels of old New England rarely stopped for lack of water while the slopes upstream from mill sites remained wooded. Steep, forest-covered granite hills could contain a deluge and then gradually deliver the water to valleys below. Streams, especially the headwaters, carried clear water and flowed perennially. The land was richly watered—by about the same amount of rainfall it receives today. But now many granite slopes are bare, and the rains rush off almost as fast as they come.

Let no one suppose that the rivers that issued from forest wilderness before settlers cleared the land were always placid and constant. On the contrary, heavy rains over a drainage basin converged upon the main channel in gigantic floods long before any man, white or red, set foot upon our continent. The primeval forests did indeed bridle the violence of rivers, and the floods spent themselves with less apparent destruction, since the valleys contained no man-made "property" to destroy. When the white man came and developed his property, he unleashed the wild violence of waters that have repeatedly laid waste the river valleys. He made arrangements for disaster, and now he must seek to correct them in some degree, as a concomitant of good water conservation.

So drastically has the denudation of watersheds accelerated runoff that stream flow once highly valuable has in many places become a dubious asset. Streams that once turned water wheels constantly are now only periodically useful for power. The Westfield River in Massachusetts is one among many with such a history. Brooks that once flowed perennially now flow only intermittently, and often with muddy water. Unhampered headwaters rush together so rapidly that the master stream becomes now and again a wild torrent that defies discipline. Floods like that of the Mississippi in 1927, that of the Ohio in 1936, that of the Missouri in 1947, that of the Columbia in 1948, that in Kansas in 1951, and those in California in 1952 and 1962, to mention a few, have become milestones from which the valley folk reckon years. They have caused tragic losses of life and property. Floods have cost fantastic sums of private and public money; more in a few years than it would cost to prevent indefinitely their recurrence. Kansas is certainly not crowded with urban or industrial development, yet the 1951 flood caused damage estimated at 2 billion dollars.[12] Flood waters spread far and wide over the level terrain with consequent damage to crops, soils, homes, and communities in an extensive area. Good soils were buried under sterile sand.

Best defense against floods evolves from wise land use: forest on slopes where trees ought to grow, grass on dry land that ought to be sod covered, and cropland tilled under good conservation practices. But immediate, emergency, flood defense requires detention of hurried waters behind barriers across the stream. Flood control is a major purpose of many of our great dam structures, though they *prevent* rather than control, holding back waters that would flood if unrestrained. Our nearest approach to flood control has been with levees such as those along the lower Mississippi. Time and again those levees have proved inadequate. We have breached them to disperse floods by releasing the waters through prearranged spillways into broad passes that direct them to the Gulf. Perhaps dissipation of force amounts to control. Confinement has been impossible.[13]

Although flood prevention has been a major objective of federal water-resources activity since 1936, and much has been done to bridle rampageous rivers, flood damages have increased during recent years. To this paradox, record-breaking floods have, indeed, contributed, but even more accountable has been the heedless development of river plains subject to ravage by torrential waters. The creation of property vulnerable to damage by floods has been progressing more rapidly than construction for containment of the floods.[14]

Dams and reservoirs serve multiple purposes

Whatever their length or height, whatever their material, whoever built them—men or beavers—dams conserve water by detaining it (Figs. 4.7 and 4.8). Whether confining farm ponds or inland seas, dams reduce flood hazards by impounding water during wet seasons for release during dry ones and by equalizing stream flow throughout all seasons. Every dam on a river system lightens the task of the ones downstream. A river with regulated headwaters flows more uniformly into the sea. Beavers in Montana build social security for wharf rats in New Orleans.

Hundreds of dams in this country are large enough to perform several valuable functions simultaneously. Each one, large or small, inevitably does something toward flood prevention. Comparatively small dams are used economically for power production where power is needed. Large ones that impound sizeable reservoirs may serve a combination of purposes—domestic water supply, navigation, recreation, industry, irrigation, landscape enrichment, and power—without overtaxing the storage capacity, but in most cases competition limits the variety of uses. Priority of use, and allocation of water among various uses, lie well within the province of water conservation. "Water over the dam" represents outright waste, and water released without doing much work represents waste only slightly mitigated. Figuratively speaking, water passed through a turbine to generate electricity has not lost anything except its head (the depth behind the dam that gives the water its power). The body remains intact, and its usefulness below the dam may be quite as great as above it, for certain pur-

poses under certain site conditions. Its utilization for power does not detract from its value for irrigation. An industry using water downstream from a power dam may gain its greatest operational advantage from the regularity of flow ensured by continuous operation of the generating plant above it.

Not all uses of reservoirs or lakes are complementary; several conflict with one another. The fluctuation of water level incidental to draw-down for power and flood prevention causes the "shore" to oscillate in a manner most disconcerting to bathers, boaters, and fishermen, and injures the wildlife habitat as well. At the same time, the change of water level combats mosquitos and other water-breeding insects—a result pleasing to health experts. High dams across steep-sided, V-shaped valleys produce powerful heads and deep, cool water, but their shores are inhospitable and difficult of access. Long, low dams across wide valleys in flat country produce extensive lakes with shores easily approached and well suited to beach development. The shallow waters become comfortably warm for summer swimming, but their expansive surfaces lose much of their volume to evaporation.

Aristocrats among reservoirs are the ones that store drinking water for population centers. From them other uses are ordinarily excluded for reasons of sanitation. Capacity permitting, they might be used for power without detracting from their primary function, but recreation and other uses involve, at best, additional problems of filtering and purification. The highest type of water use asserts its priority in many different ways.

Dams and reservoirs can serve only temporarily because, sooner or later, the storage space fills up with soil and debris washed into it. The process is called "siltation" or "sedimentation" from the terms "silt" and "sediment" pertaining to water-deposited materials. Some silting takes place under the most favorable natural conditions, and no man would presume to stop it. Where soils are protected, as by a dense forest, siltation proceeds at an exceedingly slow rate and may be almost imperceptible. Thus it would take a millennium to fill our great reservoirs. Unfortunately such conditions do not obtain over any of our major watersheds: none has a continuous, undisturbed forest cover.

Where soils have poor natural cover or are exposed by unwise land use, their erosion and consequent choking of reservoirs can proceed at such fantastic rates that the useful life of a dam may be only a few decades. Readers less than middle-aged bid fair to outlive in usefulness several of our big dam structures. Many dams, big and small, have already been filled to the top and now retain alluvial flats instead of water. One of these is shown in Fig. 4.9. At the rate the mighty Lake Mead has been filling since Hoover Dam was completed in 1935, even it will be brim-full of sediment in less than five hundred years.[15] In the immediate future, hydraulic engineers will face problems of their own creation: shall they remove the sediment or raise the dam? When must they yield to the natural forces that carve valleys?

Fig. 4.9 *Less than twenty years after construction this dam was rendered ineffective by sedimentation. Its usefulness would have been prolonged by good land management on the watershed above it. (S.C.S. photo.)*

How may they abandon a moribund project without destroying cultural adjuncts? Among our large dams are many well-planned and well-sited ones, with a life expectancy of several centuries; but, even they should be regarded as temporary expedients, lest they instill a false sense of permanent security. Annual displacement of reservoir storage capacity by sedimentation varies from a small fraction of 1 per cent in some reservoirs to more than 3 per cent in others.[16] Thus, a dam whose tributary watershed erodes rapidly may be defunct less than thirty years after construction. Conditions of the watershed as a whole determine the longevity of a dam.

If ever we could develop completely all our drainage basins and their tributary watersheds and pump out ground water exactly as fast as it goes in, we should have available *all* the water possible to obtain with the techniques now generally understood. There would be a specific quantity for all purposes, procurement would be competitive, and margins of supply would be sought through artificial precipitation of cloud moisture and the freshening of sea water. The "production" aspect of water conservation would be accomplished, and only the problem of optimum "disposition" would remain. Meanwhile, far into the remote future, we must look to production and disposition (credit and debit) simultaneously. Water conservation is clearly a matter of double-entry bookkeeping, and our ledger has entirely too many red entries at present. Let us examine the big accounts in our record and see how they might be better balanced.

Our uses of water may be grouped into two categories; those for which the water is withdrawn from a source of supply either on the surface or underground and those that entail no such manipulation. Nonwithdrawal uses include water for navigation, water for wildlife habitat, and water for outdoor recreation. Withdrawal uses include water for irrigation, water for industry, water for domestic and municipal supplies, and water for generating electricity (although one might contend that water is not actually withdrawn by passing it through turbines to a lower level). Withdrawal (or intake) water may be further subdivided into two categories of use—consumptive and nonconsumptive. After nonconsumptive use water is immediately available for re-use without appreciable reduction of volume. None has been taken away. Water used consumptively is temporarily lost, either by evaporation into the atmosphere or by incorporation in a product such as canned food or beer. It is not immediately available for re-use.

Obviously, electric generators consume no water, so that water with hydropower potential is wasted only when its energy goes unused. It is conserved by extracting the energy for useful purposes. The operation of locks on waterways might be said to divert water for navigation, however negligible the quantity. Navigation might also be regarded as a quasi-consumptive water use in the degree to which shipping soils the water and thereby renders it less suitable for other uses. Water-use classification becomes somewhat arbitrary from a practical point of view.

Our main water uses involving both withdrawal and consumption, or depletion, are represented in the accompanying diagram (Fig. 4.10), which serves as convenient orientation for examining certain debits and credits in our water budget. We shall first consider the most consumptive use, irrigation, because it is divorced from the public and industrial uses. The latter two are often associated because their problems are common to both.

Crop irrigation produces many fruits and vegetables prized both for flavor and nutritional qualities, including grapes for fine domestic wines. It contributes much to the excellence of our diet and our health and to the magnitude of our gross national product. It produces an abundance of hay that helps feed livestock on ranches and rangelands, and it also produces abundantly such surplus crops as corn, sorghum, and cotton. It is, of course, a profitable practice, but one so demanding of water where water is scarce that it appears in some situations doomed by its own extravagance.

UNITED STATES WATER BUDGET

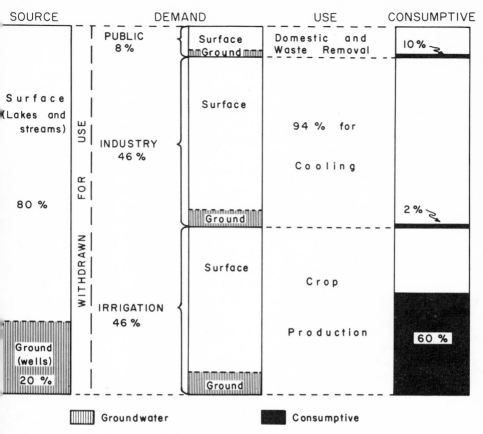

Fig. 4.10 *The degree to which any water use is consumptive correlates more or less with the length of time the water is rendered unsuitable or unavailable for reuse. Water for farms and rural communities comes mainly from wells. More than one-fourth of the water withdrawn for industrial use is saline. (Compiled from* Water Resources Activities in the United States, *Select Committee on National Water Resources, U.S. Senate, 86th Cong., 1st sess.)*

More than 90 per cent of all irrigated land in the United States lies in the seventeen Western states and Hawaii. Although more than one-fifth of the irrigation water comes from federal projects, irrigation development remains predominantly private enterprise. More than one-third of the water used for irrigation is ground water pumped from wells,[17] and pumpage is often so excessive that it amounts to water "mining." On parts of the Southern High Plains of Texas and New Mexico (Llano Estacado) withdrawals approximately equaled the annual recharge rate in 1935. By 1958 pumping had attained such excessive volume that withdrawal was 140 times as great as recharge, portending complete

Most consumptive and wasteful is irrigation

exhaustion of the ground-water reserve in about thirty years.[18] Continuous water mining necessitates progressive deepening of wells, and, unless stopped, it will eventually raise water costs so high that irrigation becomes uneconomical. A few cents per 1,000 gallons might be decisive.

Not only does irrigation entail the greatest consumptive *use* of water, but it also relates to our greatest consumptive *waste* of water—useless dissipation of potentially productive water—by evaporation and transpiration. In our Western irrigation regions where the air is warm and dry much of the time and strong winds are prevalent, 7 feet of water may evaporate from exposed water surfaces in one year.[19] Total evaporation losses attain monstrous proportions, and yet their regional magnitude is somewhat less than that of transpiration from useless phreatophytic vegetation on stream banks and flood plains.

Phreatophytes are plants that require much water and draw their supply from the zone of saturation, or ground-water storage. Alfalfa is a phreatophyte, noted for its deep roots. Unlike alfalfa, however, the water-wasting plants that concern us here have no significant economic value. More than seventy species of phreatophytes grow in the dry West. Some of them have adapted to a wide range of habitat conditions from Canada to Mexico; others, with less climatic tolerance, are limited in their regional distribution. Worst water waster of all is the saltcedar (Tamarix gallica L.), which has invaded almost every stream valley in the Southwest. A dense, vigorous growth of this species transpires as much as 5 to 9 acre-feet of water per acre occupied in a single year. This and other phreatophytes have usurped an estimated 16 million acres of land in the seventeen Western states.[20]

Altogether, irrigation constitutes our most grossly wasteful water use. Its efficiency could be vastly improved by sealing diversion canals against leakage or replacing them with pipe lines, by applying water to fields at such times and in such quantities as would be of optimal benefit to the crops, by eradicating phreatophytes, by suppressing evaporation from surface-water sources with chemical applications, and by other possible techniques. Meanwhile, according to trends already apparent, other, less consumptive uses, such as industry and recreation, will require increasing proportions of the scarce water in our dry West and realize benefits incomparably greater than those generally accruing from irrigation. Until America stands in need of extending arability to satisfy food requirements, further public development of water storage for irrigation should probably be postponed. Otherwise we shall have defunct reservoirs filled with debris when such storage becomes necessary.

In sharp contrast with irrigation, industry uses water most efficiently and least consumptively, and for good reason. Manufacturers operate competitively in our free, capitalistic system and their profits derive largely from economical procurement and utilization of materials, including water. Water costs are subject to the same scrutiny as other items of expense. Indeed, a reliable water supply, of adequate quantity and suitable quality, available at reasonable cost, may be a prime factor in the location of an industrial plant. Where the water is abundant and cheap it may be used on a "once through" basis; where it is in short supply or needs considerable treatment before it can be used, it may be re-used or recirculated several times before released from the plant. Waste of industrial water is so obviously antithetic to good management as to be, in effect, self-prohibitive. Price prescribes the conservation of water by industry without any extraneous compulsion. Perhaps the only circumstances justifying public restriction of industrial water use are those under which requirements for industry threaten depletion of supplies needed for municipal purposes; however, such circumstances have become recurrent, if not persistent, in many places.

Industrial use is efficient; domestic use is reckless

Public water use lacks the efficiency characteristic of water use by industry because it is a noncompetitive, nonprofit community service. Water for domestic use remains a very inexpensive commodity in most localities, and, being cheap, it is used "lavishly." For considerable segments of our urban population water is furnished unmetered and is paid for at a fixed monthly rate— an open invitation to waste. The low price of domestic water instills false notions of abundance and perpetuates equally false standards of water quality. Most Americans still take a glass of crystal-clear water for granted, neither marveling at its clarity nor hesitating between swallows to speculate about the number of times the transparent liquid might have been drunk before. We are prone to discount the worth of inexpensive things; whereas industry must be sensitive to water costs, the price of domestic water might be multiplied several times without reducing consumption significantly. Self-imposed restrictions on water usage can effectuate substantial diminution of demand in event of present or impending shortage, but only if the public be realistically apprized of the necessity. Self-appointed prophets of water famine have been shouting "wolf" so loudly that their trembling flock, the public, needs calm assurance that America's thirst will be quenched. We have plenty of water, and we can have more as we need it, but we must correct our slovenly habit of degrading it with filth and pouring it over the land dirty! The 10 per cent and 2 per cent, respectively, of consumptive use cited for public and industrial withdrawals of water have little more than definitive significance, because most of the water discharged by industries and municipalities is so polluted that it must be regarded as at least partially "consumed." The degree to which cities and factories degrade the quality of water below that acceptable for their use curtails the available supplies. Quality reduction and volume reduction contribute to the same problems and cannot be entirely segregated. Water abuse causes water shortage.

Most pervasive, destructive, and dangerous of all our water problems are those caused by pollution, our persistent loading of waters with almost every kind of waste in quantities exceeding natural assimilative capacities. The major pollutants, their sources and characteristics, appear in concise, tabular form in Table 1. Intensive scrutiny of the tabulation spares us a lengthy discussion here. One additional source should be mentioned, namely, the ships and other craft that pollute with oil and bilge wastes the water they ply. (Pollution, in turn, effects shipping adversely.) Note that some pollutants are living organisms, including many dangerous to human health. Many are organic substances that decompose harmlessly in the presence of sufficient dissolved oxygen. Still others are inorganic chemicals that remain stable and toxic for a long time and can be poisonous far from their origins. Some pollutants are in solution; others are in suspension. Some are natural, such as salt and silt that enter rivers and move toward the sea without human help; but, many others —among the worst—are artificial, synthetic substances so varied and complex that we know neither what their cumulative danger may be nor how to dispose of them safely. The least noxious, though most voluminous form, thermal pollution, can kill a stream by reducing its oxygen content. The evils of pollution have become more menacing to the beauty and habitability of our country than any other resource abuse.

Pollution destroys much more than water, blighting the whole landscape it touches. It has ruined or seriously damaged most of our streams and lakes and many segments of our coasts, killing the fish, driving wildlife away, and discommoding, if not actually jeopardizing, human society. The Public Health Service and other health agencies are obliged to condemn and close numerous

Water pollution befouls, withers, and destroys

Table 1

Pollutants: Common Types and Sources

Pollutant (type)	Nature of Pollutant	Common Sources	Overpollution Results in:	How Measured, Controlled, etc.
Sewage and other oxygen-demanding wastes	Putrescible organics; normally reduced to stable compounds by aerobic bacteria (which require water-dissolved oxygen).	Domestic sewage; food processing industries.	Excessive depletion of oxygen in water damages fish life; complete oxygen removal causes anaerobic bacterial action on pollutants resulting in bad colors, offensive odors.	Measurable in terms of biochemical oxygen demand (BOD); i.e., amount of water-dissolved oxygen used in aerobic bacterial decomposition of the waste. Sometimes expressed in terms of population equivalent (PE); includes oxygen demand by industrial waste as well as municipal sewage. Based on average oxygen need of 0.17 lbs./person to stabilize daily sewage and related wastes.
Infectious agents	Disease-causing organisms (bacteria, viruses).	Human and animal wastes; certain industries (e.g. tanning, slaughtering).	Need for stringent purification treatment to obtain potable supplies; losses to fishing industry (especially shellfish); curtailed recreational uses of streams, lakes, etc.	Most commonly controlled with chlorine; all bacterial and viral contamination probably impossible to remove in most cases, but concentrations are greatly reduced.
Plant nutrients	Principally nitrogen and phosphorus compounds.	Municipal sewage; industrial wastes; farms (chemical fertilizers).	Excessive growth of aquatic plant life leading to secondary oxygen-demanding pollution, offensive odors, bad taste.	Serious problem; not removed by ordinary sewage treatment methods.
Organic chemicals	Detergents, pesticides, many industrial by-products.	Domestic and industrial sewage; farms (pesticides, etc.).	Threat to fish and other wildlife; possible long-term ingestion hazards to human beings.	Very often not removed by usual sewage or water purification treatments.
Minerals and inorganic chemicals	Common salt; acids; metallic salts; cyanides; etc.	Mining; industrial processes; natural deposits (e.g. salt).	Interference with manufacturing processes; obvious or insidious toxic effects on humans and wildlife; bad odors and tastes; corrosion of equipment (industrial, navigational, power plants).	Difficult to detect and measure; removal often costly.
Sediments	Primarily soils and minerals; also some industrial by-products.	Land erosion by storms, flood waters, etc.; pulp mill and other plant effluents.	Obstruction or filling of streams, lakes, reservoirs, navigational channels; increases cost of water purification; interferes with manufacturing processes; causes equipment corrosion; reduces fish life.	Controlled by use of soil conservation and flood control methods; also by improvement of industrial technology.
Radioactive materials		Mining operations; refining of uranium and thorium; power reactors; medical and research centers.	Health hazards to all animal life; small amounts may be concentrated by aquatic life and sediments to increase long-term hazards.	Detectable by automatic stream monitoring; controlled by proper storage of wastes. Future disposal problems will become critical. Normal water treatment methods are ineffective for removal.
Heat	Heated water returned to streams and lakes.	Steam-electric power plants; steel mills; refineries; other industrial cooling units.	Reduction of water-contained oxygen, resulting in slower or incomplete pollutant decomposition and damage to aquatic life.	Minimized by recirculation and re-use of industrial cooling waters; choice of proper plant location; use of spray ponds, cooling towers, etc.

Source: *Chemical Week*, October 7, 1961. By permission from *Chemical Week*. Copyright 1961 by McGraw-Hill Book Company, Inc.

beach areas and fishing grounds every year to protect the public. Many cities on our coasts, rivers, and Great Lakes, urgently in need of outdoor recreation opportunities, have largely surrendered to pollution their waterfront advantages. Despite vigilant surveillance, outbreaks of disease have been traced to shellfish taken in polluted water. Pollution of habitats has been a major factor in the decimation of waterfowl and other desirable wildlife. Its annual destruction of habitat exceeds the rate of habitat creation and rehabilitation by all public agencies conducting fish and wildlife restoration programs.[21]

In the early days, when factories and population centers were few and scattered and rivers ran full, it was possible to pour our wastes into the streams without much danger. Dilution was adequate then, but growth and concentration of people and industry mutilated watersheds and increased water consumption, simultaneously. Cultural development reduced water "production" by clearing the land. The supply waned while the demand grew larger. Streams shrank in volume and became more erratic in flow. The production of industrial wastes and sewage grew progressively greater until many weakened streams became overloaded with filth. Now, especially in the densely populated Northeast, many a river once clear, beautiful, and beneficent has become an ugly menace. The Potomac is a national disgrace!

Polluting matter in our streams comes mainly from soil erosion, water-using industries, coal-mining operations, oil fields, and city sewerage systems. Pollution by mine acids can be greatly reduced by sealing abandoned mines. Oil field brines can be largely, and economically, disposed of by injecting them back into the ground to repressurize the remaining oil. Soil conservation reduces the volume of erosion silt. However, pollution by industrial and metropolitan wastes grows in volume, complexity, and strength without effective and adequate efforts to abate it. Raw sewage is the most objectionable of all because it contaminates water with disease germs far beyond the extent of areas visibly soiled. So common is the practice of dumping raw sewage and factory wastes into a creek or a river that, except in remote wilderness areas, few streams carry clear water. Many are open sewers traversing our most populous landscapes. Too many towns and institutions, too many pulpmills, steel mills, chemical plants, collieries, and other industries overwork the streams, using them both for water supply and waste disposal. It has been estimated, for instance, that Ohio River water, during periods of low flow, is *used* almost four times on its journey from Pennsylvania to the Mississippi.[22]

When city water systems became practical it was convenient for river towns to draw their water supply from the stream—*above the town*—and equally convenient to pour their sewage and dump their garbage into the same stream—*below the town*. Of course other towns downstream complained, but about all they could do was to install better filtering and purifying plants and to drink less palatable water at a higher price. We have imposed upon ourselves such widespread water adulteration that places with good, pleasant-tasting water are prized by discriminate travelers and home seekers.

To date we have behaved worse than swine, and it is imperative that we improve our habits. Cannot we, the intelligentsia of the animal world, dispose of our refuse without befouling our habitat? We know the means of preventing or abating pollution, and we are learning the necessity for employing them; but clear streams and pure well-water are no longer free, and we are reluctant to pay for them. From that attitude has developed our most serious delinquency in water conservation.

Observe
the cleanly swine

Our attack on water pollution is thus far a losing battle. Despite tremendous expenditure for construction of waste-treatment facilities, accelerated by liberal government aid under the Federal Water Pollution Control Act (Public Law 660, 84th Cong.), our waste load increases faster than our means to cope with it. In 1960 our surface waters were almost six times as dirty as in 1900.[23] During the interim (sixty years), municipal pollution had more than tripled in volume and industrial pollution had increased tenfold. Worst polluters are some twenty-five thousand industrial establishments with separate waste outlets.[24] Most of those nefarious outlets pour untreated wastes into waters once natural. Stream pollution by industries is twice that of municipalities. Both are disgraceful in a land otherwise incomparably fair and rich!

Treatment
of sewage and
industrial wastes
must become
standard practice
everywhere

Twenty-five per cent of municipal wastes are still dumped into our streams as raw sewage; 31 per cent receive only primary treatment, which removes one-third of the wastes before release of the water; only 44 per cent receive both primary and secondary treatment, which removes about 80 per cent of the wastes. Thus, altogether, the sewage problem is, by volume, only half-solved. Furthermore, conventional treatment (Figs. 4.11 and 4.12) extracts none of the salts, stable detergents, or certain other chemicals. They remain in the effluent, and, by percolation into the earth, eventually pollute ground water. Although waste treatment, on a tonnage basis, has become our biggest business,[25] it needs doubling now and tripling in the near future.

Fig. 4.11 *Sewage treatment plant, Kenosha, Wisconsin. Conventional treatment of municipal waste costs very little per person. Cost of this installation in 1940-1941: $475,-000, exclusive of land. In 1962 it served a population of more than 70,000 at an annual expenditure of $110,000 for operation and maintenance. (Photo by Joseph Constanti, Courtesy the City of Kenosha.)*

Fig. 4.12 *Kenosha borrows her water supply (almost 12 million gallons per day in 1962) from Lake Michigan. Shown here are the processes by which the city, having used and soiled the water, cleans it before returning it to the lake. (Courtesy the City of Kenosha.)*

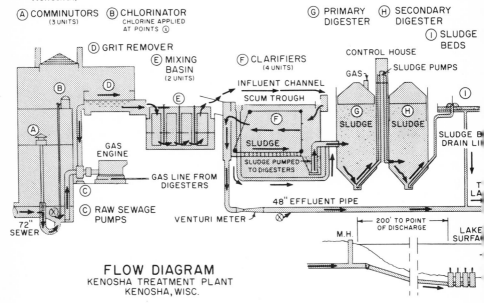

Ⓐ COMMINUTORS (3 UNITS) Ⓑ CHLORINATOR CHLORINE APPLIED AT POINTS Ⓧ Ⓖ PRIMARY DIGESTER Ⓗ SECONDARY DIGESTER

Ⓘ SLUDGE BEDS

Ⓓ GRIT REMOVER

Ⓔ MIXING BASIN (2 UNITS) Ⓕ CLARIFIERS (4 UNITS) CONTROL HOUSE

SLUDGE PUMPS

GAS

INFLUENT CHANNEL

SCUM TROUGH

Ⓑ Ⓓ

Ⓔ

Ⓕ

Ⓐ

Ⓖ SLUDGE Ⓗ SLUDGE

Ⓘ

SLUDGE B DRAIN LI

GAS ENGINE

SLUDGE

SLUDGE PUMPED TO DIGESTERS

GAS LINE FROM DIGESTERS

Ⓒ

T LA

Ⓒ RAW SEWAGE PUMPS VENTURI METER

48" EFFLUENT PIPE

200' TO POINT OF DISCHARGE

72" SEWER

Ⓧ

M.H.

LAKE SURFA

FLOW DIAGRAM
KENOSHA TREATMENT PLANT
KENOSHA, WISC.

72

Under provisions of Public Law 660 each state may, through a legally constituted Water Pollution Control Board, or any other designated agency, refer to the responsible federal authority (Public Health Service) any problem under its purview, whether interstate, intrastate, or coastal, for investigation and adjudication. In event of interstate or coastal pollution, the federal authority must prosecute the party or parties responsible for the injury; in event of injury that is intrastate the Federal government may intervene only with consent of the governor. The state agencies may, without recourse to higher authority, cite communities or industries for violations and compel them to institute specified corrective measures. Before the end of fiscal year 1962, federal action had been taken in eighteen cases, involving 250 cities and an equal number of industries, and affecting some 4,000 miles of interstate rivers and streams.[26] The several state agencies had at the same time required many delinquent municipalities and industries to correct their deficiencies. Asserted by law and implemented with fiscal authority, the public will may have turned the tide of water pollution.

The authorized agencies have little difficulty prescribing appropriate measures for alleviating municipal violations because sewage is, in essence, the same kind of stuff everywhere; the onus is on the community, and the installation of standard facilities meets requirements. Costs are ordinarily defrayed with a tax levy less consequential than irritating. However, mandatory control of industrial pollution is often more complicated. Industrial wastes are so complex and so variable from one source to another that prescribed corrective measures must be adjusted to many different situations. A fixed formula will not suffice. Enforcement of stringent regulations may curtail payrolls and profits more than economically tolerable, even causing suspension of operations. Arbitrary injunction must be tempered with deliberation and reasonable time for compliance. Many industrial wastes have become salvable as by-products by the application of new techniques, and many more such conversions will be forthcoming. (If wastes are strong enough to be damaging, they must also have strength enough to be useful when appropriate technologies can be applied to them.) The consumer public must, for its part, learn to accept as legitimate price factors any waste-treatment costs not otherwise recoverable in the production process. Clean streams are no longer free; they can be had only as we are willing to pay for them.

Our cities and institutions that continue to pollute our waters necessarily also continue to expand their filtering and purifica-

Fig. 4.13 *A dirty stream degrades the community. (Redrawn from U.S. Public Health Service.)*

tion facilities to cope with the problem. Obviously, they are wasting their efforts in attacking pollution at the wrong end. Certainly it would be better to treat the sewage at its source and keep our streams clean than to recover by straining and sterilizing a required supply of water from them *after* they have ruined the landscape through which they flow. The comparative drawings (Figs. 4.13 and 4.14) suggest how badly pollution can degrade a community and how well preventive measures can rehabilitate the blighted area. Costly as it may be initially, the prevention of pollution pays good dividends in the long run.

The emerging consensus of experts is that *all* water pollution

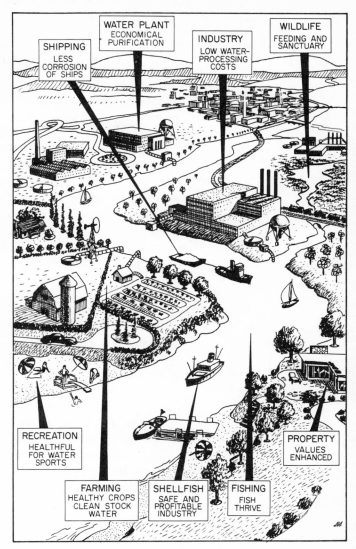

Fig. 4.14 *A clean stream promotes health and prosperity. (Redrawn from U.S. Public Health Service.)*

must be prevented entirely and that no lesser degree of abatement or control can be tolerated indefinitely. Absolute prohibition of any waste disposal that degrades water quality below its natural condition on the land or in the ground should be our ultimate objective, and until that objective is attained we shall be delinquent in water conservation. Advancement toward that goal, while concurrently expanding the total available water resource, is assured by several applications already practical and others in process of development. Brief mention of a few must suffice here.

The efficiency of water use can be greatly improved in many ways that have been amply demonstrated, but they await more

Improvement of water efficiency

extensive employment. Re-use and recirculation of water can be
very substantially expanded, with a proportional reduction in
consumption. Saving and recycling of water in manufacturing
plants have achieved such economy that our total industrial consumption of water has actually declined considerably during
recent years. Between 1954 and 1959 water consumption per
dollar value added by manufacture was reduced from 21 gallons
to 12; total industrial water use rose 53 per cent, but new-water
intake increased only about 5 per cent.[27] In water-scarce locations
steel is being manufactured at commercially competitive cost
using only 1,100 gallons of water per ton of product instead of
the national average of 65,000.[28] Recirculation of cooling water
in petroleum refineries has reduced the ratio of water to crude
oil to one-twenty-fifth of that required in a once-through plant.[29]
By recycling water ninety times, a paper manufacturer in California reduced requirements from 3,000 to 200 gallons per minute—an annual saving of 4,500 acre-feet.[30] Apparently our much-
publicized water shortage remains a matter of cost, not exhaustion.

Re-use of water following its discharge from another service instead of wasting it to air or sea has possibilities that are almost
unlimited, except that repeated re-use tends to charge the water
with salt and other substances. Concentration of impurities
eventually necessitates special treatment or replacement of the
well-worn water. Treated sewage effluent serves admirably as industrial coolant; yet less than 1 per cent of such effluent was directly re-used by industry as recently as 1960.[31] In that year a
steel plant near Baltimore, Maryland used 110 million gallons of
municipal waste water per day, after simple chlorination. Increase to 150 m.g.d. by 1965 was anticipated. The company began
using sewage effluent many years ago when water from overdrawn
wells became too saline for use in cooling the hot rolling mills.
Other cooling is accomplished with water pumped from Chesapeake Bay.[32] Municipal waste effluents can be used and re-used,
as done in certain copper plants in New Mexico. They are adequate for boiler feed as well as for cooling. They have been used
for waterflooding in secondary oil recovery. They are used in
many parts of our dry lands (especially in the Southwest) for irrigating feed, forage, and pasture crops.[33] Their aggregate use
remains small, but it will surely grow as water requirements increase.

**Artificial
ground-water
replenishment**

Artificial water storage has substantially augmented our available water resources, but thus far the storage is largely on the
surface, impounded in ponds and reservoirs. Surface storage has

such versatility of function, contributing more or less to all kinds of water requirement and management, that its development will surely continue. However, it has several inherent disadvantages that disparage it by comparison with storage deep in the ground. It occupies surface space, often in dubious competition with other land uses; it is subject to considerable loss of water by evaporation and transpiration; it is subject to seasonal temperature change that restricts its usefulness for certain purposes; it is vulnerable to direct contamination by run-off; its capacity may be constricted rapidly by sedimentation.

Underground storage of water has none of these handicaps in equal degree and has virtual immunity to some of them. It also has incomparably greater capacity, although impaired by excessive exploitation in some areas, as evidenced by land subsidence and intrusion of sea water into fresh-water wells. In most places where ground-water withdrawal has depleted the supply or threatens depletion by exceeding natural replacement, the deficiency may be compensated with artificial replenishment. Many cases attest its practical feasibility. If necessary or desirable, it might also be employed to fill subterranean voids that otherwise remain empty. (We shall note later on that underground storage of natural gas has certain implications for ground-water hydrology.)

Two principal methods of ground-water replenishment have evolved in practice—surface *spreading* of water over pervious soakage areas and deep *injection* through recharge wells drilled into the aquifer. A variant between the two involves the digging of pits and filling them with water, thereby encouraging induction. Where suitable land is available for dispersal ditches or shallow basins to hold introduced water so that it will infiltrate, spreading is the most economical method. Drilling and maintenance of recharge wells is so expensive that their use is restricted to built-up areas or for special purposes. Surface spreading can be effective for reclaiming water of low quality, such as storm or flood water, industrial waste water, and domestic sewage. Recharge wells are less useful for reclamation because low quality water tends to clog them. The two methods together have considerable application in the United States, amounting to a total artificial recharge of 700 million gallons per day in 1955, of which almost eight-tenths was from surface water and the remainder from public water supplies, industrial wastes, and air-conditioning return.

Water spreading at Denver, Colorado in 1889 was probably the first such project in the United States.[34] The practice is now most extensively used in California, in parts of New Jersey, and especially on Long Island, where several hundred recharge basins receive the discharge from storm sewers. Average recharge rate for one basin on Long Island is some 23 gallons per square foot per day. At Bountiful, Utah a spreading project has raised the water table 15 feet.[35] The efficacy of the method has been demonstrated in many places. It is operative in modified form wherever any device impedes surface run-off, be it a simple farm terrace or a dam across the Missouri.

Although employed much less extensively than surface spreading for ground-water replenishment to raise the general water level of an area, recharge wells have become important devices for improving and protecting the quality of water supplies locally. Their contribution to volume of storage is usually incidental to some other purpose. They are used for stopping salt-water intrusion into fresh-water aquifers near the coast, a function most elaborately employed in southern California and on Long Island. They are used for subterranean cooling of water in metropolitan areas where air conditioning necessitates continuous pumping—*into* recharge wells and *out of* producing wells. The aquifer caught in the middle may be several degrees warmer at summer's end than it was the previous spring. Under certain conditions they are used for driving out saline water that has invaded fresh-water wells—and for other purposes.

Replenishment of ground water by injection may be accomplished without drilling special wells by simply forcing water into the ground instead of drawing it out. A practice followed for many years in Louisville, Kentucky is to pump water down during seasons of low demand so that there will be enough to pump up when requirements are high. The same well may serve, alternately, both for recharge by injection and for timely recovery. However ground-water replenishment is accomplished, it constitutes a short-circuit of the hydrologic cycle that delays escape to the ocean or to the atmosphere.

Assuming maximum future conservation of fresh water naturally delivered to the land—by repeated use and purification and by storage on the surface and below ground—we may judiciously predict that the total available volume of such water will, even so, be less than our eventual requirements. This prospect lends national dimension to problems heretofore regional or local and warrants increasing federal concern with their solution.

Two possibilities for augmenting our fresh-water resources avail themselves: artificial precipitation of atmospheric moisture and demineralization of waters too salty for most kinds of utili-

Water augmentation by demineralization

zation as they are. Rain making remains largely experimental and cannot be relied upon for any significant hydrologic modification in the near future. Demineralization is becoming progressively more important for meeting fresh-water demands where other procurement is expensive and often precarious. Research and development by agencies both public and private have been devoted to the reduction of conversion costs so that our fundamental source of water, the sea itself, might become available for augmenting degraded supplies on the land and diluting the streams that return them to the sea.

Economical desalinization of water became a federal objective in 1952 when Congress passed the Saline Water Act (Public Law 448). Pursuant to this act, the Office of Saline Water was established in the Department of the Interior and began investigations in 1953. In 1958, with Public Law 85-883, Congress ordered a demonstration plant program consisting of five large-scale conversion facilities; one on each coast (Atlantic, Gulf, and Pacific) for desalinization of sea water and two in the interior (one in the Northern Great Plains and one in the arid Southwest) for treating brackish well water. These plants were installed and became operational as shown in Table 2. The Congress further directed that the plants be sold seven years after passage of the law, thereby averting federal competition in a business which was considered suitable for commercial expansion. Federal sub-

Table 2

Saline Water Conversion Demonstration Plant Program
(Under Public Law 85-883)

Site	*Operational*	*Process*	*Plant Size*	*Raw Water Source*	*Fresh Water Cost (per 1,000 gallons)*
Freeport, Texas	April, 1961	Long tube vertical multiple-effect distillation	1 million gallons per day	Sea	$1.00 to $1.25
Point Loma San Diego, California	January, 1962	Multi-stage flash distillation	1 million gallons per day	Sea	$1.00 to $1.25
Webster, South Dakota	October, 1961	Electrodialysis (membrane process)	250,000 gallons per day	Well (1,800 ppm)	$ .85 to $ .95
Roswell, New Mexico	May, 1963	Forced-circulation vapor-compression	Approximately 1 million gallons per day	Well (15,600 ppm)	$1.25
Wrightsville Beach, N.C.	Laboratory center for testing freezing and other separation processes.				

Source: Office of Saline Water.

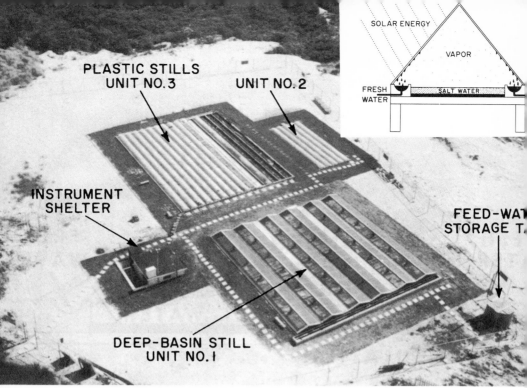

Fig. 4.15 *The Solar Research Station for sea water conversion was established in 1958 on the U.S. Coast Guard's Ponce de Leon Lighthouse reservation near Daytona Beach, Florida. The process is simple, but a large-capacity unit takes considerable space. The three still units cover 5300 square feet and yield 500 gals. of fresh water per day. (Courtesy Office of Saline Water.)*

sidy of process improvement may continue a long time because energy costs remain high (see Table 2 for plants). Solar distillation requires no process fuel, but it takes up such a large area that space and construction costs may offset fuel economy (Fig. 4.15). Since demineralization costs are more or less proportional to the mineral content of the raw water treated, it becomes apparent from Table 3 that it is more economical to remove the minerals from waste waters than from brackish ones and incomparably more economical to remove the salt from brackish water than from sea water.

Thus we may anticipate that demineralization will, at least for some time to come, contribute more toward re-use of present water supplies than toward augmentation of their volume.

Demineralization of brackish ground water has become practical in many locations. Several of our military installations, especially inland Air Force bases, are important users of desalted water.[36] Increasing numbers of industries and communities are exploiting brackish water resources.

Coalinga, California made history as the first community in

Table 3

Salt Content in Parts per Million

Fresh water	0 to 1,000
Sewage effluents	Fresh water plus 100
Brackish water	1,000 to 4,000
Salted water	4,000 plus
Sea water	18,000 to 35,000
Great Salt Lake	200,000 plus

Source: Select Committee on National Water Resources, U.S. Senate, C.P. No. 30, March 1960, 25.

the United States with a water supply derived from brackish ground-water sources. Although capacity of its original plant completed in 1959 was only 28,000 gallons per day, it freshened, by electrodialysis, water containing 2,000 parts of dissolved solids per million at a cost of only $1.45 per thousand gallons as against

Fig. 4.16 *Desalinization will be a special boon to inland areas with a scarcity of water that is naturally fresh. (Deliniation of saline surface water areas after U.S.G.S. Water Supply Paper 1374; of saline ground-water areas after* Technology in American Water Development *by Ackerman and Löf, Johns Hopkins Press, Baltimore, 1959.)*

SALINE SURFACE AND GROUND WATER IN THE UNITED STATES

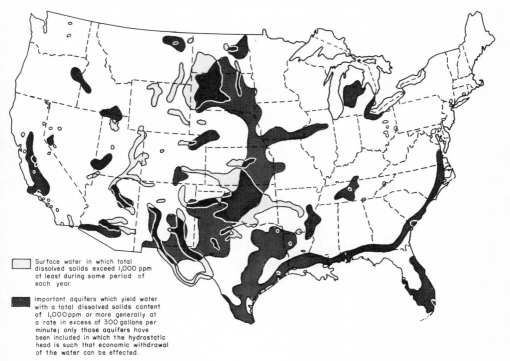

Surface water in which total dissolved solids exceed 1,000 ppm at least during some period of each year.

Important aquifers which yield water with a total dissolved solids content of 1,000 ppm or more generally at a rate in excess of 300 gallons per minute; only those aquifers have been included in which the hydrostatic head is such that economic withdrawal of the water can be effected.

a cost of $7.05 per thousand for water previously hauled in by rail. A plant with a daily capacity of 2 million gallons would satisfy all Coalinga's water needs and might reduce cost to only 40 cents per thousand gallons.[37] Another independent pioneer project was instituted by Buckeye, Arizona in 1962,[38] and other communities have been following suit. One may predict, on the basis of Fig. 4.16 that such projects will become distributed quite extensively.

As happens frequently in resource manipulation the conversion of brackish water from inland aquifers creates one problem by solving another; water desalinization yields, not only fresh water, but also prodigious quantities of salt. For instance, brackish water containing 3,000 parts of salt per million yields 3,900 tons of salt from the processing of 800 million gallons.[39] The problem of waste disposal will be increased rather than diminished by extracting salt from brackish well water, enlarging the load that must be carried to the sea. Disposal of the salt as a raw material for industry mitigates the problem somewhat, and will surely be exploited more extensively. Meanwhile, thoughtful young conservators should ponder momentous choices between grand alternatives: whether to collect all land wastes and ship them by pipe line far to sea or to desalt and ship inland sufficient quantities of sea water for augmentation of stream flow with adequate dilution? Whether to tolerate the wastage of substances from land to sea or to salvage them at their source for beneficial use on the land?

Social elements should always be taken into account in resource management, and this applies no less to water conservation than to other kinds. In the case of water, certain traditional rights and archaic laws that hinder conservation should be repealed or amended to accommodate its progress. As water problems become more acute and water requirements more competitive, they often challenge the legality of time-worn customs and test the validity of statutes. Legal obsolescence fosters neither private nor public interests.

Wrong water rights should be repealed

Basic to American water law in general is the doctrine of *riparian rights* inherited from British common law. Under that doctrine, property in land invests the owner with property in water touching the land. Only he whose land fronts on a stream has a right to the water in that stream. This principle remains dominant in American water law, especially in our humid Eastern states.

When settlement advanced into the dry American West, another water doctrine, that of *prior appropriation,* emerged—first as common law defended with violence, and later as statutory law in several states. Under this doctrine, water rights derive from priority of *beneficial use,* not from ownership of land bordering or surrounding the water. He who first uses the water has a right to it.

Thus, Western land attaches to property in water; Eastern water attaches to property in land. Neither system has acquired the flexibility that would permit equable apportionment of stream flow for various uses or among all potential users that might benefit from it. For instance, the "beneficial use" for which water is legally diverted in the dry West may be the most wasteful use to which the water could be put. Efficiency of the use counts little, if at all, in the reckoning. In parts of the Southwest, irrigation is the only beneficial use acknowledged by law, thus prohibiting water diversion for other, more economical uses. In the East, a farmer owning tremendous acreage that contributes substantially to the flow of a nearby stream may be denied any withdrawal from that stream by a mere strip of real estate separating his land from the water. How much water might his neighbor, entitled to "reasonable use," dissipate if he owned both sides of the stream?

A third doctrine became applicable to ground water, the *rule of capture,* which is no less deleterious to conservation than the other two. Under this rule the man with the biggest, deepest well may pump all the water he wishes even if he exhausts the aquifer and causes neighboring wells to go dry.

This has been merely by way of suggesting that our water laws do, indeed, need revision. The states have devoted diligent study to the problem, but few have adopted corrective legislation. "Reasonable use" puzzles the East much as "beneficial use" puzzles the West.

Except as the Federal government has jurisdiction over navigable waters carrying interstate commerce and presides over certain projects and interstate water compacts, authority over water resides in state government and may be delegated therefrom to subordinate civil divisions. The state must often adjudicate between competing or conflicting water interests.

All the water *on* a state, *above* it, and *under* it, from the top of the atmosphere to the bottom of the earth's crust, belongs to that state; yet, no state has fully integrated its authority over the three realms of water under law. Only the seventeen Western states had, before 1955, adopted comprehensive legislation for conserving the defined surface streams, and several of them also had fairly good legislation for conserving ground waters.[40] Most

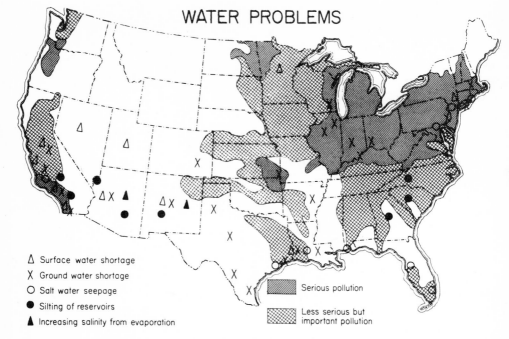

WATER PROBLEMS

△ Surface water shortage
X Ground water shortage
O Salt water seepage
● Silting of reservoirs
▲ Increasing salinity from evaporation

▨ Serious pollution

▧ Less serious but
important pollution

Fig. 4.17 *Water problems assert themselves most forcibly where they are most acute, but no region can afford neglect of its water resources. This map is only one way of indicating how widespread and serious certain water problems have become. Our water situation has further deteriorated since this map was prepared. (Courtesy American Geographical Society.)*

of the Eastern states lacked suitable water legislation and the South remained particularly negligent. Much progress has been made recently, especially with reference to area management of ground water in parts of the Southwest, but water law must be much improved generally before water conservation can be realized as it should be.

There is no simple panacea for our bad water situation, no course of action that can quickly and completely revive our dwindling water resources. Certain natural storage facilities have been permanently impaired, and water movement has been accelerated by inept land utilization. We have reduced the total amount of available water retained on the land—surface and underground—and we are shrinking it more rapidly now than ever before, apparently disdainful of signs and warnings that drain cannot exceed replenishment indefinitely. The accompanying map (Fig. 4.17) shows that large regions are handicapped by water problems. Many localities are threatened with water calamity. We have created a grave water situation, but in the main it is amenable to solution. Good land use, skillful engineering, research, education, legislation, and public concern must all be brought to bear.

**Ours
to choose
between
conservation
and rationing**

5

Our Soils and Their Depreciation

soil combines air, water, organisms, and minerals in a marvelous, life-sustaining medium often degraded by men

Soils are the foundation of our worldly goods; a basic wealth upon which our existence depends. From them comes nearly all the food we eat, much of our clothing and shelter, and most of the materials for our comfort, convenience, and pleasure. Water alone is more important to the viability of resources, but without soil water would be useless. With the exception of water and its life forms, all other renewable resources come from the soil. The importance of soil as primary producer grows ever greater with the dissipation of exhaustible resources and proportionately increased reliance upon the renewable kinds. Soils must fill in when mineral materials fade out. When we have dug out all our minerals and used them up, we shall need more soil products than ever. Rather than relaxing our dependence upon soils, our advancing civilization will reassert it more and more. There is no real evidence that we may some day detach our lives from the soils that sustain us.

He who would call his sustenance "dirt" might well speak softly and conceal his ignorance. Soils are infinitely more than just plain dirt; they are a composite of minerals, organisms, air, and water, so wondrously combined that man has never exactly duplicated their structure and composition. For a better understanding of soils, he has developed a whole field of inquiry called

They are not "dirt"

85

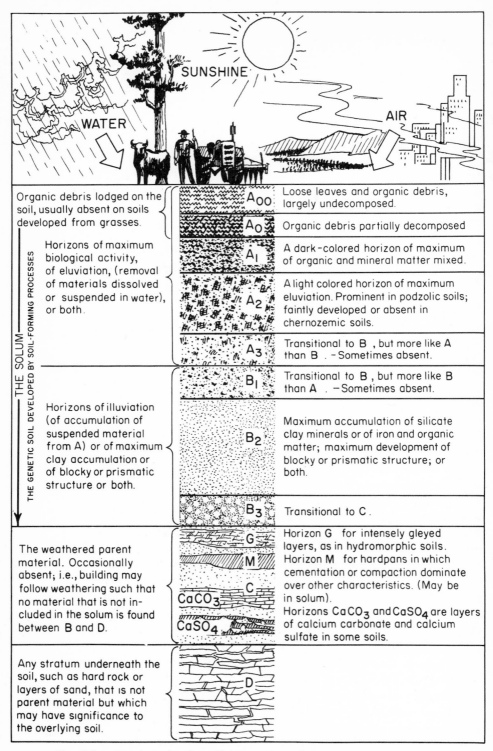

Organic debris lodged on the soil, usually absent on soils developed from grasses.	A_{00}	Loose leaves and organic debris, largely undecomposed.
	A_0	Organic debris partially decomposed
Horizons of maximum biological activity, of eluviation, (removal of materials dissolved or suspended in water), or both.	A_1	A dark-colored horizon of maximum of organic and mineral matter mixed.
	A_2	A light colored horizon of maximum eluviation. Prominent in podzolic soils; faintly developed or absent in chernozemic soils.
	A_3	Transitional to B, but more like A than B. - Sometimes absent.
Horizons of illuviation (of accumulation of suspended material from A) or of maximum clay accumulation or of blocky or prismatic structure or both.	B_1	Transitional to B, but more like B than A. -Sometimes absent.
	B_2	Maximum accumulation of silicate clay minerals or of iron and organic matter; maximum development of blocky or prismatic structure; or both.
	B_3	Transitional to C.
The weathered parent material. Occasionally absent; i.e., building may follow weathering such that no material that is not included in the solum is found between B and D.	G, M, C, CaCO_3, CaSO_4	Horizon G for intensely gleyed layers, as in hydromorphic soils. Horizon M for hardpans in which cementation or compaction dominate over other characteristics. (May be in solum). Horizons CaCO_3 and CaSO_4 are layers of calcium carbonate and calcium sulfate in some soils.
Any stratum underneath the soil, such as hard rock or layers of sand, that is not parent material but which may have significance to the overlying soil.	D	

THE SOLUM — THE GENETIC SOIL DEVELOPED BY SOIL-FORMING PROCESSES

Fig. 5.1 *Hypothetical soil profile. Note that all the layers and characteristics represented would not appear in one and the same soil.* (After Soil Survey Manual.)

86

soil science, or *pedology,* whose teachings are basic to soil conservation.

Soil development begins when simple life forms establish themselves among weathered particles of rock. The organisms help reduce the particles further, hold them in place so they can accumulate, and add their own bodies to the mass as generation after generation dies. When the mantle becomes thick enough, higher forms of life intrude and accelerate the formative process. The final result is an unconsolidated layer, several inches to several feet in thickness, containing minerals, humus, plant life, animals, air, and water, in mechanical mixtures and in chemical combinations. By suitable cooperation between sunshine, rain, and life for hundreds of years, that surface layer becomes soil; a separate entity produced by unique processes.

Most important of these processes is the downward translocation of surface materials by water percolating through the soil section. This process of taking materials near the top and redepositing them deeper down is the basic producer of soil profiles. Instead of noses, chins, and foreheads, soil profiles have layers called *horizons,* identified, top to bottom, by the simple designations, *A, B, C,* and *D.* See the drawing of a hypothetical soil profile (Fig. 5.1).

Profiles distinguish soils

The upper horizon, *A,* is the one from which percolating water removes fine soil particles, leaving the coarser materials behind. Thus the *A* horizon has become known also as the *zone of impoverishment.* Under extreme conditions it becomes so coarse and open that it loses the power to retain humus and other desirable substances and becomes a leached, sterile body of mineral matter. Its removal may be more desirable than its retention. The pale gray sand that accumulates on certain uplands in the humid East is about as lifeless as any cadaver of similar hue.

Next below lies the *B* horizon, in which the water deposits that taken from *A,* causing the *B* to become more dense and finer textured than *A.* It is referred to as the *zone of enrichment,* since it gains what *A* loses. Under certain conditions the precipitated materials develop a layer so compact that it blocks vertical movement of water. Such a hard, impervious layer is called *hardpan,* or *claypan,* an undesirable characteristic of *B* in many areas.

The two horizons, *A* and *B* constitute the true soil, or *solum,* our primary concern in soil conservation. The solum contains all the humus and all the organisms that make soil a unique body— the bridge between the geologic and biologic, the atmospheric and hydrologic. A good solum is literally crawling with organisms, containing several hundred million fungi, bacteria, and viruses in a single pound.

Under the solum lies the *C* horizon, also called *parent material* of the soil. It is simply rotten, or weathered, rock, broken down by chemical and mechanical processes. It is unconsolidated and inanimate, except as soil life invades it from above, bringing the soil section down into it, as it were. Soil development, like good stream management, begins at the top and proceeds downward. While the formative process at the bottom goes deeper into fresh material, the spent residue at the surface moves off. One might compare soil formation with the growth of the skin— new tissue builds underneath; old tissue sloughs off the surface.

At the bottom lies the unaltered geologic foundation—either loose mineral material or solid rock—often called the *D* horizon. Its physical and chemical composition has an important bearing on the qualities of the soil that forms upon it because few, if any, of our soils have remained in place long enough for the complete decomposition of their mineral constituents.

Color

Color, texture, and structure of their horizons are the most conspicuous criteria for identifying and evaluating soils. Black and dark shades of brown indicate abundant humus, and, conversely, light brown or buff indicates low humus content. A pale or ashen *A* horizon means deficiency of humus just as a sallow, washed-out look indicates ill health in humans. Bright shades of red or yellow in the *A* or *B* horizon are deceptive, since they indicate only iron content, not fertility. The more brilliant the color, the less may be the life.

Texture

Soil texture pertains to the size of the mineral particles, or grains, that make up the mass. A coarse, or open, texture, such as sand, permits water to pass through too freely and therefore lacks the power to retain humus and plant nutrients. On the other hand, soil too fine in texture, such as plastic clay, impedes water movement, lacks proper aeration (air spaces), and holds too tightly any plant foods it may contain. Between the extremes are the desirable loams—various mixtures of sand and clay that can hold air, water, and humus without overdoing it and respond well to fair treatment. See the "texture triangle" (Fig. 5.2).

Structure

Soil structure is the arrangement or grouping of soil particles, which may have profound influence on soil quality. Coarse sand lacks structure, being simply an accumulation of grains. Plastic clay may be said to have a massive structure, since the whole body tends to hang together and resist separation. Clay that divides into small loose lumps (i.e., that flocculates) is said to have a granular structure—a most desirable characteristic because it renders the clay friable (crumbly) and more easily tilled.

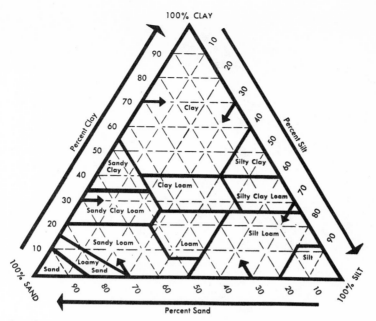

Fig. 5.2 *The corners of the texture triangle represent 100 per cent sand, clay, or silt. (Gravel and organic soils are not included.) The triangle is divided into 10 per cent portions of clay, silt, and sand. Heavy lines show the divisions between 12 basic soil textural classes. The triangle can be used only when the percentages of clay, silt, and sand have been determined in the laboratory. If you know that a soil is 20 per cent clay and 40 per cent silt, you can follow the 20 per cent line from the left-hand (clay) side of the triangle to the point where it meets the 40 per cent line from the right-hand (silt) side of the triangle. You will see, then, that the soil is a loam. (Drawing and note from Circular 758, College of Agriculture, University of Illinois, December, 1961.)*

The feel of soil, when one squeezes a handful or walks over a field, is a good index of quality. Soil full of humus and life feels spongy in the hand and springy under foot. Dead soil has the cold, fixed hardness of *rigor mortis*.

Many variables influence the rate of soil formation. Some soils have developed in a fraction of the time it took others, but under the most rapid soil-making conditions a century or two might be required. Cool, humid climates are among the fast soil makers, but it appears that they sacrifice quality for speed. They leach the *A* horizon of its best material, producing podzol soils (Fig. 5.3). Cool, subhumid climates produce soils very slowly, but their end product is superior. They produce a deep, black or brown *A* horizon, characteristic of the prairie and chernozem soils (Fig. 5.4). When one considers that humus content transmits the dark color, he can appreciate that it represents the annual residue from many, many years of grass—thousands of years might be a conservative estimate.

Soils develop slowly

Soils, like people, age at different rates, and for each, age has a double meaning. Soils old in years may be young in profile development, and vice versa. Natural surface erosion keeps many

Fig. 5.3 A podzol under forest of the Northeast. A thick layer of raw, acid organic material overlies the soil. The A horizon is white silica sand, thoroughly leached by percolating water. The B horizon is dense and compact, chocolate brown in color from its abundance of precipitated clay and organic matter. Note the location of podzols in Fig. 5.5. (Courtesy Charles E. Kellog.)

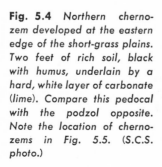

Fig. 5.4 Northern chernozem developed at the eastern edge of the short-grass plains. Two feet of rich soil, black with humus, underlain by a hard, white layer of carbonate (lime). Compare this pedocal with the podzol opposite. Note the location of chernozems in Fig. 5.5. (S.C.S. photo.)

soils perennially young; rapid leaching by water makes others prematurely old. Soil maturity indicates normal profile development; rejuvenescence means its interruption or postponement.

By any interpretation, soil forms so slowly that what we lose will be lost for centuries to come. The fraction of an inch washed off by a summer shower may represent a man's lifetime. Soil loss is more final than most men suspect. That is why it is so vitally important that we conserve what we have left. Age is not necessarily a criterion of soil quality, but environmental factors condition both age and quality of soils.

Local soil variety corresponds with the pattern of environmental conditions. In regions of uniformly heavy rainfall and constantly high temperatures, soil processes operate rapidly and continuously, producing deep soil sections—except where surface erosion is also accelerated. However, the deep soil may be extremely poor in quality because the same combination of warmth and moisture that developed it causes organic matter to decay and leach out too fast to permit production or retention of much humus. In cold, moist regions bacterial action is so slow that plant remains may accumulate as raw, acid humus. The extensive peat bogs of northern Minnesota developed that way; they show an excess of organic matter and no true soil.

Soil variety derives from climatic differences

In desert regions soils are inclined to be mineral rather than organic, because the deficiency of moisture limits plant growth, which is the main source of humus, and precludes the possibility of vertical soil development by percolating water. The small quantity of humus produced is either lost off the surface or remains near the top of the soil. Under extreme desert conditions the soil, so-called, is simply a loose mantle of rock, its original mineral content largely intact and its organic content nonexistent. The gray color of desert soil (sierozem) expresses the paucity of humus.

Between the extremes lie the climatic gradations of temperature and rainfall that produce the grand divisions of productive, conservable soils in the United States. Those divisions are shown on the accompanying map (Fig. 5.5). Within those divisions further refinement of soil variety and arrangement derives from differences in parent materials, topographic position, slope, drainage, elevation, and vegetative cover.

Major distinctions are evident between our forests and grassland soils

Major distinctions are evident between our large region of Eastern forest soils (pedalfers) and the region of Western grassland soils (pedocals). In the humid East there is enough rain to sustain a forest cover, to seep through forest litter, soil, and parent material, and to arrive at the water table. The percolat-

IMPORTANT SOIL REGIONS

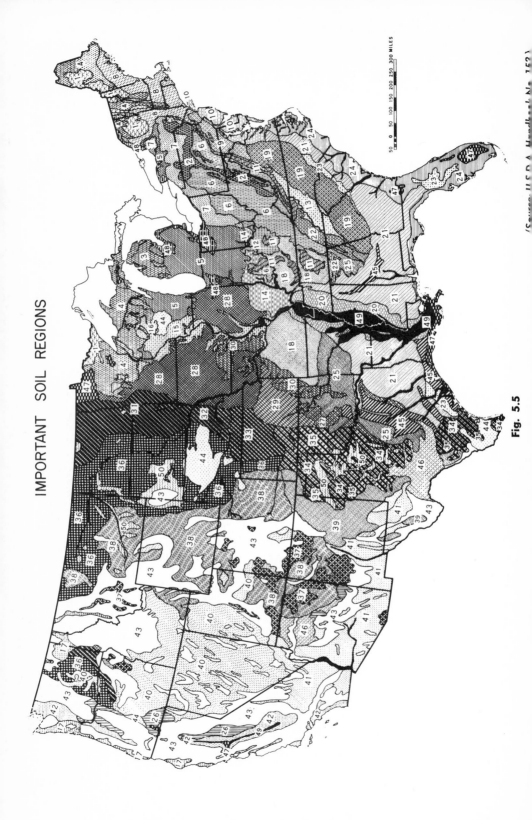

Fig. 5.5

(Source: U.S.D.A. Handbook No. 262.)

Podzols. The profile consists of a thin organic layer above a gray leached layer which rests on a dark-brown or coffee-brown horizon. The Podzol is developed usually under a coniferous forest in a cool, moist climate. Its inherent productivity for crop plants is low. The figures below refer to area numbers on the map. (1) Rough stony land, including areas of shallow Podzols. (2) Chiefly loams and silt loams, developed from sandstones and shales of the plateau and mountain uplands. (3) Dominantly sands and loamy sands, developed on glacial drift. (4) Dominantly loams and clay loams, developed on glacial drift.

Gray-Brown Podzolic Soils. The profile has a rather thin organic layer over grayish-brown leached soils which overlies a brown horizon. The soils are generally acid, at least in the surface. These soils develop in a moist and cool-temperate climate under a deciduous forest and are inherently more productive than the Podzols. (5) Dominantly loams and silt loams, developed on calcareous glacial drift. (6) Brownish-yellow silty loams or stony loams with hilly relief developed on sandstones and shales. (7) Loams and silt loams, developed on acid glacial drift and composed of sandstones and shale material. Some of these soils are imperfectly drained. (8) Dominantly stony and gravelly loams, developed on glacial drift. (9) Loams and silt loams, developed mainly on the crystalline rocks of the northern Piedmont. (10) Largely sandy loams developed on the sands and clays of the northern Coastal Plain. (11) Chiefly brown silt loams, developed on limestone. (12) Shallow soils developed on interbedded limestone and calcareous shales. (13) Loams and stony loams from granitic material with hilly to mountainous relief. (14) Silt loams with heavy clay subsoils, developed on Illinoian glacial till. (15) Silt loams developed largely from loess. (16) Imperfectly drained grayish silt loams with silty clay loam subsoils, developed from acid glacial drift. (17) Largely loams and silt loams with yellowish subsoils, developed from sandstones and shales. (18) Grayish-yellow to reddish silt loams and cherty silt loams, developed from cherty limestones.

Red and Yellow Soils. This group of soils consists of two general types of profiles that are intimately associated. Both have thin organic layers. The profile of the red soil is a yellowish-brown leached layer over a red horizon while the profile of the yellow soil is a grayish-yellow leached layer over a yellow horizon. Both develop under a warm-temperate climate. Generally, the yellow profile is more pronounced under the coniferous forest and the red under the deciduous forest. The inherent fertility of the yellow soils is relatively low and that of the red soils medium. (19) Dominantly brownish-red clay loams and gray sandy loams, developed largely from crystalline rocks of the southern Piedmont. (20) Yellow to light brown silt loams, developed on loess. (21) Dominantly gray to yellow sandy and fine sandy loams with some sands and fine sands, developed from Coastal Plain materials. (22) Largely brownish-red to red silt loams and clay loams, developed from limestone. (23) Grayish-yellow to light brown sands and fine sands of the Coastal Plain. (24) Grayish fine sandy loams, with some gray or black loams, developed in the flatwoods area of the Coastal Plain. Includes areas underlain by coralline limestone. (25) Grayish-yellow to reddish fine sandy loams and silt loams, developed from sandstones and shales. A considerable portion is hilly and stony. (26) Red soils of the north Pacific slopes.

Prairie Soils. The profile of the Prairie soil grades from a very dark brown or dark grayish-brown surface through brown to lighter colored parent material at a depth of 2 to 5 feet. It is developed in a moist temperate climate under a tall-grass prairie. Inherent fertility for crop plants is high. (27) Reddish-brown soils of variable texture, developed on sandstones, shales, clays, and sands. (28) Dark brown silt loams with yellowish-brown subsoils, developed on glacial drift and loess. (29) Dark brown to reddish-brown silt loams and clay loams, developed from limestone and calcareous shales. (30) Dark brown or grayish-brown silt loams, having heavy subsoils or claypans.

Northern Chernozem. The profile has a black or dark grayish-brown surface soil grading below into light-colored material that is calcareous at 2 to 6 feet. It is developed in a temperate to cool subhumid climate under tall and mixed grasses. Inherent productivity is high. (31) Black, silt, and clay loams, developed on calcareous glacial drift and associated lacustrine deposits. (32) Dark grayish-brown loams and silt loams, developed from loess. (33) Dark grayish-brown silt loams with claypans developed from loess.

Southern Chernozem—Dark Brown Soils. The profiles have dark brown to reddish-brown surface soils underlain by brown or red horizons, grading below into light-colored material that is calcareous at 3 to 6 feet. These soils develop in a warm, subhumid to semiarid climate under a mixed tall- and short-grass prairie. (34) Heavy or moderately heavy dark brown soils, developed from calcareous materials. (35) Predominantly red and brown sandy loams and sands, developed largely from unconsolidated calcareous sands, silts, and sandy clays.

Northern Dark Brown (Chestnut) Soils. The profile grades from a dark brown surface soil into a whitish calcareous horizon at a depth of 1½ to 3 feet. These soils develop under mixed tall and short grasses in a temperate to cool semiarid climate. (36) Dark brown soils developed on unconsolidated, calcareous sands, silts, and clays. (37) Dark brown soils, developed on heterogeneous material associated with mountainous and plateau terrain.

Brown Soils. A brown surface soil grading at a depth ranging from 1 to 2 feet into a whitish calcareous horizon. The profile is developed in a temperate to cool, semiarid climate under short grasses, bunch grasses, and shrubs. (38) Northern—chiefly brown loams, developed largely on unconsolidated sands, silts, and clays. (39) Southern—chiefly light brown to gray fine sandy loams to silty clay loams of smooth relief, developed largely on limestone or unconsolidated sands, silts, and clays.

Sierozem and Desert Soils. Grayish and reddish soils, closely underlain by calcareous material. These soils develop in an arid climate under short grass and desert plants. (40) Northern—gray and grayish-brown soils of variable texture, developed largely on loess and alluvial fan material. (41) Southern—gray, brown, and reddish soils of variable texture, developed largely on alluvial fans.

Soils of the Pacific Valleys. (42) Includes a number of variable zonal, azonal, and intrazonal soils that are too intimately associated to separate on a schematic map. These soils developed under a range of climatic and geological conditions.

Intrazonal and Azonal Soils. These soils may possess one of the two general types of profile: (a) The profile may express a local condition as drainage or parent material rather than the zonal profile of the region; (b) the profile may be too immature to express a zonal type. (43) Rough and mountainous (azonal). (44) Largely azonal sands, some of which are associated with bogs. (45) Black (or brown) friable soil underlain by whitish material excessively high in calcium carbonate. These soils developed under a prairie vegetation and are known as Rendzinas (intrazonal). (46) Shallow stony soils from limestone (azonal). (47) Marsh, swamp, and bog (intrazonal). (48) Soils largely intrazonal, developed on lake plains. (49) Alluvial soils (azonal). (50) Rough broken land.

ing water, charged with acid from leaves and pine needles, dissolves and removes calcium carbonate so actively that the soils, even those developed upon a limestone base, become acid in their chemical reaction. Called technically *podzolization,* the process tends to produce a residual *A* horizon of silica sand and a *B* horizon characterized by iron and aluminum compounds (Fig. 5.3). An east-west arrangement of podzolized forest soils results, largely, from a progressively warmer climate southward, with an attendant lengthening of growing season and a shorter annual interruption of soil processes, both constructive and destructive. Examine carefully the map of soil groups (Fig. 5.5), correlating each group with the legend and with the maps in Chapters 1, 2, and 3. Note that portions of the grassland plains receive insufficient rain to sustain a continuous, permanent forest cover, and percolating water does not ordinarily maintain contact with the water table but dissipates in the *B* horizon of the soil. Quite the opposite of acid-making trees, grasses concentrate basic compounds, especially calcium carbonate, and produce humus without an undesirable acid reaction. Water seeping through the sod takes up calcium carbonate in solution and precipitates it in the *B* horizon. Where this process, a form of *calcification,* attains notable effect—as in the black chernozem soils—the precipitate forms a solid, white layer of lime, inches in thickness (Fig. 5.4). The grassland soils lie in north-south belts; their color grades from black in the eastern belt to light brown and gray in the western belt, which is a clear expression of progressively less rainfall, less vegetation, and less humus westward. Humus shows up as a black stain on individual soil particles.

Although podzolization and calcification evince contrasts as striking as any and operate over major portions of the United States, two other soil-forming processes, latozation and laterization are also important. These are tropical soil processes, operative in Hawaii, in Puerto Rico, and in parts of the southeastern United States. Whereas podzolization accumulates silicon dioxide in the topsoil, latozation or laterization decomposes and dissipates the silicon dioxide and forms instead a concentration of iron oxides. Latosols and laterites are red and yellow in color, with horizons less distinct than in podzolics, if not entirely lacking. Tropical soils may be weathered to great depth and severely leached of plant nutrients. Laterites generally discourage cultivation because they bake to a brick-like hardness.

Local soil groups accord with topography and geology

Within the great soil regions boundaries and groupings accord with topographic arrangements and relationships. Individual soils follow rather closely the pattern of particular parent ma-

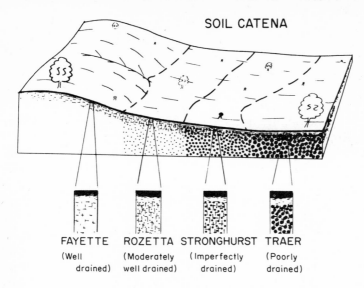

SOIL CATENA

FAYETTE	ROZETTA	STRONGHURST	TRAER
(Well drained)	(Moderately well drained)	(Imperfectly drained)	(Poorly drained)

Fig. 5.6 *A full catena of soils developed in deep Peorian loess under deciduous forest; a pedologic feature in the conterminal unglaciated portions of Illinois, Iowa, Minnesota, and Wisconsin. (Sketch by Ray Newbury.)*

terials, and their association with other soils follows the lay of the land. Where soils of common geologic origin are differentiated by topographic position and drainage, they are known collectively as a *soil catena,* as shown in Fig. 5.6. Pedologists have suggested that all soils under a given set of climatic conditions and similar topographic position will, if climate and topography have enough time to assert themselves, become identical despite any variety of original parent materials. However, few of our American soils are so maturely developed that they do not bear strong evidence of their origin. Thus, the Hagerstown "series" came from limestone, the Norfolk from sand, the Memphis and Walla Walla from loess (wind-deposited material), the Fargo from lake-bottom mud, the Gloucester from a stony mixture of material deposited by glaciers, the Chester and Cecil from crystalline rocks, the Yazoo from river deposits, and so on. Each series carries the name of the vicinity in which it was first scientifically identified, and several have extensive areal distribution. Everywhere, the particular series has its unique features of identification—color, texture, structure, depth, reaction, and others, including a certain productive capacity. A series may include several "types"—the type designation derived mainly from the texture of the *A* horizon. Locally, type may be just as important as series for practical purposes. The conservator can learn to recognize both series and types in any area with which he may be concerned. Discernment of transitional soil variants, called *pedons,* he need not attempt. He can get the information through

95

the agricultural county agent, or farm advisor, or from the local soil conservationist. He may also be able to obtain a map showing local soils distribution. A knowledge of soils nomenclature will often help him understand more clearly the practical advice of an expert.

The effects of topography in soil delineation are at least three-fold: (1) the geologic arrangement due to the differential resistance of parent materials to weathering and erosion; (2) the differences between parent soil materials themselves; (3) the various exposure and drainage conditions imposed by topographic position. In the humid East (Pennsylvania), where resistant sandstone and soluble limestone lie in juxtaposition, the latter has generally become lowland and the former highland. The sandstone begets light, sandy upland soils like the De Kalb, easily tilled but low in fertility. The limestone begets heavy, clayey soils like the Hagerstown, which is highly fertile but more difficult to cultivate. Upland soils are generally more mature than lowland varieties because of better drainage, but it should be remembered that open texture also facilitates drainage, given adequate elevation. Thus soils may be excessively drained by virtue of either coarse parent material or high topographic po-

Fig. 5.7 *Topography and geology influence soil relationships. Most soils reflect the character of their parent material, and their spatial arrangement usually follows the pattern of surface geology. (After Soil Survey Manual.)*

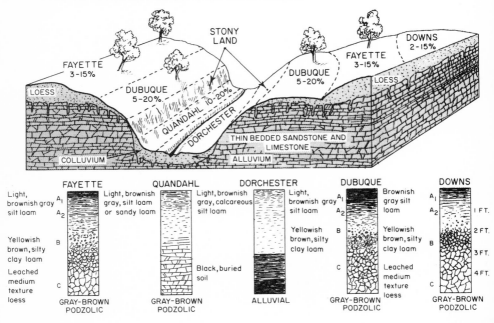

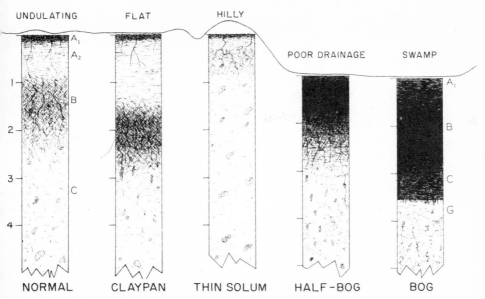

Fig. 5.8 *Topographic position and slope of the land are strong factors in soil development. A mature soil profile cannot evolve on steep, eroding slopes, nor can a normal profile develop in places poorly drained or recurrently inundated and blanketed with alluvium. (After Soils and Men. Yearbook of Agriculture, 1938.)*

sition, or by both, which is not an unusual combination. They can be made to retain more water by increasing their humus content. Figure 5.7 shows how the soils pattern coincides with geology and topography in a hilly locality of northeastern Iowa.

Slope soils tend to remain young or immature in development and become coarse in texture, because run-off removes the finer surface material and leaves a residue of larger particles. In some places the residue takes on the aspects of a surface mulch and resists the very process by which it came to be. Notable among such slope soils is the stony "phase" of the Gloucester—one reason why Massachusetts has fewer gullies than Mississippi.

In valley bottoms and on other low, flat areas, topographic position asserts itself in imperfect drainage and immature or abnormal soil development. Flood-plain soils, as in the lower Mississippi Valley, are often without profile, being simply transported and redeposited soil materials (alluvium). On low plains, such as the waterlogged flatwoods of Florida, the high water table obstructs the percolation of water necessary to normal profile development. Instead, organic matter carried through the *A* horizon becomes so compacted in the *B* that it constitutes an organic hardpan, blocking both downward and upward passage of water. The Leon and St. Johns series are good examples of this bad situation. Their use capability is extremely limited. Figure 5.8 shows various influences of topographic position in soil development.

For purposes of conservation it is not enough to describe a

soil as sand, silt, loam, or clay, on a rolling upland, on a steep slope, or on a flat lowland; other less conspicuous characteristics may be equally important in the choice of conservation methods. We have spent much time and money to refine our knowledge of American soils, and much of the information can be useful in conservation. Our soils experts may identify as many as two hundred different kinds of soil—types, phases, complexes, and variants—on a detailed map of a single locality. The conservator should recognize the functional groups, at least, because they may be the basis for land-use planning and farm management. Soil maps, soil descriptions, and soil-management recommendations are available for much of our land. The conservator should familiarize himself with those aids to agriculture for the same reasons that he should learn to identify the important tree species in forestry or the important grass species in range management. He should know the characteristics of any resource he wishes to conserve.

Turning now from soil genesis and classification to an equally brief outline of productivity factors, let us consider first what a soil must contain in order to support a healthy plant community. Staple foods—the meat, bread, and potatoes—of all common plants are compounds of nitrogen, potassium, and phosphorus, flavored with calcium. But none of the "big three" is palatable or digestible unless it be properly "cooked" and "served." Agronomists learned long ago that soil analysis by chemical test does not always mean that a substance detected is in a form plants can use. Of course, a negative chemical result means that the substance just is not present and therefore cannot be obtained by plants. However, presence of plant nutrients in the soil means little unless they be present in forms *available* to plants. Availability depends upon several factors: chemical composition and combination; humus content; organic activity; conditions of moisture and aeration. Modern utilitarian soil tests are designed to show the amounts of nutrients available to plants rather than the amounts that can be detected by chemical analysis. Certain availability tests now common involve testing extracts from the plants grown in the soils on the logical assumption that these substances would not be in the plant unless available in the soil. However, when the farmer wants a sure index of soil fertility, he sows a crop and sees how well it grows. Nature provides the ultimate soil test.

Compounds of nitrogen, phosphorus, and potassium furnish the bulk of plant foods in soil; but, plants gorged on these can starve unless they have available with the main course a number

Soil productivity depends upon availability of plant nutrients

Certain trace elements, or micronutrients, play subtle roles

of side dishes commonly referred to as *trace* elements—iron, manganese, magnesium, copper, zinc, and sulphur—and certain appetizers like barium, boron, cobalt, sodium, chlorine, and chromium. These secondary soil components, which are comparatively recent discoveries, are only partially understood and the objects of intensive continuing research. Several are believed to be essential for normal plant growth, and some are equally essential to good health in animals. The metals have particular soil value in the form of metallic salts. Though one and another serves a specific vital function in extremely small quantity, that same compound in slightly higher concentration may be strongly toxic. A little goes a long way; a trifle more can go entirely too far.

The trace elements probably have less utility as food absorbed by plants than as catalytics that release or prepare other materials for assimilation. Chicken manure, containing 0.001 per cent zinc, acts somewhat like a transfusion to certain sick nut trees (Tung) on sandy Southern soils. The trees respond to minute quantities in their diet, and many soils lack even that trace. Zinc seems to prevent specific tree ills much as iodine prevents goiter in humans. Iron and magnesium are considered essential to the functioning of chlorophyll, and others may be found equally necessary. Trace elements in the soil are like vitamins: we know they correct deficiencies, but we know little about their complex operational procedures. Much soil chemistry remains to be learned.

Unless they be dissolved in water, plant nutrients in the soil cannot be absorbed and used by the plants. The thin film of water that envelops each tiny particle of good soil contains all the plant food the soil can supply to the probing root hairs seeking it. Quantities not in solution are like packs of frozen meat in a freezer locker, and water is the only key to their release. Furthermore, plants tolerate only a certain concentration or dilution of the food-water mixture, some thinner, some thicker. Soil containing too little water to nourish the ordinary upland plants (mesophytes) is said to be *physically,* or *actually, dry*. Soil containing too much water for such plants is said to be *physiologically,* or *in effect, dry*. Some plants adapted to moisture deficiency can grow in either situation. Water and soil are partners that the conservator must often consider together.

Plant foods must be in solution

Strong acidity or alkalinity of the soil causes starvation and poisoning of plants when other properties might favor fertility. The soil factor of chemical reaction, commonly referred to as p*H*, can determine the productive capacity of a soil. To the technician, pH is "the common logarithm of the reciprocal of the hydrogen-ion concentration of a system." In plain language a pH of 7.0 indicates neutrality, lower numbers indicate acidity, and higher ones alkalinity. Soils with a pH of 4.5 or less are extremely acid; those with a pH of 9.1 or higher, very strongly alkaline. Soil reaction interests the conservator because a suitable control of pH may be the decisive factor in the conservation of certain soils.

The pH
must be within
a moderate range

Plants are more generally tolerant of acidity than alkalinity, but extremes of either are toxic. Some plants prefer an acid re-action; others prefer a basic one. Some are specific, others less particular, in their pH requirement. Most of our common culti-vated plants do best with a pH value somewhere between 6 and 8, whereas the acid forest soils need artificial neutralization to hold their reaction within that range. Application of calcium carbonate (lime) sweetens them much as bicarbonate does a sour stomach. Soils too highly alkaline, such as the very salty solonchak and solonetz might require more specific medication, like a pre-scription to correct faulty metabolism. Correct prescription must be based upon careful diagnosis of a particular situation.

Essentials of soil fertility complement each other, and paucity or defection of a single one can render the entire soil impotent.

Essentials
of soil fertility
complement
each other

Like the vital organs of the human body or the players on a base-ball team, all components of good soil are integral parts of the total organization, the character and function of each indispen-sable to the whole. Air, water, minerals, humus, flora, and fauna are merely raw materials, and no matter how precisely they might be apportioned and however thoroughly mixed, they would not be soil. They become soil only when the slow, complex, pedologic processes combine them in a balanced, reciprocating union. Un-less texture be neither too coarse nor too fine, unless there be enough humus, but not too much, unless the soil section permits water passage, yet prohibits too rapid movement, the soil will not retain the water needed to dissolve and distribute plant nutrients. Unless the solution be neither too thin nor too rich, neither too acid nor too alkaline, the plant cannot get the foods, however abundant they may be. Unless the chemical reaction be about right, bacteria and other organisms cannot continue their work of preparing plant foods and generating soil fertility. They also need air, water, organic material, and warmth in moderate proportions, and every one of these individually plays a double role of cause and effect in soil quality. Physical, chemical, and biologic characteristics of soil are so intricately bound together that a minor change in one can foment revolt in another. An established balance can be extremely delicate, and those who desire to improve it should proceed with caution.

The farmer who tills the soil summarizes all its qualities of arability and productivity in the single word "tilth," though the word pertains more specifically to the physical state of the soil in terms of its capacity for producing a particular crop. Soil in good tilth breaks and turns from the plow in smooth furrows that crumble and fall together into a friable (loose) mass upon exposure to sun and rain. Friability indicates, generally, desirable texture, structure, content of humus and water, aeration, organic activity, and chemical reaction. Dead, plastic clays that bake into clods after plowing are not only physically intractable but lack several other desirable attributes of friability. One wet plowing can injure them for several years. Compaction of a soil, in most any case, is attributable to poor physical make-up, and compaction renders correction of deficiencies doubly difficult. But good tilth means more than easy cultivation and high productivity; it means responsiveness to practices for maintaining or improving fertility. Tilth is to soil what health is to people, and the two conditions may be closely associated.

Good tilth enables high productivity

Many soils, like many men, were created poor, but unlike men of low birth, soils born poor have no higher destiny unless they be aided by men. Soil conservation, American style, has long since outmoded the old idea of soil "maintenance," which suffices only for soils naturally fertile. Since such are restricted in area, conservation must be directed toward soil "building," increasing rather than merely maintaining the "given" soil fertility.

Some soils were created poor

Our subhumid grasslands have extensive areas of soils so rich that they can produce many crops without serious impoverishment. For them the maintenance of natural fertility might be a satisfactory objective. But on either side of those grasslands on the "wet-dry" scale, soils are generally so anemic that they need a transfusion after bringing forth a few crops, if not from the very first. Deficiency of humus is symptomatic of soil anemia. Dry lands lack the vegetation necessary for humus to accumulate; humid lands under forest lose both humus and plant food to leaching water. Where there is enough rain to produce forest there is enough to cause considerable leaching of the soil as well. Our pedalfers, inherently low in fertility, can only briefly sustain a profitable agriculture without specific treatment to strengthen them. Our failure to maintain, where in fact we should have improved from the very beginning, accounts for much of the lost soil and mutilated land so tragically apparent in the Southeast.

Nor has our ruin of soils been confined to poor ones, or to the South. The soil-mining cotton aristocrats appear less guilty when one remembers that most of the soil they abused was *poor* when they got it. Other men, in other places, have spent *good* soil i.e., they have embezzled more from larger funds. Wheat and corn farmers, respectively, have dissipated more soil riches than have cotton planters.

When our European ancestors arrived in the New World they set about resolutely to make the virgin soils produce their utmost. First with iron plows, later with steel; first with scythe and cradle, then with reapers, binders, and combines they harvested crop after crop, heedlessly or unwittingly draining the soil of its fertility. They took from the soil all it could give, with little or no regard for its replenishment. They bled it white, depleted its plant nutrients, and complained when yields dwindled. They blamed everything except themselves when worn-out fields could no longer reward their abusive handling. Sons grew poor where their fathers had prospered, because the soil was spent or wasted away. The space was the same, but it was barren space, like the empty drifts in exhausted mines. Only then did the agrarian heirs come to realize that their soil had been impoverished by extractive utilization, that removal exceeding replacement had sapped the base beyond its own capacity to revive, and that their "indestructible" heritage had so gravely depreciated that it must be counted partially destroyed. It was a rude awakening, but it inspired a soil-conserving program which, if fully prosecuted, will spare our nation the disastrous depletion of soil that has ruined civilizations.

By overcropping our plowed soils, by overgrazing our grasslands, by overcutting and burning over our forest areas we have diluted and dispersed our basic wealth for quick gains, creating urgent need for salvage and repair. We have spent the base by two means: *exhaustion* in place and physical *removal*. The latter we call *soil erosion;* the former, *soil depletion.* Erosion is more obvious—even spectacular—and cannot go far unnoticed unless one refuses to see it. Depletion is much more elusive and insidious, because it leaves the soil body more or less intact, though with lowered fertility and reduced powers of recovery. Clearly, constant removal of any soil substance faster than the pedologic processes can regenerate it will, inevitably, exhaust the supply of that substance unless positive steps be taken to make up 'the deficit. That simple fact might be grave enough, but much more serious than the individual loss is its disruption of soil balance and impairment of the entire soil body. From the production viewpoint, the lack of one essential element can negate the effectiveness of others. Abundance of one cannot offset the deficiency of another. Since crops vary in their required proportion of nutrients, repeated sowing of one particular crop on a given plot of soil will first exhaust the nutrient for which that crop has the biggest appetite. The plant will suffer malnutrition when its favorite dish is consumed no matter how much other food is left. Finally, the available diet becomes so ill-balanced that no plant can thrive unless the soil be given artificial supplement— nitrate, phosphorus, potash, or other plant food. If crops are varied from year to year (rotated) they tend to equalize the removal of nutrients, thereby prolonging the life of the soil; but, in the end the variety will simply exhaust the soil more thoroughly. Whatever the planting scheme, *crops sold off the land represent soil substance,* and unless output be compensated with input the soil "goes broke," like a bank whose withdrawals consistently exceed its deposits.

Soils severely worn and depleted become afflicted, as it were. They lose more than the substances removed. They lose the normal health and function of the biotic soil community much as the human body sickens when one or more of its vital organs or glands fails to work properly. Soil poverty is not amenable to immediate alleviation by simply applying measured parts of exhausted elements to replace losses. The soil-making processes, the assimilating activity of soil flora and fauna, both normally slow, may be retarded almost to the point of cessation, and soil so nearly lifeless can respond only gradually to good treatment. It cannot recover instantly under any medication, however large the dosage. The malady can be arrested rather quickly, but full recovery takes longer.

Were it not for the fact that soil morbidity ultimately infects man we might be unconcerned about it. But *man victimizes himself when he abuses the soil,* and the insidious infection often reaches a stage too far advanced for easy control before the victim detects its presence. This contagion spreads by devious means, and breaks out in various forms. Crop yields decline, the children grow ill and morose, buildings sag and rot, broken implements stand rusting, and parents work harder and harder for less and less, often jeopardizing health and being. Necessities become luxuries, homes become squalid, prayers more fervent, and faith less assuring.

Ultimately, soil morbidity infects man

By the time a predatory cultivator realizes the measure of destruction he has wrought, he lacks all too often both the moral courage and the material means wherewith he might make restitution. Soil impoverishment depreciates land values and discourages the occupant; where both confidence and collateral be shaky, who will lend the funds with which to rehabilitate? Soils apparently intact can be so thoroughly depleted by abusive occupance that their renewal cannot be accomplished without public aid. Where there is little evidence that subsidy may be amortized, it is better economy to retire them from private use by public purchase and to endeavor to salvage the people from their self-made destitution. Disheartened people and the soil they have worn out are a very poor combination.

There is one consoling virtue of soil depreciated in situ: while the body remains, one can hope it will revive, given proper care and sufficient time. Fortunately, we have learned that soils wear out. We know the signs of weakness, and we have begun to treat the malady before it gets out of hand. Experience has taught us the unmitigated truth that rapacious men who sack and sell the soil condemn their kin to scavenging.

Weakening by one ailment invites infection with another

Serious as they may be, the direct consequences of soil depletion—crop failure, low income, malnutrition, poor plants, poor animals, and poor people—are perhaps less considerable than the concomitant deterioration of soil itself. Man has often more or less damaged the soil where he has cultivated, grazed, or logged it. Rarely has he repaired the damage. Frequently and over extensive areas he has so aggravated the damage that complete ruin resulted.

Depletion invites further injury by erosion or leaching, or both, because loss of humus reduces the capacity for absorbing and retaining water. Without good water storage, artificial application of plant nutrients can be only partially effective, because they are too rapidly carried away—either in percolating water or in run-off, depending upon soil texture, structure, and topographic position. It follows that the production of plants with which to restore humus content will be slow and often costly beyond economic feasibility; there is no short-cut to renewed soil vigor, no detour to soil fertility without humus.

Farmers, communities, and nations have gone by the board when they lacked the vision, the means, or the food reserve necessary to the replacement of dissipated soil humus. Whether by burning, washing, or blowing away, *loss of humus* is the crucial factor in soil wastage. It has made desert out of grazing land, and ghost towns out of forest villages. It hastened the fading of cultures once effulgent—Cretan, Sumerian, Persian, Athenian, Phoenician—and it scourges with hunger and famine the redundant Chinese and Indians of our modern era.

Depleted, deteriorated soils have little resistance to other destructive forces. Injury tends to become cumulative. More violent and absolute than exhaustion by wear is the destruction of soil by dissection, dismemberment, and removal that we call *soil erosion*. Soil erosion is an abnormal operation of the natural process whereby high places are reduced and low ones are filled up. Infinitely slow if left to itself, the process becomes radically accelerated under man's inept intervention. The activating forces, gentle and restrained on nature's leash, become monstrous and diabolical when man misbehaves and cuts them loose. Indignantly they tear apart and take away what previously they helped construct and ordain. Loosed by man, they dissolve and scar, transport and bury that without which he cannot prevail.

Erosion tears the soil apart and carries it away

Wind and water, erstwhile man's indispensable servants, become his most formidable adversaries when he bares the soil to their attack. The wind, purveyor of water to the land, turns hostile in its absence, and the life-giving water, unbridled, destroys the life it would sustain. Without wind and water man could not exist, but when by his own erring they do him harm, he is quick to place the blame.

The agents, wind and water, get the blame

Man is awed by the power that marches sand dunes across the desert or levels a city, by the relentless attack that moves mountains into the sea. He flees for his life before gale or torrent but forgets that unprotected soil is also defenseless against them. Might a few inches of soil resist what mountains of stone cannot endure? Certainly not! Winds that can plane a rock desert smooth make quick work of loose, dry soil, pulverized by tillage implements or disrobed and trampled by the hooves of hungry animals. Running water, which grooves the rocks and fashions valleys under the restraining hand of nature, makes game of a soft soil mantle exposed to its unfettered caprices.

In a single day of carnage, wind or water can carry away the product of centuries, and the soil in dust clouds or muddy streams has lost its usefulness. Perhaps no usable soil, or land, is totally immune to the ravages of wind or water. Indeed many soils, and expansive areas of land, feel the destructive fury of both wind and water, each in its season. Over the United States as a whole, as over the world, water erosion has probably destroyed much more soil than wind and affects a much larger total producing area. Both of these destructive agents are shown at work in Figs. 5.9 and 5.10.

Vociferous man and his silent accomplice, gravity, are instigators of the criminal plot—the latter mutely constant, the former blindly prodigal and unscrupulous. Man makes the arrangements

The instigators, man and gravity, pass the buck

Fig. 5.9 *Soil on the move: a dust storm in Colorado. The carrier is wind, but men have prepared the cargo for transport!*

Fig. 5.10 *Soil on the move: water ruining a field in Oklahoma. (S.C.S. photos.)*

Fig. 5.11 *Eviction is the ultimate penalty for land abuse. The farmer who lives in this shack (Colorado) was evicted by drought and wind because he plowed the wrong land. (Note the half-buried plow beam.)*

Fig. 5.12 *The cotton planter who lived in this house (South Carolina) was evicted by running water because he plowed the land too much, the wrong way. (S.C.S. photos.)*

and gravity does the dirty work. Had man learned that elementary lesson well enough when first he herded animals or tilled the soil, we could abbreviate this gloomy discourse. Unfortunately, man is not yet fully convinced that the soil he surrenders to gravity inevitably drags him down with it. *When the soil goes man must go too* (Figs. 5.11 and 5.12). Ours to pity rather than condemn the individual who, seeking livelihood, plows too high on the hill or runs more cattle than the land can carry; ours to examine critically the culture that imposed the need and the society that condoned the act. With malice toward neither, the striving individual penalizes both himself and his society.

In response to a seemingly insatiable market in Europe, young America developed a lucrative, commercial agriculture, in which row crops such as tobacco, cotton, and corn were entirely too prominent for the good of the land. (They still occupy much of our land, as may be seen in Fig. 5.13.) Clearing, burning, and planting ensured quick profit, and when the soil weakened there was more to clear. Men prospered by a single cash-crop specialty. They kept the soil stirred during the growing season and naked to the elements all year. They plowed straight furrows up and down the hill, except where slopes were too steep to permit it.

Fig. 5.13 *Intertilled crops, such as corn, cotton, and tobacco, incur greater erosion losses than close-growing crops, such as small grains or hay. On sloping land, row crops should be grown in narrow contour strips instead of entire fields as was once the custom. (Bureau of the Census map.)*

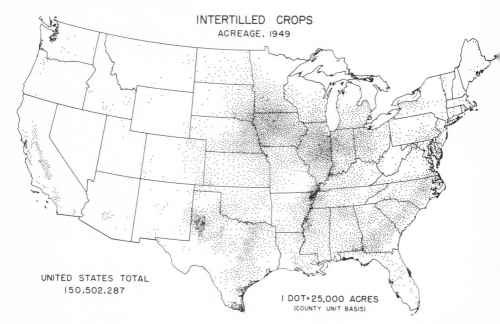

INTERTILLED CROPS
ACREAGE, 1949

UNITED STATES TOTAL
150,502,287

I DOT=25,000 ACRES
(COUNTY UNIT BASIS)

Fig. 5.14 *Whether the agent is wind or water, erosion involves removal, transportation and deposition. Where eroded debris comes to rest it may ruin undisturbed soil by burying it. This field in Minnesota is being damaged by drift from the left.*

They got their wealth and lost the soil whence it came. Worse still, they inaugurated a sort of land-use psychology that spread westward with settlement and tinges our land economy to this day: the fascination and gamble attendant upon a specialized land-use enterprise. We are justifiably proud of large, square fields, mammoth cattle spreads, and gigantic logging operations. We like to boast about *big* harvests, *big* herds, and *big* lumber stacks, without enough thought for the land whence they must come. Cutting a wide swath is traditionally American, but we need to transpose the tradition into good land management and soil husbandry. Then we shall have something we can always boast about without flinching—record production coincident with increased potential of a permanent base.

Destructive, or accelerated, erosion takes a variety of forms, and each form does several kinds of damage. Being simply an artificially activated operation of the natural geologic process, every form involves *removal, transport,* and *deposition* of soil materials. Points of origin and destination bear the brunt, with lesser injury along the route. *Wind* blows the soil away from one place and buries other soil when it deposits the debris (Fig. 5.14). It brings injury to plants and animals in the path of blowing dust and grit, increasing the difficulty of re-establishing enough life to stem subsequent attacks. Soil movement by *slipping* downslope in a mass removes the soil bodily and pushes it onto

Destructive erosion does several kinds of damage

109

Fig. 5.15 *In the foreground (Texas) soil has been buried by erosion silt.* (S.C.S. p

the soil below. It leaves raw edges and surfaces at the top, and distorted, hummocky soil at the bottom. *Water* wreaks havoc with soil from the impact and splash of the raindrop to the dumping of mud into the ocean. It robs the upland, scarring what it does not remove, it pollutes the streams and chokes their channels, and it buries under detritus the soils and alluvium of valley and lowland (Fig. 5.15). It reduces water storage at its source, it renders water courses inadequate for the discharge of excessive run-off, thereby magnifying stream erosion and flooding. It destroys plant and animal life (including man and his works) from its most inland point of origin to its seaward point of destination. Wash from a corn field in north Alabama can ruin an oyster bed in Mobile Bay more permanently than it affects the meadow immediately below the corn. Wash from their watersheds fills reservoirs with silt, negating the usefulness of costly dams and appurtenances. Wash spread over stream banks and lake shores spoils them for recreational use and wildlife habitat. From beginning to end, in scores of ways, soil erosion by water damages and disfigures our country.

Erosion by surface run-off, the most widespread and destructive, falls into three major categories: sheet wash; slope channeling or rilling; gullying. It is appropriate that we examine the salient features of each.

Sheet wash wears the soil away on areas inadequately covered. As the term implies, it peels off the top a little at a time and often goes unnoticed during its initial stages. The process begins with the pounding and splash of raindrops, which suspend fine soil particles in water, clog soil pores with the soupy fluid, and agitate a sheet of the mixture that moves off as surplus.

Sheet wash wears bald spots

This sheet erosion is invited by loss of humus, compaction, nakedness, and any other reduction of soil capacity for absorbing and retaining water. A forest floor devoid of litter, a pasture slope too closely grazed, a plowed field left bare, facilitates the process. When tree roots become exposed, or when bare earth shows through grass or grain, the process is well advanced. When the trees appear to have hoisted themselves out of the ground, or the thin spots in field or pasture have changed their hue, the attack has inflicted serious injury. The *A* horizon, the *B* horizon, or the entire soil section may have been taken by stealth. When a farmer observes that fields once of uniform color have become brindled, he might mark down in his almanac that sheet wash has robbed him. The clues are very obvious.

Once begun, sheet wash accelerates as the affected area becomes less receptive to water. Run-off from the bald spot tends to cut channels or incipient gullies below it, like infection spreading from an open wound. Here, as with many cases of resource abuse, damage and loss are cumulative and progressive; Fig. 5.16 shows the process.

Slope channeling, technically a form of rill erosion, rips loose topsoil away so swiftly and boldly that its audacity amazes even the trained observer. One heavy shower can literally "cut to ribbons" the freshly tilled soil on a steep slope, carving channels so deep that they expose the plow-sole as a flight of stairs (Fig. 5.17). Where plow depth equals or exceeds the thickness of the *A* horizon one does not need calculus to figure out that the loss of topsoil will be proportionate to the part of total surface space occupied by such channels. A thousand years of soil can be half gone in an afternoon thunderstorm, carried away in little rills of water.

Slope-channeling rips away the top soil

Up-and-down farming expedites channeling; contour plowing impedes it. In either case, cultivation that fills the grooves after one rain invites further loss to the next. Many a well-meaning

Fig. 5.16 If this were in color, the foreground would be red. Sheet wash has removed the topsoil, and gullies have begun to develop in the subsoil. Soil erosion is a self-accelerating process because the eroded area absorbs less water and thus increases run-off. (Courtesy T.V.A.)

Fig. 5.17 Slope channelling or rilling (Washington). (The author has observed the removal of almost half the soil, to plow depth, during an afternoon thunderstorm.) Note how the channels are enlarged toward the bottom, evincing the gathering volume and force of water as it runs down. Erosion may be accelerated quite as much by length of slope as by steepness. (S.C.S. photo.)

farmer smoothes a carved-up field, oblivious to the fact that the remnants he stirs become *more* vulnerable to attack. He considers the storm damage repaired when the channels are filled, failing to associate with the channeled slope the sediments spread out below it. He may view with detachment the recurrence of sheet wash or rilling until declining productivity precludes the possibility of effectual and economical countermeasures.

Rills are to gullies as acorns are to oaks, but they are seeds of destruction instead of growth. A few hundred million years ago a little rill began the world-famed Grand Canyon of the Colorado. There was no man to accelerate the cutting of the Canyon; nature did it unaided, and very slowly. Men have induced canyon cutting in many parts of our country, and even Missourians have "shown" themselves guilty, as clearly evidenced by Fig. 5.18.

Gullying rends the whole earth mantle

Gullying does not stop with the soil but rends the whole earth mantle right down to bedrock. Unrestrained, it makes of little grooves tremendous V-shaped or vertical-walled trenches that almost defy containment. It can begin with a mere scratch on the surface and produce an excavation in which battleships could be concealed. The scar of a log snaked out of the woods, the rooting of a razorback hog, the drip from the eaves, the discharge from a spot of sheet wash, or wheel tracks, footpaths, cow trails (Fig.

Fig. 5.18 *This gully in Missouri was later blocked and converted into a farm pond. Note the man standing about mid-way down this incipient canyon. (S.C.S. photo.)*

Fig. 5.19 *Gullied cow lane (Kansas). Packed and worn by animals, the soil becomes vulnerable to both water and wind erosion. Such ruin as this can be averted by timely shifting of cow routes. (S.C.S. photo.)*

5.19), or pig pens, poultry yards, cattle corrals, or grading, filling, excavating—every one, and many another, has commenced gullying of titanic dimensions.

Early in their development gullies become "triple threats" to the land. Removal and deposition are direct damages, but the ditches soon become obstacles to animals and machinery, thereby restricting or prohibiting the use of areas between them. Interdiction defeats farmers much as it does troops on a battlefield. Unless it be accessible for use the best of soil has little value.

In advanced stages of gullying the land lies completely dissected or mutilated. Under certain conditions mature gullies assume parallel courses downslope, producing veritable badlands of V-shaped grooves and sharp-crested divides, the site entirely stripped of soil and vegetation. Under other conditions, as in the loess bordering the lower Mississippi, they assume forms much more grand and grotesque, with vertical, ragged sides that cave in, tons at a time, like cliffs tumbling into a chasm. In both cases the destructive work proceeds headward and laterally like the spread of a festering wound, gaining momentum as it destroys, until those who began it are helpless to stop it.

Few people see in a gullied landscape the real loss depicted there, the work of millennia wasted in decades. More of us must

114

learn the implications of severe gullying, the most spectacular form of water erosion. With all our technology we cannot rebuild quickly what nature took aeons to create.

"What goes up must come down" applies to soil as well as to anything else, and when the translocation involves segments of soil otherwise intact the shift may be identified as *mass movement*. Landslides and earth flows are violent and sudden mass movements. So far as these phenomena are natural we can neither accept blame nor in every case prescribe preventive treatment; but, where our use, or abuse, of the land apparently activates or accelerates any of them, it behooves us to examine our fault.

Mass movement of soil also accelerates

Pasture land appears particularly susceptible to soil creep or slipping, and it may be that the weight of the animals and the paths they wear across the slope are contributing factors. Slips are common features on steep pasture slopes in southeastern Ohio and adjacent areas, where smooth rock underlies the soil. They are also common on the gently sloping grazing lands of the Great Plains, in eastern Montana and southward. They may be seen in upland pastures and steep fields most anywhere in the nation. The one pictured in Fig. 5.20 happened in the Northwest.

Fig. 5.20 *Erosion by mass movement may be induced or accelerated by inept use of the land. This slip occurred in Washington because the entire slope was cultivated without erosion-preventive applications. (S.C.S. photo.)*

The *slumps and flows* characteristic of hillsides in Muskingum County, Ohio are probably typical soil slip features. A section of soil breaks away and slips a few feet downslope, leaving a minia- ture scarp or series of scarps about its upper side, while the soil is pushed up into peculiar hummocks at its lower margin. The scarp may be a few inches to several feet in height; the mass may possibly be an acre in area, though usually much less. The movement, once begun, tends to recur until it leaves a dent in the hillside and a jumbled mass of soil debris at the bottom. The dent in the hillside loses its soil and becomes droughty, while the billowing area below it loses its normal structure and becomes poorly drained. The "stepped-crescents" of the plains are similar, but in them the slipped mass is usually thinner and the identifying features considerably subdued. Modifications of *slumping, slipping,* and *flowage* have damaged our soils in many places, but the aggregate consequences certainly do not equal those of run-off water or of wind.

Terraces apparently made by animals are probably both cause and effect of mass movement—the indirect results of overgrazing, disturbed water behavior, and rupture or weakening of the bind- ing that healthy sod and deep plant roots maintain.

This is not to say that grazing is the only way by which our use of the soil accelerates soil erosion by mass movement. We jeopardize forest slopes, too, whenever we injure or destroy the mass of roots that secures the soil or the litter and humus that detain water. We accelerate the caving and slumping of stream banks with every upstream employment of land that hastens run- off. Here is another of the manifold relationships between one conservation problem and another: impaired water storage, which directly curtails soil fertility where it occurs, is indirectly respon- sible for soil destruction elsewhere.

Much has been said about *steepness of slope,* or grade, in con- nection with soil erosion, but not enough about the *length of slope,* which may be equally important. Other factors being equal, the *length* and the *steepness* of a slope gauge the vigor of attack by water.

Length and steepness of slope gauge the vigor of attack

Perhaps the simplest statement of grade is in terms of per cent, a 1-foot vertical drop in a 100-foot horizontal distance constituting a 1 per cent slope. A 100 per cent slope equals the hypotenuse of a right triangle with both legs equal, one vertical and the other horizontal. By plane geometry it equals a 45-degree angle; by common sense, an incline too great for ordinary cultivation. The Southern mountaineer calls it "steep as a horse's face," and he knows that it is physically impossible to plow it up and down.

With a "hillside" plow that can be flipped over at each end of the field to throw the furrow downslope both going and coming, he has always farmed on the contour, often without any thought of employing it to save his soil. Where the soil lasted until modern conservation came along, the hill farmer was a ready convert to a practice he already simulated under compulsion.

A negligible portion of our land surface lies flat enough to escape accelerated erosion under cultural use without specific precautions. Water erosion takes place on slopes of less than 1 per cent grade, whose incline may be difficult to detect visually except by observing run-off. Wherever water can run off it can also erode! In parts of the Corn Belt on flat glaciated plains, the terrain is so nearly level and the drainage so sluggish that intermittent creeks weave their way off the land by meanders cut through some of our richest soils. They relegate to permanent pasture much land otherwise highly desirable for cultivation.

Erosion by mass movement does little damage on slopes of 3 or 4 per cent, but on slopes only twice that steep it may be active. *Flatness of terrain saves very few soils from erosion.*

Second only to the grade factor comes the length of the slope, especially as it influences water erosion. Grade lends velocity per se, but *length builds up volume all the way down,* as clearly shown in Fig. 5.17. Obviously, volume incidentally increases velocity and multiplies destructive capacity by augmented flow and intensified impact. On a uniform slope each unit of area contributes a comparable amount of the run-off. Theoretically, if each acre discharges as run-off 10 barrels of water from a rain, then 4 acres in a row downslope should discharge 40 barrels. Each acre in turn takes a worse lacing than the next one above it, and the lowest one gets the whole attack assembled by the others. That explains how gullying, like the self-made man, begins at the bottom and works up. The longer the slope, the more severe its erosion by water.

Wind, the horizontal movement of air, while it has little respect for grade, is nonetheless responsive to aspects of terrain. Flatness that stems eroding water gives wind the free sweep it needs to attain menacing force. Level or gently undulating uplands bear the brunt of wind erosion. Surface irregularities and lesser obstacles, such as trees, brush, or hedgerows, cause friction and turbulence that moderate the attack. Windward exposures suffer maximum deflation, and sheltered situations receive the wind-borne debris. Wind, too, takes away from one place and deposits in another (Fig. 5.14), but, unlike water, wind erodes uphill more actively than downhill.

Wind has less respect for grade

Although wind wreaks more havoc in dry regions, it also erodes humid lands whenever drought affords the opportunity. During open winters and dry spells in our humid East, considerable soil blowing takes place. Muck on valley floors, where one might think the wind impotent, falls easy prey to wind erosion when the light organic material is dry. The soft material of our Coastal Plains blows quite extensively, not only along the shore, but also on exposed sites far inland.

The dust on a footpath or a dirt road, a playground or cow lane, may yield to wind when water fails to move it. Sunken roads in loess, whether in moist Mississippi or in dry Mongolia, are at least partially the product of wind erosion. The free air of the troposphere is charged with salt blown off the oceans and dust blown off the lands. If it were not so there should be less precipitation for lack of condensation nuclei. The dust originates with wind erosion. When it attains a density visibly apparent, land somewhere is losing its soil; when it obstructs vision, soils nearby are in full flight.

As previously mentioned, few areas are entirely secure against water erosion. The same can be said for wind. However, there is much more soil destruction by water in our dry West than there is by wind in our moist East. Predominance of one over the other is a matter of degree, variable from time to time and place to place.

Climatic conditions influence human activities everywhere in many different ways, among them the selection of land-use enterprises and the provocation of accelerated erosion under a particular type of land use in any location. Climate is the framework, no less than the land itself, against which we have poorly planned and pursued the employment of our soils. We have failed to comprehend, or refused to acknowledge, the full significance of climatic elements in relation to land use and erosion.

Extremes and vagaries of climate are crucial factors

Averages, or means, most accurately computed, are at best inadequate or misleading for land-use planning. *Departures* from the norm, periodic or cyclic *fluctuations,* erratic *extremes* and *variations,* are the *crucial factors in soil erosion.* A severe freeze in Louisiana can ruin the cover crop intended to protect the unfrozen soil. A January thaw in Minnesota can erode soil that would normally lie frozen so solid, or so deeply buried under snow, that no erosion would be possible. Soils that can absorb a monthly rainfall of 5 inches, even when it comes in five days, can erode badly if the total falls in one day. Worse has happened, and the excess is disastrous where the average is harmless.

Spring drought in the spring-wheat country, where spring is ordinarily the rainy season, has ruined both crops and soils when wind stripped the top off the pulverized fields and exposed the seed. A series of dry years on the southern Great Plains created the Dust Bowl tragedy, about which more will be said in the chapter on the grasslands. Land use geared to the *wet* cycle failed when the *dry* one arrived.

Too much rain, or not enough, temperatures too high or too low, heat or cold, wetness or dryness out of season, extremes of climate and vagaries of weather—these are the recalcitrants that have eluded our best efforts of adaptation.

How much has our young nation sacrificed? More than any of comparable age in history. Many of our good farm lands have surrendered more topsoil than they retain. Many a present-day farmer in eroded parts of our Southeast has never tilled any considerable area of *A* horizon. Many are farming the *C* horizon, parent material deserted by its offspring. Unless they move away they may never farm anything better than parent material. Many dry-land farmers are cultivating soil remnants and drifted soil debris. Correction of past error is impossible, and improvement of the inhospitable situation is difficult because the means have been lost or impaired. Nor is there any regional sanctuary from soil erosion. The deep, rich soils on the rolling plains of Iowa, Illinois, and Indiana are down to the *B* horizon in many places. (Indeed, many eroded soils to which the best modern farming practices are applied produce more than ever before, but how much greater still might their yield be if those practices could have been applied to them undamaged?) The general extent and severity of erosion may be seen in Fig. 5.21.

Our losses are staggering

Indirect losses are also great—almost beyond comprehension. Soil erosion pollutes our streams, reducing their values for water supply, recreation, and wildlife habitat. By sedimentation it chokes stream channels and estuaries, rendering them less capable of discharging the concentrated run-off from eroded lands. It imposes extravagant expenditures for dredging and other measures to keep our waterways and harbors navigable. It silts our reservoirs. It increases floods and decreases our developed and potential water power. In short, it complicates all the major aspects of water conservation and robs us of the wherewithal to take corrective action.

Erosion complicates our water problems

Worst of all, unchecked erosion would compromise our enviable American society and threaten the highest material standards on earth. It would humiliate and frustrate our people. The

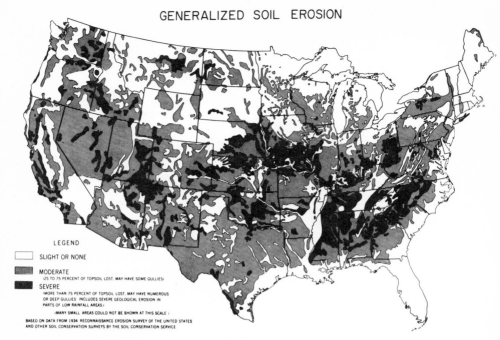

GENERALIZED SOIL EROSION

LEGEND

SLIGHT OR NONE

MODERATE
(25 TO 75 PERCENT OF TOPSOIL LOST, MAY HAVE SOME GULLIES)

SEVERE
(MORE THAN 75 PERCENT OF TOPSOIL LOST, MAY HAVE NUMEROUS
OR DEEP GULLIES. INCLUDES SEVERE GEOLOGICAL EROSION IN
PARTS OF LOW RAINFALL AREAS)

(MANY SMALL AREAS COULD NOT BE SHOWN AT THIS SCALE)

BASED ON DATA FROM 1934 RECONNAISSANCE EROSION SURVEY OF THE UNITED STATES
AND OTHER SOIL CONSERVATION SURVEYS BY THE SOIL CONSERVATION SERVICE

Fig. 5.21 *The national survey of soil erosion revealed that few areas remain intact; most of the cropland and grazing land has been severely damaged. (S.C.S. map.)*

erosion menace is not everywhere equally present, but no region has complete immunity. In some places, as in the "blow" area of the southern plains, its ravages have recurred almost unabated. The early 1950's were a painful reminder of the "Dirty Thirties." Erosion weakens our regional economies and social structures, attendant upon personal hardship and community distress. Erosion remains a serious national problem, both economically and socially.

Foreclosure, bankruptcy, and forced migration are end products of soil erosion, and emergency relief cannot compensate the victims. We cannot recover personal pride and self-confidence with disaster funds. The by-products of soil wastage—dispossessed, disillusioned, disheartened people—are not always capable of full recovery by any means. Our *real* national strength reposes in the people. Our greatest resources, those for whose aggrandizement we strive to conserve all the others, are *human*. If we would conserve them, let us look well to the defense of our soil.

6

Soil Conservation

soil conservation holds the soil in place, maintains or improves its health and fertility, and increases its capacity for sustained production

Our losses of soil have been grievous, and the continuing losses are great; but, during three decades of scientifically organized soil defense we have made such gains that many other nations, young and old, look to us for example and advice.

We cannot recover soils eroded away, and we cannot repair damaged soils beyond a degree permitted by situation and circumstance; but we can hold and fortify those soils that remain. Couched in military terms: we cannot regain all the ground we have lost, but we can hold the line and advance rather than retreat. Our tactics, as yet imperfectly developed, have even now such demonstrated effectiveness that we need only apply them more widely and more vigorously to ensure for ourselves and posterity the soils now surviving, with higher productivity and greater resistance. (In Fig. 6.1, see how soil conservation transformed an eroded farm.) Meanwhile we must develop a better public sense of values. We must learn that soil inches per acre guarantee social security more realistically than dollars per month.

The futility of employing land without soil for soil-using purposes is obvious. By the same token, one cannot conserve the soil where none exists, as for instance, on certain deep sands of our coastal plains or on the bare rock exposures of mountains

Fig. 6.1 *With good treatment we can heal and rejuvenate much of our worn and wounded land. Shortly before this picture was taken (North Carolina), the grassed hillside to the left of the fence resembled the gullied slope on the right (which was also mended later). (Courtesy T.V.A.)*

and deserts. Only if population pressure becomes extreme, as in parts of the Old World, can such sands and slopes be laboriously covered with soil artificially developed or transported from other areas. Meanwhile, the apparently unproductive spaces may be playing such subtle parts in the total scheme of things that their true worth eludes us.

Time, place, and *condition* must dictate the choices of method and technique. *Condition* means the state of the soil to be conserved, especially its erosive quality and its relative health. *Place* connotes all the geographic attributes that influence soil development, soil use, and soil erosion—climate, vegetation, topographic position, and so forth. It also involves the established land economy and cultural practices. Applications must be chosen and adapted to suit the situation: wind defense where wind is the miscreant, water defense where run-off does the damage, and so on. Within our space limitations we cannot detail the specially endorsed methods region by region, but we can indicate, now

Time, place, and condition indicate the modes of treatment

and then, how the general methods discussed have specific pertinence to certain parts of the country.

Time is of the essence! Procrastination has already enlarged the problem tremendously, and every delay makes it greater. But, there are more tangible time factors to be regarded, such as the importance of countering wind injury during a wet cycle when nature lends a hand, or the importance of conducting costly engineering when funds are available. Waiting spreads the injury, increases the cost of treatment, and renders the cure less positive and permanent.

Land-use planning is the first line of defense against soil damage. Had we better arranged our schemes of land use to accord with land capabilities from the beginning, our task would have been comparatively easy. But, because we consigned our land to various uses almost haphazardly and lost or damaged much of the soil, our planning must be remedial more than preventive, applied to soils in all stages of deterioration. We are land planners of necessity, not by choice.

Planning for regions, communities, or political units is a proper function of groups and governments at the various levels. Execution of any plan depends upon public enlightenment and cooperation. Good civic leadership is the key to water-power development, establishment of community parks and forests, and a host of other public improvements. But land planning for soil conservation cannot be implemented without the participation of private landowners. They are not only the producers of our crops and animals, but also the keepers of our soils. They must be convinced, instructed, and often assisted in the wise use allocation of the space they own. Consistent with our democratic principles, we have not forced farmers to conform, unless we count the condemnation and acquisition of land for such public developments as reservoirs, roads, communication, and transmission lines. Perhaps one of the payments for democracy has been the loss of soil incidental to absolute ownership and almost unrestrained use of the land. If that be true, which it may well be, the costs can be reduced by educating the people for democracy *and* conservation simultaneously. The combined process is implicit in group planning for area improvement.

The best laid plans often miscarry or fail of execution when economic necessity or opportunity intervenes. A farmer may be fully convinced that a certain tract should be planted to trees, but he cannot meet next year's mortgage payment with seedlings. A rancher may have to choose between overgrazing or selling

Land-use planning is the first line of defense

We formulate and implement our plans without duress

"The best laid schemes o' mice and men . . ."

his animals on a weak market. A timber grower may be offered so much for one clean cutting that he abandons his sustained-yield program. Tempted by high wheat prices, the plains farmer may risk plowing up the grass he sowed to guard his soil against wind erosion. Thus in scores of ways those who live on the land are inclined, if not compelled, to compromise the plans to which they subscribe in principle.

If his first attempt fails—if his trees burn, if his young grass withers, or if his range erodes despite carefully regulated grazing, the conforming individual loses heart and confidence. One bad year, one accident, and he bolts the planned program. Short-range reverses can blind him to long-range advantages.

Impetuous, independent men, fluctuating prices, weather, and catastrophes, must be taken in stride by the planner, but he cannot be entirely successful without a checkrein on the human element. Cognizant of that, the Soil Conservation Service, early in its brilliant career, placed its assistance to landowners on a cooperative basis to ensure execution of recommended farm plans. To enlarge the work toward regional scope, the Service organized (usually along county lines) conservation districts under enabling acts passed by state legislatures. Thus came into being the individual obligation and community organization which gave the movement the latitude and continuity essential to its success. Demonstration farms showed district members the methods and advantages of conservation farming. Many nonmember individualists also observed the good work and adopted similar practices on their own land. Many who resisted district organization initially became its staunch supporters when they had proof of its merits.

Management can prevent soil injury

Once the land is consigned to its proper use—be it *crop, pasture,* or *forest*—the next step toward soil conservation is skillful management under the chosen use or uses. Unless one follows through, his planning goes for naught. Having determined a pattern, the land operator becomes forester, grazier, or farmer, or any combination of the three. He may abandon or restrict his specialization and strengthen his economic stability by producing a greater variety of goods. Variety of produce and stability of producer are a combination conducive to good soil management and conservation.

Continuity of tenure is basic to proper soil management, because a constructive program means several consecutive years of scheduled activities. Immediate gains, this year or next, must often be disdained in order that more substantial ones may accrue later. The vision to defer and the means to sustain the wait must be at hand. Lacking either, especially the latter, the operator cannot be a *keeper* of the soil but must be instead a scavenger scratching desperately to exist this year, and maybe next. Men struggling to survive cannot be concerned about anything beyond the immediate future. Short-term tenants and sharecroppers are often at once the products and the victims of poor land. Destitute people on sterile land can improve neither themselves nor the soil without assistance. Expert advice cannot help them unless they are also assisted in applying the recommendations. Cognizant of these deterrents to soil conservation, Congress has appropriated vast sums of money to encourage farm ownership and to assist the owners in converting to good farm management.

The object of management is the maintenance or improvement of soil health and fertility, and in soil maintenance an ounce of prevention is, if anything, worth more than a pound of cure. Skillfully accomplished, the objective may be attained without serious disruption of productive land use; but if attention be deferred until health and fertility are impaired, the best opportunity has passed, and procedures will almost invariably interfere with regular production. "A stitch in time" is infinitely more applicable to the tiller of soils than it is to the patcher of little boys' breeches.

An ounce of prevention is better than a pound of cure

Except in organic soils such as muck and peat, which require special treatment, soil maintenance or improvement depends primarily upon *retention and addition of humus,* the vital soil component most transitory under productive soil employment. As retainer of water and nutrients and the medium for an active biotic community, soil humus is the mainstay of soil health and fertility. Unless humus be present in sufficient quantity, heavy soils become compacted and intractable; light ones, too loose and porous. Without humus, clays lack pore space for air and water, and sands lack the body with which to resist the leaching-out of plant nutrients by percolating water. Humus tends to bind the soil together, thereby increasing its resistance to erosion. Humus releases available nitrogen as it decays, thereby promoting plant growth. It improves the physical condition of the soil so that plants can respond well when other plant foods are added. Humus facilitates tillage and promotes good tilth.

If the humus naturally accumulated in grassland or even forest soils were retained, our soil problems would be much simpler. When we dissipate humus by burning or trampling the forest floor, by close-grazing the range, or overcropping tilled areas, we deprive ourselves of the prime factor in soil maintenance. Once lost, that factor is difficult to re-establish, because the vegetation whence it must come is retarded.

Soil fatigue and soil wear resemble emaciation and infection of the human body. If weakness be detected early and preventive measures taken promptly, the trouble will usually right itself without specific or radical treatment.

In early stages several ills respond to common treatment

In early stages many ills respond to common treatment; care and nourishment rather than medication. Retaining health is much easier than regaining it. If a fair portion of soil product, such as plant residue or animal waste, were always returned to the soil whence it came, soil ills would rarely become so grave as to require elaborate and costly palliatives. But too few of our husbandmen love and understand their soil well enough to guard its health before it has failed.

Advanced organic ailment requires specific medication

Advanced organic ailment requires specific medication, and the prescription may be very complex. A tonic cannot cure a diabetic, nor can humus remedy excessive soil acidity. Treatment generally beneficial may aggravate the particular systemic derangement. If the soil be too acid one must sweeten it; if the duodenum ulcerates one must soothe it.

Soil afflictions engendered by abuse are so numerous and varied that all cannot be described here. They fall into three major categories: *physical; chemical; biological.* There is a degree of reciprocity among the three, but the first demands greatest attention because it controls the other two and is therefore of primary importance. Physical soil ailment can usually be diagnosed as a deficiency of one or more vital elements or the wearing away by erosion. Deficiencies may be corrected by incorporating the material in short supply, be it nitrogen, phosphorus, potassium, humus, calcium, or any other. That done, and a reasonable balance regained, wear will be less active, if not stopped altogether.[1] When diagnosis shows humus content below par, its replenishment should come first, the better to assimilate any other additions. Early recovery can be assured unless deficiency and wear have proceeded so far that only nature with her infinite means and patience can afford a cure.

Serious physical injury may require surgery

Serious physical injury may require surgery. When the attending physician, the land-user, plows around a gullied hillside or abandons a worn-out field, he admits tacitly that he cannot successfully treat the injury and that he is obliged to amputate the damaged portion. In the case of the exhausted field, he turns his badly handled patient over to nature for such recuperation as she may ordain. In the case of the wounded hillside, he may be able to isolate the gangrene and prevent its spread. He may reduce the bleeding by localizing the wound. Our country is dotted with such land surgery. It devolves upon soil conservation, pursued individually and cooperatively, to defend against further injury the soil that remains and recover or revive wherever possible that which we have lost or ruined.

Many areas require only slight modification of established land-use practices; others demand complete revision of utilization. In some areas adequate conservational procedures show a quick profit over and above their total cost; in others adequate measures demand an expenditure per acre many times greater than the highest price quoted by a real-estate agent.

First, the soil or whatever is left of it must be *stabilized,* held in place. "A rolling stone gathers no moss," and soil on the move collects no fertility. The farmer-conservator cannot improve soil that is actively eroding any better than the surgeon can operate while his patient cavorts about the hospital.

First, the soil or soil remnants must be held in place

All erosion preventives are, in effect, soil stabilizers, and in many cases several must be applied simultaneously, lest none be effectual. Increase of humus content, increase of pore space for air and water, a dense, unbroken surface cover, dispersal of run-off, and moderation of wind velocity—all contribute toward fixing erosive soil in place. The function of each, always constant, varies in relative importance from one situation to another. For instance, one might gain nothing by adding humus to muckland, whereas its incorporation with salvable parent material where nothing better remains might well be the signal step toward its conservation.

Unless it is bare and dry and pulverized, soil cannot be very badly damaged by wind. When the soil is so dry that the wind can easily remove it, it is too dry to produce a protective vegetative cover. Conversely, when the soil is moist enough to resist wind action, it has moisture enough to grow protective vegetation as well. Thus, defense against wind erosion hinges upon water conditions.[2]

Soil cannot blow badly unless it is bare and dry

Since soil-blowing is a natural hazard to flat lands under low and erratic rainfall, it is man made only to the extent that man breaks or weakens the protective covering and reduces soil capacity for absorbing and storing water. He can correct his error by establishing and maintaining a *cover* as good, or better, than the original one nature provided and by ensuring that the soil receives and retains water just as effectively as it did before he disturbed it.

Sores of sheet wash will heal under a proper bandage.[3] Straw,

Sores of sheet wash heal under a bandage

stalks, leaves, brush, sawdust, or other material, spread over the wound to intercept raindrops and to prevent the spatter effect that causes irritation, serve in much the same manner as a wet wrapping over a burn. If the gall be large and deep it may be necessary to retire it from use temporarily. The application of a thick blanket initially, and the addition of new layers as older ones decay and settle, can mend a deep sore in a few years. However, results cannot be very satisfactory if the bandage is ripped off annually and the wound probed with a plow. Temporary, seasonal bandaging does well just to reduce festering and spreading.

Horizontal tillage checks slope channeling

Horizontal tillage checks slope channeling and incipient gullying by dividing slope length into shorter segments. by breaking the gradient, or by interrupting both slope and grade. Horizontal, or contour, tillage means the performance of cultural operations crosswise of the slope (on the level) instead of up and down.[4] (A contour is a line drawn on a map or on the ground, all points of which lie at the same elevation.) Since water runs downhill, any obstruction on the contour impedes its flow and reduces its erosive power. The principle is as simple as that. Its application on the land is illustrated in Fig. 6.2.

Fig. 6.2 *Contour tillage (almost horizontally) is a basic application in soil conservation. This layout in Pennsylvania shows two additional devices for managing run-off-diversion terraces and a farm pond. A clean-tilled orchard needs conservation measures similar to those applicable to any other row crop. (S.C.S. photo.)*

Fig. 6.3 *Strip cropping is an effective elaboration of contour tillage, employing strips of close-growing crops such as hay alternating with intertilled crops such as corn. Run-off from heavy rain can cut a long slope planted entirely to corn, but it cannot gather great destructive force across a few rows. Such wash as may occur is intercepted and dispersed by the next hay strip below. Thus strip cropping breaks a slope into segments. The sweeping curves of strip cropping harmonize with the natural design of the land. (S.C.S. photo.)*

In practice there are numerous contour tillage devices, and some of them are developed to a high degree of technical perfection. Plowing furrows along the contour is the simplest form. Each furrow acts as a dam against water moving downslope. Strip cropping is another simple form. It is a mere matter of alternating contour strips of close-growing crops such as hay and grain with strips of row crops such as cotton, corn, and tobacco that require clean tillage. Each close-growing strip, itself receptive to water, disperses the run-off and captures the silt lost from the tilled strip above it. Strip cropping is both practical and artistic, as may be seen in Fig. 6.3.

Another device for controlling slope wash and conserving water is a system of terraces or diversion channels—almost but not quite accordant with contours, so that the slight pitch will lead water off laterally instead of running over the terrace ridges.[5] There is no essential difference between a field terrace and a

129

Fig. 6.4 *The channel-type terrace such as pictured here, in Louisiana, conserves both soil and water. It impedes erosion run-off and spreads the water over a wide soaking area. It presents no obstacle to normal tillage operations, including harvesting. (S.C.S. photo.)*

diversion channel except that the latter is a larger structure with a broader trough, to discharge uncommonly heavy run-off. See in Fig. 6.4 how a channel-type terrace catches water, spreads it out, and causes it to soak into the soil.

Terracing has been the object of much experimentation to determine the most effective construction under various conditions of soil, slope, climate, and cultural utilization. Early attempts with terracing failed because the ridges were built exactly on the contour, with both troughs and ridges too steep and narrow. Heavy rains broke over the ridges and cut them to pieces. They were obstructions to normal tillage operations, with little compensation in the form of water storage. Field testing evolved the broad, "easy" terrace now in vogue, which discharges excess water laterally into preplanned and permanent disposal channels, such as the one pictured in Fig. 6.5.[6] It has extensive storage and soakage area for water and interferes very little with mechanized tillage. Terracing has recast the rural scene in many parts of America and has given many communities a new lease on life. The word *contour* has become important in the American language. Many who cannot read it know its practical application; many others must learn.

Contour tillage serves either preventive or corrective purposes, depending upon the timeliness of its employment. In American history it will rank high among the great scientific achievements of the twentieth century. We may add new variants, such as stubble-mulching and subtillage[7] to take fuller advantage of its soil and water conserving capabilities, but the simple, basic, concept remains constant: restrain and detain run-off at its origin, and both soil and water will be conserved.

Gullies respond to blocking and planting despite their forbidding aspect. Only against the cavernous kind with precipitous walls are man's efforts to erase often frustrated. Some gullies initiated by men will probably scar the earth long after the human species has departed. About the best we can do with the manmade canyons is to deflect run-off away from their heads so it cannot tumble over the brink and undermine the walls. We can hope to slow down headward destruction and perhaps even arrest it after a time, but to fill in and smooth over all the monstrous holes already dug would be prohibitive in cost, if not physically impossible.

Gullies respond to blocking and planting

Fig. 6.5 *Grassed waterways are devices whereby converging run-off or that debouched by horizontal diversion channels may be discharged without dissecting the land. In some highly productive farming areas, on terrain that is almost level to only gently undulating, they are the most conspicuous conservation features. When properly developed they yield good cuttings of hay, as shown here on this farm in Illinois. (S.C.S. photo.)*

Fig. 6.6 *Decapitation is the first step in subduing a gully. This project was begun by deflecting run-off away from the head. Log dams, or "gully blocks" were then emplaced, commencing with the uppermost. Tons of boulders were deposited below each spillway to absorb the impact of the waterfall and prevent its undermining the structure. The sides of the gully were graded smooth and planted to black locust, small grain, and lespedeza. The full treatment was completely successful, resulting in a stabilized condition. This was a public project near Spartanburg, South Carolina. (S.C.S. photo.)*

V-shaped or U-shaped gullies may be arrested and gradually refilled by constructing "check dams," or gully blocks, across them at appropriate intervals, closely spaced on steep slopes and farther apart on gentler ones.[8] Each block establishes an artificial base level and causes debris to fill in behind it. For maximum results the blocks must be built first across the head of the gully, then progressively farther down its length. With gullies as with streams, beheading gets positive results. Figure 6.6 shows one way of doing it.

Hardy vines, grasses, shrubs, or trees can effectively stop gullying under certain conditions, particularly if active gullying be arrested with dams prior to planting. In the Southeast, kudzu and honeysuckle have stopped many gullies without any aid beyond the planting. Trees wrought the change observable in Figs. 6.7 and 6.8. Either process can quickly blanket a deep earth wound and heal it in a few years. Perhaps honeysuckle is too

132

Fig. 6.7 *Quick rehabilitation of gullied land may be prohibitive in cost, but the process of natural healing can be facilitated by planting hardy species.*

Fig. 6.8 *Black locust made the gain on this farm in Illinois in only three and one-half years. (S.C.S. photos.)*

efficient; farmers who have fought it as a weed have been known to reckon gullying a lesser evil. However, now that they can kill the vine with toxic sprays, they should be less prejudiced.

Repair of dissected land involves engineering

Land completely dissected by gullying is extremely difficult to rehabilitate by damming and planting, because each gully requires its own series of dams or blocks, and the intervening raw ridges slough and crumble so rapidly that plants cannot attach themselves securely. Stabilization by vegetation takes a long time.

Only drastic measures can quickly mend dissected, denuded land, and in many cases the costs are not justifiable in terms of recovered productivity. Where remaining earth materials have *substance* to warrant the expenditure, the torn land can be stabilized by contouring and terracing it with a bulldozer or other heavy machinery. The plants can then take hold and begin the slow process of developing new soil in place of that which washed away. Without adequate private means or public assistance, an owner of man-made badlands may either view them with detachment or look the other way. He can help nature bind them with vegetation, but he cannot expect much gain from them during his lifetime. They may not even be a legacy for his grandchildren to cherish.

Cultivation should enrich rather than impoverish

Soil abuse was once so nearly universal in the United States that we had almost come to accept shrinking production from aging fields as a foregone conclusion. But now we have determined that the age of a cultivated field has no significance as an index to its productivity. We must revamp our land-use psychology, and there are good indications that we will. No changing current of American thought could possibly be more prophetic. We have begun to employ our soils according to their quality. We have made some produce more abundantly than when they were broken. But we have done it the hard way, with artificial means and narrow perspective. When we learn to enlist the natural forces ready to serve us and view the soil as a sacred trust we dare not violate, then shall we be on the only sure road toward soil enrichment coincident with continuous crop production. Genuine soil conservation cannot be realized without that approach and that conviction.

Replenishment should approximate withdrawal

If enrichment by tillage be temporarily waived, at least replenishment should approximate the withdrawal of essential elements. Anything less than that must be deemed uneconomical and antisocial. Until we know exactly what we take from the soil in each crop we harvest, we cannot be sure of restoring the losses entirely; but, we certainly can make general restitution insofar as we do know the food requirements of that crop. By scientific analyses of soil and plant tissue we are narrowing the margin of chance.[9] In their annual farm operations good farmers place replenishment on a par with yield, knowing that future years will compensate.

Any alert, experienced farmer recognizes the inherent advantages of general farming or animal industry over cash cropping. He knows that in meat, milk, or eggs he sells less soil off his farm than in wheat, hay, or cotton. One such farmer, on being praised for his lush meadows, explained very candidly, "I sell only what can walk off the place. My biggest loss is the phosphorus in the bones." Of course our friend lost more than phosphorus, but he voiced a sound idea in soil conservation. The waste of energy incurred by converting vegetable calories into animal calories represents economy in terms of soil.

Thorough tillage stimulates soil organisms and soil processes that convert soil material into plant food, thereby promoting productivity. By the same token, good tillage hastens the assimilation and availability of materials contributed to the soil, artificially or otherwise. Unless the supply of raw materials for plant foods be replenished, tillage simply pirates the nutrients until they are exhausted. Piratical cultivation has exhausted many of our soils. We have thus overworked one function of tillage and neglected another. Only when we equalize or reconcile the two can we perpetuate the fertility of our cropland; neither theorizing nor experimentation will suffice. Farm owners and farm operators must determine that cultivation "doubles in brass"; otherwise the "orchestra" goes out of tune.

If ever a strong back and a weak mind qualified a man for farming, that time has passed long ago. In order to make a fair profit, and at the same time keep the factory (the soil) in good repair, the modern farmer must be intelligent and well informed. Increased mental requirements have not materially offset the need of a strong back, however. Mechanization has not done away with physical labor on the farm, as anyone who has plowed corn stubble with a tractor can attest. Keepers of arable soil need both brain and brawn to discharge their trust properly. Each must be planner, mechanic, accountant, producer, and conservator all wrapped up in one. All of us depend upon their versatility, now and for the future.

Crop rotations promote soil balance and economic stability. The "single cash-crop culture" once dominant in several farming regions depleted the soil rapidly and afforded the farmer only one source of income. All the eggs were in one basket, a most precarious arrangement. Whenever the crop failed or the market

Crop rotations promote balance and stability

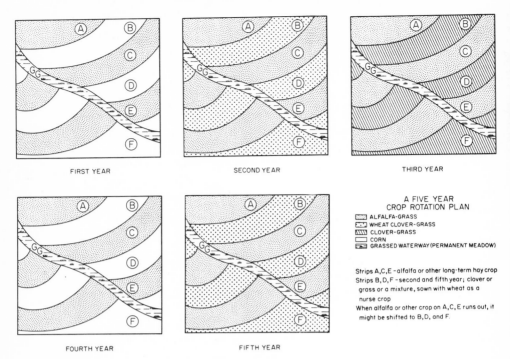

FIRST YEAR   SECOND YEAR   THIRD YEAR

FOURTH YEAR   FIFTH YEAR

A FIVE YEAR
CROP ROTATION PLAN

ALFALFA-GRASS
WHEAT CLOVER-GRASS
CLOVER-GRASS
CORN
GRASSED WATERWAY (PERMANENT MEADOW)

Strips A,C,E - alfalfa or other long-term hay crop
Strips B,D,F - second and fifth year; clover or grass or a mixture, sown with wheat as a nurse crop
When alfalfa or other crop on A,C,E runs out, it might be shifted to B,D, and F.

Fig. 6.9 *A variety of crop rotations may be used on a single farm. Any rotation system adapted to the land helps conserve the soil, and also affords the farmer a more diversified and stable economic base on which to operate. (After F.B., No. 1981.)*

slumped, the farmer had nothing with which to ease the pinch. When his soil weakened under repeated planting to the same crop without respite, he found himself in a grave predicament.

A partial answer to both problems lay in *crop variety*—the several crops "rotated" from one field to another in a more or less regular sequence.[10] Rotation schemes were nothing new to our "general" farmers, but to certain of the cash-crop specialists, such as wheat growers and cotton planters, they meant complete revision or replacement of the conventional system. Transition has been slow, but few areas remain in which some form of *cropping system* has not displaced the degrading single crop. In many places suitable rotations have become a standard practice. The five-year rotation shown in Fig. 6.9 is only one of many that have become popular.

Diversified crops in well-ordered sequence benefit both soil and farmer in a number of ways, their inherent advantages variously manifest from one place to another. They vary from year to year the drain of any particular plant nutrient, thereby helping to maintain better composition and physical condition of the soil. A good rotation helps to maintain the supply of humus and nitrogen, keeps the soil protected more, if not all, of the time, and increases total yields. It counteracts the development of toxic substances, varies the feeding range of roots, helps control insects and diseases, and improves crop quality.[11] It affords opportunity for better weed control, better use of fertilizer, and a more equitable seasonal distribution of labor requirements. Aside from its assistance toward holding the soil and maintaining its fertility, crop rotation also ensures the farmer a more regular income with which to operate. Unfortunately, rising costs of mechanization are discouraging crop diversification in the degree to which a farm must be equipped with special implements for each kind of crop it produces.

Especially effective in a soil-conserving rotation are the close-growing grasses and legumes sown for pasturage or meadow. A thick grass sod protects the surface against baking and washing. Its mass of roots bind the soil in place, open it to air and water, and add humus as the roots die and decay.[12] The legumes (clover, alfalfa, lespedeza, and so on) penetrate the soil with their roots and perform the distinctive service of enriching the soil with nitrogen taken from the air. Peanut or locust, herb or tree, leguminous plants possess special nitrogen-fixing equipment that places them in a class by themselves as soil builders.[13] However, when they are grown as field crops in a rotation their full benefits cannot be realized unless they be plowed under or grazed. Good use of a legume may be seen in Fig. 6.10. Harvested for hay and sold, their fixation of nitrogen may be poor compensation for their drain of potash and calcium. Farmers who grow peanuts for soil improvement and sell both nuts and vines cheat the soil and deceive themselves; the crop should be harvested by swine, not with machinery. Attractive prices for peanut oil, peanut hay, and peanut butter have often negated the good intent of peanut growing to conserve the soil.

Grasses and legumes are especially effective

Alfalfa holds top rank among our leguminous forage crops. It is a deep-rooted, hardy perennial that produces highly nutritious hay or silage. It is adapted to a wide range of temperature and moisture conditions and flourishes for several years from one sowing, under favorable conditions. Its dense, rapid growth requires frequent cutting, making it an excellent weed eradicator. A major detraction from its popularity is its requirement of a "sweet" soil and a generous supply of calcium. It abhors acidity and will not make hay on acid soil without the application of lime.

Idleness will not energize the soil, nor will soil be idle unless

Idleness will not energize the soil

Fig. 6.10 *Cover crops protect the soil after clear tillage or when other crops have been harvested. Legumes are favored because they add nitrogen while giving good protection. This vetch in a Texas pecan orchard was plowed under as green manure. (S.C.S. photo.)*

it is too dry or too cold for anything to grow in it. (Summer fallowing to store moisture in dry farming is not idleness in this sense.) Fields left untended get no rest unless they are too weak to support plant growth. Weeds (plants out of place) soon occupy the "idle" space and draw upon the store of nutrients in the soil. A rank stand of weeds can tax the soil quite as heavily as a crop grown for harvest. Soil substance given to the production of noxious weeds usually represents flagrant waste of a natural resource.

Something may be said in defense of weeds, because they are not altogether evil. Under certain conditions they are genuine assets. A good weed cover can be a very strong deterrent to erosion, by either wind or water. It can also add considerable organic matter to the soil, particularly if it be plowed under when it is lush and green. A lesser virtue of weeds is their indication of soil fertility. Pity the farmer who has no weed problem, because his soil probably cannot bring forth much of what he sows either.

There can be no vacation for soil during the growing season unless it be kept bare by tillage—a dangerous invitation to erosive forces. Furthermore, such an enforced rest period cannot energize the soil except as it may store needed moisture and encourage the conversion of soil contents into available plant foods.

Like a typical vacation, it is often more exhausting than energizing.

Problems unsolved by fallowing or idleness are most adequately met by keeping a vegetative cloak on the soil as much of the time as possible. Plantings made for the purpose of protecting the soil are referred to as *cover crops* (Fig. 6.10). When they are sown into another crop being grown for harvest, as between rows of corn after the last cultivation, they are called *catch crops*. In any case, plants that grow quickly and produce a thick, heavy stand are preferable.[14] Suitable species comprise a long list; some adapted for winter cover, others for summer cover. Their service is particularly valuable during such time as a regular money crop does not occupy the space and whenever or wherever heavy snow or deep freezing fails to defend the soil.[15]

Cover crops are not only protective while they grow, they are also a valuable source of humus and fertilizer (green manure). A heavy stand plowed under, or worked into, the soil adds many tons of organic material per acre and is an excellent substitute for barnyard manure.[16]

Their nitrogen-fixing characteristic makes annual legumes particularly desirable for use as cover crops. A great variety of clovers, peas, and beans have come into popular favor. Many of our foreign plant introductions have gained American citizenship through outstanding service as leguminous cover and green manure crops. Crotalaria, kudzu, lespedeza, and ladino clover are solid, though foreign-born, citizens.

Organic wastes are of the soil and belong to it.[17] Unless they be returned to the soil, it loses its power to produce. They are the vital fiber of the soil, whence, in life, all organisms draw their strength. But in our artificial, mechanized culture, we are liable to overlook that salient fact and distinguish too precisely between the quick and the dead. We are prone to forget the endless chain of life that transcends our creature existence. Starvation taught the Chinese to respect it. Let us profit by their experience before we, too, feel the sting of that lash.

Organic wastes are of many kinds, and not all are wasted from the standpoint of proper return to the soil. However, entirely too many, defamed as "trash," or "filth," or "refuse," are conveniently disposed of or destroyed and diverted from their proper destination, the soil.

Organic wastes include: the garbage that pollutes our streams; the pile of leaves burned in the alley; the sawdust heaps that smolder at sawmill sites; the straw piles burned after threshing to destroy weed seeds and to clear the space for plowing; and a

Cover crops afford more than soil protection

Organic wastes belong to the soil

Fig. 6.11 Crop residues should be returned to the soil. They help protect the soil; they reduce evaporation and induce water to infiltrate; and eventually they become humus. (S.C.S. photo.)

host of others. The man who buries the garbage in the garden, or makes compost of leaves he rakes, or spreads a straw pile as manure after it has settled and rotted, deserves a badge of distinction as a conservator.

A current trend that bears watching is the "salvage" of crop residues for fabrication into marketable products: wall board from cane bagasse or corn stalks; furfural from corncobs and hulls of oats, cottonseed, and rice; "soft-grit" blasting material of ground-up corncobs for cleaning precision machine parts; plastics from "flour" of straws, stalks, cobs, hulls, or nut shells; corrugated shipping containers from small-grain straws; cigarette paper from seed-flax straw; paper pulp from wheat straw; and many, many others. American farmers produce an estimated 250 million tons of dry residues annually, of which about half may be available for industrial use.[18] Can we spare them? Can our soils get along without them? We may discover that residues left on the ground as mulch, plowed under for humus, or used as litter for animals are more profitable in the long run than those sold off the farm for industrial utilization. The organic wastes shown in Fig. 6.11 may be exactly where they belong—on the field that produced them.

There is probably no complete substitute for *stable or barnyard manure as a soil builder and fertilizer,* and we are producing too little of the precious, odoriferous, stuff. When oxen, mules, or horses drew our farm implements we had much more manure and less area in need of it. Now, autos and tractors have largely replaced work animals, and manure has become a scarce, costly commodity while the fields in need of it have expanded. A twentieth-century dilemma reposes in the fact that exhaust

Animal manures are the best fertilizers

fumes from a tractor have no fertilizer value. The saving of crop area once used for animal feeds may be deceptive.

More diversification of farming systems, which include considerable animal industry (beef, dairy, swine, sheep, poultry), is a sure way to offset our reduced numbers of work stock. Grazing animals help fertilize their pasture; but stall-feeding, with abundant litter or bedding to catch and absorb the wastes, produces a greater volume of manure with more strength and a slower rate of decomposition and dissipation. The stable variety, spread on the land promptly upon removal from the stall, has no equal for soil improvement.[19]

The alert farmer-conservator conserves even the manure with which he helps to conserve his soil. He spreads it on the land raw (green), before it loses any of its strength. If he cannot apply it fresh from the stable, he stores it in a roofed, watertight pit until such time as he can best apply it. Manure piles that have lain in sun and rain, until they have faded on top and burned (molded) inside, have lost much of their power to reinforce the soil. Americans need a finer appreciation for the pungent odor of freshly spread manure about a countryside. They could take lessons from their European cousins.

Commercial, chemical fertilizers cannot entirely replace manure and other organic material used to enrich and reinforce the soil. The organics fit better into the natural scheme of things, improving the soil community at the same time as they contribute to soil fertility. Almost squarely in contrast, the prepared concentrates give immediate (artificial) stimulation. They may be likened to the *emergency rations* in a soldier's field pack intended to tide him over when other food is temporarily unavailable. Used in a similar manner, commercial fertilizers serve a most valuable purpose in soil conservation, but when used indiscreetly they can sterilize more than they fertilize.[20]

Prepared concentrates resemble emergency rations

Excessive use of chemicals can distort or destroy the biotic balance in the soil and reduce its powers of recuperation. Repeated applications can make a bad condition even worse, until finally each crop becomes entirely dependent upon a measured dosage calculated to mature it. Soil so abused degenerates into an inert, mineral mass, whence roots struggle to extract their measured rations in order to hold the plant upright for exposure to sunshine. Soil can be killed, and virtually embalmed, by excessive chemical applications.

Concentrated fertilizers have become indispensable to scientific agriculture and contribute substantially to the high yields and superior quality of our crops. Technological fertility has outmoded

142 *Soil Conservation*

native or natural fertility to a very large extent. However, neither nutrient solutions applied in liquid form nor soluble minerals applied in granular form can be effective unless organic content of the soil is also replenished. Only in the presence of sufficient organic matter to contain and dispense them are the dissolved concentrates available to plants and not rapidly leached away into ground waters. Liquid fertilizers go to work quickly but may also be lost quickly.[21] Commercial fertilizers are used in prodigious quantities in the United States. They were applied to 133 million acres of land in 1959, distributed as shown in Fig. 6.12.

Lest the uninitiate be confused, let it be explained that all bagged and bought fertilizers are not of the concentrated kinds about which we have cautioned. Such natural materials as dried dung, dried blood, cottonseed meal, bone meal, fish meal, ground phosphate rock, and many others also come in bags—effective but expensive substitutes for stable manure and crop residues.

All depends upon the humus-water partnership

The success of other soil-conserving measures is contingent upon a propitious humus-water partnership. Much has been said about the merits of each partner, but neither can be effective without the other. Only where there is sufficient humus to govern

Fig. 6.12 *Machines and chemicals have revolutionized American agriculture. Commercial fertilizers may be most profitably applied to land that is inherently most productive. (Bureau of the Census map.)*

ACREAGE ON WHICH COMMERCIAL FERTILIZER WAS USED, 1959

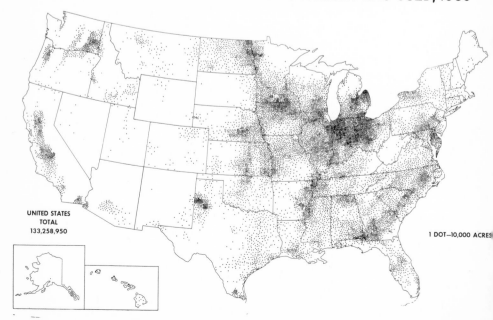

UNITED STATES TOTAL 133,258,950

1 DOT—10,000 ACRES

Fig. 6.13 *Subsurface tillage and stubble mulching to conserve both soil and water is especially advantageous on dry farmlands. Steel sweeps, drawn through beneath the surface, loosen the soil without turning it over. The half-buried straw (stubble) improves water absorption and reduces the wind hazard. Photo taken in Montana. (S.C.S. photo.)*

its receipt and release can soil water serve its full purpose as vehicle for plant nutrients; only where water is adequate but not excessive can humus develop normally from organic materials and maintain a healthy soil body.

There are many ways of fortifying the soil with humus. Whether it be worked into the soil or spread on the surface as a *mulch,* any kind of organic matter is raw material of humus. A flat rejection of one method and acceptance of the other would be wrong because related factors vary widely from place to place. Farmers in the subhumid and semiarid regions employ an innovation called *stubble-mulch* farming, or *subtillage,* wherein they loosen the soil by running blades through it several inches below the surface instead of turning it over as with a plow.[22] The stubble, held at the surface and protruding above it, as shown in Fig. 6.13, guards admirably against wind erosion, besides admitting and holding water effectively. The practice has proved desirable in other regions but might not be suitable in all areas.

If humus be abundant, how else may one strengthen the humus-water partnership? By *water-spreading,* another device which involves holding and spreading excess water over broader area in order that it may soak in where it would otherwise run off.[23] Broad terrace basins and other contour depressions induce water soakage. Farm ponds in dammed-up gullies, or wherever the terrain favors them, accomplish water spreading by holding back run-off so more of it soaks into the ground. Furrows such as those pictured in Fig. 6.14 can be a crucial factor in storing soil water where precipitation would be inadequate without them. Many soil conservation practices, specific in their apparent function, contribute to the dual purpose of enriching soil humus and moisture content, simultaneously *conserving both soil and water*. Those two major resources must be treated jointly, not independently.

Calcium carbonate combats acidity

For many of our soils the control of acidity is a necessary conservational measure. (Alkalinity is the crucial problem in certain portions of the dry West, and sulfur or gypsum the standard antidote.) [24] The Eastern forest soils tend to be naturally acid, their soluble alkaline compounds leached out by percolating water. Where the soil material is acid (silicious), and the forest deposits raw, acid humus through which the rain percolates, calcium is rapidly dissolved and carried away. Even soils derived from limestone and resting on a limestone base become highly acid. Fortunately, the condition is easily corrected where there is limestone beneath the soil.

It is a simple process to quarry the limestone; crush it or "burn" it, and spread it on the land. While it dissolves and passes through the soil, it counteracts acidity. That is exactly what is

Fig. 6.14 *Contour furrows (listing) to catch winter precipitation can be a decisive factor in valleys of the dry West. Photo taken in New Mexico. (S.C.S. photo.)*

done in practice. Lime (calcium carbonate) is the neutralizer, and the competent land user tests his soil at intervals to determine how much he should apply.[25] He may prefer burned lime for immediate reaction, or raw, ground, or crushed lime for longer endurance. He may choose to "lime" with *basic slag,* the black, waste-bearing limestone flux from iron smelters. Thus, a waste that has purified one resource is salvaged to conserve another.

Liming can be a vital operation in the rehabilitation of depleted soil. The organic matter and humus added to give such soil "backbone" are themselves nitrogenous and tend to be acid. Their beneficence may not be fully realized unless calcium carbonate is also added to complement them and to combat acidity.

Last, but probably not least, soil conservation requires attention to the elusive *trace elements* (micronutrients) that guard the health and fertility of soils in much the same manner as vitamins guard those qualities in humans and other animals. A perfect ratio of nitrogen, potash, phosphorus, and calcium is no guarantee of high productivity. Deficiency of a single trace element in a soil otherwise rich can cause critical deficiency in plants and can starve the animals that feed on those plants.[26]

Study and research magnify our respect for the elusive trace elements

Cows graze themselves thin on knee-deep pasture unless the soil under the grass contains cobalt. Tung trees need zinc; citrus trees, manganese; apple trees, boron. The trace elements influence each other's effectiveness and that of the major fertilizer materials. They make themselves felt in such minute quantities, and their functions are so delicate, that the novice should not tamper with them. Let the land user call an expert when he suspects "trace trouble."[27]

Since *one objective of soil conservation is maximum and permanent productivity,* the conservator should endeavor to understand the trace elements insofar as the soil chemist can advise him. If all ordinary applications achieve unsatisfactory results, one or more of the minor elements may be at fault. They exact thorough, scientific investigation. They comprise a challenging frontier in soil conservation. In them we may find many questions we cannot now answer.

We have always had among us men with "green thumbs" who to the limits of their knowledge, would guard the soils they use as the priceless property those soils really are. But green thumbs have never attained a majority; the more numerous "plow-sow-reap" men have dominated our use of the land. From colonial times until recent date such men wasted our soils without restraint, often wantonly, sometimes of sheer necessity.

We have made gratifying progress toward conserving our soils

Then came a reckoning in the midst of calamity. In the early

1930's the coincidence of severe drought and economic depression wreaked such havoc with American agriculture that the problem became a national issue of the first magnitude. The Congress reacted courageously and positively with legislation that initiated, among others we shall mention later, a nationwide program of soil conservation. During trying years, 1933-1936, the Federal government, with the rare vision of dedicated leadership, enunciated three basic policies to conserve our soils and to prosper our agriculture; they established two public agencies to implement the policies. Crop-acreage limitation, technical-advisory assistance, and cost-sharing subsidy of farm improvement became acknowledged functions of government. The Soil Conservation Service (SCS), established in 1935 (Public Law 46, 74th Cong.) was charged with the technical and advisory aspects; the Agricultural Stabilization and Conservation Service (ASCS), evolved under the Soil Conservation and Domestic Allotment Act of 1936, assumed responsibility for compliance with regulations and disbursement of payments to eligible landowners and operators for applying approved conservation practices on their land. (Federal subsidy varies considerably from one application to another but has averaged about 50 per cent of costs.)

These two agencies, the SCS and ASCS, remain the prime movers of soil conservation in the United States, and to them we owe much of the incomparable progress in American agricultural efficiency during the three past decades. The magnitude of their tangible accomplishments may be judged from the following partial tabulation, but their intangible, long-range benefits cannot be tabulated. Neither of these agencies owns or administers any land; both work directly with private owners and users of land who voluntarily avail themselves of the services; each operates through elected county (or parish) committees responsible to a central state office, which, in turn, maintains liaison with national headquarters in Washington, D.C. Both have such extensive compass and impinge on so many aspects of conservation that we shall have occasion to mention them several times in subsequent chapters. As of 1961, 2,900 soil conservation districts had been formed, comprising 96 per cent of the nation's farms and 92.5 per cent of its land in farms (1,038 million acres; 3,560,000 farms and ranches). Twenty-three states had been organized into districts in their entirety.[28] In less than three decades of public determination and cooperative effort, America's defense against soil erosion is so well organized and the work so far advanced that our land may be fairly secured against wastage thirty years hence.

The Agricultural Conservation Program, 1936-60 Inclusive
Selected Conservation Practices

Storage-type reservoirs	Structures	1,665,000
Checks and drops for erosion control	Do	3,034,000
Spreaders and diversion ditches	Miles	125,600
Leveling irrigated land	Acres	7,158,000
Contour stripcropping	Do	5,794,000
Standard or broad-base terraces	Do	25,442,000
	Miles	1,380,000
Field stripcropping	Acres	104,794,000
Contour farming	Do	138,829,000
Crop residue management	Do	153,640,000
Special tillage of cropland	Do	138,181,000
Subsoiling	Do	12,492,000
Vegetative cover	Do	774,498,000
Liming materials	Tons	422,803,000
Tree planting	Acres	2,991,000
Timber stand improvement	Do	2,342,000
Conservation drainage	Do	40,149,000
Competitive plant control on grazing land	Do	42,168,000
Livestock water developments	Structures	1,584,000

Source: Department of Agriculture Appropriations for 1963: Hearings before a Subcommittee of the Committee on Appropriations, House of Representatives, 87th Cong., 2 sess., Subcommittee on Department of Agriculture and Related Agencies Appropriations, Part 4. (Washington, D.C.: Government Printing Office, 1962).

In view of such abundant production—crop surpluses far outdistance market demands and accumulate beyond storage levels that could be useful in any eventuality—one might hastily conclude that land improvement is neither necessary nor desirable and that agricultural efficiency compounds an economic burden already heavy. This would be, however, faulty and dangerous reasoning from at least two points of view: stored reserves of food and fiber render America unique among the nations, reinforcing her superior defensive posture; improvement of efficiency and productivity reduces land requirements for agriculture, thus releasing space to other uses more immediately needed. No problem of abundance must be permitted to impede our cultural progress; the consequences would soon be more costly than any temporary overproduction! Artificial price stabilization and manipulated equation of supply and demand should, however, be temporary expedients lest even they become deterrents to technologic innovation.

Rather than being discouraged by the surplus problem, land conservation has, in fact, been concomitant with crop reduction. Our early attempts to reduce production by acreage limitations, as with the Agricultural Adjustment Act of 1933, failed in their

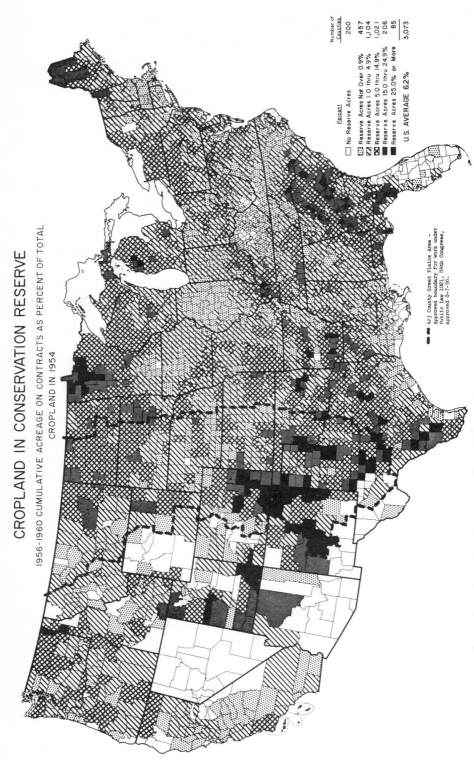

Fig. 6.15 *The Soil Bank program diverted from cultivation much land that had produced surplus crops and much that was marginal or submarginal despite subsidy. (U.S.D.A. map.)*

immediate purpose whilst inducing conservation proficiencies that have strengthened our agriculture ever since. Under that much maligned law many farmers learned the usefulness of cover crops and green manure, for instance. Acreage restriction (allotment) prescribed by the law taught them a fundamental of land economics especially important to conservation: the best land warrants the most intensive cultivation; the poorest land, the least. They concentrated their energies on select plots of land and caused them to yield more than previously obtainable through dissipation of effort on much larger areas of lower quality. Production efficiency largely negated acreage allotment as a means of curtailing surplus. The Agricultural Adjustment Act of 1933 should be honored as a magnificantly successful failure! More recent and temporary acreage limitations, such as under the Feed Grains Program first applied in 1961, have more immediately retarded storage accumulations.

Especially noteworthy for simultaneous surplus reduction and land conservation is the "Soil Bank" or "land reserve" idea promulgated in the Agricultural Act of 1956 (Public Law 540). This law made provisions for diverting a tremendous aggregate of land from the production of crops and pasture to continuous protective vegetation under contracts of three to ten years' duration. By the end of 1960, after which no new contracts were authorized, producers had voluntarily placed about 28.70 million acres on 306,182 farms in the "conservation reserve" at an average annual rental rate of $11.85 per acre.[29] Approximate distribution of the reserve lands is shown in Fig. 6.15. During the period, 1957-1961, the program *avoided* production of some 671 million bushels of corn, 568 million bushels of grain sorghum, 517 million bushels of oats, 219 million bushels of wheat, 25 million tons of hay (or equivalent forage), more than 1.65 million bales of cotton, and lesser, but proportionately significant quantities of other commodities.[30] As of July 15, 1961, cost-share assistance had become allowable for sowing down to grass and legumes almost 19 million acres, for planting trees on more than 2.15 million acres, for constructing 6,531 ponds on 16,600 acres, for planting special wildlife cover on some 306,000 acres, and for flooding for wildlife habitat more than 12,000 acres.[31] The entire program is administered by ASCS. The Soil Bank has inestimable portents for the future because much land in reserve will become retired from food and fiber production indefinitely and will serve more immediate needs for wildlife habitat and outdoor recreation.

7

Spoliation and Restoration of Our Dry Grasslands

nature demands that we mend and maintain the protective grass cover to conserve our dry grasslands

Third among our regenerative resources we shall consider the great, natural pastures that dominate much of the landscape, philosophy, and economic history from the hundredth meridian westward, from the Canadian to the Mexican boundary.[1] Before the advent of white men, grazing land of various types occupied an estimated area of 850 million acres,[2] including almost all of the Great Plains region east of the Rockies, and large portions of that vast complex west of the Rockies known as the Intermontane Basins and Plateaus.

In nature's arrangement, satisfactory to the Indians, only forested slopes and a few spots of barren desert interrupted the great expanse of dry grasslands. White men have dotted the realm with forest cutover and irrigation projects, assaulted it with plows along its entire eastern "front," and gnawed holes in its cover with excessive herds and flocks. They have respected and understood the grasslands even less than they have waters and soils.[3]

A natural grass cover is fairly indicative of climatic limitation that inhibits forest growth by dearth of moisture or warmth, or both—but the frontiersmen were stayed by neither climate nor plant ecology. They learned by trial and error, erring magnificently and learning indignantly.

Where grasses and shrubs or forbs prevail against trees—as on

150

the plains and in the Western mountain valleys—there is barely
enough occasional rain to keep those plants alive, and not enough
to sustain a natural succession of ordinary trees. From approximately the hundredth meridian westward, the plains, plateaus,
and valleys receive less than 20 inches of rainfall annually on the
average, and in many places less than 10 (Fig. 3.2 on page 30).
If those 20 inches—or even those 10—came without fail, marginality might admit some compromise, but it happens climatically that *where the least rain falls it is also the least reliable.*
Departures from the "normal" are the rule rather than the exception; where the balance is most delicate, it is most frequently upset. The 20-inch isohyet (rain line) oscillates radically eastward
and westward; life on the plains blooms and withers as the rainfall waxes and wanes. Droughts come so frequently (Fig. 7.1)
that they should be anticipated by the land user and accepted
by all residents as a regional handicap.

Grassland
makes
the geographic
transition
between forest
and desert

Fig. 7.1 *Erratic rainfall is a natural characteristic that men have often failed to respect
in the drylands. Deficient moisture means that land utilization must be restricted accordingly. Averages of precipitation cannot be used as criteria of land capability because
the recurrent drought years fix the limits of productivity. (U.S.F.S. map.)*

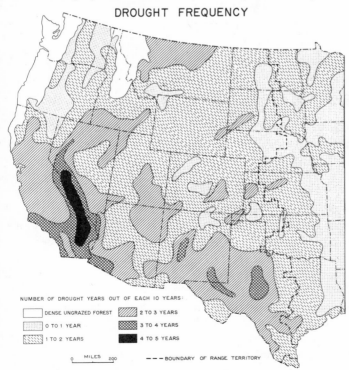

DROUGHT FREQUENCY

NUMBER OF DROUGHT YEARS OUT OF EACH 10 YEARS:

DENSE UNGRAZED FOREST   2 TO 3 YEARS
0 TO 1 YEAR   3 TO 4 YEARS
1 TO 2 YEARS   4 TO 5 YEARS

0   MILES   200   - - - BOUNDARY OF RANGE TERRITORY

Fig. 7.2 *Blue grama is one of the "meek" that have "inherited" the steppes. On this short-grass range just west of Sheridan Lake, Colorado, the hardy species tenaciously survived severe drought and overgrazing. (U.S.F.S. photo, June 1940.)*

In good years the grasses flourish, producing abundant seeds, deep roots, and strong bulbs and crowns. Those plant parts can survive extreme drought by remaining dormant, then burst into verdure and bloom when the rains come again. Grasses and forbs, with such special equipment as bulbs and rhizomes that survive drought in dormancy, bridge the gap between forest and desert. Giant cacti go them one better by storing up water when it comes, but none of our ordinary trees can compete. The lowly grama grasses hold their ground where the mighty oaks must yield. Recurrently decimated by drought and wind long before man's intervention magnified those hazards, the short grasses possess amazing powers of survival (Fig. 7.2).

From Indiana westward the pioneers to the northern Middle West sailed veritable seas of grass in prairie schooners to a region where by some strange quirk of fortune needle grass, bluestem, and other stalwarts had driven a deep wedge of *tall grass prairie* eastward into the forest. Many dropped anchor in the rich, black soil, and when the Homestead Act of 1862 gave each wagon's "skipper" a quarter section for the asking, settlers soon

The prairie
schooner sailed
broad seas
of grass

152

filled the billowing prairies and broke the sod to sow wheat. That episode was not inconsistent with natural attributes—in fact, it fashioned our bountiful "bread basket"—but west of the prairie, west of the Mississippi, the schooners ran into cross winds and shoals. Many ran aground, others went adrift, and our grassland problem began because they had crossed the western boundary of *tall* grass and invaded the *short* grama and buffalo grasses without thinking anything of it (Fig. 7.3).

Fig. 7.3 *Vegetation reflects the degree of natural limitation and indicates the general use capability of an area. In many places natural range conditions can be improved artificially, as by clearing and seeding, much as certain soils inherently poor can be made productive by appropriate tillage and fertilization.*

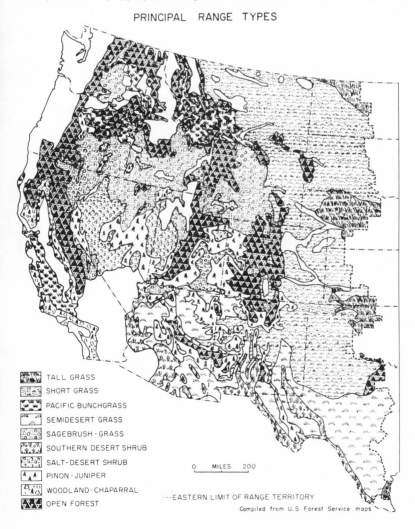

PRINCIPAL RANGE TYPES

TALL GRASS
SHORT GRASS
PACIFIC BUNCHGRASS
SEMIDESERT GRASS
SAGEBRUSH-GRASS
SOUTHERN DESERT SHRUB
SALT-DESERT SHRUB
PINON-JUNIPER
WOODLAND-CHAPARRAL
OPEN FOREST

0   MILES   200

---EASTERN LIMIT OF RANGE TERRITORY

Compiled from U.S. Forest Service maps

Nor can we blame the pioneers; experts today cannot quite agree on the location of that boundary, except to say that it is a transitional, shifting zone rather than a precise, fixed line. Nature does not draw many sharp boundaries. Be that as it may, when Americans occupied the short-grass plains and the more desiccated shrub and bunch grass country farther west, they collided head-on with *arid* and *semiarid* conditions, entirely lacking in experience to cope with them (note the complex pattern of range types in Fig. 7.3). They did not know that sod-making grass species tighten their belts and disperse themselves in bunches where moisture is insufficient to sustain a complete cover. They knew not how thin the ice they trod in their westward race for riches.

The race began promptly upon cessation of domestic hostilities in 1865, and in a few years there developed in the dry West that "leather-pounding," six-shooter era of American history that, for good or ill, holds our schoolboys entranced in TV and Saturday movies—Hollywood has capitalized where many stockmen went bankrupt. The great cattle empire was short-lived, for the cattle man lived violently in a violent land. Nature plagued him with scorching droughts and freezing blizzards which often took ruinous toll of his herds. The range was open and public, and Colt's "equalizer" was his best claim to water holes and grass. Sheepmen, "nesters" (farmers), poachers, and rustlers were the bane of his existence. Fortunes were quickly made and as quickly lost, grasses dwindled and markets slumped, railroads, homesteaders, and prairie dogs encroached upon the cowpuncher's wide-open spaces. Settlers chose land with water on it, and every new farm deprived the stockmen of a grazing-area tributary thereto often several times as large as the farm itself. And the *stronger land bond* would not be denied: the plow unhorsed the saddle.

Coincidence made doubly tragic our peopling of the dry grasslands. Settlement advanced upon them when a cycle of wet years gave them extraordinary powers of deception. Nature played a mean trick on the rough-and-ready cowboy who, in righteous wrath, defended the range as it was and died without knowing his wisdom.

But the temporarily lush and fertile areas could not be withheld from the land-hungry people desirous of plowing, fencing, and establishing permanent homes. They came and plowed up the incomparable native grasses, many species of which possessed the remarkable faculty of curing on the root and retaining considerable nutritional value where they stood, making hay gratis for winter feeding.[4] Not only did we permit settlement—we en-

AVERAGE SIZE OF COMMERCIAL FARMS, 1959

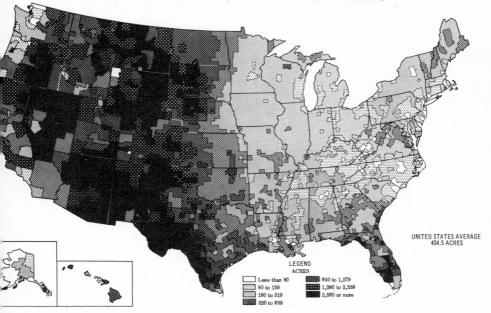

LEGEND
ACRES

☐ Less than 80	▦ 640 to 1,279
▨ 80 to 159	▦ 1,280 to 2,559
▨ 160 to 319	■ 2,560 or more
▦ 320 to 639	

UNITED STATES AVERAGE
404.5 ACRES

Fig. 7.4 *Apparently Congress was too conservative even when it increased the home-stead unit to a whole section. Many ranches now contain several square miles of land. (One section = one square mile = 640 acres.) (Bureau of the Census.)*

couraged it. When climatic reverses exposed the true marginality of this land, the Congress sought to conceal rather than correct its stupendous error. In 1911 it passed the "enlarged" Homestead Act, allowing the grassland settler 320 acres; and when even a half-section proved inadequate for the support of a family, it doubled the ante again with the "stock-raising" Homestead Act of 1916. Even then, Congress was too conservative, as may be seen in Fig. 7.4.

At first thought, 640 acres of land might be regarded a fine gift, but in the drier, more westerly rangelands whole sections did not always suffice, especially as they were doled out in rectangular pattern without regard for streams or other water supply. Many areas remained unclaimed—parts of the public domain we could not give away; until Congress passed the so-called Taylor Grazing Control Act in 1934, these were grazed without discretion by any rancher who could drive his animals to them. "First come, first served" was the maxim of competing stockmen. In order to maintain their operations, especially in dry seasons, they overgrazed the public range (and their own too, for that matter) and denied it the respite essential for recovery. The weakened cover gave way to erosion by wind and water, weeds overwhelmed more palatable species, and forage values dwindled to a fraction of their original carrying capacity.

Barbed wire, patented in 1874, foreshadowed the end of the Great Plains cattle empire, and, in 1886-87, when a combination of drought, blizzard, and overgrazing brought disaster to flocks and herds, the steel plow resumed with renewed vigor its empty campaign against spurs, saddles, six-shooters, and branding irons. Big farmers took over where bigger graziers had failed, apparently blind to their own impending failure. They plowed until virtually nothing plowable remained unturned. They brought bigger and better machines to pulverize more thoroughly soils never intended to know anything more mechanical than the hooves of a cow. From gang plows and six-horse teams they progressed to steam engines and gasoline tractors, the more quickly to turn the soil after each successive crop of wheat or cotton. They cut a broad swath for big stakes; those who "hit it right" got rich.

Sobered by drought, wind, and crop failure, many adopted dry-farming methods to store two years' moisture for one crop; many a wheat farmer in Kansas, the Dakotas, and the Palouse of eastern Washington owed his survival to clean fallow and dust mulch. Others elected to "stir it all every year and hope for enough rain to make a crop." Those wishful thinkers cursed the drought six days of the week and prayed for rain on Sunday, and despite their most fervent pleas they were the first to feel the pinch when drought persisted. Even he who practiced dry farming exposed his soil to wind erosion during dry spells and to water erosion when the torrential rains came; to exercise caution on the one hand he incurred a risk on the other, and in his attempt to store moisture, he forfeited the soil he was trying to moisten. Even dry farming failed when extreme desiccation persisted. (Improved soil-conserving techniques have by now rehabilitated many farms that once literally blew away.)

What with drought and deluge, wind and flood, blizzard, dust, hail, and grasshoppers, farming of the dry grasslands has always been a precarious business. Had we but known their limitations and taken precautionary measures in time we might have saved their original mantle of soil (and sod, as well, where necessary), and spared ourselves a major problem of American conservation. However, as with many another resource decision, we procrastinated until deterioration proceeded almost beyond repair and visited upon our dry-land folk such hardship as our democratic society will not countenance. True, the grasslands had witnessed many booms and busts before—homes built and soon deserted, fields tilled briefly and then abandoned, happy arrivals and sad departures—but the aftermath of World War I brought catastrophe on such a scale that we were finally compelled to recognize the inherent marginality of the grasslands.

High wartime prices for wheat invited the plow to the very edge of the desert; comparable prices for beef and wool over-populated the abused, constricted range.[5] The stress of war and the fever of postwar inflation made demands on the dry lands far beyond their limits of sustained production. With abandon unforgivable even under stress, we sapped them beyond their powers of recuperation, during the most auspicious climatic circumstances they can experience. We spent them.

Then came drought and depression almost simultaneously and with tragic consequences. The cattle market crashed in the early 1920's, making many stockmen war casualties, while rainfall and wheat prices continued favorable to agriculture. Land prices soared and farming expanded, almost unopposed by range interests. But the ill-founded prosperity was short-lived. In 1931 drought announced its return, and in 1934 it reached unprecedented severity.[6] Hot, dry winds lashed the open plains, scorching the remaining grasses and ripping into the soil laid bare by plowing or overgrazing. Farmers drilled their seed deeper than usual, and it "blew out" of the ground instead of sprouting. The soil took flight in billowing clouds of dust and drifted like snow along the ground, engulfing fences, farmsteads, and the barren stream courses. As double punishment for trespassing, the angry winds sought to bury the soil they could not tear away. The scourge drove eastward with moderated intensity as far as central Minnesota, bringing a brief visitation of tumbleweeds, and so weakening heavily grazed oak woods that a certain unscrupulous bark beetle took the opportunity to kill them; ungrazed woods showed only slight injury.

War, weather, and ignorance had fashioned the so-called Dust Bowl in the Panhandle-west Kansas region (Fig. 7.5), and damage was also serious in Nebraska, the Dakotas, and other dry states. An exodus of farmers and families was inevitable,[7] and many who stayed should have gone. Some departed when their soil went; some needed the prodding of successive crop failures. Some gave up when the well went dry, and some were expelled by foreclosure. Many "stuck it out" until they had nothing left but the mortgage. The catastrophe was of such proportions that in 1934 the Federal government intervened to mitigate the tragedy and prevent its recurrence.

Shocked by the destitution and forced migration of people from the interior of our own country, the Congress set about to examine the causes and devise corrections. It made embarrassing

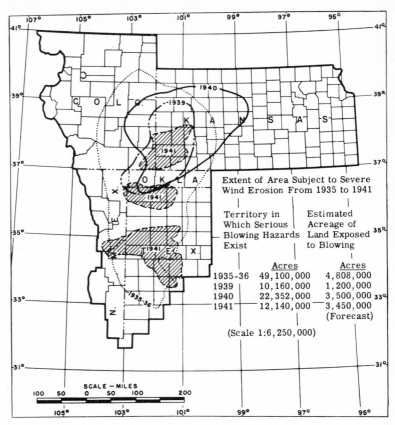

The following table appears within the figure:

Extent of Area Subject to Severe Wind Erosion From 1935 to 1941		
	Territory in Which Serious Blowing Hazards Exist	Estimated Acreage of Land Exposed to Blowing
	Acres	Acres
1935–36	49,100,000	4,808,000
1939	10,160,000	1,200,000
1940	22,352,000	3,500,000
1941	12,140,000	3,450,000 (Forecast)

(Scale 1:6,250,000)

Fig. 7.5 *Blow area map, Southern Great Plains. Wind fashioned the Dust Bowl in collaboration with men and drought. Soil drifting and dusting scourged the dry grasslands long before they were plowed or grazed, but their inept appropriation by settlers exposed them to hazards against which nature had previously afforded a goodly degree of protection. (S.C.S. map.)*

We could not prohibit drought, so we passed a law against its consequences

discoveries. It found that the portion of the United States composed of rangeland had lost something like half its productivity, as shown graphically in Fig. 7.6. Uncontrolled grazing and crazy homesteading had surrendered the best soil to wind and water erosion. Denuded watersheds poured devastating floods over the lowlands, and choked with mud the life-giving streams and irrigation projects. Decimation of predators had permitted their prey, the prolific rodents, to multiply until they menaced both forage and soil. Noxious weeds and insects were spreading and thriving at the expense of valuable grass species. In short, our violations of the delicate balance between life and moisture had

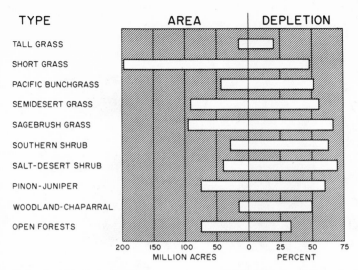

TYPE	AREA	DEPLETION
TALL GRASS		
SHORT GRASS		
PACIFIC BUNCHGRASS		
SEMIDESERT GRASS		
SAGEBRUSH GRASS		
SOUTHERN SHRUB		
SALT-DESERT SHRUB		
PINON-JUNIPER		
WOODLAND-CHAPARRAL		
OPEN FORESTS		

200 150 100 50 0 25 50 75
MILLION ACRES   PERCENT

Fig. 7.6 *Area and depletion of range types, 1936. Drought and economic depression during the early thirties climaxed range despoliation and threatened the entire range economy with disaster. This graph is from a comprehensive study of the problem made by the Forest Service at the request of Congress. The study became a basis for important legislation affecting the range resources. (After The Western Range, Senate Document No. 199, 74th Cong., 2nd sess., 1936.)*

so seriously damaged a major segment of our national economy that its repair would be extremely slow and costly.[8]

Passage of the Taylor Grazing Act in 1934 began a program of federal proprietorship over the public rangelands that continues today, with refinements added by practical experience during the intervening years. Pursuant to the act, a Division of Grazing was established in the Department of the Interior and homesteading was stopped until the new agency could determine the suitability of subject lands for settlement. In 1939 the new agency became known as the Grazing Service, which, in 1946, was joined with the celebrated General Land Office to form the Bureau of Land Management. The latter, the BLM, has since been the principal steward of our federal lands, its authority extending over some 467 million acres (Fig. 7.7), of which about 172 million are rangelands. The Bureau administers about 158 million acres of the federal range in fifty-eight organized grazing districts in eleven Western states and the remainder in scattered parcels of land outside the districts.[9] More than 18,500 ranchers pasture these rangelands under permits issued by the BLM and pay a modest fee per animal-unit-month for the privilege.[10] The equivalent of some 8 million head of domestic livestock from dependent ranch units graze the federal ranges each year.[11] Liaison between range users and the responsible federal agency (BLM) is maintained through a system of stockmen advisory boards, state

Taylor Grazing Act and Bureau of Land Management

159

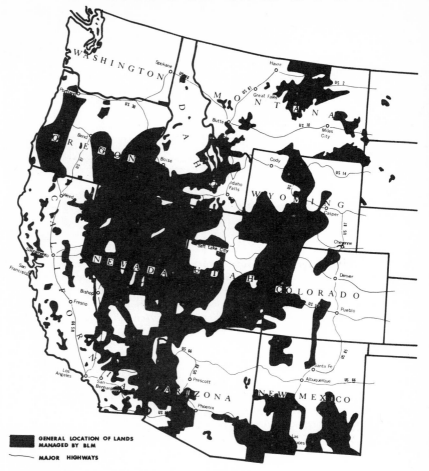

Fig. 7.7 *Over the grand, far-flung public estate represented here, together with most of Alaska, the Bureau of Land Management has administrative responsibility for natural resources whether subaerial, subaqueous, or subterranean. (B.L.M. map.)*

advisory boards, and a National Advisory Board Council. The national body has representation from many land-resource interests—forestry, minerals, recreation, urban development, local government, wildlife, *and* livestock.[12] Although duly concerned with the economic welfare of private land operators, the BLM has the primary responsibility of improving, conserving, and maintaining the *public* rangelands by regulating grazing, preventing the deterioration of soils and vegetation, and protecting the watersheds, wildlife, and other appurtenant resources.

Charged with direct assistance to both farmers and ranchers in the dry realm, and of the same "drought-depression" vintage as the BLM, are two agencies already mentioned, the Soil Conserva-

160

tion Service and the Agricultural Stabilization and Conservation Service. Thus, one agency protects the public lands; two others assist with the conservation of lands privately owned. Progress has come in both directions, as we shall see.

In 1937 Congress passed the Bankhead-Jones Farm Tenant Act, which authorized federal purchase of submarginal farmland from private owners disheartened or evicted by drought or other hardship. Under provisions of this act and subsequent legislation, the federal government repossessed by outright purchase many thousands of plains farms and removed the previous occupants to areas more suitable. During the period 1940-1955 the number of farms on the plains was reduced more than one-fifth—from more than 500,000 to less than 400,000.[13] Most of the land vacated became public property—an estate of scattered derelict homes on an acreage aggregating tens of millions. Many tracts thus acquired became parts of national grasslands. Many have been added to National Parks, National Forests, and grazing districts. Some are reserved for wildlife and other purposes. Many might

Fig. 7.8 A ten-row shelter-belt, three-quarters of a mile long, six years old, in Seward County, Nebraska. Such a barrier moderates surface wind velocities for a distance many times greater than the height of the trees. (S.C.S. photo.)

well be sold to private owners if suitable land-use restrictions (and liabilities) could be made conditions of each sale.

A unique federal project inspired by the "Dirty Thirties" was the planting of a gigantic windbreak the length of the plains, from North Dakota to Texas. Young men in the famed Civilian Conservation Corps, under Forest Service supervision, planted 85 million trees and shrubs of species selected by experts as most resistant to the harsh conditions and set them out in north-south strips, athwart the westerly winds.[14] (This was only one of many worthy accomplishments of the CCC.) A good specimen of tree strips may be seen in Fig. 7.8. By skillful arrangement of species east to west,[15] so that the shorter, hardier ones bear the brunt of the wind, and by careful attention in the early years, a high percentage of survival has been obtained. The comparative suitability of areas for such shelter-belt planting is shown in Fig. 7.9.

The shelter-belt idea was not new, but its demonstration in America had been limited to farmstead windbreaks. The planted strips have proved locally effective in reducing wind

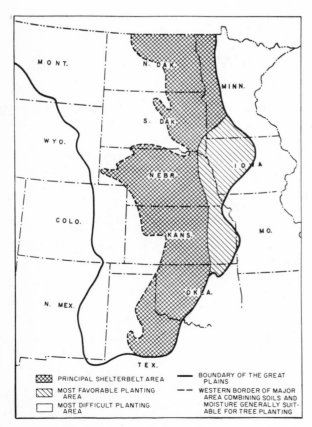

Fig. 7.9 Great Plains Region: major areas of practicable tree planting. Cultivation has inhibited any natural invasion of trees, but artificial plantings have survived and grown remarkably well. (U.S. F.S. map.)

Fig. 7.10 *An effective pattern of field and farmstead wind-breaks in Foard County, Texas. The light-colored field in the foreground lies exposed and wind-blown; those bordered by trees show little evidence of drifting. (S.C.S. photo.)*

velocities, but many more are needed if they are to moderate surface winds over any considerable area. Wet years and prosperity returned before the Prairie States Forestry Project could be completed. World War II came along, and there was no time for planting trees in the grasslands.

The war clouds coincided with wet seasons on the plains, and wartime prices for cotton and wheat made the new verdure seductively green. It enticed newcomers to farms abandoned a decade before and even tempted many Dust Bowl veterans to plow up grass anew. On the southern plains they plowed 4 million acres of grassland between 1942-1952, but only 1 million of them were suitable for permanent cultivation. On the northern plains the fever ran lower, but even there they plowed hundreds of thousands of acres incapable of sustained farming.[16]

Since the war, the planting of farm windbreaks has continued, largely under the sponsorship of the Soil Conservation Service. In our erratic dry regions, where wet years bring the opportunity for improvement, farmers must be encouraged to exercise better prudence than the man who ignores a hole in the roof when the weather is fair. Field windbreaks, such as those pictured in Fig. 7.10, are effective deterrents to wind erosion during drought, but the trees should be planted during a wet period.

Specific procedures for conserving the grasslands cannot be recommended with the same degree of confidence as those for humid farmlands and forests, because our grassland economy is very young, its environmental setting extremely heterogeneous, and the systematic study of its regional attributes and cultural developments only recently begun. Americans sawed lumber for two centuries before they roped steers in Texas. Logging is logging, whether the object be black spruce or white oak; sheep and transhumance (seasonal shift from summer to winter pastures) in the Rockies bear little resemblance to cattle and year-long grazing on the southern plains or summer grazing and winter feeding on the northern plains. Trees have become veneer and cellulose, but, to most of us, grass remains just grass, without qualification.

By the very nature of its environment, range conservation is highly complex, and in practical application it becomes beset with many complications. To begin with, the geographic diversity of the range land itself is extremely great. Twelve major range types compose our dry grazing lands, with many local variations of plant ecology, carrying capacity, seasonal usefulness, reliability of year-to-year forage production, and so forth. The system and relative importance of grazing in the land economy varies widely from one locality and operation to another. (The BLM has identified and studied twenty-seven distinctive ranch types, with many different sizes in each category.) Range users adjacent to farms or irrigation projects have ready access to supplemental feed and forage, while those far removed from any considerable cultivated area lack the stabilizing margin of supply thus afforded. Seasonal ranges complement each other and are often indispensable one to the other in grazing systems long established. To gain maximum benefit from seasonal ranges their use must be properly integrated—mountain pastures for a part of the year, and open lowland pastures for the remainder. Range users who graze seasonal ranges must be afforded access to them, with the privilege of moving their animals (trailing) across intervening areas. Trailing creates special problems of conservation because the transit area is subject to excessive grazing and wear by the many herds or flocks that traverse it.

Most perplexing from the standpoint of range management and policy are areas in which lands administered by divers federal agencies are intermingled, as in central Utah. There, range administered by the Bureau of Land Management lies wedged between National Forest ranges, with a generous mixture of state and private land thrown into the bargain. Whenever any difference of policy obtains between the agencies involved in such a confused situation, the disparity generates controversy that adds to the confusion. Closer coordination of all federal activities in the range country will improve the regional economy and increase its value to the nation. Such projects as the Public Land Range Appraisal proposed jointly by the Forest Service and the Bureau of Land Management in 1962 augur well for the future. The Forest Service administers 64 million acres of grassland. Both agencies are handicapped by inholdings and fragmentation of lands. The Bureau of Land Management needs more liberal authority to exchange public for private holdings to consolidate operational units.

Only a few general suggestions for grassland conservation may be postulated without fear of valid contradiction. Where recurrent drought has caused the soil to blow away and repeated farming ventures to fail, we should certainly restrict the plow, or exclude it entirely, until such time as necessity requires, and technology enables, us to moisten the earth artificially whenever it threatens to fly. Terracing, strip cropping, stubble mulching, and all the other soil- and water-conserving practices that suffice against moderate drought cannot prevail against severe, protracted desiccation, because soil devoid of moisture cannot produce the vegetable matter necessary for its protection. Where no plants grow there can be no replenishment of the stems and roots that bind the soil.

Restrict the plow and return the grass

When rain returns it comes violently (dry lands are cloudburst lands), and the soil, planed smooth and hard by wind, absorbs but little, suffering severe erosion by the excessive run-off. The comparative flatness that facilitates wind action would deter water action were it not that showers are usually torrential. Where drought and wind fill and level works designed to hold water when it comes, the conservator has only one safe and sane alternative—*return of a permanent grass cover.*

Farmers have repeatedly pushed dry, upland agriculture too near to the desert and have been pushed back in the lean years. Many farms that failed have reverted to public trust, and many more may revert with future droughts. It is quite appropriate that the precarious establishments should be added to the National Land Reserve, because private owners cannot ordinarily afford to rehabilitate them even with the liberal public aids available. Regrassing by sowing, like reforestation by planting, requires considerable outlay without immediate returns.[17] Native grasses, like native trees, will reclaim their own province, given time, but they would take a quarter- to a half-century to cover

certain galls left by the plow.[18] We elect to protect the remaining
soil more promptly by artificial seeding to hardy species, such as
tested exotics or those native to the area. We had begun to salvage abused areas by "sowing them down" when drought, the
"twenty-year locust" returned to the plains in the early 1950's,
and the winds whipped up a Dust Bowl bigger than any before.
This siege of desiccation disrobed another 3 or 4 million acres,
which, when added to the 10 to 12 million previously laid waste,
comprised a sorry total of some 14 million acres that needed re-
clothing with grass.[19]

Public reaction was commensurate with the devastation; Congress established a special Great Plains Conservation Program
(Public Law 1021) in 1956, listing ten states affected—Colorado, Kansas, Montana, Nebraska, New Mexico, North Dakota,
Oklahoma, South Dakota, Texas, and Wyoming—and authorizing the Secretary of Agriculture to enter into cost-sharing contracts with farm and ranch operators for ten years or less in
counties he would designate as "susceptible to serious wind
erosion by reason of their soil types, terrain, and climate and
other factors." The act further specified that: "Such contracts
shall be designed to assist farm and ranch operators to make, in
orderly progression over a period of years, changes in their cropping systems and land uses which are needed to conserve the soil
and water resources of their farms and ranches and to install the
soil and water conservation measures needed under such changed
systems and uses. Such contracts may be entered into during the
period ending no later than December 31, 1971."

Actual work under Public Law 1021 commenced in 1957 and
became authorized for the vast region outlined in Fig. 6.15 on
page 148. By the end of 1962 a total of 10,702 contracts had
been signed, covering more than 25.6 million acres in 375 counties. The contracts involved about 3.3 million acres of cropland,
of which 762,573 acres were scheduled for conversion to permanent vegetation, including 200,000 acres of Soil Bank land
(identified immediately below). As of mid-1962, some 324,000
acres had been converted from Public Law 1021 resources alone.[20]
Development of other conservation measures or installations,
such as terracing, stock-water ponds and tanks, strip cropping,
tree windbreaks, and water spreading, had progressed at a comparable rate.

Also in 1956, the Congress initiated the Soil Bank program,
under which a vast aggregate of Plains land, including many
entire ranches and farms, was placed in conservation reserve. At
the end of 1961, almost 9 million acres of cropland on the Great

Great Plains Conservation Program

Fig. 7.11 *Results of good and bad management on Southwestern Grassland range type, New Mexico. The range in the foreground was damaged by over-grazing and improper seasonal use. The five-strand barbed-wire fence protected the adjoining area from similar abuse. (B.L.M. photo.)*

Plains were retired to native grasses and more than 2 million acres to forest tree plantings.[21] Both the grass and the trees were expected to remain indefinitely.

Many areas never plowed have been badly depleted by running too many animals on them, by grazing them so closely and continuously that preferred forage species could not maintain normal vigor and reproduction, and by trampling them along trails between pastures and around overused bedding or watering places. The wear of too many animals has broken the cover, compacted and exposed the soil, thinned and weakened—even exterminated—the desirable grasses, and encouraged weeds and rodents. It has caused such general deterioration in many places that natural recovery cannot come about unless the number of animals be drastically reduced or the grazing system be modified to give depleted areas "sabbatical leave" for recuperation. System modification usually boils down to some form of regulated or controlled grazing, which has in fact largely replaced the old catch-as-catch-can that once prevailed. Management of grazing produced the spectacular contrast shown in Fig. 7.11.

Range management for sustained yield is often more complex than sustained-yield forestry and differs as widely in practice as the fenced ranches common to the Great Plains and the more extensive unfenced ranges prominent in the intermontane regions. Especially on the northern Great Plains, stock raising has become a semiagricultural enterprise, with hay and feed crops produced for wintering and fattening the cattle. Where the quality, or potential quality, of the range warrants the expendi-

Damage
by overgrazing
responds to
"undergrazing"

Fig. 7.12 *Arrangement of watering places can be used to distribute animals and get uniform grazing of the range. Stock tank or farm pond impoundment conserves both land and water, as demonstrated in Sandoval County, New Mexico. (S.C.S. photo.)*

ture, fencing solves the control problem (Fig. 7.11); however, on ranges of low carrying capacity, public or private, less costly methods must be employed. One shepherd can control a tremendous band of sheep (1,000+) and a man on horseback can ride herd on many cattle. A high degree of control can be achieved by systematic arrangement and timely relocation of "salting" and watering places.[22] Salt attracts all kinds of range livestock, and cattle cannot roam far from their drinking water. Artificial ponds (tanks) such as the one pictured in Fig. 7.12, piped to watering places, can help distribute grazing pressure as desired. See also in Figs. 7.13 and 7.14 how water may be stored for animals in desert situations.

Several systems for grassland conservation have evolved, all conceived to recover depleted areas and to maintain the pastures in a high state of production, without drastic curtailment of the established economy. Temporary removal of all livestock would solve the whole problem, but it would waste the resource and ruin a valuable industry. *Deferred grazing,* the exclusion of animals from an area until the grasses mature their seed and send out new rhizomes, permits reproduction of species where early grazing would preclude the possibility. *Rotation grazing,* the timely shifting of animals from one pasture or tract to another, gives each area in turn a period of rest during which to regain its strength. The two systems are often combined in what the experts call *deferred-rotation* (Fig. 7.15), a very popular and economical system in practice.[23] In some places, *alternate grazing* to sheep

Figs. 7.13 and 7.14 *Since about 1951, deep pit type charcos have become especially popular for impounding livestock water on arid Indian land in the Southwest. These are on the Navajo Reservation at Concho, Oklahoma. Their depth gives them a favorable ratio between storage capacity and surface evaporation area. By the end of 1962 some 3,500 of these structures had been built on Indian rangelands. (Courtesy Evan L. Flory; Bureau of Indian Affairs photos.)*

and cattle yields maximum proceeds with minimum drain because sheep and cattle have different tastes; the woolly animals selecting grasses and forbs less palatable to the bovines, and vice versa.

Where the need is apparent and land values permit, the range stockman may well employ certain soil- and water-conserving measures that serve on steeper land in the humid regions, such as contour terracing or furrowing and water spreading. He may bandage a wind gall or "blowout" as if it were a spot of sheet wash. But his real objective must be to make whole, and keep whole, the protective, productive grass cover that fits his locality. Grass must be his *means* and his *medium* for conservation and continued prosperity.

Management that maintains health and balance suppresses grassland pests that can otherwise attain destructive proportions. Prairie dogs and jack rabbits seem to thrive on depleted range where weeds have successfully invaded the grasses. If fifteen jack rabbits eat as much grass as one sheep, seventy-five of them equal

Mechanics can help the grass

169

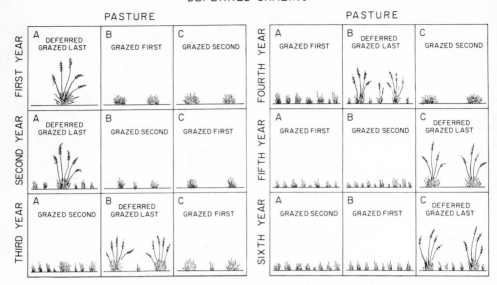

DEFERRED GRAZING

Fig. 7.15 *Deferment of grazing permits the forage grasses to mature their seeds and reproduce their species naturally. A pasture deferred one year for seed production is also deferred the next so that the young plants may become well established before subjection to cropping. Three pasture divisions may be continually rejuvenated with a six-year rotation.* (Redrawn and reproduced with permission, from A. W. Sampson, Range Management, copyright 1952, John Wiley & Sons, Inc.)

Fig. 7.16 *Under favorable conditions a depleted grass range recovers quickly. One year of good rainfall made this change on a meter quadrate of pasture near Ness City, Kansas. Heavy grazing and protracted drought had reduced the basal cover of forage grasses to only 12.6 per cent of area in the fall of 1940.* (See Fig. 7.2.) *A year later the grasses covered more than half the square.* (Redrawn from Ecological Monographs, January 1944 [Albertson and Weaver.])

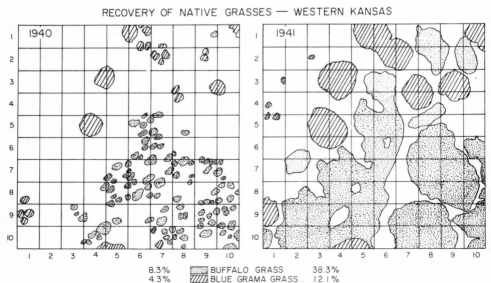

RECOVERY OF NATIVE GRASSES — WESTERN KANSAS

8.3% ▨ BUFFALO GRASS 38.3%
4.3% ▨ BLUE GRAMA GRASS 12.1%

one animal unit.[24] (Carrying capacity of pasture or range is usually stated in terms of animal units, acres, and months, one animal unit being *one cow* or *five sheep*.) A few hundred rabbits on a small ranch become expensive subjects for nature study. Prairie dogs become a double liability; not only are they voracious eaters of good grasses, but their burrowed "towns" are physical hazards to livestock. Kangaroo rats lay up such stores of grass seed that numbers of them interfere seriously with natural re-seeding. Rodents in normal numbers perform certain beneficial functions in grassland soils, but out of hand they degrade their own habitat. Range management might well include a more len-ient attitude toward the flesh eaters that prey on rodents.[25]

Health and balance suppress grassland pests

A healthy, vigorous range checks the spread of noxious and poisonous weeds that infest denuded areas, endangering live-stock, sheltering rodents, and resisting the return of forage plants. Against insects, and diseases too, maintenance is the secret of defense in grasslands as well as in forests. If unmolested, grasses —like trees—will solve many man-made problems without man's assistance. In effect, good *range management* simply reduces artificial barriers to natural self-perpetuation of the biotic com-munity. Figure 7.16 shows how quickly a depleted native pasture

Fig. 7.17 *The most desirable forage plants are commonly the best watershed protectors. Water conservation becomes a free bonus for good range management. (U.S.F.S. dia-gram; after* The Western Range.)

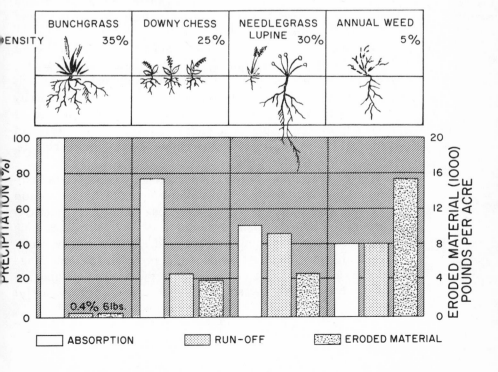

can recover. Figure 7.17 shows that good forage species are also good protectors of the land.

As the tree farmer needs advice from a forester, so the grazier needs advice from an agrostologist (grass expert). The forester has the advantage of big subjects, but the agrostologist deals with plants so small and so numerous that his observations and conclusions are less easily understood by the novice. Even when the grazier becomes something of an agrostologist himself, he may be sorely tempted to run his animals onto the young, tender grasses when his better judgment tells him grazing ought to be deferred. Sacrifice of superior forage in order that the grasses may reproduce themselves requires stronger will power than the leaving of valuable trees in selective logging. But stockmen are learning that deferment in grazing as in forestry pays high dividends in the long run.

On our public ranges least of all can we afford any compromise of grazing restrictions. Let no blustering rancher or politician embarrass the inspector who orders animals off knee-deep pasture. The inspector has probably determined that the tall stuff is avoided by the animals and that the desirable species at the bottom need rest in order to hold their own in the competition.

The dry grasslands contribute much of our meat, fiber, and leather, but their annual production must conform to the vagaries of their marginal climate. Flocks and herds must be adjusted to the limitations of moisture—not to deceptive *averages* of rainfall, nor to the good wet years, but to the frequent crucial years and seasons when drought rides the range.

He who stocks to capacity in favorable years risks the loss of both livestock and range during lean ones. Better that he "waste" some forage one year than that he starve his animals and kill his grass the next. If he grazes his range to 75 per cent of its capacity in "normal" years and 50 per cent in bumper years, his herd or flock is probably as big as it ought to be for a fair degree of stability.[26] If he narrows the margin he gambles with climate, and climate deals the cards.

When by reseeding, caution, and patience we recover the millions of acres now denuded and prohibit henceforth such wanton abuse, we shall have solved a most pressing problem in American conservation. Our grassland economy may never have the stable security of general farming in the humid East, but as meteorologists and climatologists become more proficient at long-range weather forecasting, we can increase total production and anticipate hazards. Not by environmental *control*, but by careful

[margin notes]

One role
of the
agrostologist

Climatic
marginality
must be
respected

adjustment may we better utilize and conserve our valuable grass-land resources, since we cannot control the cycles of climate.

Adjustment is progressing rapidly on dry lands, both privately and publicly owned. As of 1962 private landowners had, with liberal public assistance, achieved the corrective changes previously noted. Meanwhile the public rangelands were being analyzed and appraised by the Bureau of Land Management in a comprehensive inventory to determine capabilities and optimal utilization. Early in 1962, the analysis and adjudication work had been accomplished on about one-half the land in grazing districts and was programmed for completion by 1967. Among many other improvements and installations scheduled for completion were the building of 14,500 miles of additional fences, the seeding of 2 million acres, the controlling of brush on 2 million acres, the controlling of noxious and poisonous weeds on 3 million acres, the treating of land by pitting, scarifying, and terracing on 200,000 acres, and the building of 7,000 additional water-control structures (wells, springs, stock-watering ponds, detention dams, and water spreaders).[27]

After more than a century of abuse and devastation of our plains and rangelands, we are now determined to mend them and use them without further spoliation. By joining private and public forces to rehabilitate and conserve them we shall realize their full, though limited, potential. When future droughts visit them the land will be less vulnerable to attack and the inhabitants more secure against calamity.

Programs both private and public conserve the dry lands

8

Our Forests and Their Exploitation

forest products and forest influences are indispensable to our American culture

Soils have value only in terms of their product—vegetation— and forests represent the most conspicuous vegetative development. They flourish where soil, water, and sunshine in good combination afford a favorable habitat for plants. Trees are the aristocrats of the plant world, and a community of them composes the "high society" called forest. That society claims for itself those environments favorable to it and relegates to grasses, forbs, and shrubs those areas climatically or otherwise less hospitable.

Except in rainy tropical regions, where enervating heat and humidity have retarded cultural progress, forest cover generally indicates conditions conducive to a high order of human occupance. Population densities, industrial and commercial developments, in the modern world pattern show remarkable geographic coincidence with the arrangement of middle- and high-latitude forest regions. Deserts and semiarid grasslands stimulated man's initial rise from barbarism to an advanced state of civilization, but our modern Western culture matured in forests, not by chance but by the liberal provision of human wants—food, shelter, fuel, and abundant raw materials for manufacture into other necessities.

Forests provide a great variety of useful materials, many of them indispensable to our everyday living. Without the bounty

174

of our forests, we could not have gained the superior economic position our nation enjoys, nor might we envisage maintenance of national prestige in the future.

Forests provide a great variety of useful materials

Out of our woods come tall *poles* on which to string lines for communication and power transmission, *piling* to support wharves and other structures over water or soft earth, *cross-ties* to support railroads and heavy traffic, *logs* for lumber and veneer with hundreds of uses, *bolts* for cooperage, shingles, matches, pencils, and a hundred other purposes. From our woods come *posts* for fences with which to protect our crops and control our animals, *timbers* to shore up mine passages and excavations, *cordwood* for fuel and pulp. From our woods come *bark* for tanning leather, *pitch* for naval stores, *sap* for sugar and sirup, *nuts* for food and feed and flavoring, *raw materials* for goods and services upon which our economic standards and social customs depend.

From wood comes paper, cellulose, cellophane, rayon, explosives, alcohol, dye, medicine, charcoal, acetic acid, tar, plastics, and other industrial products. On paper made of wood we print our newspapers, magazines, books, all sorts of informative and educational matter, our records, contracts, and valuable documents. On wooden railroad ties we travel for business and pleasure and ship the bulk of our domestic commerce—much of it in wooden containers. Wood protects the lives of our miners, knocks all our home runs in baseball, houses many of our people, adds the allure of rayon fabric to our ladies' attire, helps win our wars, helps furnish our homes, fences the scrubs from our thoroughbreds, and imparts the fine quality that distinguishes a violin from a fiddle.

The virtues and uses of forest products could not be listed, much less evaluated, on the pages in this book. We are constantly making substitutions, but we are even more rapidly developing new uses and greater requirements. We could not live normally and happily without them, yet thus far we have done little to ensure a perpetual supply.

The incidental, indirect, and less tangible forest benefits have untold value, greater perhaps than the entire aggregate of all forest materials. Would any decent citizen, other than the gatherer and the vendor, hang a price tag on a Christmas tree or a wreath of greenery, when its true worth shows only in the sparkle of children's eyes? Could anyone place a monetary value on the aesthetic glory of New England's woods in autumn or on the inspirational grandeur of the great trees on the Pacific Slope? Are not trees associated with the fondest childhood memories and the

Less tangible forest benefits have untold value

nobler thoughts of most Americans? Our forests would be invaluable to us without any utility other than their sentimental, psychological influences.

Forestry is unequalled as a means of conserving soil and water. Forests on our watersheds, often referred to as *protective forests,* prevent soil erosion, detain surface waters and release them flowing clear and regularly, and replenish ground-water reserves by induced percolation. The deep soil under a healthy deciduous forest—may have storage capacity for 14.5 inches of rain.[1] Our best water reservoirs are those that *grow* about the headwaters; not the ones *built* downstream. Without *green storage,* be it forest or sod, above them, man-made reservoirs can be only moderately effective and short-lived. A major portion of our forest land needs no commendation to the conservator beyond its function in the regulation of stream flow, the prevention of stream pollution and silting, and the prevention or moderation of floods!

Many forms of wildlife are forest dwellers, and they thrive best where their forest habitat remains intact and healthy. A vigorous forest harbors an abundant population of birds, game animals, and lesser of the fauna. In clear, cool forest streams and lakes live choice species of fish. In and about those waters live waterfowl and fur bearers. Bear or beaver, moose or mink, turkey or partridge, fox, deer, or hare—big game and small keep to wooded places more than to the open. Hunting, fishing, trapping, or nature study is generally more challenging and rewarding in the forest than outside it. Woodlands are about as important to wildlife conservation as they are to the conservation of water and soil. For that reason sportsmen are often enthusiastic, if not always proficient, forest conservators. They recognize that forestry improves hunting and fishing by improving wildlife habitats.

Our forefathers wrought a nation out of wood

Perhaps no other environmental attribute has exerted so potent an influence over American history as have the great forests to which our forest-bred ancestors from Europe laid claim in the New World. Our forefathers virtually wrought a nation out of wood. Trees were to them both help and hindrance. They cut them and burned them to clear land for crops. They built their houses of logs, furnished them and heated them with wood. They bridged the streams with timbers and floored, walled, and roofed the bridges with planking. They blocked streams with wooden (crib) dams to develop water power with which to saw lumber, to grind meal, and to forge tools. They traveled in wooden boats and wooden wagons. Their plows had wooden beams, and they drew them with oxen under wooden yokes. Even their household utensils were largely of wood. They hafted with wood the axes for chopping their way into the continent. Wood was both obstacle and facility.

The colonists nurtured our infant nation on wood. The forests yielded the wherewithal to enact the fabulous chapters of colonial commerce and seamanship. From the forests came the timbers and planking, the masts, yards, and bowsprits, the rosin and tar with which to seal the seams. Wooden ships carried wooden cargoes, and the European market was America's plum. We shipped masts, ship timbers, and naval stores as fast as we could, but demand exceeded supply. We built ships for fishing and whaling, ships to carry a rapidly expanding foreign trade, ships for a powerful Navy, ships to sell to our commercial rivals across the Atlantic.[2]

Wooden ships carried wooden cargoes

Before the advent of steam power and steel hulls during the last quarter of the nineteenth century, our wooden men-of-war, mounting iron cannons, secured our position as a formidable naval power. Our sleek clipper ships outsailed everything else afloat. Even now wooden boats bring in much of our fish, and wooden bottoms carry a considerable portion of our commerce.

To the early settlers along our Eastern seaboard the deep, dense forest seemed inexhaustible. They found only limited, scattered clearings, and the pristine wilderness stretched westward beyond the farthest horizon they could comprehend. Who might have foreseen that the tremendous expanse of standing timber would be decimated in a hundred years? (See Fig. 8.1.) Apparently there was wood for every conceivable purpose, and wood to burn! Fire, which has since become a major menace to our forests, was then an effective tool for penetrating and subduing them. Burning was neither malicious nor wasteful. It was an expedient by which men carved fields and farms out of the wilderness and forced the sylvan frontier.

The deep, dense forests seemed inexhaustible

Settlement chopped and sawed and burned its way westward into the interior. In many places, notably in the broad-leaved forests of the southeastern highlands, it was convenient to kill the trees by girdling, thus admitting sunlight for crops planted among the weathering trunks. Farms spread westward into the great forest. Crops displaced trees, cows evicted the deer, roosters crowed where ruffed grouse once drummed, men and their tamed retinue dispersed the wild things and usurped their domain. Wild fowl and other game, without which the pioneers would have starved, shrank before the advance of saw and ax and musket. Civilization subdued the wilderness.

Settlement chopped, sawed, and burned itself into the land

Halfway across the continent, settlement was at the expense of

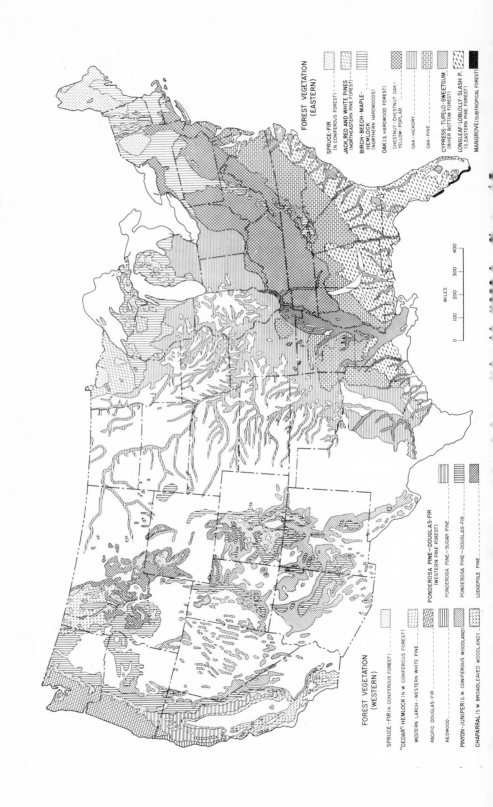

FOREST VEGETATION
(WESTERN)

SPRUCE-FIR (N. CONIFEROUS FOREST)

"CEDAR"-HEMLOCK (N.W. CONIFEROUS FOREST)

WESTERN LARCH-WESTERN WHITE PINE

PACIFIC DOUGLAS-FIR

REDWOOD

PINYON-JUNIPER (S.W. CONIFEROUS WOODLAND)

CHAPARRAL (S.W. BROADLEAVED WOODLAND)

PONDEROSA PINE-DOUGLAS-FIR
(WESTERN PINE FOREST)

PONDEROSA PINE-SUGAR PINE

PONDEROSA PINE-DOUGLAS-FIR

LODGEPOLE PINE

FOREST VEGETATION
(EASTERN)

SPRUCE-FIR (N. CONIFEROUS FOREST)

JACK, RED AND WHITE PINES
(NORTHEASTERN PINE FOREST)

BIRCH-BEECH-MAPLE-
HEMLOCK (NORTHERN HARDWOODS)

OAK (S. HARDWOOD FOREST)

CHESTNUT-CHESTNUT OAK-
YELLOW-POPLAR

OAK-HICKORY

OAK-PINE

CYPRESS-TUPELO-SWEETGUM
(RIVER BOTTOM FOREST)

LONGLEAF-LOBLOLLY-SLASH P.
(S. EASTERN PINE FOREST)

MANGROVE (SUBTROPICAL FOREST)

MILES
0   100   200   300   400

forest. Trees and men were mortal enemies, and the human conquest was altogether too thorough. Forests retreated to lands undesirable for cultivation. Game grew scarce, streams waxed rampageous and muddy, and despoliation continued. Halfway across the continent, forests helped and hindered the progress of settlement. Once funneled through the gaps in the Eastern highlands, settlers went down the Mississippi tributaries by raft or boat and emerged upon the open prairies. In the South they found few natural openings before they reached the dry plains of Texas and Oklahoma. The human tide hesitated at the edge of the grasslands to muster courage for the strange crossing; then, braced against the forest, it resurged over the unwooded plains in wooden wagons.

Coincident with the spread of settlement and national growth, lumbering outgrew its crude beginnings in New England and became a full-fledged business of exploitation. It was *extractive, destructive,* and *moderately lucrative,* and it invaded all of our great forest regions shown in Fig. 8.2. It proceeded from region

Lumbering invaded the great forests one by one

Fig. 8.2 *Forest regions of the contiguous United States. From each of the five Great Forests came a timely episode in our economic history; in each is a special promise for the future. Coastal Alaska comprises a separate segment of the Pacific Forest; Interior Alaska constitutes the "sixth estate." (U.S.F.S. map.)*

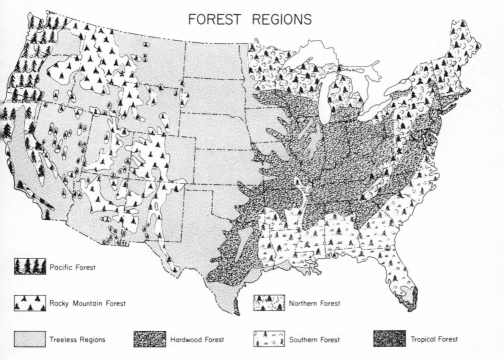

FOREST REGIONS

Pacific Forest

Rocky Mountain Forest

Treeless Regions

Hardwood Forest

Northern Forest

Southern Forest

Tropical Forest

PRODUCTION OF LUMBER IN THE
UNITED STATES, BY REGION, 1899- 1958

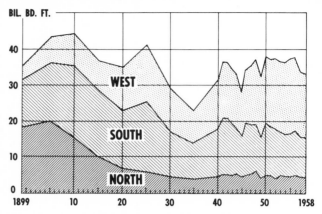

Fig. 8.3   *Timber has become a mainstay in the South. (U.S.D.A. graph.)*

to region as destructive exploitation in one shifted industrial opportunity to another (Fig. 8.3).

By the historic impact of initial colonization, the mixed forests of New England were the first to be logged commercially. American lumbering emerged from the colonial sawmills, commencing with white pine, hemlock, and spruce in northerly areas, and yellow poplar and chestnut southward. Then, as now, leading lumber species were softwood,[3] mainly conifers. From the beginning, oaks and other hardwoods contributed ship timbers, tight cooperage, furniture and implement parts, but their mixed stands and specialized uses spared them from the main assault. The specific gravity of green hardwood logs also discouraged their cutting during the era when logs were almost universally floated to the mill down the stream that drove the saw. Mean paradox, indeed, that the waters regulated by forest were the prime facility for forest removal! Sawmills were our first commercial application of water power, probably as early as 1631,[4] and water power helped make lumbering a top-flight American industry.

Northeastern white pine ruled the shifts and fortunes of American lumbering for more than two hundred years.[5] In quest of that prized species, major logging operations shifted from Maine to New York, to Pennsylvania, and on in turn to Michigan, Wisconsin, and Minnesota.

After the Civil War the famed pineries of the Upper Lakes region dominated the American lumber industry for more than a quarter-century. The mythical Paul Bunyan and his great blue ox, Babe, handled huge pine logs like match sticks and sent them down the rivers in gigantic "drives." Bemidji, Minnesota claims Paul Bunyan as a native son and celebrates his fantastic mythical career.

Paul Bunyan logged the North Woods

Cutting was done in winter when the cold north country lay frozen and snow-covered. Good wages lured rough-and-ready lumberjacks away from civilization to the isolation of remote logging camps. During the short winter days they rent the crisp air with the ring of axes, the swish of crosscut saws, the crash of falling trees, loud shouts of "timber," and profanity as keen edged as the ax bits.

With large teams of horses they hauled the great logs in great pyramidal loads secured with "log chains" to wide sleighs with steel-shod runners. They piled them systematically, either on a frozen stream, or on its bank whence they could tumble them into the water after the ice went out. Men called *drivers* rode the logs downstream to the sawmill, guiding them with pike poles or peavies to prevent stranding or jamming. When jams did occur the drivers broke them up promptly to start the logs moving again before the drive became hopelessly tangled. Not infrequently it was necessary to loosen a jam with dynamite. The whole system was "rough"—on both men and timber. Many logs that were sound on the stump reached the sawmill badly battered or splintered.

Before the turn of the century the South became prominent in lumbering, and by 1910 it outranked the declining Northern pineries as a source of lumber. Southern yellow pine took the place of northern white pine. Longleaf became the leading lumber species, and held sway for about as long as had Upper Lakes pine before it. Longleaf and slash (pitch pines) were the source of our naval stores, but lumbering outranked turpentining, and the resinous trees were felled for lumber. Northern capital and equipment invaded the "Piney Woods," took out the finest specimens, and destroyed any others that stood in the way.

Yankees helped slash the southern "Piney Woods"

Never before, nor since, have men so quickly and ruthlessly "slashed" a forest as they did the Southern coniferous forest, the most extensive of its kind. Rebel or Yankee, the Southern lumber baron operated under a "cut out and get out" policy. Labor was cheap and plentiful, the terrain flat to gently rolling, and the weather never severe. Techniques of logging and sawing had improved, at least insofar as speed was the criterion of efficiency. Saws were largely steam driven, the boilers fired with slab and cull logs. (Many logs then used for fuel would be considered high

grade today.) So thorough was the extraction that such a stand of longleaf as shown in Fig. 8.4 is now rare.

The remarkable stands of longleaf, slash, shortleaf, and loblolly were soon cut out, Southern yellow pine lost its pre-eminence, mills closed down, and the transient, extractive industry sought new realms to exploit and desecrate. Had not the swamp environment discouraged its logging, the rot-resistant bald cypress would certainly have fared no better than the pines.

Next to bear the brunt of ax and saw was the magnificent, virgin forest of the Pacific Northwest. Douglas fir (Fig. 8.5), in the royal line of conifers, succeeded to the crown relinquished by longleaf pine. In the new "court" were redwood, Western white pine, sugar pine, Western hemlock, and several other tall timber blue bloods.

Despite rugged terrain and remoteness from market, the Pacific Coast forest suffered mass attack while our doughboys were fighting World War I in Europe. Opening of the Panama Canal in 1914 precipitated full-scale assault against the heaviest stands of timber on the continent. Water transport made Western lumber competitive in our Eastern markets. Lumber from the

Despite remoteness and difficult terrain, the Pacific Northwest suffered mass attack

Northwest has constituted a major item of Canal freight ever since.

In the Northwest, logging became highly complex and mechanized in order to handle giant trees in rough topography. Tractors and power-yarding machinery have all but replaced horses and hand labor; chain saws have replaced the backbreaking crosscuts. Today improvements of techniques and equipment are continually increasing the speed and efficiency of logging operations. The cutting of trees has become big business, involving high finance. From the generations of experience that evolved the modern methods came also a certain respect for conservational applications. The modern logger operates under legal restrictions designed to protect his business against suicide.

Latest contributor to our lumber industry is the Rocky Mountain forest region, yielding Western white pine from its northerly areas and the desirable ponderosa pine from widely scattered stands. Logging of the Rocky Mountain slopes completes the regional circuit of soft-wood lumbering in the United States. We have cut a wide swath about the nation. To appease our hunger for lumber we have shipped it by sea halfway around the

The Rockies closed the lumber circuit

Fig. 8.5 *An over-mature stand of Douglas firs in Washington dying of old age. Such timber should be logged so that a new generation of trees might grow in its place. (American Forest Products Industries photo.)*

continent and then hauled it overland more than halfway across for delivery.

From Maine to Washington State the original cut was wondrously rich, and its taking shamefully extravagant as viewed in retrospect. However, from a practical point of view the initial logging of our conifers was simply good business at an opportune time. The trees were ripe, and the demand was strong. Then, as now, profit was the motive of lumbermen, and a few of them got rich. However, competition was keen, and the market accepted only the best. The economic climate dictated many wasteful practices; the entrepreneur had little choice if he wished to operate. The old-time logger deserves our praise rather than our blame, for he produced a material that contributed more to the building of America than any other we possessed. Had he been faint-hearted and sentimental, our rich stands of virgin timber would have fallen and rotted without benefit to anyone. Was it not better to salvage a portion, even by destructive methods, than to let all of it die of old age?

The timber harvest hastened America's rise to commercial prestige and industrial greatness. It helped build our Navy, our fishing fleets, and our Merchant Marine. It helped bring the fertile Midwestern plains to fruition. It facilitated revival of the South after ravage and economic collapse. It was the dominant factor in the opening of the great Northwest. But the price was high—so high that the consequences cannot be quickly and easily evaluated or corrected. It compelled us to invoke forestry and conservation lest destructive extraction be complete and final. It became possible and necessary to estimate saw-timber reserves by groups and species, as in Table 1.

In the wake of the sawmills—North, South, East, and West—lay charred and desolate cutover lands. Most atrocious was the slashing of the South, where many millions of acres were ruthlessly logged and burned. Burning was not a necessary concomitant of logging, but what with deep pine "straw" on the forest floor, turpentine faces on the trees, wood-burning locomotives on logging spurs, steam engines in the mills, and careless workers smoking tobacco, fire stalked the lumber camps. Many a sawmill closed prematurely because fire claimed part of the cut; none could operate in a fixed location after all suitable logs had been cut within the radius of economical hauling.

When the tributary area had been cut over the operator closed down his mill and moved the "steel" to another site or another region, leaving behind him a smoking sawdust pile, a rambling

Ripe crops made bountiful harvests

In the wake of the sawmills lay charred desolation

skeleton of weather-beaten boards, and several shacks full of
destitute families. By arson or accident, many mills burned down

Table 1

Timber Volume by Species, in the United States and Coastal Alaska

Species group	Growing stock	Live saw-timber
	Billion cu. ft.	Billion bd. ft.
Eastern softwoods:		
Southern yellow pine	49	174
Other Eastern softwoods	25	68
Total	74	242
Eastern hardwoods:		
Oak	53	146
Sugar maple, beech, yellow birch	19	51
Gums	18	51
Other Eastern hardwoods	61	133
Total	151	381
Western softwoods:		
Douglas-fir	98	532
Ponderosa and Jeffrey pine	43	224
Western hemlock and Sitka spruce	43	208
True firs	38	184
Sugar and Western white pine	10	57
Redwood	6	36
Other Western softwoods	43	165
Total	281	1,406
Western hardwoods	11	28
All species	517	2,057

Source: "Timber Resources for America's Future," *Forest Resource Report No. 14*, Forest Service, U.S. Department of Agriculture (Washington, D.C., 1958).

before closure. If there be any sight more depressing than the gray-black army of stumps standing as sentinels of barren cut-over, it must be the weathered ghost towns in which the monstrous destruction once centered. One cannot view the aspect and reflect upon its implications without a surge of mixed emotions —anger, pity, shame, and contempt. One may countenance the creation of ghost towns with the exhaustion of ore bodies, but he cannot condone the "mining" of timber!

Clean cutting was bad enough, but the burning that accompanied or followed it left scarcely anything alive. The young pine candles (seedlings) that might have flourished under the unobstructed sunlight died young in the flames. The nearest seed

Fig. 8.6 *Cut-over, burned-over area in Colorado. Destructive cutting and burning left an aftermath of maimed land. Many similar shambles have punctuated the history of American lumbering. (S. T. Dana, U.S.F.S. photo.)*

trees accidentally left standing were so few and far between that they could but slowly resow the great, scorched voids between them. How well they *did* repopulate the barrens has been described as a major miracle of American forestry.

Where original stands admitted no light in which their off-spring could grow, as under the great Douglas firs of the North-west, there was nothing destructive about clear cutting limited areas; in fact, it is considered good practice to this day. But, when an aftermath of fire destroyed forest duff and soil humus it handicapped the next generation of trees. In our epic of forest exploitation the fire that accompanied logging has been much more villainous than the loggers. Desolation such as that depicted in Fig. 8.6 may be found in many localities once richly forested.

In the big "show," hardwoods played minor roles, but they had their own special contributions to make. Oaks furnished ribs and beams for ship hulls. Hickories furnished tool handles and wagon parts. From birch came shoe pegs. From walnut came gunstocks. And from a score of other species came material for many other specialized uses. But the hardwoods stood so mixed and scattered that the removal of any individual species merely thinned the composite forest stand. Clear cutting for commercial purposes was neither expedient nor feasible.

Dispersal, mixture, and special utility spared the hardwoods from the main assault

186

The central Eastern hardwoods, composing the largest of our forest regions, escaped the systematic large-scale exploitation for lumber that laid low our conifers. Clearing for farms took more hardwoods than did commercial logging. Valuable hardwoods survived the adjacent softwoods because the market demanded a greater volume of pine than of oak and because the hardwood mixture was difficult to log profitably.

Now steel, paper, plastics, and other materials have displaced hardwood for many purposes. Steel drums have largely displaced tight cooperage (barrels and kegs); paper cartons have largely replaced wooden crates and boxes. Plastics have become prominent in furniture and interior finishing. Hickory, once important in the manufacture of wheeled vehicles and horse-drawn implements, has shrunk to the role of handle material and become a "weed" species. Oak retains prominence as flooring; cherry, walnut, birch, and some other species remain popular for furniture and interior finish. Unfortunately the hardwoods take so long to replenish that the remnants of any favored species must be made to last as long as possible.

Soils under the hardwoods are generally more fertile than those under the conifers and are therefore more desirable for agricultural use. Farmers cleared the hardwoods to get at the soil much as miners strip away the overburden to get at the mineral. The remnants of hardwood left standing are largely in farm wood lots and on land unsuited for agriculture. High unit value now subjects good hardwood specimens of favored species to constant search and collection despite patchy distribution.

When the grand whirl of "quick rich-long poor" lumbering headed for its last roundup we had to swallow our pride and accept what we had previously rejected. Weed species and second growth gained favor. Eastern hemlock, Southern slash pine, Northern jack pine; gum, beech, lodgepole, and tamarack; woods that cracked or splintered or twisted, woods full of knots or worm holes; most any lignified stem big enough to make two-by-fours became saw timber.[6] For pulping and synthetics a long list of nondescripts became respectable citizens of the forest community; saplings made as good cellulose as patriarchs. Technology and economics revamped our ideas about forests and forestry. We entered a new era of wood, and 152 different species of trees became commercially important.[7]

Weed species and second-growth gained acceptance

Wood became a primary raw material for a variety of industrial innovations, not simply lumber and timbers. Prices rose and quality fell, but stumpage could be appraised in terms of cellulose (and lignin) instead of board feet. Portable sawmills

We entered a new era of wood

shifted precariously from place to place about the cutover lands, cutting scattered patches of trees that had attained merchantable size. Competent lumbermen turned their attention to forest protection and reproduction to ensure the permanence of their operations. Notably in the Northwest, where most of our virgin saw timber is located, lumber manufacturers adopted policies and practices whereby their factories might operate continuously and indefinitely. Sawmills became permanent community assets.

The most revolutionary aspect of the "new forestry" was that pulpwood became a crop on land abandoned by lumber barons only two or three decades earlier. Fast-growing softwoods stole another march on the hardwoods because the speed of regrowth became a critical factor. Spindly pines, firs, and spruces produce cellulose faster than the nobler oaks, birches, and hickories.

Despite destructive exploitation in the past, we have abundant timber reserves still remaining and tremendous forest resources regenerated on land whence original stands were once obliterated.

When our forebears began felling trees in the New World that area which now composes the forty-eight contiguous states had a billion acres of forest.[8] Now, including the states of Alaska and Hawaii, our forest lands aggregate some 786 million acres, of which 489 million acres comprise the commercial forest area from which timber harvests are available. The remaining 297 million acres of American forest land are classed as noncommercial—land that is incapable of yielding usable wood products, is economically inaccessible, or is reserved for such purposes as parks, wilderness, game refuges, and military installations. The United States contains 8 per cent of the world's total forest area and 15 per cent of the land being operated for forest products.[9] More than one-third of our country remains forested; commercial forests occupy one-fourth of our land.[10]

Neither Hawaii nor the island possessions of the United States may ever contribute much to the nation's wood supply because they contain less than 1 million acres of commercial forest, most of it better employed for purposes other than timber production. However, Alaska, the largest American state, contains two great forest regions—coastal and interior—the latter remaining almost entirely unexploited (Fig. 8.7).

Coastal Alaska comprises a heavily forested area of some 16.5 million acres, preponderantly of Western hemlock and Sitka spruce, in timber stands comparable with those of western Washington and Oregon. The region yields considerable quantities of saw timber and pulpwood and could sustain harvests immensely greater than those now economically feasible.

We have abundant timber resources despite destructive exploitation in the past

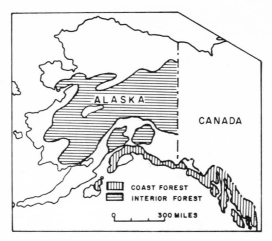

Fig. 8.7 *The forests of Interior Alaska bear little resemblance to the luxuriant Coastal ones. (U.S.F.S. map.)*

COAST FOREST
INTERIOR FOREST

300 MILES

FOREST REGIONS ALASKA

Interior Alaska contains some 120 million acres of forest land, of which about one-third might be classed as commercial forest land. These 40 million acres support an estimated 32 billion cubic feet of timber, including 180 billion board feet of saw timber, with an annual net growth of some 4 billion board feet. The forest is mainly white spruce and paper birch. The commercial area is almost equal to that of Oregon and Washington combined and contains about 60 per cent as much saw timber as the state of Washington. Yet it remains almost unexploited.[11] The Bureau of Land Management administers the forest land of interior Alaska.

Regional distribution of forest lands in the contiguous states and coastal Alaska is shown in Fig. 8.8. Note that the Eastern forests are largely commercial; the eastern United States contains three-fourths of our commercial forest land, which is most extensive in the Southern and Upper Lakes regions. Commercial forest occupies major proportions of total land area in several Eastern regions, exceeding one-half in four of them: New England, 86 per cent; South Atlantic, 60 per cent; Southeast, 59 per cent; and west Gulf, 57 per cent. Highest percentage of commercial forest land in the West is 43, and that is in the Pacific Northwest, our major source of saw timber.[12] (The heaviest, tallest timber stands and the greatest lumbering operations in the world are in the Pacific Coast forests of the United States and Canada. Douglas fir yields more saw timber than any other species.)

Almost all the Western forests are coniferous; about two-thirds of the Eastern ones are broadleaved. The Eastern hardwood types constitute slightly more than half the total acreage of our com-

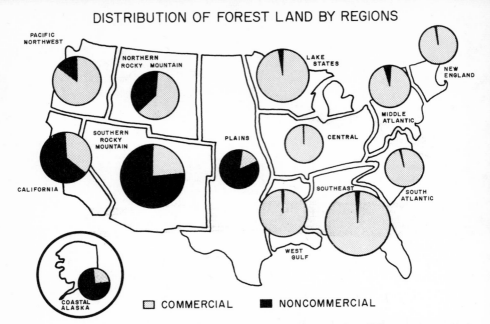

DISTRIBUTION OF FOREST LAND BY REGIONS

☐ COMMERCIAL ■ NONCOMMERCIAL

Fig. 8.8 *The eastern United States, and especially the South, will become increasingly important as a source of forest products. ("Timber Resources for America's Future.")*

mercial forest area. Most extensive is the oak-hickory type, which occupies 112 million acres or 23 per cent of the total. Second in area is the loblolly-shortleaf pine type on 12 per cent of the total acreage. Although Eastern hardwoods predominate, the East also contains an aggregate area of softwoods equal to that of the West. Comparative areas of various types may be noted in Fig. 8.9, and their general locations approximated in Fig. 8.1.

Total volume of our forest-growing stock (live, standing timber) is some 517 billion cubic feet, including more than 2,057 billion board feet of saw timber.[13] Net growth each year exceeds the cut, so a margin between supply and demand has become appreciable during recent years.

Volume and trends in American consumption of major timber products are represented graphically by Fig. 8.10. Note the downward trend in fuelwood and the upward trend in pulpwood during almost three decades. Consumption of lumber, the principal timber product, has decreased during recent years, and imports have also curtailed the domestic production. The United States has been a net importer of lumber since 1941. The domestic wood harvest has been greatly supplemented by imports from Canada, whence came about 80 per cent of our newsprint from 1945 to 1955, and about 60 per cent in recent years. In individual years we have imported a third of the hardwood plywood used in the United States and thirteen times as much veneer as we have exported (veneer imports in 1955 were 52 million square

190

feet).[14] Were we to meet all wood requirements from domestic sources we might soon revert to a deficit between harvest and growth volumes because imports contribute 10 per cent of our total consumption.

Fig. 8.9 *Total areas of hardwoods and softwoods are about equal, but the types have unequal regional distribution. ("Timber Resources for America's Future.")*

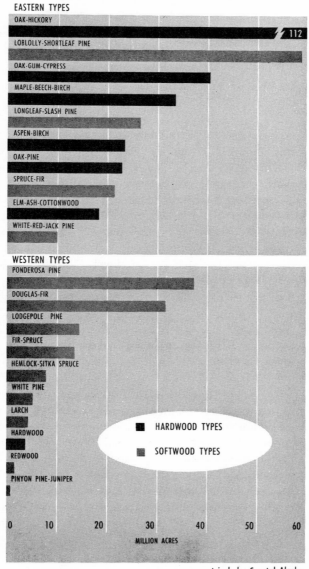

HARDWOOD AND SOFTWOOD TYPES
ABOUT EQUAL IN AREA

west includes Coastal Alaska

CONSUMPTION OF TIMBER PRODUCTS IN THE UNITED STATES 1900-1958

(INCLUDES NET IMPORTS OF EACH PRODUCT)

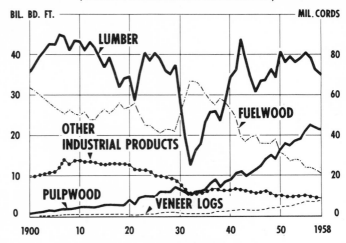

Fig. 8.10 *The increased production of pulpwood is mainly in the Southern Piney Woods. (U.S.D.A. graph.)*

As a national average, each American uses, in various ways and forms, 78 cubic feet of wood each year, about the equivalent of 1,000 board feet of lumber and almost a short ton in weight.[15] Among his annual requirements are 436 pounds of paper, representing more than half a ton of wood. (Much of this becomes litter that defiles the American landscape.) This rate of consumption per capita may not persist; but, the least population increase reasonably predictable will soon raise our total wood requirement above its present level. Only by diligent conservation can we ensure optimal contribution of forestry resources to economic progress. Their present importance to our economy is readily recountable.

Forest industries in our national economy

The 1958 Census of Manufactures showed that "Forest Industries" ranked third in the nation in the number of establishments with twenty or more employees, surpassed only by "Food and Kindred Products" and "Apparel and Related Products." The forestry group ranked fourth both in total number of employees and in annual payroll and fifth in value added by manufacture.[16] Forest industries employed 1.6 million persons and had a payroll of 7 billion dollars a year—a substantial contribution to gross national product. Some 57,000 establishments were engaged in the forest industries, including 46,000 sawmills, 800 paper and paperboard mills, 350 pulpmills, 300 plywood and veneer mills, and 200 cooperage mills.[17] Their yield of materials alone would be reason enough for conserving our forests, not to mention their value for other purposes. The noncommercial forests, most ex-

192

tensive in the West and especially in the Southwest, have inestimable worth for watershed protection, recreation and residence, and wildlife habitat. Forests utterly worthless as a source of wood may be much more valuable than those most heavily timbered.

Less than one-third of our noncommercial forest land is privately owned; most such land is federal. However, 73 per cent of our commercial forest land is owned by private individuals and firms. Farmers have 34 per cent of it, forest industries, 13 per cent, and a variety of individuals and concerns the remaining 26 per cent. In the West only about 33 per cent of the commercial forest land is privately owned, mainly because so much remains in federal ownership. In the North private owners have 81 per cent of the commercial forest land; in the South they have 91 per cent.[18] Fifty-seven per cent of all private forest ownerships are in the North, averaging only 55 acres each; 40 per cent are in the South, averaging 97 acres each; and only 3 per cent are in the West, with an average size of 310 acres. The nation's private, commercial forest lands are in more than 4.5 million ownerships, ranging in size from only 3 acres to more than 2 million. The average size of private ownership is only 79 acres.[19] Figure 8.11 shows at a glance the ownership classes of land whence our timber crops must come.

Various forest industries own 23,450 tracts of commercial forest land, many of them large. More than 1.1 million forest properties are held by individuals, groups, and corporations, apart from

Dispersed fragmentation of ownership complicates forest management

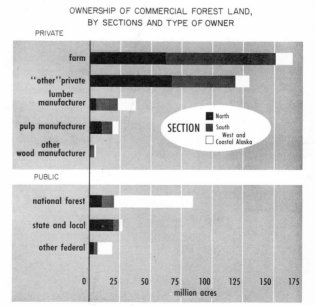

Fig. 8.11 *Our national wood supply has millions of custodians, but many remain unaware of their appointment. ("Timber Resources for America's Future.")*

OWNERSHIP OF COMMERCIAL FOREST LAND, BY SECTIONS AND TYPE OF OWNER

PRIVATE
farm
"other" private
lumber manufacturer
pulp manufacturer
other wood manufacturer

SECTION
■ North
■ South
□ West and Coastal Alaska

PUBLIC
national forest
state and local
other federal

0   25   50   75   100   125   150   175
million acres

VALUE OF FOREST PRODUCTS SOLD
DOLLARS, 1959

UNITED STATES
TOTAL
$187,386,362

1 DOT—$100,0(

Fig. 8.12 *Values represented here are those realized by farmers only, whether from maple syrup, pine gum, logs, pulpwood, or other products. The map does not show proceeds from nonfarm logging operations. (Bureau of the Census map.)*

industrial tracts and farms. The greatest number of private forest properties are more than 3.3 million farm woodlands, of which the West has only 64,000.[20] Average size of these farm forests is only 49 acres.[21] In aggregate they constitute a major, though only partially realized, source of our domestic forestry products. Their contribution to farm income is distributed as shown in Fig. 8.12. They would produce several times their present yield if properly managed. To enhance their productivity, as well as that of other small, scattered woodlands, poses a special problem in forest conservation, as we shall see. However, neither fragmented ownerships nor diversity of forest conditions and proprietary circumstances need be unduly frustrating.

Self-perpetuation is a fundamental function of all living things, trees included. Given a fighting chance, forests repossess areas from which they have been removed. If we would have clear streams with trout in them, more water and fewer floods, thriving factories and inspiring vacations, books to study and comics to read Sunday morning, we need only help our forests to survive and reproduce their species. We need practice only those forestry and conservation measures that pay their own way. Despite all our past abuse the living trees will continue to serve us unless we exterminate them willfully. They can pay us well for a fair degree of protection and management.

Trees will serve us if we practice conservation

194

9

Forest
Conservation

forest conservation perpetuates our abundance of timber and magnifies the beneficence of forests

Forest conservation demands patience and foresight in its practitioners because logs do not grow overnight. The planter of trees must wait several years for the fruits of his labor. The logger who cuts down all the trees at once has to wait many years for another harvest. The keeper of a forest who wishes to change its composition without destroying it cannot do so in a season, as a farmer rotates his crops; the change may take a lifetime, or more. Regeneration of good grass cover on a worn-out range can be further advanced in one year than the regeneration of a mutilated forest in a decade, or even a quarter-century. Forestry serves best both the individual and the nation when it is pursued with proper perspective—a view toward future prospects and needs.

Short
perspective
fails
in forestry

If the nation's wood requirements are to be met satisfactorily several decades hence, forest conservation must be expanded and accelerated *now,* not when timber famine threatens. It is to avert future scarcity that Americans, even while reveling in plenty, have become concerned about conditions of their forest resources and means for improving them. Several general aspects of those resources warrant brief review here as prelude to subsequent discussion of particular facets that bear on the total situation.

By projecting population growth and the demand for wood against probable over-all increase of forest productivity, it becomes quite apparent that the United States has no more commercial forest land than will be needed. Although forestry has heretofore given ground to almost every other kind of land use, it will become increasingly competitive and gain a higher priority. Meanwhile better management for improved productivity will become practicable on many areas now in poor condition or entirely neglected.

Timber status and prospect

Much of the commercial forest land, so-called, is almost devoid of trees at the present time. About one-fourth of all such land is less than 40 per cent stocked with trees; some 40 million acres have less than ten trees where 100 trees should be growing. About 50 million acres need planting if they are to become productive reasonably soon.[1] At the rate we have been going, this task would take more than a quarter of a century.

Although the nation's growth of timber is increasing, especially in the South, the quality of standing timber available for harvest has declined. Three-fourths of the forest land lies east of the plains, but two-thirds of the saw-timber volume is in old-growth stands of the Pacific Coast region, much of it on National Forests. In Coastal Alaska, California, Oregon, and Washington, comprising only about one-fourth of the nation's commercial forest land, stands 70 per cent of the saw timber.[2] Some 50 million acres of heavy, virgin forest should be harvested much faster than is being done because the timber is overmature, and delay entails waste. In recent individual years the cut on National Forests in the West has been much less than the volume allowable under the long-range Forest Service program, because the price of lumber was too low relative to stumpage for profitable logging and milling. While much of the best saw timber ages and deteriorates on the root, old-time carpenters ridicule prevailing market-grade standards with facetious definitions; one has it that "Number 2 Common" means two knots to the foot. As the old-growth forests of the West are logged over, our main dependence for saw timber must, inevitably, shift toward the more extensive forests of the East. Fortunately, most Eastern species have attained a favorable growth-cut/saw-timber ratio, so there need be no dearth of wood in the nation after the magnificent Western forests have been felled.[3]

Wise men in positions of public trust, cognizant of the inherent inadequacies of the individual, began long ago a participation of government in forestry matters. As early as 1817, the Federal government established the Santa Rosa Live Oak Timber Reserve in Pensacola Bay, Florida, to guarantee a source of ship timber for the Navy. That was our first positive attempt to protect the public interest in forests against selfish private enterprise.[4] The reserve contained only 30,000 acres and was short-lived, killed by narrow politics. Timber reserves for the Navy came and went, totaling 264,000 acres on the Gulf Coast in 1868. The last of them was not removed from our land-office records before 1923.[5]

In 1891, with the establishment of the Yellowstone Park Timberland Reserve, began the great National Forest system which now encompasses some 186 million acres.[6] In 1897 Congress *opened certain forest reserves to use,* paving the way for scientific forestry in America by legal regulation, demonstration, and experiment. In 1960 our National Forests contributed a record 12.2 billion board feet of timber,[7] besides providing grazing lands for almost 4 million domestic animals,[8] protecting many major watersheds, and harboring an abundant variety of wildlife and tourists.

Until 1905 the General Land Office in the Department of the Interior administered the forests, and the Department of Agriculture had the professional foresters, but in that year the lands were transferred to the Department of Agriculture to get the material and the know-how together. Since then the Forest Service has advanced the conservation of several durable resources, very appropriately concerning itself not only with trees, but also with the grasslands, wildlife, and other resources within its vast and numerous administrative units. Figure 9.1 suggests the magnitude of the task. As of 1961 the National Forest System contained 155 National Forests and eighteen National Grasslands, their aggregate area about 88 per cent west of the Mississippi.[9]

The functional versatility of the National Forests became public policy in 1960 by enactment of the Multiple Use-Sustained Yield Act (Public Law 86-517), which directed that the National Forests be administered for "outdoor recreation, range, timber, watershed, and wildlife and fish purposes." [10] In reality, the functions prescribed by this act were not new to the Forest Service, but previous authority to develop them stemmed from legal implication or from scattered fragments of legislatoin. First prescribed use of forest reserves was for timber, in 1897, to which was added recreation in 1899. First purchase of land for National Forests was authorized to protect the headwaters of navigable streams, under the Weeks Law of 1911, which also established a program of federal-state cooperation in fire protection. The Clarke-McNary Law of 1924 extended the purchase policy to include the watersheds of navigable streams and lands for the production of timber and greatly expanded federal cooperation with the states, not only for protection of forests against fire but

Our great National Forest System

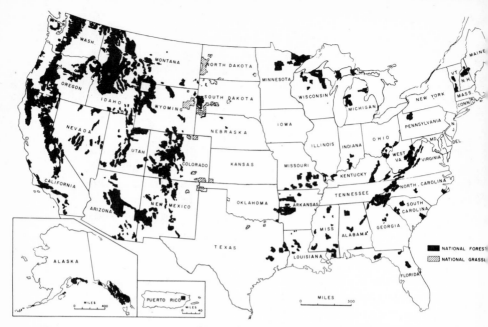

Fig. 9.1 *The manifold services of the National Forests include watershed protection, timber production, range and wildlife conservation, forestry demonstration, wilderness preservation (see Chapter 13) and others. They contribute to every class of natural resources. (U.S.F.S. map.)*

also for providing farmers with planting stock and for cooperative work in farm-forestry extension.[11] In 1960, thirteen Forest Service tree nurseries distributed 137 million seedlings and transplants.[12] Following the enactment of Public Law 86-517 the Service accelerated its comprehensive program for conserving all natural resources under its jurisdiction, a program already well advanced. Full development of all its land units for maximum usefulness by the year 2000 is the long-range goal. Progress toward that goal is impeded by the irregular shape and interrupted pattern of various land units; within the exterior boundaries of the National Forests and National Grasslands lay some 40 million acres of privately owned inholdings in 1961.[13] Acquisition of these inholdings, by exchange or purchase, to consolidate the public properties into compact blocks of land is progressing; however, a problem of such dimensions cannot be solved hurriedly.

The National Forest System and the Forest Service have such historic continuity and serve so many facets of American conservation that their mention in several contexts throughout this volume should be readily understandable. Forty-five states contain National Forest areas, the largest federal forest ownership being in Alaska (some 20,742,000 acres). Each of six others has

National Forest land approximating more than 10 to more than 20 million acres, and in descending order of acreages are: Idaho, 20,352,000; California; Montana; Oregon; Colorado; Arizona, 11,409,000. Almost one-fifth of the eleven contiguous Western states is National Forest land.[14] These federal forest lands are very real assets to the several states as sources of both monetary gain and of sundry intangible benefits. One-fourth of the revenues produced by National Forests and Grasslands is remitted to the counties in which they lie. The direct payments, federal expenditures for roads, fire protection, and other services, together with employment afforded local residents, exceed the taxes that might be collected if the lands were privately owned. Forest Service lands yielded revenues amounting to 148.2 million dollars in 1960, largely from timber sales.[15] (If a county disdains participation in organized fire protection, even when its receipts from National Forest land are more than its share of costs would be, the voting citizens ought to be ashamed!)

The Forest Service is by no means the only agency that administers federal forest land and conserves our public timber resources. Under a congressional act of August 28, 1937 the Bureau of Land Management operates a sustained-yield forestry program on more than 2.6 million acres of prize timber in western Oregon revested to the United States in 1916. (The land was granted by Congress to the Oregon and California Railroad in 1866.) The Bureau has jurisdiction over a total of almost 46 million acres of commercial forest land in its various and far-flung areas of responsibility. Also managed for sustained yield are almost 6 million acres of timber on Indian lands in twenty-three states, mainly tribally owned. Forestry is important to the Indian economy because less than 10 per cent of the 52 million acres held in trust for the Indians is suitable for farming and most of the remainder is open range.

B.L.M. and Indian forests

State forestry, now an important facet of conservation, began in the colonies with certain fire-prevention measures and penalties for timber theft, but it did not settle down to serious business before 1885. In that year New York began the acquisition of the Adirondack and Catskill Forest Preserves. During the last half-century state governments and state police powers have contributed tremendously to the advancement of American forestry. In 1961, thirty-six states held title to a total of 19,747,921 acres of forest land (706 areas) in various use categories.[16] The Fulmer Act, passed by Congress in 1935, afforded the states federal aid in the purchase of lands for state forest purposes.

(It should be noted that forest ownership by the states is a

minor part of their forestry activities. It is by departments of
state government (forestry, conservation, or other) that public
aids to forestry, whether of federal or state origin, are actually
put to work on private forest lands. The state, usually operating
through counties, administers cooperative fire protection, technical assistance, management regulations, taxation, etc.)

Forests owned by cities, counties, institutions, and communities
have also come into vogue—largely a twentieth-century development. We have more than thirty-six hundred such forests in
forty states—the pride of many people. They contain some 4.4
million acres.[17]

Whatever the level of government under which they are retained, public forests generally serve multiple purposes. Many of
their benefits are difficult to appraise in terms of money, but
most of them will, under good management, yield enough timber
to defray all costs of purchase and administration over a period
of years.[18] They have inestimable value as object lessons in forest
conservation. There is room for many more community forests,
and conservators in many places are encouraging the movement.

Although many public forests conserve timber quite incidentally, they lend forestry the long-range perspective difficult to
achieve under private ownership. Best of all, they are living
proof that forests can produce a perpetual supply of materials
without curtailing their unique services in soil defense, water
development, wildlife habitat, nature study, and recreation.
Their educational values probably surpass all the other benefits.
Where might we better develop a forestry consciousness than in
the woods? Where might we more forcibly indoctrinate the public with respect and responsibility for the forest than in a well-
supervised camping or picnic area?

Perhaps nothing else has equaled the National Forest purchase
program in resolving our problem of submarginal land. Substantial aid has also come from the forest departments in various
states. By sale or default private owners have surrendered white
elephants in the form of cutover, burned, or scrub areas. The
public agencies have gathered them in, often in consolidated
blocks, and initiated systematic rehabilitation. Private liabilities
have become public assets by removing them from tax rolls and
placing them under capable stewardship. Public purchase and
consolidation of denuded forest land reduces submarginal farming and enlarges our potential forest production. This is not to
say that all such acquisitions should remain permanently under
public ownership. Advances in technology and changes in economic climate may warrant their future return to private hands.

**Public forests
often serve
more than
they conserve**

Private holdings, large and small, contain the bulk of our potential timber supply, but almost all of them serve in some multiple capacity. Whatever its primary purpose, almost every woodland contributes in some degree to the conservation of other resources: soils; water; wildlife; and so on. While a few forest tracts are retained privately for recreational or sentimental purposes, woodlands owned by private citizens or corporations must in the main either yield a profit on an investment or produce supplementary income in money or kind.

Private holdings contain the bulk of our potential timber supply

Forty-five per cent of the nation's softwood saw timber is on National Forests, and 11 per cent of it is in other public ownerships. The public and the forest industries together own almost three-fourths of such timber, but a much smaller share of the hardwood volume. The National Forests contain only 6 per cent of the hardwood saw timber. Three-fourths of the annual cut has been of softwoods, almost one-half of it comprised of Douglas fir and Southern yellow pines. Our merchantable timber is largely in public and industrial ownerships.[19]

Those ownerships support the large-scale *industrial* operations and are the prime movers of American forestry. The entrepreneurs employ many people and make big investments against stiff competition. They must be strictly practical and efficient to show a fair profit. They are making their plants permanent fixtures by cropping the forests instead of mining them. Some purchase and contract to log publicly owned timber (as on the National Forests) according to restrictions and specifications laid down by responsible agents of government. They harvest, process, and sell the major produce of our forests. They plan by the century rather than year to year, and many schedule their logging sequence over immense "circles" of operation. They manage the forests well, being compelled to do so, either by public regulations or to enhance corporation earnings—or both.

Industrial forests are competitive; farm wood lots supplementary

The small private ownerships present quite another management situation, although they support many wood-using industries of local economic importance. Few of these small properties are managed and maintained as well as the large industrial and public ones, and many are entirely neglected. Most are in poor condition, and their productivity is very low. Their improvement is essential because, collectively, the small forests are, potentially, our greatest future source of timber.[20]

The small units in commercial forestry are operated in a variety of ways. Many owners sell stumpage by the acre, and the buyer comes and cuts it. All too often anything goes, because the buyer shies away from restrictions on the manner of cutting.

Economic expedience brushes forestry aside in such cases. Other
owners cut their timber and sell the logs at a mill or plant within
market distance. Most interesting, and in many cases most conservational, in this category are the small owner-operated forests
and woodworking plants, particularly characteristic of rural New
England and the Appalachian highlands; these, however, are
scattered far and wide in the wake of transient exploitation. It
is true that few are now entirely supplied from a single woods
property, but with wood cut from several small properties many
such plants have operated continuously while the big "shows"
came and went. Their products range from tool handles, neck
yokes, and chair dowels to barrel staves, headings, meat skewers,
and lollypop sticks. They stabilized American forest industry
locally when the big mills ran out of timber and moved on.
Scattered about the country are thousands of such small wood-
using plants, especially numerous in hardwood areas. Considering
that wood sold for $1.00 on the stump acquires, by harvesting,
transporting, processing, fabrication, and distribution, almost
twenty times that worth to the ultimate consumer,[21] it becomes
apparent that a small woodworking establishment may be a vital
asset to the rural community.

Farm woodlands constitute the most problematic and numerous category, and the most neglected segment of our forest potential. The problem lies deep-rooted in farm tradition and
responds but slowly to scientific ministry. In the East, farm wood
lots are portions of the farm rejected for cultivation; on the
plains, they are planted groves of quick-growing, short-lived trees
to protect the house and barns from the bite of cold northerly
winds. Such windbreaks may never have much commercial value,
but the former should by good management boost farm incomes
and our national timber crop vastly more than they ever have,
or do at present. Few farmers know how valuable their farm
woods might be, because they have regarded them mainly as
space for cattle to roam when other pasture needs respite. Figure
9.2 shows the distribution of pastured woodland on farms, and
Fig. 9.3 shows the distribution of those protected against grazing
animals.

Not so long ago, when farmers were less articulate and less
subsidized, the farm woods, especially in hardwood country, furnished many materials for the farm establishment. Fuel for stoves
and fireplaces, rails and posts for fence repair, poles to brace
haystacks and stakes to hold the tops on grain stacks, tongues and
whippletrees for horse-drawn implements—wood for this and
wood for that came out of the trusty wood lot. But farmers, in-

WOODLAND NOT PASTURED

ACREAGE, 1959

UNITED STATES
TOTAL
71,636,066

1 DOT—25,000 ACRES

Figs. 9.2 and 9.3 *Heaviest concentration of nonpastured farm woodland is in Appalachia and the Southeast. Rough topography on the one hand and dominance of such cash crops as cotton, tobacco, and peanuts on the other are largely accountable. Long-leaf-slash pine forests of the southeastern Coastal Plain may be pastured with impunity —unless periodic burning accompanies the grazing operation. Forests grazed in the dry Southwest are generally of little value for timber. Grazing of livestock is most deleterious to good forest management in the hardwood forests of the Northeastern and North Central regions, as shown by Figs. 9.10 and 9.11. (Economic Research Service, U.S.D.A. and Bureau of the Census, U.S.D.C.)*

WOODLAND PASTURED

ACREAGE, 1959

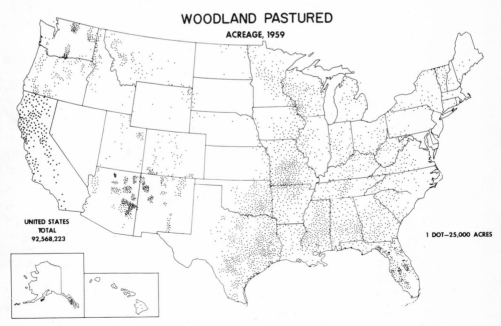

UNITED STATES
TOTAL
92,568,223

1 DOT—25,000 ACRES

cluding those in hardwood country, have modernized, commercialized, and mechanized until they buy their fuel, buy the wire and steel for fences, use tractor-drawn implements with steel hitches, and in a hundred other ways shun the use of wood for reasons of economy as well as convenience. Why chop wood when the labor costs more than equivalent coal or oil delivered? Can one neglect his cows and chickens to "lay up" wood when their regular tending pays more than the price of a wood substitute? Not in this age of cash and calculation!

Their *subsistence* functions largely past, farm woods fall from grace unless they too be *commercialized*. The trend is well advanced, but progress is slow because it takes time to sell 3.4 million farmers an idea, no matter how good it is.

Pulpwood cutting has become a rewarding off-season activity on many farms, notably in the South where a merchantable crop of pine comes up from seed in fifteen to twenty years[22]—profitable tree crops have been grown in considerably less than fifteen years. Farmers have also learned the high value of saw timber, but too few of them can resist a tempting offer for acre stumpage. They should know that a few selected trees cut now and then bring much more remuneration in the long run than one clear cutting can possibly give. Thus far they have so badly abused their woods that the typical farm forest has only 1,900 board feet of saw timber per acre—about half the average stand on commercial forest land generally. By comparison, the public forests have 7,500 board feet per acre, or almost twice the national average.[23]

With forestry as with soil conservation, farmers must *see* the "miracle" before they believe. Once convinced, they find in forestry a welcome adjunct to other crop systems, a splendid addition to farm diversification, and a steady source of supplemental income. Public forest agencies, both state and national, assist the farmers as a matter of good policy for the common weal. Timber operators assist the farmers in the vicinity of their plants as a matter of good business to ensure a better supply of available raw material. Epitome of rapport and cooperation between private forest owners and wood-using industries is the American Tree Farm System that began in the Douglas-fir region in 1941 and attained in only two decades the prominence represented by the accompanying tabulation (Table 1). This progressive national movement is sponsored by American Forest Products Industries, Inc., representing companies that process or manufacture forestry goods. Affiliates certify tree farms in their respective regions upon application of the woodland owners and

Table 1

Tree Farm Progress Report
January 1, 1963

State	Number 1/1/61	Number 1/1/63	Total Acreage 1/1/61	Total Acreage 1/1/63
Alabama	1,974	2,184	6,180,444	6,399,047
Arizona	4	4	70,243	70,243
Arkansas	1,069	1,135	3,596,426	3,627,720
California (redwood)	119	123	641,510	644,966
California (western pine)	247	252	2,215,796	2,220,853
Total California	366	375	2,857,306	2,865,891
Colorado	8	8	79,252	79,252
Connecticut	61	74	56,192	59,761
Delaware	1	1	176	176
Florida	544	672	5,978,752	6,249,913
Georgia	1,222	1,754	5,586,566	6,451,098
Idaho	652	666	1,002,597	1,045,570
Illinois	202	227	21,043	21,688
Indiana	382	428	68,834	74,082
Iowa	123	135	8,719	9,041
Kentucky	150	172	104,943	109,809
Louisiana	1,514	1,758	3,916,621	4,085,863
Maine	486	534	445,120	459,983
Maryland	37	40	21,478	22,630
Massachusetts	211	243	81,840	90,066
Michigan	853	923	1,246,163	1,342,531
Minnesota	1,284	1,401	671,320	718,910
Mississippi	2,946	3,154	2,846,662	2,950,074
Missouri	114	129	180,056	189,647
Montana	60	62	967,071	1,023,894
Nebraska	30	50	2,092	2,571
Nevada	1	1	12,984	12,984
New Hampshire	316	425	227,005	295,868
New Jersey	27	38	12,796	14,476
New Mexico	4	4	155,040	155,040
New York	220	235	145,208	158,307
North Carolina	872	1,044	1,507,238	1,618,498
North Dakota	148	165	4,002	4,407
Ohio	561	588	138,848	156,261
Oklahoma	140	148	988,857	991,275
Oregon (eastern)	149	152	1,821,767	1,840,411
Oregon (western)	302	325	2,611,314	2,773,428
Total Oregon	451	477	4,433,081	4,613,839
Pennsylvania	649	708	303,290	328,005
Rhode Island	42	42	7,262	7,262
South Carolina	463	518	1,883,321	1,976,107
South Dakota (western pine)	2	2	20,960	20,960
South Dakota (Plains)	209	220	13,918	15,735
Total South Dakota	211	222	34,878	36,695
Tennessee	642	704	1,087.527	1,101,350
Texas	1,510	1,629	3,802,137	3,863,137
Utah	1	3	2,960	9,803
Vermont	92	117	154,072	180,663
Virginia	432	448	1,024,422	1,044,670
Washington (eastern)	317	316	742,791	748,434
Washington (western)	404	426	3,504,567	3,573,780
Total Washington	721	742	4,247,358	4,322,214
West Virginia	79	90	250,977	252,633
Wisconsin*	441	613	1,211,651	1,249,891
Wyoming	2	2	40,672	40,672
Total for 47 States	22,312	25,092	57,665,086	60,383,445

* Includes sixteen industrial forests.
Source: American Forest Products Industries, Inc., Washington, D.C.

a professional inspection to ascertain that the properties in question are well managed and protected. Recognition as a tree farmer imposes no obligation and conveys no reward except the pride in good stewardship. Farm woodlands and other small, privately owned forests comprise about 80 per cent of the certified tree farms.[24]

Different kinds of ownership occasion differences in forest management. Different timber stands, pure or mixed, big or small, or of various sizes, demand discretion in the choice of logging and restocking methods. The great variety of forest industries imposes several distinct requirements as to modes of cutting and handling. Good forestry on the part of a farmer with a few walnut logs to sell may not resemble even remotely the equally good forestry of a timber grower with a large acreage of pine of pulpwood size. There will also be obvious disparity between the wood-using plant that works purchased wood and the one that depends mainly or entirely upon company-owned forests. Conservation cannot attain full bloom against the grain of economics, but any detailing of the economic intricacies influencing forestry in the various forest regions lies far beyond the scope of this survey. Merely a brief sketch is apropos here of *common problems* and *approved solutions* in forest conservation generally.

Fire has probably destroyed more of our forest than we have cut and continues to take a heavy annual toll despite our efforts to prevent it. Great forest fires, such as the Hinckley (Minnesota), the Peshtigo (Wisconsin), the Tillamook (Oregon), and the Bar Harbor (Maine), seared tragic pages into American history. Many thousands of fires gnaw away at our forest resources every year. During the decade 1940-1950 an average of 21.5 million acres of our forests went up in smoke *each year*—i.e., we burned annually an area the size of Maine.[25] Since then we have made such gratifying progress against forest fire that the national burn in 1960 was somewhat less than 4.5 million acres, in 1961 only 3.04 million acres—less than one-twelfth the 38 million-acre burning in 1935. The Smoky Bear campaign of the Forest Service and the "Keep Green" program of American Forest Products Industries have proved how effectively education can promote conservation. Both should be continued with undiminished vigor because fire will always endanger the forest. Complacency would invite recurrent catastrophe!

Fire protection remains the fundamental forestry requirement. Without it all other forestry measures come to naught, like derelicts with neither power nor mooring. Unless it be provided first, every other effort becomes a bad risk. None of our forests is fire-proof; fires have burned big holes in every one, even those in cool, moist New England. Drought comes to all of them, and dry woods are so much tinder. Obviously a long dry season as in southern California increases the fire menace. However, one should also note that such a climatic condition produces scrub rather than forest, so that burning is less destructive of timber than it is damaging to watersheds.

Seed sowing and tree planting are wasted labors if the resultant growth succumbs to fire. No forest industry can attain desirable stability and permanence where its basic requirement—a continuous supply of wood—may suddenly "evaporate" from the scene. Most of the destructive forest fires are of our own doing, either by accident or intent. Carelessness with matches and cigarettes, failure to kill campfires, trash fires left unattended, and other equally irresponsible acts cause about half of the fires. Almost one-third are set purposely by people who think burning improves the range or eradicates pests, by people who want "clean" woods, and by persons mentally warped who start fires "just for the fun of it." Only about one in eighteen can be blamed on railroad and lumbering operations. Less than a sixth result from natural causes, mainly lightning—lightning starts many more, but attendant rain puts many of them out before they can do much damage. The fact that we ourselves, the recipients of the bounty, put the torch to our forests is indeed a sorry reflection on our intellectual attainment.

Woods burning for the improvement of grazing is a major deterrent to forestry in the South. Most of the burning fails in its purpose, because the forest grasses are generally too sparse and too low in nutritional value to afford good range, and at best they have only limited seasonal utility. Good pastures have been developed in the Southern pine region, but burning was not the sole means of their improvement. Seeding of suitable forage plants was probably a more important factor. Burning of forest range probably improves it more for quail than for cattle.

All wildfires in the forest are not equally destructive; there are degrees even in burning. Fire that stays on the floor and lacks the intensity with which to consume tree trunks can run through a forest without direct injury to the main stand. However, such *surface* or *ground fire* destroys litter that shielded the soil, absorbed rain, and would have enriched the humus content. Apparently harmless, the lightest kind of ground fire may do considerable damage to the forest environment.

Another kind of wildfire called *crown fire* takes the roof off the forest, leaving charred trunks and snags in its wake. It can race

Fig. 9.4 *A forest fire may kill the entire biotic community, leaving sterile space to which life returns but slowly. Dead trees and snags become highly inflammable, and should be cut down lest they kindle a further scorching. (K. D. Swan, U.S.F.S. photo.)*

through a stand of conifers with the speed of the wind that drives it, beheading the big ones as it goes and killing more deliberately anything that grew under their canopy. All crown fires are disastrous, but at their worst they are conflagrations beyond compare, destroying completely the biotic community they ravage and leaving only dead, sterile space behind them.

Those which consume virtually everything combustible we may well call *soil fires* because they destroy the organic matter in their paths, including soil humus, right down to the mineral foundation (Fig. 9.4). They destroy not only present life but also the prospect of rehabilitation for an indefinite period. Soil fires are one of man's most abominable visitations upon his worldly habitat, wiping out, as they do, the entire biotic community and the soil it helped produce through ages of operation. Without life the soil process stops, re-establishment of life forms and redevelopment of a soil mantle become exceedingly slow processes. *Soil fires are the third-degree burns of forest.*

The place to stop our sacrifice of forests to fire is with the cigarette, the campfire or bonfire, the incendiarist, the spark from a machine. A single thought of caution can save thousands of acres of forest and soil, millions of dollars worth of property, hazardous man-hours of firefighting, human communities, herds and flocks of game—whole segments of our environment that we now erase by carelessness or ignorance.

Precaution and prompt detection are the best firefighting tools

Prevention or "presuppression" is the first and best defense

208

against forest fire; prompt detection the best tool with which to combat it. A full-blown, raging forest fire almost defies control. Prompt arrival on the scene is the essence of fire fighting, and arrival cannot be prompt unless the fire be spotted when it starts and its location reported accurately to the nearest available source of men and equipment. Lookout towers on commanding heights of land, connected by telephone with volunteer crews and equipment stations, stand as symbols of *organized* fire protection; more recently airplane patrols and radio communications have entered the spotting service.

Fire protection is maintained on more than 93 per cent of state and private forest lands, financed jointly by federal, state, and local governments. It demands and deserves public and private cooperation. It must be inclusive in coverage, because no forest area can be safe against fire unless adjoining lands on all sides are also guarded. It must be an *organized* system; otherwise it becomes a piecemeal failure.

First and foremost the system must maintain constant vigilance whenever the forest is dry and easily ignited. Hundreds of "measuring" stations have been established to keep us posted on the degree of fire danger at all times; through them, inflammability is scientifically determined and officially reported. The system must include emergency crews ready to respond on short notice, tools and equipment at strategic locations, and vehicles for speedy dispatch to any detected smoke in the woods.

Defense against forest fire should be commensurate with the danger. Weather, forest condition, and terrain are major factors. Woods drenched with rain or blanketed by snow are safe. Woods far from the haunts of men are comparatively safe, except where lightning starts most of the fires, as in the Rocky Mountains and the Pacific Coast forests. But dry autumn woods, infested with excited hunters whose gear includes everything *except* ash trays, are veritable powder kegs. *Late summer and autumn demand special vigilance.* Fires in flat, open woodland are more easily suppressed than those in heavy timber on rugged terrain. Prevention assumes maximum significance where suppression is most difficult.

An acreage of saw timber or thrifty young growth may warrant careful maintenance of a *fire lane* about the periphery to keep out fire, and *fire breaks* within to limit the spread of any fire that may jump the outer barrier. Lanes and breaks must be gauged to the particular situation, but in any case they should be broad enough to ensure a fair degree of security. Plowed strips a few furrows wide serve well for seedlings, but they are inade-

Defense should be commensurate with the danger

Fig. 9.5 *A fire lane or fire break helps protect a forest against invasion by fire or, as pictured here, helps localize and subdue any fire originating within the forest. This is a carpet grass fire break and road transecting commercial timber property in Florida. (W. R. Mattoon, U.S.F.S. photo.)*

quate for stopping a crown fire in tall conifers. A fire break-fire road combination such as that pictured in Fig. 9.5 serves well both as fire barrier and logging facility. A broad strip of pasture might be even better.

The fire danger can be no greater than the extent and value of the forest. Grass, not forest, becomes the casualty of wildfire on our Western rangelands, and the consequences of range burning are usually less serious and less permanent than those of forest fire. Not only are the grasses less susceptible to injury than is a forest, but they recuperate much more quickly.

No forested community can afford to risk the tragedy of fire. As the forest goes so goes the forest community. A few fatal hours can reduce to ashes the works of one generation and the hopes of another. In all our forest regions fire means loss of livelihood, be the principal income from lumber, as in the West, from pulp, as in the South, or from tourists, as in many parts of the North. Forest products and forest services contribute *directly* to the well-being of most Americans, yet comparatively few people pay serious attention to the fire menace before it robs their own pockets or curtails their water consumption.

No forested community can risk the tragedy of fire

210

Considering the manifold communal services of forest, one observes with embarrassment that in this, the enlightened twentieth century, private timber growers are at the mercy of an unconcerned public. That regrettable circumstance prompts the private owner to restrict public privileges. Because a few inconsiderate picnickers, hunters, or fishermen lack decent respect for private property, the owner "posts" his woodland against all comers. In self-defense he excludes many good citizens whose presence in the woods would actually enhance its safety. Sportsmen's organizations all over the country are doing much to solve the problem, by exemplary behavior in the woods and by active participation in defense against fire. Though good hunting and fishing is their objective, they recognize that forest fire kills game and fish, destroys choice wildlife habitats, and may permanently change the wild population of an area. Chain reactions characterize both natural and social aspects of conservation.

Private timber growers are at the mercy of an unconcerned public

Small owners control a major portion of our forest area and hold the key to the future of our forest industries, but fire loss, or fear of it, discourages many from employing forestry practices they would otherwise prefer. The most enthusiastic tree farmer loses heart when his young planting burns. The eastern Tennessean who set a large hillside with walnut for his grandchildren and saw the thrifty young planting killed by fire in one afternoon could hardly be expected to plant it over again. Fire is a deterrent to the planting of any species, and more especially of the slow-growing hardwoods. The slower the growth of a tree the longer its exposure to fire and other hazards before it can acquire any value.

Unable to afford adequate precautions against fire on separate, scattered parcels of forest, the individual or corporate owner must look to cooperative organization and governmental support for necessary fire protection. The basis for such organization and support dates back to 1911, when the Weeks Act authorized them. Federal cooperation with states and private forest owners in organized protection against fire was strengthened by the Clarke-McNary Law, as previously mentioned; and the provisions have been liberalized by amendments, notably in 1944 and 1949. However, as recently as 1961 more than 30 million acres of state and private forest land and 50 million acres of federal forest land remained without protection.

Organized fire protection is a sound public investment

Economic irony resides in the fact that the South, where wood grows fastest, has been most delinquent in combating fire. Considering that slash and longleaf are the only American pines yielding both pitch and wood and that they produce pulpwood, poles, and sawlogs in less time than Northern species, it is most unfortunate that their protection against fire has been neglected.

In parts of the Northeast, where forest services frequently outweigh the value of wood, fire prevention measures are rigidly enforced. The forest-conscious Yankees in Massachusetts mean business when they order that "No bonfire may be built without a permit from the District Fire Warden." If the clambake is rained out, which one anticipates in Massachusetts, another fire permit —and another bushel of clams—must be procured for a future *day and hour.* Conservative New England is *conservative* in more ways than one, and forest protection can be calculated to pay off. Who would render a financial statement on New England's autumn foliage? How much water power would be lost if the upper Connecticut Valley were burned over? How much tobacco would floods ruin in the Valley? How many tourists would cancel their reservations?

Consider the metropolitan nucleus farther south, and the *direct influence* of *remote* forest fires on it. For example, how thirsty would New York be if the Catskills burned over? How many would ski at Lake Placid if the vicinity looked like the Tillamook Burn? Indeed, organized fire protection defies appraisal, but it is probably worth more than twice what it costs anywhere. Common sense ought to nettle our delinquent areas to participate. Its demonstrated merit foreshadows its eventual extension to all our forest lands. Delay is wasteful and will surely occasion much regret. We cannot be content with anything short of complete coverage because neglect in one region penalizes another. A fire in Washington raises the price of houses in Ohio, a fire in Mississippi increases the cost of *The New York Times,* and a burn in Minnesota can shrink the catch of shrimp off Louisiana.

Controlled burning, prescribed by a competent forester, is a very versatile aid to forestry. Under certain conditions it is the **Controlled** quickest, cheapest means of clearing ground for sowing or plant- **burning** ing, removing litter that would prevent seeds from contacting the **aids** earth, and destroying noxious competitive growth. In trained **forestry** hands it can be a technique for *selective* forest reproduction at much less expense than by conventional methods.

Travelers to the "Deep South" would be somewhat less revolted by the numerous smokes in the woods if they knew that there, where destructive fire is most rampant, *constructive* burning is also exceptionally useful. Fire combats fungus on young pine seedlings, becoming a useful sanitation measure. Controlled burning of young growth may be used for sorting a mixture of conifers and hardwoods, killing the oaks and sparing the more resistant pines, a practical method of species selection.

Protective burning has several variations, all of them helpful in averting fire damage. They are a special version of the backfire, the last, desperate resort against a full-blown wildfire. "Once over lightly" causes no injury to longleaf a few inches in diameter, but the same trees, worked for turpentine years later, would be extremely susceptible to injury if pine straw, twigs, and dead grass were permitted to accumulate on the forest floor meanwhile. Thus, it is often wise to burn the debris every year or two to prevent fire with dangerous intensity. Burning also serves to maintain fire lanes and fire breaks where general burning is not advisable. Thus for many special purposes, fire can be employed to promote that which it usually threatens.

In harvesting the forest, men have been almost as indiscreet as with fire. Logging has left areas almost as devastated as if they had been burned. With heavy machinery and steel cables men have taken what they wanted and knocked down whatever stood

Fig. 9.6 *Slash pine plantation near Homerville, Georgia. The trees were planted during the spring of 1929 and thinned for pulpwood during the winter of 1941-42, when they averaged 7 to 10 inches d.b.h. Thinning yielded 52 cords from 40 acres, worth $7.00 per unit (1¼ cords) loaded on railway cars—thus paying for the planting as well as improving the stand for future crops. (Leland J. Prater, U.S.F.S. photo.)*

in the way. They have left rejected trees and parts of trees scattered about where they fell, like engraved invitations to fire; nor have they yet mended their ways entirely.

Logging need not be ruinous; in fact, it can be beneficial to the forest. Loggers who remove mature trees and culls without damaging the younger, healthy ones improve the forest incidental to its harvest. By taking out the trees that have stopped growing and by releasing the space to vigorous ones that can use it, they accelerate increment (growth of wood) by reducing competition. When a tree in a commercial forest shows little or no annual increment, it is wasteful to leave it standing, but a conservation of space, rain, sunshine, and soil to cut it down.

Logging
need not be
ruinous

A step further, and one arrives at *selective cutting* and *sustained-yield* management. The two phrases may be related—even synonymous—in practice, but not necessarily so. Each has a distinct meaning, and, independently or jointly, neither is as simple as one might suppose.

Selective cutting may entail "selection" on the basis of any one among several criteria, or an appropriate combination of them. It may be done for the purpose of thinning a stand so that the undisturbed trees can grow larger and more valuable (Fig. 9.6), or of removing diseased and decaying trees while they retain some usefulness and before they infect others. It may be done to remove weed trees, deformed trees, and trees with broad crowns (wolf trees) that take up space they cannot pay for. Such *selection* of a stand is aptly referred to as *sanitation* or *salvage* cutting; it is illustrated in Fig. 9.7. Chosen specimens are *not* cut; they are left to grow.

Selective
cutting
and sustained
yield

Selective cutting conventional style, as shown in Fig. 9.8, removes the choice, large trees and those making least growth, leaving the others to mature for a subsequent crop. In mixed stands, with trees of various sizes, selection can be extremely complicated, especially when culling for stand improvement and *harvesting* for maximum market value are accomplished in the same logging operation.

Selective cutting constitutes a form of perpetual *forest cropping* conducive to maximum, sustained-yield production under the most varied forest conditions and economic circumstances. Cutting a few trees per acre one year, a few the next, or several years later, one species or several as the mixture affords and the market demands, brings continual income without depleting the stand or selling at a disadvantage. Except where peculiarity of species or uniformity of stand, or both, favor another plan, selective cutting ensures optimum sustained yield and superior

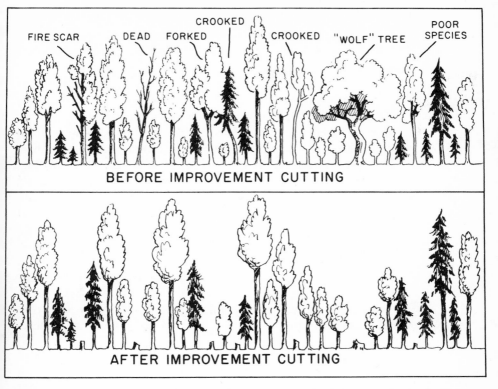

FIRE SCAR   DEAD   FORKED   CROOKED   CROOKED   "WOLF" TREE   POOR SPECIES

BEFORE IMPROVEMENT CUTTING

AFTER IMPROVEMENT CUTTING

Fig. 9.7 *A conservator would not overdo sanitation and release cutting. He would leave, here and there, a hollow tree for squirrels or raccoons and a dead snag for flickers or bluebirds. (After Farmers' Bulletin No. 1989, U.S.D.A.)*

Fig. 9.8 *Selective logging of Ponderosa pine in Oregon. Removal of mature trees gives younger ones the space they need for vigorous growth. (Ray N. Filloon, U.S.F.S. photo.)*

forest conservation. It is the only practice whereby one can take crop after crop of timber without deterioration of the forest environment and curtailment of multiple forest services.

However, nature and economics often indicate or dictate *clear cutting* of timber much as a Kansas farmer reaps wheat. Complete clearing of patches or strips, while it may be somewhat adverse to other forest functions, may show the best profit from forest products. Commercial logging as commonly done requires costly preparation for efficient felling, bucking, skidding, yarding, loading, and hauling. Anyone who assembles all the necessary machinery and gear for economical operation must have a "cut" of sufficiently large volume. In uniformly *large* stands, as of virgin Douglas fir in the West, the added cost of selective logging is not ordinarily justified because all the trees are mature. Any left standing would soon depreciate in value. Furthermore, Douglas fir fails to reproduce itself satisfactorily except in clearings. Block, or patch logging, as shown in Fig. 9.9 has proved advantageous. Clear cutting may under certain operating conditions be advisable also in uniform second growth, as of slash

Fig. 9.9 *Block or patch logging of uniformly ripe forest in the Pacific Northwest. Patches cut out will be sown by seed dispersed from blocks left standing. The land produces timber perpetually. (Unfortunately, Douglas fir may set viable seed only once in several years). See also Fig. 19.15. (American Forest Products Industries photo.)*

pine grown for pulpwood in the South. The Southern pines need sunshine for satisfactory restocking and give way to the more shade-tolerant oaks and other deciduous trees unless openings be large enough. A few seed trees per acre left uninjured by the loggers may repopulate an entire area as shown in Fig. 9.16 on page 229.

Where it is economically feasible, as in mixed farm woods or in high-grade mixed timber, selective cutting tree by tree is the best guarantee of sustained yield, but sustained-yield management need not be abandoned just because one must resort to clear cutting. A sort of crop rotation becomes the alternative. Theoretically, an owner of land that produces a merchantable crop of pulpwood in fifteen years can get a crop every year indefinitely if he divides his property into fifteen blocks and clear-cuts one block each year. By careful attention to reproduction, natural or artificial, the first block harvested should be ready to cut again in its turn, fifteen years later.

In practice several variations of management secure the objectives of sustained-yield forestry—continual cropping, perpetual restocking, maximum dollar yield, and minimum interference with protective values. The Norris-Doxey Act of 1937 provided for increased technical aid to farmers with forest-management problems, and in 1951 the law was expanded to include non-farm forest owners. Congress has constantly broadened the public sponsorship of forestry to ensure the nation a supply of wood.

Several states (fifteen in 1961) require by law several practices on privately owned forest lands to ensure their continuous and satisfactory productivity, with severe penalties for violation. The laws variously specify such details as minimum tree size that may be cut, number and size of seed trees to be left standing, disposal of slash, prescribed method of cutting (as strip harvest of spruce in the Northwest), and caution against damage to forest by logging operations. Some require a license or permit to operate; some provide for planning, supervision, or inspection of logging operations and management by a designated state agency.[26]

Farm-woodland conservation practices have been adopted by many thousands of farmers during recent years. By the end of 1959 the Agricultural Conservation Program had made cost-sharing payments for forestry on more than 4.5 million acres, including considerable area in every state. As much as 16 per cent of all ACP payments made in a state were for forestry practices.

Lumbermen have done worse with the crop they gather than with its growing. About twenty years ago less than a half of the saw timber cut served any useful purpose other than for fuel, and one-third of it was wasted completely. Almost half the waste was *slash*—the trees destroyed, and parts of trees abandoned, by loggers. The other half resulted from *primary manufacture, sawing,* and *pulping.*[27] Slash, slab, shavings, and sawdust, a million tons a year, were not to be sneezed at; but, until they could pay their way to market and give their handler his hire, they were "no good" and had no value. Their conversion to *economic* goods posed a knotty conservation problem; one only partially solved today. Approach to a solution has come through *integrated logging* and *integrated use* of the cut—logging for several species and grades of timber in one operation and supplying materials for a variety of purposes. When a logger cuts out of a mixed stand oak for a flooring plant and pine for a lumber mill he does integrated logging. When he takes from one oak tree a log for flooring, bolts for barrels, and shorter lengths for furniture parts he refines the integration. But he cannot operate that way unless he has access to a market for each quality and length he cuts; he logs for a living.

In like manner can the sawmill operator salvage materials when the opportunity affords. Given the market, he can convert slabs into dimension stock or parts for boxes and crates, and press shavings and sawdust into briquettes for fuel. The sawyer saws for a living and welcomes any opportunity to make a salable by-product of salvaged waste.

Substantial improvement has been made. By 1952 almost two-thirds of the timber cut for lumber was utilized; wasted residues of logging and milling had been reduced to 26 per cent of the total harvest.[28]

We could forbid loggers and sawyers to waste wood, but if we did compel them to salvage wastes that are not merchantable we might cause greater waste by restricting their operations; it is better conservation to use even half a ripe tree than to let the whole tree fall down and rot away. Complementary organization of primary forest industries has begun and will surely develop as the price of wood increases. By-products plants are becoming profitable adjuncts to permanent wood-using factories much as the recovery of sulfuric acid complements copper smelting, gas and volatile oils the coking of coal. Technical advice and public assistance can achieve much more than all attempts to *prohibit waste* by legal mandate. Sustained yield and integrated use are logical, economical partners. One implements the other, and both are gaining prominence. Liquidation cutting and one-product operations have made of themselves forest scavengers, and practical considerations are starving them to death. One-product forest industry parallels single cash-crop farming. Both systems destroy the base upon which they depend and cannot long endure. Integration is to forestry as diversification is to agriculture.

Taxation can be a potent instrument for conserving our forest resources, but we have not employed it skillfully. Certain states have literally taxed their forest right off the land by neglecting to adopt tax laws in support of deferred-yield forestry. A tax on standing timber compels the owner to cut enough of it to defray that tax. Where land under reforestation bears a tax assessment, the owner is almost forced to commence cutting as soon as the most vigorous trees attain minimum merchantable size. If *disparity* of levy distinguishes between commercial and noncommercial forest land, the commercial category is penalized for being productive. Taxation of standing timber can tax it right off the land. Many of our forest states actively encourage good forest management with favorable taxation.[29] *Tax exemption* for land under forest reproduction and *deferment of tax on standing timber until it is cut* (yield tax) are the measures most commonly applied. In 1961, eight states had exemption laws and fifteen had yield laws.[30]

The collection of a tax when timber is sold has proved difficult and costly, but when based on number rather than on volume of logs, it has brought benefits even beyond its basic purpose by inducing owners to grow mature timber. It has exposed many cases of timber "thieving," a particularly noxious form of larceny that hinders forestry in many places.

Unless the tax system favors him, the ordinary private owner cannot hold on to cutover while it restocks. He surrenders title to the state by tax delinquency. In due time an enterprising scavenger with a portable sawmill redeems the land by paying the back taxes (often partially remitted), cuts it over as thoroughly and quickly as he can, and lets it revert to the state again. The vicious circle continues, serving badly both private and public interests, until such time as the state either assists the private owner by a liberal tax policy or retains title to the land indefinitely. Tax revision can stop the scourge of recurrent tax reversion.

To a country boy, grown and far from home, the clang of a cowbell brings acute nostalgia. He recalls how sweet was its music when he, all alone in the dark, found the cows at the far end of the woods. But cowbells do not harmonize with forestry as they do with boyhood recollections. The bell-cow with her following gets little grass for much roaming, and, by passive "brute" force, slowly thins the green canopy above her.

Intelligent
taxation
encourages
forest
conservation

Cowbells
do not
harmonize
with forestry

Fig. 9.10 *Healthy, ungrazed oak-hickory woodlot in Illinois. The floor is a living reservoir for water, but very poor pasture. A growing generation of trees will replace the old ones. (B. S. Meyer, U.S.F.S. photo.)*

Fig. 9.11 *Overgrazed hardwoods in North Carolina. Understory and duff have been destroyed by the hooves of animals. The result is neither pasture nor forest. Cattle and trees are poor partners. (E. A. Johnson, U.S.F.S. photo.)*

Grazing and forestry are two primary land uses much better divorced than combined. When they are mixed the forest usually suffers. Since half of our forests are on farms, and most farm woods are grazed much more severely than is good for them, the grazing problem looms large in forest conservation. Strictly man made, the problem is readily soluble by man's own adjustment of land use. Of course, the carefully regulated grazing in our National Forests is on open areas within the forest rather than among the trees.

Large herds or flocks in the forest trample the duff and litter to pieces, pack the soil, destroy young growth, and impair conditions generally (compare Figs. 9.10 and 9.11). They restrict or eliminate altogether all the normal services of forest, such as water storage, soil defense, wildlife habitat, and wood production. Only in special situations is their presence beneficial. They can turn the tide of battle where pine seedlings wage a losing fight with oaks (browsing goats are especially efficient). Of course, they can remove the fire hazard by wearing the forest floor clean and hard, but such conditions are almost as bad as the consequences of burning.

As a general rule, the farmer who would grow timber should *fence livestock out,* and not in. If he wishes some shade for his animals, let him fence into his barnyard or pasture a part of his woodland and cross that part off his forestry ledger. If he be a Southerner concerned with pine growing he may need a rifle to drive off rooting razorback marauders that kill young seedlings and lay the soil open to erosion. However, wild hogs are not pasture animals in the normal sense. Figure 9.3 indicates that farmers have begun to distinguish between pasture and forest.

Two species of Southern pine—longleaf and slash—play a dual role in American forestry, yielding a major portion of our pulpwood crop and almost all of our naval stores. Popularly known as the pitch pines, they are the species worked for turpentine. In the warm southerly climate, where men take life "tolerably easy," the trees have a longer growing season and may produce wood at more than twice the rate of their Northern cousins.

Modern turpentining practices minimize forest damage

The history of turpentining carries the same stigma of waste and destruction that has characterized our exploitation of forests for lumber and timbers. The old methods of tapping were "extractive." Great wounds were cut into the trees, much of the resin was left on the trunk or in the "box" gouged into the base of the tree to catch it, fire ignited the bleeding wound and burned it deeper, and bugs and decay completed the mayhem. Trees tapped for gum resin lost their value as saw timber, because the

choice log, the bottom one, was ruined for lumber. Young trees
were bled to death, and many stout patriarchs died of torture.

When the original stands had disappeared it became necessary
to use a new device for catching the resin; the second-growth
trees were too small in diameter to permit cutting out an adequate "box." Thus came one step toward conservational turpentining—gutters and cups were attached to the tree. By experiment and demonstration the "streak"—the diagonal wound—has
been reduced gradually to a fraction of its original depth and
width. Acid applied after shallow (bark) chipping stimulates gum
flow so one streak lasts two weeks instead of one, thus producing
as much and as long from half as high a "face" (the entire
chipped area on one side of a tree). By narrow streaking, by beginning the face low on the trunk, and by working only one face

Fig. 9.12 *High naval stores face on longleaf pine (Florida, 1930). Working to such
height on a tree ruined the butt log and was uneconomical from the standpoint of gum
production. (F. Hayward, U.S.F.S. photo.)*

Fig. 9.13 *Modern turpentining practice. Working low, short faces, as shown here on
longleaf and slash pines in Georgia, produces gum more economically, while the tapped
trees also grow into valuable timber. (American Forest Products Industries photo.)*

per tree instead of two, timber values are not seriously curtailed and growth losses are small relative to gum yield. (Compare Figs. 9.12 and 9.13.)

Improvement of gathering and distillation has greatly reduced waste. Gum spirits of turpentine and gum rosin have become permanent crops in our southeastern states, from North Carolina to Texas. The industry reached its peak in 1908 and declined steadily until 1960. It was expected to die, but the regrowth of the pitch pines has exceeded all expectations. As if in anticipation of its demise, there began in 1910 the wood–naval-stores industry, which extracts the pitch from old stumps, a unique form of salvage. More recently, technology made possible the recovery of spirits from the liquor discharged by pulpmills using the sulfate process, which is a form of salvage even more gratifying because it reduces water pollution. Production of sulfate turpentine began in 1928; production of tall oil rosin began in 1949.[31]

In recent years more than one-half of the turpentine produced has been of the sulphate variety, and almost two-thirds of the rosin produced has been distilled from old pine stumps. In 1961 only about one-fourth of both turpentine and rosin production came from living trees.[32] The use of turpentine as paint and varnish vehicle (thinner) has declined as synthetic formulations have been developed, but its use in industrial chemicals is increasing. More than one-third of the rosin is used as a size in the manufacture of paper; almost another third goes into chemicals and pharmaceuticals (mostly adhesive tape); most of the remainder goes into paints, rubber, chewing gum, and printing inks.[33] Minute quantities make music or improve the game of baseball. A complex "tall oil" obtained from stump wood has special uses in *conserving* materials, particularly in the flotation process for concentrating minerals.[34]

The Federal Naval Stores Conservation Program initiated in 1936 encourages good practices in the production of gum naval stores (from trees). In 1961, 5,126 producers worked about 38 million faces (three laborers can handle a "crop" of 10,000 faces). In 1959 about 2,500 producers qualified for ACP payments by applying good forestry in the turpentine woods.

Georgia produces about 82 per cent of the entire American gum crop; Florida ranks second, then Alabama, Mississippi, Louisiana, and South Carolina, in that order. "Turpentining" is also done in southern North Carolina and southeastern Texas. Fourteen of the twenty gum-processing plants operative in 1961 were in Georgia.

In 1960 American production of naval stores from all three sources was 2 million drums of rosin (520 lb net) and 605,000 barrels of turpentine (50 gals). Prices have been erratic, but future demands, both domestic and foreign, will probably rise substantially and productive rank of the sources will change.

Already declining, the wood-distillation industry will end when available stumps have been processed. In 1961 about 73 million tons of longleaf and slash stump wood remained, almost two-thirds of it in Florida and Georgia. (More than half the stump wood processed in 1960 came from Florida.) The West had some 24 million tons of ponderosa stumps, more than one-half of them in Oregon. Much of this stump wood could be exploited without serious injury to growing timber. Sulfate–naval-stores production, related directly to the pulping of resinous woods, will expand tremendously. (About 80 to 90 pounds of tall oil are recovered per ton of sulfate pulp.)[35] Production of gum, the oleoresin taken from living trees, could be seven times as great as it was in 1960 (622,000 bbls). About 160 million saw-timber–size longleaf and slash pines remained unworked in 1960. Gum-processing plants have been operating at less than one-half of total capacity.[36] Efficiency could be greatly improved if warranted by market demand. Integration of timber and gum production might be expanded tremendously. Boiled down to a thick tar, the gum from pines was originally used to preserve ropes and to caulk the seams of ships. Hence the term *naval stores*. The United States remains the world's leading producer and exporter of naval stores, accounting for almost one-half the totals.

Insects, diseases, parasites: the most destructive forest enemies

Up to this point we have dealt with problems of forest conservation largely man made, and therefore nicely within our province to correct or arrest. We venture now into a brief exposition on a major forestry problem essentially natural in origin, and less amenable to specific correction. *Insects and diseases take a much heavier toll than forest fires,* but while we have substantially reduced fire loss and may almost eliminate it, we have made only limited gains against pests and cannot be confident of thwarting their future inroads. The myriads of bugs, bacteria, and fungi that infest his realm try the forester's mettle much as the trace elements in soils try the agronomist's. Minute forms of life can steal us blind in the forest before we see them, and when their work becomes apparent it is often too late to apply effective countermeasures. They are the *most insidious and elusive* and the *most destructive* enemies of our forests. Their rank among other destructive agents may be seen in Fig. 9.14.

Beetle, caterpillar, worm, or sawfly—a single species of insect

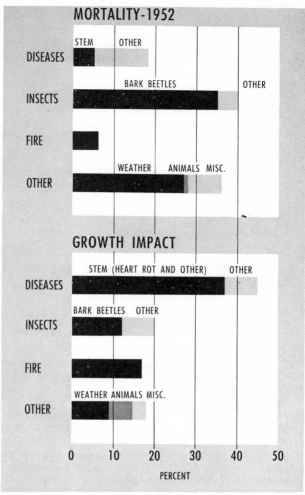

MORTALITY AND GROWTH IMPACT ON SAWTIMBER IN THE UNITED STATES

MORTALITY-1952

DISEASES — STEM | OTHER

INSECTS — BARK BEETLES | OTHER

FIRE

OTHER — WEATHER | ANIMALS MISC.

GROWTH IMPACT

DISEASES — STEM (HEART ROT AND OTHER) | OTHER

INSECTS — BARK BEETLES | OTHER

FIRE

OTHER — WEATHER ANIMALS MISC.

0   10   20   30   40   50

PERCENT

includes Coastal Alaska

Fig. 9.14 *Pest control has lagged behind fire prevention. (From "Timber Resources for America's Future.")*

on a rampage has damaged seriously, and even killed outright, tremendous stands of choice timber. The spruce budworm in the North, the Englemann spruce beetle in the Rocky Mountains, the Douglas-fir tussock moth in the West, and many other infamous "bugs" have, time and again, made the most ruthless logging operation look like a Sunday-school picnic.

Wilts, blights, rots, galls, cankers, and other infections are more insidious than the insects and equally ruthless. Traveling by wind or water, carried by insects, birds, and other forest creatures (even by man himself), they are extremely difficult to

contain and no easier to exterminate. The chestnut blight spread
the length of our Eastern hardwood region from New England
to the southern Appalachians, killing virtually every American
chestnut tree. We were unable to check it. The oak wilt, first detected near the northwestern edge of the central hardwoods
region, threatens the life of a choice hardwood family. Many
fungi are essential to the health of the forest, and we should
protect them. How shall we destroy the bad ones without also
destroying the good ones?

Various parasites cause serious forest damage by weakening
and deforming their host trees and exposing them to more dangerous infestation and infection. Perhaps the worst parasite is
the dwarf mistletoe (five species), which does great damage to our
Western conifers, more especially in ponderosa pine of the southern Rockies.

Did we intimate that we, the people, have little to do with the
incidence of forest pests? We spoke too glibly. Several tree killers
have been brought to America from overseas, among them the
chestnut blight, which all but wiped out one of our most durable
and versatile hardwoods, the Dutch-elm disease, which threatens
several species with a similar fate, and the white-pine blister rust,
which jeopardizes a chosen species in Eastern forest reproduction.
Through forest exploitation we have often upset the natural balance that held the pests in check. By poor housekeeping we have
bred pestilence and by bruising and burning we have exposed the
trees to attack. We have violated the communal organization of
forests and may stand to pay dearly for the offense.

Our campaign against forest pests follows two lines of action:
direct (frontal) attack to stop or prevent an epidemic; the enlistment of natural forces (grand strategy) to oppose any threat of
violence. The latter technique depends mainly upon *management*
that maintains natural forest conditions and healthy, vigorous
growth. It is the forester's "cold war," the safe, sure way to victory
without shooting. The former technique involves armed combat
to subdue a hostile enemy; DDT sprayed from an airplane is the
standard tactic. But in a "hot war" we cannot always kill the
enemy without also striking our own "guerrillas" and potential
collaborators. Let no one but a trained forest pathologist or
entomologist declare this kind of war and let him do so only as
a last resort. As with any war, victory may be more apparent than
real.

To maintain reasonable security against the ravages of insects
and diseases we need public enlightenment and area organization much as for fire protection. Just as with fire, detection and

prevention are better than costly suppression, and every forest area is a potential threat to others in the neighborhood. Against either fire or epidemic, cooperation is essential and should be inclusive. But the novice cannot spot an impending disease as he can a fire; that is for the trained scientist. Continuous research, systematic survey, and improved silvicultural practice are urgent needs. The Forest Pest Control Act passed by Congress in 1947 authorized necessary surveys in both public and private forests. It made forest pest control, officially, the national problem that it is. As later implemented, that act provides for an annual pest survey in order that epidemics may be detected before they reach disastrous proportions. Under this law and the Lea Act of 1940 the Forest Service cooperates in pest control on sizable state and private forest properties. Several states require private landowners to control forest pests much as they are required to combat weeds. In event of serious threat they may get state or federal aid in suppressing it.

Wild denizens of the forest perform acts both beneficent and injurious to the vegetation that feeds and shelters them. Terrestrial and arboreal creatures—feathered, furred, or hooved—disperse seeds as if in payment for those they eat, but in their regular round of activity they also carry diseases from one benefactor to another. Birds that sow cherry pits miles from the tree may carry diseases even greater distances. Squirrels plant nuts but also eat buds and spread fungi. Mourning doves destroy many noxious seeds but also eat the first, tender shoots from pine seeds. Rabbits and other bark eaters injure or kill young saplings by girdling them. Deer and other browsing animals (leaf and twig eaters) can be so destructive of young hardwoods as to eradicate them. Mice and other seed-eating rodents can be a grave handicap to reforestation by seed sowing. In actual cases reproduction of certain conifers by sowing has succeeded only when poison was sown beforehand to decimate the rodents.

Forest wildlife performs both constructive and destructive functions

One cannot review even casually the contradictions in animal behavior without pondering the ruling force of nature's balance and asking himself whether man, the superior species, is not most frustrated by his own failure to conform. A case in point is artificial sowing and planting, where nature, given the initiative, would do the work free of charge.[37] Had men more fully comprehended that fact during the initial stripping of our forests and made only moderate provision for its normal operation, reforestation would have been spontaneous and our present forest situation would be much more favorable. Where forest once stood it would have risen again, quite promptly, had Paul Bunyan and

Cooperation with nature reproduces forest better than sowing or planting

his breed been content to chop somewhat smaller holes in the mantle or at least left a few more scattered remnants. Where forests have once prevailed they would return without our solicitation—quickly to sites unimpaired and slowly to places from which, in our destructive exploitation, we caused the soil or its substance to escape. In the East, North, and South the deed was done before we knew the error of our ways. We learned in time, however, to save seed blocks or strips (seed-producing trees) in parts of the virgin forest in the West, and thus secure natural restocking of intervening clear-cut areas. Figure 9.15 shows the seed-block system in operation. We also discovered that Southern pines will quickly propagate, given the opportunity (Fig. 9.16).

Natural reproduction is by far the cheapest means of reforestation. With selective cuttings, reproduction takes place continuously even under very light cropping and requires no special attention if the grower will be content with a future preponderance of shade-tolerant trees (broadleafed species, mainly). If he wishes to retain certain sun-loving conifers, either in pure or mixed stands, he must so manage the present forest that adequate openings admit sunshine to the floor. Excepting a few, such as hemlock, conifers are intolerant of shade, requiring more or less direct sunshine for healthy development. Unfortunately the shade-tolerant species are not generally discouraged by abundant sunshine, and being more versatile, they often tend to overwhelm the more sensitive needle-leafed species where the two types are mixed. To secure coniferous reproduction from such admixture may entail special measures against hardwood sprouts. Goats have been employed, but selective toxic sprays are likely to be the best answer. In pure coniferous stands where clear cutting and *seed blocks* are advisable, suitable ground conditions may be the main reproduction problem demanding attention. The tiny, featherweight seeds must be given access to the soil. Very often enough surface is laid bare by logging operations, but some kind of mechanical stirring, or burning, may also be necessary. Volunteer reproduction for sustained yield under clear cutting is best ensured by systematic logging of alternate checkerboard "blocks" (Fig. 9.9), or parallel "strips." The patchwork system for quick, natural restocking, while most economical and profitable, is also nicely compatible with protective forest functions.

Where for any reason natural reproduction fails, the timber grower has a choice between the direct sowing of seed and the planting of nursery-grown seedlings. In large operations successful reproduction has been accomplished by seeding from an airplane, which is much cheaper than planting but also less cer-

Fig. 9.15 Seed block left standing when a mature, even-aged forest was logged scientifically in the Pacific Northwest. On high ground, which ensures maximum seed dispersal, individual trees would be subject to wind-throw. (Courtesy West Coast Lumbermen's Association.)

Fig. 9.16 Natural reproduction of slash pine, the prolific regenerator of southern forests. A few seed trees per acre produced a plentitude of seeds. Self-sowing by longleaf pine has been less spectacular because it produces good seeds only infrequently. (L. J. Prater, U.S.F.S. photo.)

tain to produce a suitable stand. The development of tree-planting machines made possible economical planting on large properties, just where planting was most delinquent. Mechanical tree
planting has become a custom business much as grain threshing
used to be. Such planting has transformed many ghastly cutover
areas, notably in the Upper Lakes region and the South.

Meanwhile, many large wood users, such as lumber and paper
companies, have established nurseries to supplement those maintained publicly, in order that small, private forest owners might
have ample planting stock at very little, if any, cost. This has
been one of the most reassuring developments in American
forestry, its intrinsic value probably surpassed by its promotion
of desirable social attitudes. Tree planting has made America
forestry conscious, because a planted area is the most obvious
evidence of forestry, even to the casual tourist who drives by it
smoking a cigar. The planter was probably more firmly impressed
by aches in his back and blisters in his hands. The diagram
series in Fig. 9.17 shows how he might have done the job.

By the end of 1961, we had 20,133,000 acres of planted forest,
most of it on farms and on other private properties. Accelerated
by the Soil Bank program, the annual tree-planting rate exceeded
2 billion seedlings (about 2 million acres) in both 1959 and 1960.
Most of this planting was done by hand, and most of the trees
are conifers native to the areas. True, many plantings are of poor
quality, on worn-out, or eroded, soil, on sand so deep or rock
so bare that the hardiest species cannot produce a timber crop of
high quality. But most of them occupy land otherwise wasted,
saving soil and water as they grow into useful, serviceable forest.

Silviculture, the science and practice of growing trees as a
crop, will probably be an everyday word in American conversa-
tion before our grandchildren manage our affairs and formulate
our policies. All the planting and management to date are a mere
beginning compared with what can be done under intensive silvicultural practices. Application of genetics research bids fair to
double the productivity of trees. Tree farming has barely begun
in America; our forestry remains largely haphazard and half-
hearted. We are inclined to plant trees where nothing else will
grow, ignoring the fact that many species demand comparatively
good soil for satisfactory development, that many areas lack even
the meager substance to keep alive those species least exacting.

But, on the other hand, we hear much talk about the wisdom
of soil and site selection, optimum spacing, plant breeding and
selection, planting season, disinfection and immunization, cultivation, pruning, and soil fertilization. The tree-farm movement may

**Intensive
silviculture
may gain
greater
prominence
in the
American scene**

TREE PLANTING

KEEP THE ROOTS OF YOUNG TREES MOIST.

① DRIVE MATTOCK INTO GROUND AND OPEN SLIT BY RAISING HANDLE.

② PULL MATTOCK BACK TO OPEN SLIT. INSERT TREE TO COLLAR OR ORIGINAL GROUND LEVEL.

③ HOLD TREE IN A VERTICAL POSITION; THEN CLOSE SLIT WITH MATTOCK.

④ USE HEEL OR BALL OF FOOT TO TAMP GROUND FIRMLY, REMOVING ALL AIR POCKETS.

SPOT METHOD
WHERE SOD IS HEAVY, REMOVE 18" SQUARE BEFORE PLANTING.

TRENCH METHOD
USED WHERE SOIL IS VERY FIRM.

CUTTINGS

MAKE SLIT WITH A SPADE OR STICK (A). ALMOST OR ENTIRELY BURY CUTTING AT A SLIGHT SLANT AND TAMP SOIL FIRMLY (B).

Fig. 9.17 *Commercial tree planting may not always be economical, but in many situations planting by hand is the best means of reforestation. Supervised tree planting by school children or college students should be more productive of future conservators than of timber.*

be prophetic of genuine timber cropping in the future. In the offing one can visualize turpentine orchards for pitch and lumber, walnut groves for nuts, veneer, and gunstocks, "fields" of pine for pulp—grown and harvested like wheat, corn, or oats. And one may hope that there will be those sufficiently visionary and unselfish to plant acorns, so that someone in the twenty-first century may sell white oaks for several hundred dollars apiece. Even now a good, big one on a northerly exposure and reasonably near a market may be worth more than $100.

Economic and technologic progress advance forest *conservation by preservative treatment* of wood to increase its versatility and to extend its useful life. Established at Madison, Wisconsin in 1910, our Forest Products Laboratory is now the largest institution in the world for the study of wood and its uses. Investigations at Madison, and elsewhere, have brought to light amazing discoveries, and have perfected, among many others, techniques for increasing the durability of timber products. Preservative treatment triples the life of a railroad tie and does about as well for a telephone pole. Of the estimated 230 million wooden fence posts set in the United States each year the life of some is multiplied as much as ten times after preservative treatment. Most of these are dipped right on the farms where they are used.

Wood preservatives might better be called *conservatives*

Creosote, the old stand-by, and pentachlorophenol are the leading preserving materials, used on 87 per cent of the wood treated in 1961. The latter, being clean and odorless after application, and permitting painting of the treated wood, has the advantage over creosote of being suitable for interior use. Both are most effective when forced into the wood under pressure; pressure treatment accounts for more than 90 per cent of the total.[38]

More than 380 wood-preserving plants operate in the United States, with most of them in the Southeast. One such treating plant is pictured in Fig. 9.18. Paul Bunyan would surely have swallowed his bale of tobacco had he been told that a fence post of pine might be made to last thirty years, challenging white oak, chestnut, or black locust for endurance.

In 1961 wood-preserving plants pressure treated almost 5.5 million poles, 80 per cent of them Southern pine, 17.2 million crossties (half of them oak and almost a third of them from other hardwoods, 96 per cent of them sawn), and 24 million fence posts (87 per cent of them Southern pine). The plants also treated 518 million board feet of lumber and timbers and gave fire-retardant treatment to about 12 million board feet. Total volume of wood treated by the wood-preservation industry in 1961 was about 215.4 million cubic feet.[39]

Fig. 9.18 *Preservation is an important form of wood conservation. These tramloads of ties, poles, and posts are going into pressure cylinders for impregnation with hot creosote at a Charleston, South Carolina plant. (Courtesy the Koppers Company, Inc.)*

Through numerous public agencies and private organizations forestry advice and assistance are available to everyone. Our schools and other social institutions, already actively assisting, can do much more to conserve our forest resources. If every school child could be privileged to plant one forest tree, our forest problems might dissipate in a generation. With no other natural resource does our entire citizenry come into such direct, conscious contact as it does with the forest, and to no other natural resource is public interest and responsibility more vital. Let the public be adequately informed of the contributions forests make to our individual and national well-being, and the forests will prosper. Unless we be fools, we shall never be short of wood. Our forest lands have such potential productivity that, should trade relations permit, we might one day export even paper pulp and newsprint instead of importing them.

Through conservation we can have all the wood we need

10

Conservation Patterns on the Land

drainage divisions and land management accordant with land capability set the pattern for conservation

**The land
is our base
of operations**

All resources are attached or related to the land. The soils, water, and vegetation introduced in the preceding chapters are the crucial attributes of land. By their adequacy or paucity they influence the usefulness of land for various purposes. On the other hand, the conservation of soils and water depends more upon the use of the land than upon any direct manipulation of the soil or of water itself. From the land, its soils, and its waters come most, if not all, of our biotic resources.

The land provides the surface space necessary to exploit and process resources, including the minerals brought up from below. As container and producer of resources, land holds resource status in its own right; but more important than that, it is the frame of reference for understanding and conserving the other resources. It is the base from which the conservator must work. It is the map on which we plan the strategy of conservation. It is our maneuver area for isolating, attacking, and solving a wide variety of conservation problems.

**Land use
sets
the pattern
for conservation**

The apportionment of a land area among particular kinds of use may actually be a most important conservation measure, but let us regard it rather as a prelude, or preliminary, to the specific treatment of resources that pertain to that land. Let us not consider the types and arrangement of land use an end in themselves,

234

but merely an adjustable pattern into which we fit the appropriate conservation measures. This idea should be borne in mind as the reader progresses through the following chapters, because they proceed on the assumption that land management has a further end in view. He should be aware that soil conservation pertains mainly to cultivated land, that good forestry conserves soil, water, and wildlife incidentally, that reseeding and management does the same for the dry grasslands, and that areas preserved as wilderness are immune to the ordinary ills that trouble us elsewhere.

Whether for the nation as a whole or for an individual farm, the appropriate allocation of space (land) to various uses is a prerequisite to conservation. It is to the conservator as fire protection is to the forester. Unless it be accomplished first, all other measures may come to naught. Only after use-allocation has been made wisely and well can the success of other applications be fully realized. The entity with which we must deal first in conservation is *land*—soil, or water, or anything else takes its place as part of the picture of land use.

In a preceding chapter it was suggested that all *terra firma* is not soil covered, that the terms *land* and *soil* are far from synonymous. There is much land without any true soil upon it, much that has never had soil, and much on which soil may never develop. When one considers the spread of lands naturally devoid of soil and the extent of others from which the soil has been lost he might become more concerned about land than soil. Certainly land occupies more space, but without soil it is generally neither highly productive nor readily improved. Bread comes from soil, not from land devoid of soil; without bread, who would there be to fret about wasting the land barren of soil?

There is much land without soil

Soilless areas are of several different kinds, ranging in composition from the thick organic deposits accumulated in bogs and marshes to the deep, sterile sands of old beaches and dunes. Soil surveyors recognize thirty-four types of land which must be mapped without any soil designation.[1] Certain mucklands can be made highly productive by drainage and specific treatment. From many of them come superior truck crops, especially roots, tubers, and bulbs that need soft earth in which to grow.

The sands, on the other hand, are not only naturally unproductive but lack the capacity for retaining materials that might be applied to make them productive. Some sand areas have more value for glass manufacture or military maneuver than for plant growth. Locally they serve a useful purpose as recharge areas for groundwater.

Where the country rock sticks out of the ground there is, obviously, no soil; and fragmentation, such as in "shoe-peg" shale, does not make it much less barren than if it were solid. The disintegrated material will admit rain and roots and may sustain a forest cover though true soil be lacking. Trees like the cedar, with extensive lateral roots to support them, take hold where flat-rock strata lie too near the surface to permit normal soil development and where inclined strata crop out at intervals with soil pockets between them.

Where loose stone blocks or boulders occupy the ground there is no soil in the ordinary sense, and unless the mantle be completely stabilized the most tenacious plant species survive with difficulty.

Areas of stones or exposed rock have been classified in American soils literature as *stony land* and *rock land* respectively. The sterile, sandy areas have been mapped as *undifferentiated sands and gravels,* without soil designation. The literature has dealt more kindly with the more deserving bog and marsh areas, referring to them variously as *organic soils, muck,* or *peat.* In the arid West are extensive areas from which winds and torrential rains strip off mineral materials before any soil can form in them. Such bare areas have been described as *badlands.* Aridity prohibits vegetation from covering their nakedness. These and other soilless land types compose a tremendous aggregate area.

The land itself holds resource status

Whichever nomenclature one prefers, he should appreciate that, although good land has soil on it, land without soil can also be useful. *Land, per se, holds resource status!* For land that lacks soil, conservation becomes largely a matter of wisely planned, limited utilization. The presence of soil broadens the choice of land use and increases the economic feasibility of other conservation measures. So much has been said about *soil* conservation and so little about *land* conservation that the latter might appear to be neglected. However, neglect has been more apparent than real. It has been assumed that most of our land has some trace of soil upon it and that soil and land conservation are too closely allied for separate treatment. The assumption has been confusing. Land and soil may be considered together in planning the use of an area, but each must be treated separately for good management and conservation.

The primary land uses occupy most of the space

Crops, pasture, and forest occupy so much of our land and yield so much of its produce that they have come to be known as the *primary* land uses. Those three surface adaptations contribute most of our food supply and the greatest variety of our raw materials. Without this *primary* triumvirate on the land all our dig-

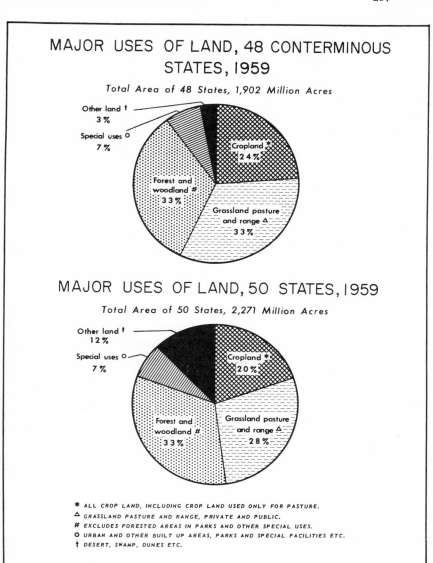

MAJOR USES OF LAND, 48 CONTERMINOUS
STATES, 1959

Total Area of 48 States, 1,902 Million Acres

Other land † 3%

Special uses ○ 7%

Cropland * 24%

Forest and woodland # 33%

Grassland pasture and range △ 33%

MAJOR USES OF LAND, 50 STATES, 1959

Total Area of 50 States, 2,271 Million Acres

Other land † 12%

Special uses ○ 7%

Cropland * 20%

Forest and woodland # 33%

Grassland pasture and range △ 28%

* ALL CROP LAND, INCLUDING CROP LAND USED ONLY FOR PASTURE.
△ GRASSLAND PASTURE AND RANGE, PRIVATE AND PUBLIC.
\# EXCLUDES FORESTED AREAS IN PARKS AND OTHER SPECIAL USES.
○ URBAN AND OTHER BUILT UP AREAS, PARKS AND SPECIAL FACILITIES ETC.
† DESERT, SWAMP, DUNES ETC.

Fig. 10.1 *The percentages are subject to changes, but only gradually. These graphs represent the economy of the country as a whole. (U.S.D.A. graphs)*

ging in the earth for minerals and all our fishing in the sea would come to naught. The three are, indeed, primary—fundamental! The proportionate space each occupies in the United States may be learned from Fig. 10.1; their regional importance from Fig. 10.2.

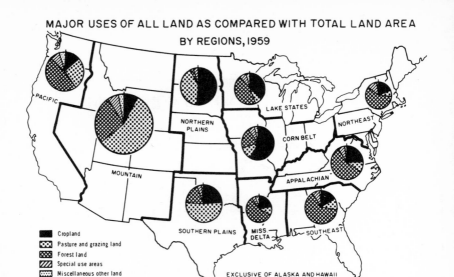

Fig. 10.2 *Resources and interests of one area may be quite different from those of another. Regional land economy becomes a prominent factor in regional planning and conservation. (U.S.D.A. map.)*

The magnitude and health of our agricultural, pastoral, and forestry industries gauge the state of the Union as a whole and dominate the economy of almost every section of America. The crop/pasture/forest ratio greatly influences the source of livelihood, mode of living, and even the politics of states and regions. Of course, it determines also the comparative regional interest in the various resources and their conservation (Fig. 10.3). One should not expect a sheepman in Wyoming to be much concerned about forestry, nor a logger in Idaho to worry about water and forage for sheep. Neither should one suggest that a wheat farmer on the black Dakota plains can apply the same soil conserving measures as a hog farmer in Iowa or a dairyman in Wisconsin. But one can hope that a furrier in Manhattan who likes butter and biscuits, lamb chops and pork roast, and his kitchen finished in ponderosa pine appreciates that he enjoys the fruits of the primary land uses. Our urban population was almost 70 per cent of the total in 1960, according to the current definition of "urban" used in the census. In the decade 1950-1960 the urban population increased more than 29 per cent while the rural decreased 0.8 per cent.[2] It is therefore important that the city dwellers know where and how their bread is buttered. They need reminding that farmers, ranchers, and lumbermen are entrusted with the permanent source of their material well-being— our productive land.

Special cultural developments constitute a fourth major category of surface land use, covering approximately 7 per cent of

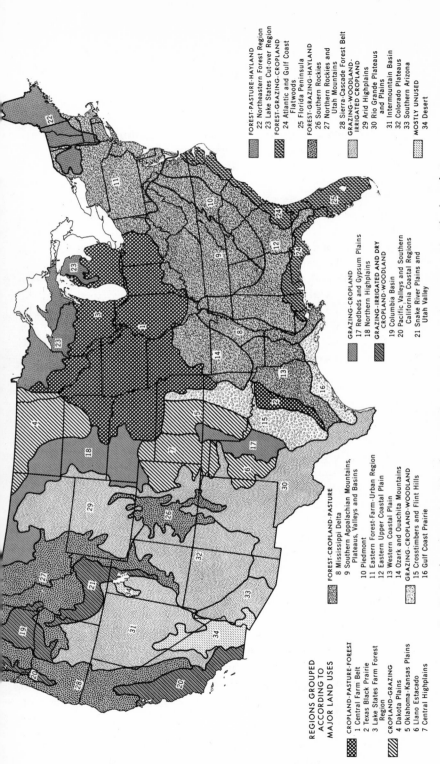

REGIONS GROUPED ACCORDING TO MAJOR LAND USES

CROPLAND-PASTURE-FOREST
1 Central Farm Belt
2 Texas Black Prairie
3 Lake States Farm Forest Region

CROPLAND-GRAZING
4 Dakota Plains
5 Oklahoma-Kansas Plains
6 Llano Estacado
7 Central Highplains

FOREST-CROPLAND-PASTURE
8 Mississippi Delta
9 Southern Appalachian Mountains, Plateaus, Valleys and Basins
10 Piedmont
11 Eastern Forest-Farm-Urban Region
12 Eastern Upper Coastal Plain
13 Western Coastal Plain
14 Ozark and Ouachita Mountains

GRAZING-CROPLAND-WOODLAND
15 Crosstimbers and Flint Hills
16 Gulf Coast Prairie

GRAZING-CROPLAND
17 Redbeds and Gypsum Plains
18 Northern Highplains

GRAZING-IRRIGATED AND DRY CROPLAND-WOODLAND
19 Columbia Basin
20 Pacific Valleys and Southern California Coastal Regions
21 Snake River Plains and Utah Valley

FOREST-PASTURE-HAYLAND
22 Northeastern Forest Region
23 Lake States Cut-over Region

FOREST-GRAZING-CROPLAND
24 Atlantic and Gulf Coast Flatwoods
25 Florida Peninsula

FOREST-GRAZING-HAYLAND
26 Southern Rockies
27 Northern Rockies and Utah Mountains
28 Sierra-Cascade Forest Belt

GRAZING-WOODLAND-IRRIGATED CROPLAND
29 Arid Highplains
30 Rio Grande Plateaus and Plains
31 Intermountain Basin
32 Colorado Plateaus
33 Southern Arizona

MOSTLY UNUSED
34 Desert

Fig. 10.3 *The geography of land use sets the national pattern for conservation. The boundaries on this map are not static, but subject to deliberate change. They tend to coincide with those in Fig. 10.11. (U.S.D.A. map.)*

our total land.[3] They compose a long list of divers social and economic demands for space, all of which are indispensable to our culture. Some are highly productive of material wealth, while others are creative of less tangible values; however, none contrives to bring forth any direct fruit from the land it occupies. All buildings, roads, streets, railways, communication and transmission lines, parks and playgrounds, airports and flying fields, dams and reservoirs, oil wells and tank farms, military reservations, mines and quarries, race tracks and cemeteries are cultural land uses. They are expanding constantly, often usurping space highly prized for primary production. It is estimated that special land uses will continue to divert from agriculture about 1 million additional acres annually until 1975 for use as sites on which to build factories, shopping centers, homes, roads, airports, institutional facilities, etc.[4]

Many special uses are only temporary, destined to shift in the course of a few years, but they leave scars that heal slowly. The recovery of abandoned building sites, roadbeds and railbeds, mined areas, or even burial grounds for productive use affords better opportunity to conserve land than many a project of reclamation by drainage. Unfortunately, recovery is often a bigger task than the original conversion of a field to a special use, because soil removed, or mutilated, incidental to construction work is not so easily replaced.

The four great categories of land utilization, and the numerous classes of use within each, compete for the space they occupy—the most discriminate laying strongest claim to the land. Among the primary uses, cultivated crops take first choice, pasture takes second, and forest retires to areas poorly suited to either of the other two. Ordinarily, a special use prevails against any one of the primary ones because it attaches a higher value per areal unit either in terms of earning power or in special desirability. The most intensive cropping about a city retreats farther into the country with every onslaught of subdivision and suburban expansion. Roses, cows, or asparagus tips cannot resist filling stations, drive-ins, and tourist courts.

For special purposes—such as residential, commercial, or industrial use—the location and form of the land become criteria of valuation. Inherent fertility loses its significance as a measure of quality; the space becomes "real estate," and it yields artificial dividends instead of genuine produce. Special cultural uses rob the land of its normal resource status, subordinating productive capacity to site factors. Competition for space in our metropolitan areas long since necessitated detailed planning and restriction of land use by zoning ordinances or similar regulations

Special uses aggregate a large total area

Fertility ratings yield to site factors

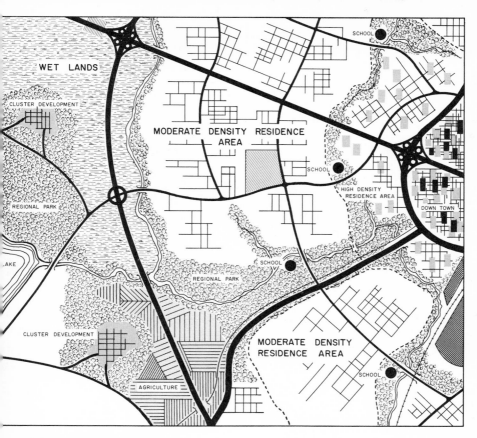

A VARIETY OF WAYS THAT RECREATION CAN BE BUILT INTO AN ENVIRONMENT

1. Natural drainage channels can be preserved as a network of functional open space.

2. Wet lands and flood plains can be zoned to prevent undesirable development and preserve the natural, scenic, and wildlife resources.

3. Appropriate areas for regional parks can be acquired.

4. "Cluster" development can be employed to combat uneconomic and undesirable sprawl.

5. Open space easements can be purchased to preserve rural scenery, and the subdivision of unsuitable areas should be prevented.

6. Residential parkway roads can be developed to follow the route of drainage channels and to border other open areas, such as lakes, marshes, and school grounds.

7. Hunting, fishing, and hiking easements can be purchased to provide increased recreation use of private lands.

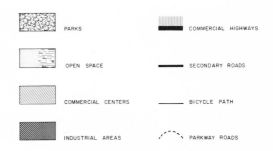

PARKS	COMMERCIAL HIGHWAYS
OPEN SPACE	SECONDARY ROADS
COMMERCIAL CENTERS	BICYCLE PATH
INDUSTRIAL AREAS	PARKWAY ROADS

Fig. 10.4 *Unless a projected subdivision includes sufficient reservation of open space, its development should not be authorized. Every expansion should be consonant with a comprehensive plan. (Adapted from O.R.R.R.C. report.)*

to protect public interests against haphazard private promotion.

The expansion of urban and built-up areas at the expense of established primary land uses should not be condoned without regard for land-capability factors. The spread of suburbia and exurban clusters such as represented in Fig. 10.4 should be di-

Quality should be respected in any land-use conversion

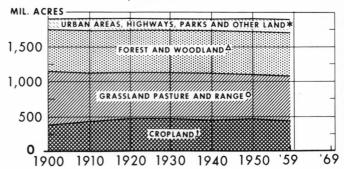

THE TREND IN LAND UTILIZATION

48 Conterminous States

MIL. ACRES

URBAN AREAS, HIGHWAYS, PARKS AND OTHER LAND*

1,500 — FOREST AND WOODLAND △

1,000

GRASSLAND PASTURE AND RANGE ○

500

CROPLAND †

0

1900 1910 1920 1930 1940 1950 '59   '69

* URBAN AND OTHER BUILT AREAS, HIGHWAYS, RAILROADS, AIRPORTS, PARKS AND OTHER LAND.

△ EXCLUDES FORESTED AREAS RESERVED FOR PARKS AND OTHER SPECIAL USES.

○ INCLUDES GRASSLAND PASTURE AND RANGE, PRIVATE AND PUBLIC.

† CROPLAND PLANTED, CROPLAND IN SUMMER FALLOW, SOIL IMPROVEMENT CROPS, LAND BEING PREPARED
FOR CROPS AND IDLE.

CROPLAND AVERAGES ARE FOR THE YEAR PRECEDING THE DATE OF THE INVENTORY EXCEPT FOR 1959.

Fig. 10.5 *Note particularly the changes in cropland acreage because they reflect the main developments in land economy. (U.S.D.A.)*

Fig. 10.6 *(Schematic drawing from S.C.S.)*

OUTLINE OF THE LAND-CAPABILITY CLASSIFICATION

MAJOR LAND USE SUITABILITY (Broad grouping of limitations)	LAND-CAPABILITY CLASS (Degree of limitations)		LAND-CAPABILITY SUBCLASS (Grouping of land-capability units according to kind of limitation. This table shows examples only.)	LAND-CAPABILITY UNIT (Land-management groups based on permanent physical characteristics. This table shows examples only.)
SUITED FOR CULTIVATION	I	Few limitations. Wide latitude for each use. Very good land from every standpoint.		
	II	Moderate limitations or risks of damage. Good land from all-around standpoint.		
	III	Severe limitations or risks of damage. Regular cultivation possible if limitations are observed.	Limited by hazard of water erosion; moderately sloping land.	Moderately sloping, slightly acid soils on limestone.
				Moderately sloping, highly acid soils on sandstone or shale.
			Limited by excess water; drainage needed for cultivation.	
			Limited by low moisture capacity; sandy land.	
	IV	Very severe limitations. Suited for occasional cultivation or for some kind of limited cultivation.		
NOT SUITED FOR CULTIVATION	V	Not suited for cultivation because of wetness, stones, overflows, etc. Few limitations for grazing or forestry use.		
	VI	Too steep, stony, arid, wet, etc., for cultivation. Moderate limitations for grazing or forestry.	Grouping of sites according to kind of limitation.	Sites significant in management of ranges, pastures, forests, etc.
	VII	Very steep, rough, arid, wet, etc. Severe limitations for grazing or forestry.		
	VIII	Extremely rough, arid, swampy, etc. Not suited for cultivation, grazing, or forestry. Suited for wildlife, watersheds, or recreation.		

Fig. 10.7 (From: "The Measure of Our Land," S.C.S.)

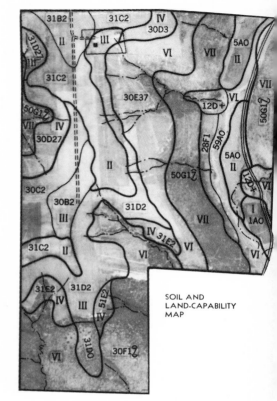

SOIL AND
LAND-CAPABILITY
MAP

Description of the Capability Classes on This Farm

Here are descriptions of the land-capability classes on this farm. The kinds of soil in each class are listed at the end of each class description.

Class I land is very good land from all points of view. It is nearly level and does not wash away readily. The soil is deep and easy to work and holds water well. Since it has few limitations that restrict its use, the farmer who runs the farm can use it safely in most any way he chooses—for cash or feed crops, for pasture or trees, or for wildlife food and cover. Of course good soil-management practices are required to keep it productive.

1AO—Arenzville silt loam, 0–2 percent slope, uneroded

Class II land has some natural condition that somewhat limits the plants it can produce or that calls for some easily applied conservation practice if it is plowed. Most of the Class II land on this farm is sloping enough to let water run off at a speed that carries soil away when it is in corn, soybeans, small grain, or other similar crops. Some of it is wet land that needs drainage.

5AO—Rowley silt loam, 0–2 percent slope, uneroded
31B2—Dubuque silt loam, deep, 2–5 percent slope, moderately eroded
31C2—Dubuque silt loam, deep, 5–10 percent slope, moderately eroded

Class III land has more serious or more numerous limitations than Class II. These limitations may be natural ones such as steep slope, sandy or shallow soil, or too little or too much water. Or the limitation may be erosion brought on by the way the land has been used. Thus Class III is more restricted in the plants it can grow or, if cultivated, calls for conservation practices more difficult to install or to keep working efficiently. When used for cultivated crops on this farm it needs these conservation practices because of slope or previous erosion, or both.

30B2—Dubuque silt loam, 2–5 percent slope, moderately eroded
30C2—Dubuque silt loam, 5–10 percent slope, moderately eroded
31D0—Dubuque silt loam, deep, 10–15 percent slope, uneroded
31D2—Dubuque silt loam, deep, 10–15 percent slope, moderately eroded

Class IV land has very serious limitations that restrict the plants it can grow or that call for very careful management if it is plowed. On this farm it is either steeper or more severely eroded than the Class III land, or both.

30D2—Dubuque silt loam, 10–15 percent slope, moderately eroded
30D3—Dubuque silt loam, 10–15 percent slope, severely eroded
31E2—Dubuque silt loam, deep, 15–20 percent slope, moderately eroded

On this farm, all the fields in land-capability Classes I, II, III, and IV are also good for pasture or hay,

The large Roman numerals show the land capability. Heavy lines outline the capability classes. The three-part symbol of Arabic numbers and letters shows the kind of soil, slope, and erosion in that order.

for trees, or for wildlife food and cover. In fact, they could produce better yields of these permanent-cover crops than the fields in Classes VI and VII, which are best suited to permanent cover.

Class VI land has limitations that make it generally unsuited to the common cultivated crops—such as corn, soybeans, or small grain—but it can produce good pasture or hay. On this farm, it is also well suited to trees. Very steep slopes are the limitation of most of the Class VI land on this farm.

12D+—Stony colluvial land, 10–15 percent slope, uneroded
30E3—Dubuque silt loam, 15–20 percent slope, severely eroded

Fig. 10.8 *Conservation Farm Plan. Application of the plan usually begins with a compromise between the ideal envisioned and the adjustment immediately feasible. (From S.C.S.)*

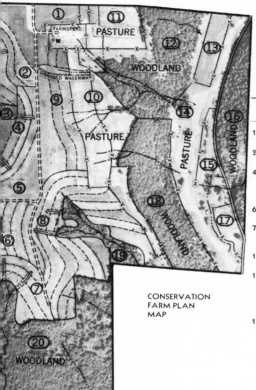

CONSERVATION
FARM PLAN
MAP

The circled numbers on the different fields key with those in the table that gives detail about the conservation measures.

Conservation measures planned for this farm

Field	Conservation measures
1.........	Contour tillage; 5-year crop rotation—1 year corn, 2 years small grain, 2 years clover and timothy.
2, 5, 9....	Contour stripcropping; 5-year rotation—1 year corn, 1 year small grain, 3 years alfalfa and timothy.
4.........	Contour stripcropping; 5-year rotation—Center strip: 1 year corn, 1 year small grain, 3 years alfalfa and timothy. Outside strips: 1 year corn, 2 years grain, 2 years timothy and clover.
6.........	Contour stripcropping; 5-year rotation—1 year corn, 2 years small grain, 2 years clover and timothy.
7, 8......	Contour stripcropping; 5-year rotation—1 year corn, 1 year small grain, 3 years alfalfa and timothy; strip near woods to be permanent hay.
13, 15....	Contour tillage and drainage to remove excess water; 4-year rotation—2 years corn, 1 year small grain, 1 year pasture.
17........	4-year rotation—2 years corn, 1 year small grain, 1 year pasture.
	Conservation treatments for all cropland: All waterways seeded and kept in sod. All fields limed and fertilized as needed.
12, 18....	To improve stocking and increase production, about 6,000 white pines to be interplanted in the openings of the 2 fields.
	Natural reproduction of hardwoods to be encouraged in all improvement and harvest cuttings. To improve quality of later cuts, trees cut during the first 5 years to be confined to the poorest trees, such as those with crooks, low forks, and scarred butts. Thereafter, each 5 years about 750 board-feet per acre to be cut; trees to be selected so as to keep the woodland producing. Fields to be divided into 5 equal units and 1 unit cut each year. Den trees to be kept for wildlife.
16........	Management will be the same as for fields 12 and 18 except each 5-year harvest cut to be 1,000 board-feet per acre.
19, 20....	Management the same as for field 16; about 3,000 white pines to be interplanted in the openings. Shrubs for wildlife to be allowed to come in along field borders.
3.........	Wildlife land: Open grassy and shrubby areas to be kept. Some hardwood trees to be cut for lumber to allow better wildlife plants to grow. 200 conifers to be planted for winter protection for wildlife.
10, 11, 14.	Conservation treatments for all pastures: Limed and fertilized. Worn-out areas seeded to grass and clover mixture. Newly seeded pasture to be grazed lightly the first year. Amount and time of grazing to be regulated. Pastures rotated to provide alternate grazing and resting periods of about 2 weeks each. Weeds and tall grasses mowed at least once each year. Livestock kept off legume pasture during September. Grazing on sweetclover regulated so that it will reseed itself.
Farmstead.	Fence to be replaced with a multiflora rose living fence.

30F1—Dubuque silt loam, 20–30 percent slope, slightly eroded
59A0—Alluvial land, poorly drained, 0–2 percent slope, uneroded

Class VII land is not only unsuited for cultivated crops but it also requires careful management when used for grazing or forestry.   Its limitations on this farm are shallow soil and eroded steep slopes that wash easily and need extreme care to prevent more erosion.

50G1—Rough broken land, 30–45 percent slope, slightly eroded

This farm does not have any Class V or Class VIII land.

rected toward the peripheral land least desirable for agricultural use wherever the choice is possible. Soils most productive of crops may be the least desirable as a home site, and vice versa. Convenience of situation, economic opportunity, and social choice may all be respected; but community interests are better served by more discriminate space allocation. The open spaces shown in Fig. 10.4 may be superb for recreation although of little value for other purposes. Much land conservation would result if all shifts of land from primary to special uses were subject to judicious selection on the basis of minimal land quality adequate for the special purpose to be served.

We have barely begun the scientific and selective allocation of rural land to primary uses that should precede any application of specific conservation techniques. We have talked much about soil conservation with reference to arable (plowed) land and said very little about conserving land by changing its use. We have accepted traditional land-use ratings too readily and observed land-use trends (Fig. 10.5) without thought of interference. But the conservator will not be bound by tradition. He has no qualms about retiring an infertile field from cultivation and planting trees on it. Neither does he hesitate to challenge the validity of acreage trends as land-use criteria unless they are correlated with production trends. Good land conservation does, in fact, cause progressive divergence of acreage and production curves—higher yield from less area.

Other factors being equal, *superior land receives the most intensive attention; inferior land, the most extensive.* (Intensive land use applies much labor and/or capital per unit of land—heavy investment in small acreage. Extensive land use involves much land and little expenditure per acre.) Good land rewards well the keeper who tends it, but poor land makes less promise of such reward. Land cannot repay tillage costs exceeding its limits of production. Simple economic theory relegates unproductive land to idleness, and practical technology, including conservation, cannot always abrogate the time-worn theory. Conservation relaxes economic restriction on land utilization by physical improvement of the land. It is a moot point whether the elevation of wasteland to pulpwood cropping represents better conservation than the conversion of a pulpwood stand to saw timber, or whether pasture land made arable or pasture land simply given higher carrying capacity be the better achievement. In any case, the degree of *increase in productivity attained* should be the criterion. And, unless added production can defray improvement costs the improvement represents waste rather than conservation—a futile attempt to elevate the land above its in-

Quality of use and quality of land tend to coincide

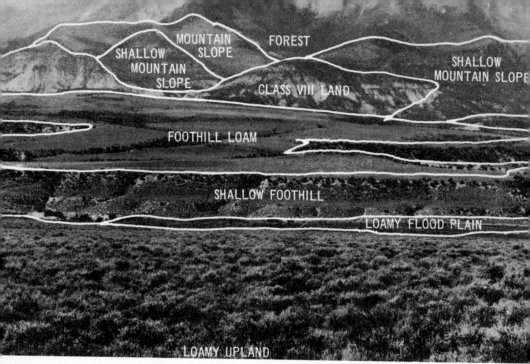

Fig. 10.9 *Range classification takes into account not only physical site factors but also the composition and condition of the plant community. (S.C.S. schematic diagram.)*

herent use capability. The conservator cannot make fertile crop-land out of rough, stony waste any more than a tailor can fashion a woolen garment out of cotton shoddy. Instead, each can only do his best with the material at hand, letting his product conform to the fabric. To the conservator such conformation means the employment of land for its optimum productive use, be it crop, pasture, or forest; intensive, extensive, or in between. *The first step toward good land conservation is the classification and use*—the allocation of unit areas on the basis of capability ratings.

The Soil Conservation Service evolved a practical system of land classification that identifies according to use capability eight classes of land in farms, as illustrated by Fig. 10.6. The first four classes are suitable for crops, the next three adaptable to grass and trees, and the next class is useless except as wilderness or wildlife habitat.[5] From I to IV, each class demands progressively more careful use for successful crop production; from V to VII, each class becomes more limited in its usefulness for pasture or forest (Fig. 10.7).[6] A land-use plan according to land capability may be a farmer's most constructive conservation measure. Without a good plan, other conservation practices cannot be effective. Figure 10.8 shows the steps by which a farm plan is evolved.

A system for classifying rangeland was also developed, based mainly on site factors as indicators of potential forage production (Fig. 10.9), but with plant ecology taken into account. In this

Land use according to capability improves the farm, the region, and the nation

247

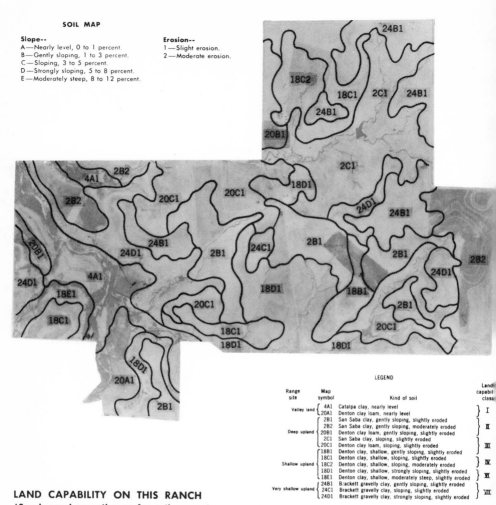

SOIL MAP

Slope--
A—Nearly level, 0 to 1 percent.
B—Gently sloping, 1 to 3 percent.
C—Sloping, 3 to 5 percent.
D—Strongly sloping, 5 to 8 percent.
E—Moderately steep, 8 to 12 percent.

Erosion--
1—Slight erosion.
2—Moderate erosion.

LEGEND

Range site	Map symbol	Kind of soil	Land capability class
Valley land	4A1	Catalpa clay, nearly level	} I
	20A1	Denton clay loam, nearly level	
	2B1	San Saba clay, gently sloping, slightly eroded	} II
	2B2	San Saba clay, gently sloping, moderately eroded	
Deep upland	20B1	Denton clay loam, gently sloping, slightly eroded	
	2C1	San Saba clay, sloping, slightly eroded	} III
	20C1	Denton clay loam, sloping, slightly eroded	
	18B1	Denton clay, shallow, gently sloping, slightly eroded	
	18C1	Denton clay, shallow, sloping, slightly eroded	} IV
Shallow upland	18C2	Denton clay, shallow, sloping, moderately eroded	
	18D1	Denton clay, shallow, strongly sloping, slightly eroded	} VI
	18E1	Denton clay, shallow, moderately steep, slightly eroded	
	24B1	Brackett gravelly clay, gently sloping, slightly eroded	
Very shallow upland	24C1	Brackett gravelly clay, sloping, slightly eroded	} VII
	24D1	Brackett gravelly clay, strongly sloping, slightly eroded	

LAND CAPABILITY ON THIS RANCH
(See legend on soil map for soil names)

Class I is very good land from all points of view. It is nearly level and does not wash or blow readily. The soil is deep and easy to work. It holds water well and is at least fairly well supplied with plant food. The rancher can use it safely in most any way he chooses, such as for cash or feed crops, grassland, or wildlife land. It needs only good soil-management practices to keep it productive.

Class II land has a slight erosion hazard and requires some conservation treatment if cultivated. These practices usually are easy to apply and keep up. It can be used for cultivated crops, grassland, and wildlife.

Class III land has more serious or more numerous limitations than Class II land. These limitations may be natural ones—such as moderate slope or shallow soil. Or the limitation may be erosion brought on by the way the land has been used. Thus the use of Class III land is more restricted than that of Class II, and if it is cultivated it needs more conservation treatment.

Class IV land has serious restrictions that limit the plants it can grow or that call for very careful management if it is plowed. Also, the number of years favorable for cultivated crops are apt to be few.

Class VI land has severe limitations—shallow soil or steep slopes—that make it better suited to range than to cropland. It is moderately productive for range if proper grazing management is followed. Reseeding if needed and pitting and water spreading can improve pastures and ranges on Class VI land.

Class VII land has very shallow, gravelly, or droughty soils. They are the least productive soils on the ranch. It is impractical to try to improve this range by reseeding, pitting, and water spreading because the soils are too shallow. However, range condition on this kind of land can be improved through proper grazing use.

RANGE SITES ON THIS RANCH
(Soils are listed in the legend for soil map)

Valley range site is the most productive range site on the ranch. Soil are deep, fine-textured, and nearly level to gently sloping. They are subject to overflow now and then.

Deep upland range site is productive and well drained. Soils are fine-textured, generally more than 20 inches deep, and gently sloping to steep.

Shallow upland range site is moderately productive; soils are shallow, fine-textured, droughty, and undulating to steep.

Very shallow upland range site, occupying ridge tops and steep slopes, is the least productive on the ranch. It consists of very thin clayey soil over marl and limestone bedrock.

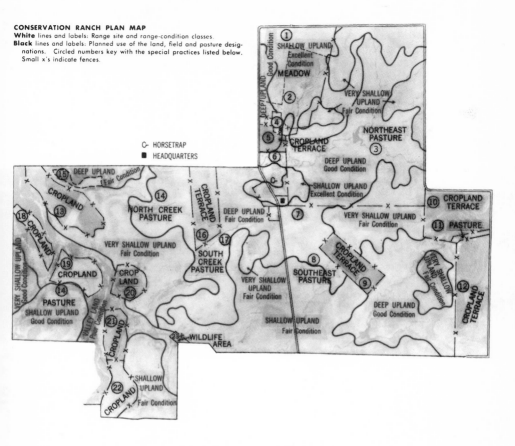

CONSERVATION RANCH PLAN MAP
White lines and labels: Range site and range-condition classes.
Black lines and labels: Planned use of the land, field and pasture designations. Circled numbers key with the special practices listed below. Small x's indicate fences.

C- HORSETRAP
■ HEADQUARTERS

CONSERVATION MEASURES

CULTIVATED FIELDS

General Practices

Weeds in tame pastures will be mowed high to avoid cutting grass seeded for grazing.
Fire lanes will be maintained along public roads and other hazard areas.
One hundred to two hundred pounds of phosphate per acre will be applied each year to sweetclover fields.
Terraced fields will be cultivated on the contour.
Grain fields will not be grazed after March 15.

PASTURES

General Practices

The goal of range management will be to improve all ranges to good or excellent condition.
The goal on each range site will be to increase the key forage plants as follows:

Valley range site—
1. Big bluestem
2. Indiangrass
3. Switchgrass
4. Little bluestem

Shallow upland range site—
1. Little bluestem
2. Sideoats grama
3. Hairy grama

Deep upland range site—
1. Little bluestem
2. Indiangrass
3. Big bluestem
4. Sideoats grama

Very shallow upland range site—
1. Little bluestem
2. Sideoats grama

Fig. 10.10 *Conservation Ranch Plan. Sustained yield management is applicable to pastures as well as to fields and forests. (From S.C.S.)*

system, shown in Table 1, range condition is classified according to the percentage of present vegetation that is climax for the range site.[7] Here then is a scheme whereby native pastures may

Table 1

Rangeland Classification

Range-condition Class	Present Vegetation That Is Climax (*per cent*)
Excellent	76 to 100
Good	51 to 75
Fair	26 to 50
Poor	0 to 25

be classified for use. A ranch planned accordingly is represented graphically in Fig. 10.10.

Planned land management on farms and ranches places on the land the intricate, detailed pattern of conservation. The entire handiwork begins with the design by land classes on individual fields and pastures and culminates in the regional mosaic of watersheds and river systems. To these we shall return later in this chapter.

Modern land utilization and conservation revise a traditional connotation of intensiveness. In the "good old days," pasture and forest were never more than extensive land uses. Stock raising and lumbering were expansive enterprises loosely attached to the land. Now much of our beef comes from intensively used land and from pastures carefully prepared, sown, fertilized; in places pastures are even irrigated with portable sprinkler systems during periods of drought. We are also developing silviculture to a degree that intensifies the use of land for producing forest. Eventually land in saw timber may receive as much attention as land in fruit orchard. Conservation breaks the old-fashioned parallel between type of land use and intensiveness of use and enforces the stronger parallel between land quality and intensiveness, with less and less regard for type of enterprise.

Conservation also faces up to the economist's problem of marginal and submarginal land by classification and selective use. (Marginal land is land that will barely yield its operator a livelihood under prevailing use; submarginal land will not meet his simplest needs for food, clothing, and shelter.) In this province the planning aspects of land conservation have special significance. Land submarginal in small cultivated tracts can often be

Adjustment of land use corrects marginality

used profitably for grazing or forestry in larger blocks. Our legis-
lators acknowledged that fact when they amended the Homestead Act to populate the plains. Their fault when they doled out
our dry grazing lands lay in being too conservative rather than
too rash. They overestimated land capabilities because they
lacked the experience necessary to judge them. Perhaps they did
foresee that abusive practices would render submarginal a large
acreage of land in the humid eastern portions of the country;
much of it ruined by robber crops, but even more of it damaged
by misappropriation for uses above its capabilities. In any event,
the problem of submarginal land (and submarginal tenants) attained national proportions long before we took concerted action
to solve it.

The urgent need for salvage and reassignment of misused land
invoked our modern planning and conservation movement. We
learned that hunger stalks the man who plants cotton where slash
pine ought to be or wheat where grass ought to grow, that marginality may stem from human error more often than from any
fault of the land, and that self-imposed pain can be self-alleviated.
We learned that much land submarginal under cultivation can
be profitably grazed or forested.

Why do people penalize themselves by cultivating submarginal land? Because they are victims of any one among several
circumstances and lack the wherewithal to correct the situation
or to remove to a better locale. Abandonment of land under
the compulsion of poverty, malnutrition, and disease is the tragic
price many Americans have paid for unwise land occupance. A
major objective of land planning is to salve that misery and guard
against its recurrence.

Circumstances have prompted maladjustments

As mentioned previously, the settlement of better lands in the
Old West caused poor farms in New England to lie idle. The
stony hills could not compete with fertile plains. *Comparative
quality* made many fields in the East submarginal. Settlement
of land anywhere without discriminate selection condemns un-
lucky settlers to submarginality. That has happened in several
places about our country. We condoned, and encouraged, private
ownership of land which could not support the owner. Selection
comes by painful trial and error and by forced migration of any
residents in excess of the number the land can adequately and
permanently sustain. See by comparing Figs. 10.3 and 10.11 how
land use coincides or conflicts with land capability on a regional
basis.

The Dust Bowl demonstrated conclusively the tragic consequences of wrong land occupance. Abnormally high prices ac-

GENERALIZED LAND RESOURCE AREAS

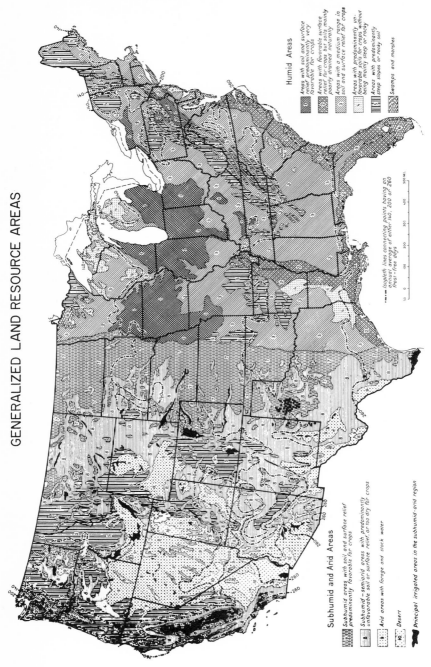

Humid Areas

- Areas with soil and surface relief predominantly very favorable for crops
- Areas with favorable surface relief for crops but soils mainly poorly drained naturally
- Areas with a medium range in soil and surface relief for crops
- Areas with predominantly unfavorable soils for crops without being mainly steep or rocky
- Areas with predominantly steep slopes or rocky soil
- Swamps and marshes

Subhumid and Arid Areas

- Subhumid areas with soil and surface relief predominantly favorable for crops
- Subhumid–semiarid areas with predominantly unfavorable soil or surface relief, or too dry for crops
- Arid areas with forage and stock water
- Desert

Principal irrigated areas in the subhumid-arid region

Isopleth lines connecting points having an annual average of either 140, 200 or 260 frost-free days

Fig. 10.11 *Land capability on a national scale. Represented here is a composite of attributes by which the comparative quality of large areas may be gauged. It warrants systematic study, including correlation with several previous maps (Figs. 1.3, 2.2, 3.2, 3.5, 5.5, 10.3, and others) that depict geographic components separately. (U.S.D.A. map.)*

companying war pressure for food pushed cereal crops, particularly wheat, beyond their safe limits of aridity. Decline in market demand and price asserted the submarginal character of the "boom" expansion. Price fluctuations have often caused, or exposed, the marginality of land for a particular use.

Many Americans live on land that became submarginal at their own hands or the hands of their ancestors. Such unfortunates have victimized themselves, but their plight is nonetheless a problem for the planner-conservator. His the task to correct and rehabilitate, whatever the origin of the trouble.

Extractive industries, such as mining and "destructive" lumbering, have left in their wake men without wages and families dependent upon submarginal land. By this and other processes destitution and submarginal land have become associated in a scavenger-carrion partnership. Dissolution of that tragic partnership depends upon planned land use.

Whereas farms with a variety of land classes may be planned and conserved economically if they include sufficient portions of good land, those lacking good land lack also the capacity for significant internal improvement. Their conservation is best accomplished by consolidation into larger units for less intensive employment or by retirement from private ownership and use by public appropriation.

We consolidate poor land and intensify our use of good land

Farm subsidy or bounty that keeps farmers on submarginal land simply prolongs the agony of sane economic adjustment and aggravates a bad condition. Crop-acreage restrictions, on the other hand, encourage better tending of select parcels and voluntary retirement of poorer parts of a farm to less intensive use appropriate to their quality. Acreage restrictions have compelled many farmers to learn that it is more profitable to concentrate energies and means on a little good land than to dissipate them over a much larger area of poor land. The curtailment of acreage intended to protect commodity markets has achieved more valuable and permanent results in the realm of land-use improvement.

Land was an abundant commodity during the entire formative period of our great nation, and west of the mid-continent it became freer than water. When the United States had extended its dominion to the Pacific Coast the Federal government held title to most of the lands west of the Mississippi in a grand "public domain." There followed the phenomenal era of westward expansion implemented by lavish gifts of land under various plans calculated to speed settlement and private ownership. What was the good of land that yielded no taxes?

Public ownership enables special utilization and conservation of land

The Homestead Act of 1862 and subsequent liberalizing

PUBLIC LAND * AS A PERCENT OF TOTAL LAND AREA, APRIL 1, 1950

(COUNTY UNIT BASIS)

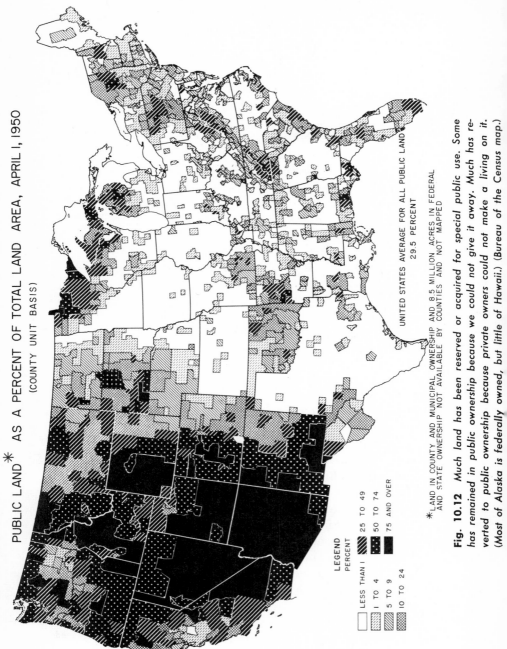

LEGEND
PERCENT

LESS THAN 1
1 TO 4
5 TO 9
10 TO 24
25 TO 49
50 TO 74
75 AND OVER

UNITED STATES AVERAGE FOR ALL PUBLIC LAND
29.5 PERCENT

* LAND IN COUNTY AND MUNICIPAL OWNERSHIP AND 8.5 MILLION ACRES IN FEDERAL
AND STATE OWNERSHIP NOT AVAILABLE BY COUNTIES AND NOT MAPPED

Fig. 10.12 *Much land has been reserved or acquired for special public use. Some has remained in public ownership because we could not give it away. Much has reverted to public ownership because private owners could not make a living on it. (Most of Alaska is federally owned, but little of Hawaii.) (Bureau of the Census map.)*

amendments, the Timber and Stone Act of 1878, and other legal devices for giving land away brought settlers to the plains and valleys of the West. Liberal land grants encouraged the building of railroads, roads, and canals to facilitate settlement. Swamp and overflow lands were given to the states within which they lay. The Federal government disposed of the public domain with a vengeance. Not before 1934 was the wild giveaway spree checked. There remained very little "open" land upon which a private owner might make a living.

Meanwhile, men of vision had begun a national program of salvaging and reserving certain lands for permanent public use and administration. In 1872 Congress established Yellowstone National Park—the initial step toward our great National Park system of today. In 1891 Yellowstone Park Timberland Reserve was set aside—the forerunner of our national forests. Congress decided that vast areas of our great land might best serve the people if held in public trust, at least for an indefinite period. States, counties, towns, and communities have followed the example until publicly owned lands now aggregate tremendous totals. The public ownership approximated in Fig. 10.12 is largely federal. As of 1962 the government owned almost 768 million acres, including almost 99 per cent of Alaska and more than 250,000 acres in Hawaii. Smallest proportion of federal land was in Connecticut—only 0.2 per cent of that state's area.

With the modern planning and conservation era came a complete about-face in our attitude toward public ownership of land. Public acquisition became the means of removing from submarginal land the unfortunate tenants struggling to live on it, thereby diverting both land and human resources to better purposes. Most of the displaced tenants were relocated on land better suited to their use. The states discovered that tax-delinquent land may not always be "redeemed" by the payment of back taxes, that its repeated resale means repeated human suffering, and that its depopulation and retirement at public expense is good economy. Acting upon this knowledge and for the common weal, we have returned to federal ownership some 50 million acres once privately owned, about half of it in National Forests.[8] We have abandoned counties and dissolved their governments. We have returned submarginal land to its proper tenants— trees, brush, birds, snakes, foxes, and other wild things, none of whom demands subsidy. Many expansive units of our land have been wisely adjudged most useful in their natural state, and only the public can afford to own and preserve a wilderness. Only public ownership, under a democratic government, can

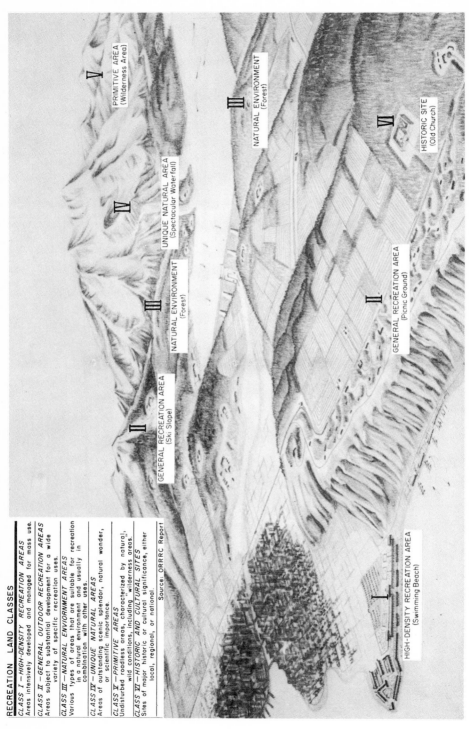

RECREATION LAND CLASSES

CLASS I — HIGH-DENSITY RECREATION AREAS
Areas intensively developed and managed for mass use.

CLASS II — GENERAL OUTDOOR RECREATION AREAS
Areas subject to substantial development for a wide variety of specific recreation uses.

CLASS III — NATURAL ENVIRONMENT AREAS
Various types of areas that are suitable for recreation in a natural environment and usually in combination with other uses.

CLASS IV — UNIQUE NATURAL AREAS
Areas of outstanding scenic splendor, natural wonder, or scientific importance.

CLASS V — PRIMITIVE AREAS
Undisturbed roadless areas, characterized by natural, wild conditions, including "wilderness areas."

CLASS VI — HISTORIC AND CULTURAL SITES
Sites of major historic or cultural significance, either local, regional, or national.

Source: ORRRC Report

V PRIMITIVE AREA (Wilderness Area)

IV UNIQUE NATURAL AREA (Spectacular Waterfall)

III NATURAL ENVIRONMENT (Forest)

III NATURAL ENVIRONMENT (Forest)

VI HISTORIC SITE (Old Church)

II GENERAL RECREATION AREA (Picnic Ground)

II GENERAL RECREATION AREA (Ski Slope)

I HIGH-DENSITY RECREATION AREA (Swimming Beach)

Fig. 10.13 The lake might accommodate several seasonal activities in turn and attract one kind of participant or another most of the year. (Panorama from O.R.R.R.C. report.)

256

hold in trust for future generations the open spaces and wild lands we want them to inherit. Therein lies a unique governmental responsibility for conservation.

Acknowledging the vital importance of outdoor recreation to the American way of life and the urgent necessity of providing the people adequate opportunities to enjoy such recreation, the Congress created in 1958 an Outdoor Recreation Resources Review Commission (Public Law 85-470) "to study the outdoor recreation resources of the public lands and other land and water areas of the United States, and for other purposes." The Commission delivered its monumental report, including twenty-seven pertinent Study Reports in as many separate volumes in January, 1962. From this elaborate ORRRC report will be several items in Chapter 13. The Commission proposed the classification system for recreation areas depicted in Fig. 10.13 as a management guide.

Lands in recreation classes III, IV, V, and VI, as schematically represented in Fig. 10.13, can fully serve their aesthetic purposes only if held in perpetuity by the government. Those in classes III and V would not generally be profitable as private enterprises because they must have considerable size, and they attract few people. Indeed, ready access and heavy traffic would destroy the very qualities for which they are preserved. In public trust they yield no significant revenue; in private ownership they would probably not yield sufficient income to defray any taxes. Many in class IV have, in fact, been acquired by private interests and successfully commercialized—the Natural Bridge in Virginia, for example. However, their worth as private enterprises comes by nearness to heavily populated areas or main routes of travel. Whether owned privately or publicly, the "high-density" and "general" recreation areas (classes I and II), should be in vicinal proximity to the human agglomerations they serve; the primitive or wilderness areas must be more remotely situated, which, by nature, they are. Thus, our system of outdoor recreation areas, as classified according to natural attributes and social benefits, has its own various pattern on the land. The classification is a useful guide for developing a suitable system in balance with present and future needs.

Classes of recreation land may be functionally arranged

Trends in land economy, by design or otherwise, point the way to future land conservation. Good trends express conservational progress; bad ones foreshadow complication or obstruction. As noted above, there is a trend toward *more intensive use of good land and more extensive use of poor land,* both facilitated by acreage restrictions and government acquisition. The latter is

Trends in land economy are guideposts of conservation

FARM PRODUCTION PER ACRE AND PER ANIMAL

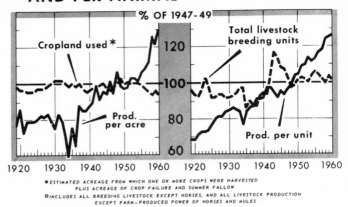

Fig. 10.14 *Phenomenal improvement in production efficiency has distinguished American agriculture. We have so greatly increased yield—per acre, per animal unit, and per man-hour—that we need less cropland and fewer farmers. (U.S.D.A. chart.)*

largely an application of land-use planning; the former a by-product of artificial economic stabilization. Both contribute to land conservation. Their constructive results may be inferred from our substantially increased production during recent years while our total crop acreage remained about constant. Land selection has magnified the advantages of improved plant strains and the application of mineral fertilizers.

Another current trend relating to intensified use of our better land involves the revision of traditional land-use ratings on the basis of enterprise. Local intensification of stock raising and timber growing on good land shifts grazing and forestry into higher cash-yield brackets, elevating them nearer to parity with conventional cropping. It appears likely that the transition will gain momentum as we refine our adjustment to the land. The conservator may anticipate the time when Americans will meticulously regulate cattle grazing and cultivate timber crops under systems long since perfected by Europeans.

The land planner needs to recognize and analyze all land-use trends with a view toward meeting future land requirements without waste and without jeopardizing our standard of living and our national strength. We know that our nation has a total land area of more than 2.2 billion acres, exclusive of some 42.4 million acres of inland waters, and that our population exceeds 190 million. We know that we are growing crops on just about all the land that can be tilled economically at present—458 million acres in 1959 [9]—and that our population continues to increase. Population grows while land area and potentially arable acreage

Our population increases while land area remains constant

258

remain constant. How then may we continue to satisfy the mounting demand for food, to say nothing of other products of the land considered essential? Thus far we have met the challenge with increased yields per acre under scientifically improved agriculture (Fig. 10.14). Conservation, though as yet not fully applied, has contributed much to that efficiency. Estimates of anticipated increase in production per acre between 1950 and 1975 range all the way from 33 to 75 per cent.[10]

We need not fear hunger any time soon, nor even quite remotely, but when our arable acreage has been pressed by mechanization, fertilization, seed selection, breeding, and complete husbandry to yield its utmost—our population still increasing—we shall be compelled to expand our crop area. We could develop for crops some 80 million acres more capable of production than many now cultivated,[11] and we could round off the increase to 100 million acres without sacrifice of standards.[12] We have no immediate need for expanding our crop acreage, but future food requirements may compel us to do so. Then we may bring water to all the irrigable acres in the dry West and resow to crops those fields once retired from crop production in the humid East. And should the pressure for food be unrelenting, wise men may condone drainage of wet land to avert hunger. The planning against future land requirements must not be ignored by conservators of today, although future procedures may change greatly to accord with changing circumstances.

We are far from our limits of production

As our nation fills with people we need ever wiser cultural adjustment to our land and ever more judicious allotment of space to increasingly competitive uses. Upon planner-conservators devolve the responsibility for progress to the utmost social growth our land resources can sustain without undue sacrifice of the *base*. Their success will be commensurate with the degree to which they keep pace with needs and events. Their ideas cannot be static; their concepts must be continuously adjusted to changing conditions. Their work cannot be done "once and for all" because the very progress they ensure sets them new tasks. Land use and land economics must keep pace with the changing situation, and conservation must be adapted to the new frame of reference.

We must continuously refine our adjustment to the land

Conservation planning transcends individual land ownerships. Its compass includes entire cities and states. It applies to all lands and all land appurtenances, whether public or private, rich or poor, wet or dry, flat or steep, populous or empty. It involves not one or a few, but all associated resources whence comes the wealth of communities and regions. The programmed applica-

Watersheds as planning regions

tion of conservation should, therefore, be organized on the basis of identifiable spatial units, each with a common resource denominator of concern throughout the unit. The bonding medium for community organization might be any resource or combination of resources with which the area is well endowed; however, water, the land's lifeblood, has no equal as the amalgam of community interests with regional dimensions.

The natural drainage systems on the land—the hydrographic divisions of our country—constitute a ready-made framework for regional resource development. With those systems, variously identified as *watersheds* or *drainage basins,* much of our area and regional planning has become associated. By American definition a watershed is the area—the total area—drained by one stream, whether it be an intermittent creek that discharges the run-off from a few acres or a river whose tributaries drain half a continent. All the land from which surface water runs to one outlet is a watershed. In legislation and in common usage, however, the term *watershed* has acquired an erroneous connotation of limited size, applicable to small streams and headwaters of larger ones. The terms *basin* and *valley* have become customarily reserved for areas drained by sizable rivers. One might say that a large river *basin* has several *tributary valleys,* each with a number of small *watersheds comprising its headwaters.* This may not be accurate terminology, but it helps us correlate our thinking with the comparative magnitude of hydrologic entities, their inherent problems and opportunities, and the appropriate scope of planned development for each size. Small watersheds, for instance, are not ordinarily suitable for hydroelectric generation.

Although the entire scheme may not exist in every case, a general idea to be kept in mind is that each farm field contributes to the drainage of the farm, that each farm contributes to the drainage of a small watershed, that each small watershed contributes to the drainage of a larger tributary, and that each tributary drains into a master river or the sea. The management of raindrops—where they strike—ultimately helps regulate the stream into which they run. If all its tributaries be regulated, the main stream may also be manageable. The little headwaters might be likened unto Aesop's bundle of sticks.

Ideally, the management of drainage systems should begin on their upper reaches and progress downstream; but in practice our hydraulic applications, as a matter of expediency, have often begun with the trunks of streams rather than with their branches. Historically, the Army Corps of Engineers has discharged its civil responsibilities for flood control and navigation by building large dams and locks; the Bureau of Reclamation, operating in the seventeen Western states, has also erected many large structures to impound water for irrigation and other purposes. Project engineering under these agencies has, perforce, taken into account the inherent unity of a stream system, but neither has been authorized to conserve land resources about headwaters. The Weeks Law passed in 1911 authorized the purchase of forests to protect watersheds important to navigation, but the integrated conservation of other lands had not yet emerged. After that time public regard for drainage-system planning appeared in many desultory legislative references, but only with the advent of the "inspiration" emergency era of the early 1930's did it reach full bloom, with passage of the boldly conceived Norris Act (1933) creating the Tennessee Valley Authority.

The TVA is a unique corporate agency of the United States government, charged with the comprehensive, unified development of the Tennessee River system and the assistance in the orderly conservation of all resources in the Tennessee Valley. It was constituted to demonstrate the practicality of integrated watershed development and to execute a regional plan for an entire river system under centralized administrative control.[13]

TVA, demonstration of integrated valley development

The Tennessee Valley was a good place for the great experiment. The Tennessee had been a rampageous stream and a heavy contributor to Mississippi floods. The valley contained little industrialization that would involve relocation costs. The valley populace was so hard hit by the national depression that its traditional thrift and self-sufficiency proved inadequate, and potential construction and industrial workers were on relief. This depression emergency reduced local opposition to the project.

The TVA development might have been better than it is if it had applied the principle of beginning with headwaters and progressing downstream. However, other considerations dictated that the lower dams be erected before the upper ones. Except for navigation, many somewhat smaller dams might have been better than a few big ones; less emphasis and publicity on electric power might have made the valley a better proving ground for other regional developments.

Whatever its faults and failures, its successes and achievements, the TVA has inestimable value as a research laboratory for regional planning and conservation. It is a unique project of profound interest to planners and conservators everywhere. By scientific selection of sites and designs for a *system* of dams, the Authority has gone far toward acquiring maximum multiple

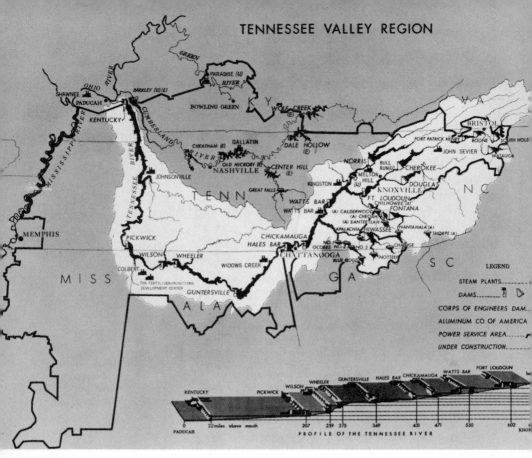

Fig. 10.15 *The integrated TVA system. Although several dams are privately owned, all are operated as integral parts of the unified system. Upper dams store potential flood waters during wet seasons and release them during dry ones. Flow of the main river is regulated so well that it is navigable year-round up to Knoxville, for craft drawing nine feet of water. Total lift from Paducah to Knoxville is 515 feet—in a distance of some 650 miles. Water from certain upper tributary dams generates electricity thirteen times before it joins the Ohio at Paducah. (TVA map.)*

utility of an entire watershed (Fig. 10.15). The system consists of thirty-one major dams and reservoirs that regulate effectively the outflow from a watershed 41,000 square miles in area. Since the first multiple-purpose project went into operation (Norris Dam, 1936), the system had averted, by the end of fiscal year 1961, flood damages that would have amounted to more than 149.5 million dollars.[14] Annual freight traffic on the lower river had attained a ton-mileage of 2.3 billion,[15] and the lakes attracted in 1960 more than 42 million (person-day) visitors.[16] In event of conflict among multiple purposes, flood prevention has precedence; navigation and power secondary rank. Recreation and wildlife are by-products of primary functions; improvement of agriculture and forestry is an integral part of resource development, while also reducing the sedimentation of reservoirs.

The TVA must not be appraised on a short-sighted–cost-profit basis. Its value as a proving ground for unified watershed development has infinitely greater significance, and its greatest contributions may be intangible. More or less incidental to the primary objective of flood prevention came some 650 miles of safely navigable waterways, dependable water supply, new and varied recreational opportunities, conservation of soils, forests, and wildlife, and vital contributions to our national defense. The modern Tennessee Valley is living proof that all our renewable resources are mutually interdependent and that their conservation can be best accomplished by careful coordination of selected improvements within a defined spatial unit. One particular resource may dominate the scene, but it should not be permitted to exclude others from appropriate attention. Total improvement must be the main objective whatever the initial line of departure.[17]

One cannot question the unique position of water as the fundamental resource, and the TVA has shown how well it serves as the center of reference for regional planning and conservation. A river is simply a distinct unit of circulating water, but all its branches, or limbs, are integral parts of the body. All parts belong, and all must be attended. The primal character of water and the unitary behavior of a stream may well dominate not only the theory, but also the future practice, of conservation in general. Water divides may well attain much greater importance as boundaries than any arbitrary line between states. Our national domestic economy might some day revolve about river basins. At such time we may turn to TVA and other valley experiments for help with such perplexing questions as these: Should any valley authority be established without the express wish or approval of citizens resident in the area involved? Should the local people themselves organize and operate any such project? Should many small dams be built in preference to a few big ones? Where should the priority of work be between the trunk stream and its tributaries? Should dams be merely sited by the central authority, and the sites leased to private companies? Should structures publicly built be leased or sold to private interests upon completion? Should the power market be held within the minimum seasonal output of hydroelectric plants, or should supplemental thermal (i.e., fuel-burning), power units be installed to absorb the load during periods of slack water? Should any state be deprived of its best (river bottom) land by reservoir flooding in order to protect the land of another state downstream from flood damage? How

National economy might revolve about river basins

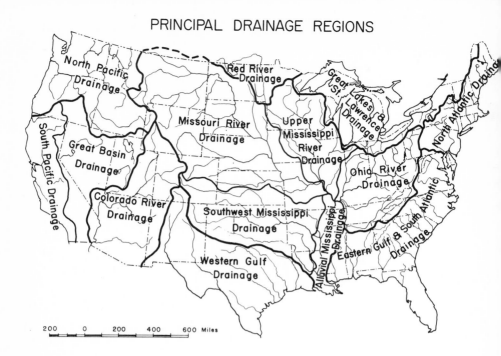

PRINCIPAL DRAINAGE REGIONS

Fig. 10.16 *Our national economy might revolve about the major drainage basins, with development appropriate to each of their tributary divisions. (After map by National Resources Board.)*

should costs and indemnities be computed and distributed? In any case, what should be the minimum life expectancy of a project to justify its execution? Is the forty- or fifty-year amortization plan a valid criterion of project feasibility?

The map of principal drainage basins (Fig. 10.16) shows a logical division of our nation into compartments for water management and other conservation programs. In most of these watersheds work is already well advanced. Watersheds, large and small, are in various stages of planned, unified development, modeled more or less after the TVA. They operate under a variety of administrative structures: some intrastate; some interstate; some in groups of states or parts of states; at least two (involving the Delaware and Susquehanna Rivers), with several states and the Federal government cooperating; and several under international treaties. For adequate water-quality control, if for no other purpose, we need coordinated surveillance over every stream system from one end to the other, as was instituted on the Ohio before its sanitation made much progress.[18]

Do not exaggerate watershed virtues

Although they are, indeed, manifold, the merits and potentials of watershed management should not be exaggerated. Watershed boundaries are definite and convenient but not sacred or in-

264

violate. Many divides, or water-partings, between watersheds have been artificially breached. The city of Denver draws water from headwaters of the Colorado River by tunnels driven through the Continental Divide, and without moral stigma.

The limitations of a river for producing hydroelectricity should be acknowledged. The most powerful river, *fully harnessed,* may be utterly inadequate as energy source for a populous valley. Only slightly more than one-fourth of the power generated by TVA in 1961 came from hydroelectric plants.[19] The usefulness of rivers for power is being enhanced considerably by the hydraulic legerdemain exposed by Fig. 10.17.

Even in watersheds such as the Wabash, which is notoriously prone to flooding, water disposal for flood prevention must not be so drastic that storage for other purposes becomes inadequate. Water requirements for thermal-electric power generation are

Fig. 10.17 *Pumped-back storage renders thermal-electric and hydro-power combinations even more complementary than otherwise. During periods of slack power demand, water from the lower pool is pumped back behind the main dam in readiness for turning the water turbines to meet peak power demands. With or without pumped storage, the so-called "auxiliary" steam plants have become the principal facilities. (Conceptual drawing from 1961 Report, the Secretary of the Interior.)*

Fig. 10.18 *The TVA's Kingston steam plant, largest steam-electric station in the United States. (See its location in Figure 10.15.) The plant has nine generating units with a combined rated capacity of 1,440,000 Kw and a capability of 1,600,000 Kw. Its efficiency ratio (Kw-Btu) is among the highest in the country. At full capacity on all units, the plant consumes about 14,750 tons of coal per day and uses about 1,177 million gallons of water. The condenser cooling water (almost 93 per cent of water used) is heated 13.05° F. between intake and discharge. (Courtesy Gilbert Stewart, Jr.; T.V.A. photo.)*

second only to those for hydropower (Fig. 10.18); provision should be made to store enough floodwater for operating steam plants during drought.

Most important of all, one should remember that full implementation of a watershed plan or program, involving all the land and other resources, cannot be achieved quickly! The Tennessee leads the field, however, in both unified engineering and in integrated conservation. Though well planned and farthest developed, the TVA project, after three decades of operation, still awaits much of the land-use rehabilitation essential to its full realization. While forests burn and red mud runs into the reservoirs, the plan remains only partially executed. No amount of engineering can conserve a drainage basin without the aid of good land utilization.

The idealist might wish all watersheds completely reforested, but the practical conservator must arrive at a workable compromise between water management and land occupance. If we eject farmers from our drainage basins, where will they farm? If there be no food, who will use all the water? In valley bottoms agriculture, grazing, and forestry will inevitably yield space to water storage, but on the slopes that feed the reservoirs they must be reconciled with water "production." Few wilderness areas remain available for water storage, and fewer still lie sufficiently near settlement to render their water presently valuable for controlled use. Highly industrialized valleys, such as the upper tributaries of the Ohio about Pittsburgh, prohibit the kind of watershed development that involves big dams, because it would cost entirely too much to relocate industrial plants and facilities. For the visible future at least, such industrialized valleys cannot be dammed and flooded for water storage as was the Tennessee. Their improvement will be served better by small dams and good land-use management at their headwaters. Conservation of land and soil about its tributaries is in any case the most effective and permanent way of regulating the main trunk of a stream.

Extension of unified river basin development depends upon centralized planning and coordination by state and national agencies. Whether we like it or not, certain aspects of water conservation exceed the scope and capability of any private enterprise. Delinquent public action to reduce flood damage and extend vital waterways reflects lack of public understanding. We have just begun flood prevention. We debated for half a century the unique opportunity afforded by the Great Lakes–St. Lawrence system for transportation. A threatened shortage of domestic iron ore and increasing dependence upon imported ores opened our eyes and brushed aside selfish sectional interests. The life of our inland steel empire was insured by Congress in 1954 when the St. Lawrence Seaway project was finally approved.

Public concern with the conservation of land and water in small watersheds became formalized in 1954 with passage of Public Law 566, the Watershed Protection and Flood Prevention Act. Under that act, as amended, local residents may organize their own corporate authority over the watershed in which they live, not to exceed 250,000 acres in area. They may then receive technical assistance from the SCS and cost-sharing benefits from the ASCP for planning and executing comprehensive development of the small watershed, the fundamental management unit (Fig. 10.19).

As of December 1, 1961, 365 such projects, encompassing some

Public Law 566

Fig. 10.19 *Looking headward up Pleasant Valley in Winona County, Minnesota. This little watershed is fringed by wooded drainage divides unsuitable for cultivation. Each small tributary, best observable left of center, has a miniature watershed of its own that drains into the main stream. All the runoff from the entire watershed flows out at lower right, and thence mingles with waters of another drainage system. (S.C.S. photo.)*

21 million acres, had been authorized for operations; 693 projects, totaling about 49 million acres had been approved for planning; and the Soil Conservation Service had received 1,605 additional applications for assistance on almost 113.5 million acres.[20] Some 470 flood-water–retarding structures had been completed before the end of fiscal year 1961. Development activities under other land and water management laws were also progressing rapidly.

In a national inventory of soil and water-conservation needs accomplished in 1958, 13,000 small watersheds were delineated in the contiguous forty-eight states; of these, almost twelve thousand have a size suitable for projects under Public Law 566.[21] Some eight thousand three hundred of them need project action of one kind or another, and many have multipurpose potential. However encouraging, our work thus far is but a prelude to the organized land management we must ultimately achieve. When headwaters (small watersheds) become well managed, such downstream rampage as depicted in Fig. 10.20 will be bridled at its source and the master streams will be more amenable to useful regulation.

The multiple-use concept pertaining to land has been so fre-

DOWNSTREAM FLOOD DAMAGES IN THE UNITED STATES

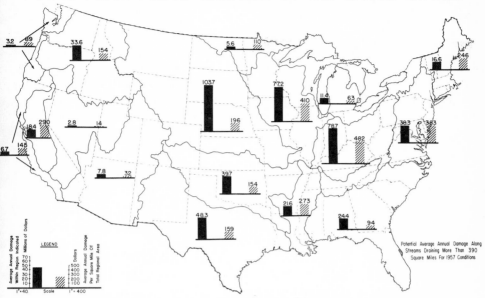

Fig. 10.20 *Big dams become more effective when adequately reinforced with many small ones upstream. (Corps of Engineers map.)*

quently enunciated in legislation, both by direction and implication, that the instances cannot be cited here. Suffice to say that any appropriation of land for one special use exclusively has become suspect and subject to close scrutiny and deliberate adjudication. No longer do our superhighway engineers officiously sight the shortest distance between two points without some regard for the quality of the land they will mutilate! In most management projects the planner must, by law, give heed to possible integration or combination of land uses, whatever his primary objective. No project contemplated under Public Law 566 can be approved before the plans have been coordinated with agencies representing wildlife and other interests. Neither will the Federal Power Commission, which has final authority over site selection and construction of power installations, issue a license before determining that the proposed project will achieve maximum use of one resource with the least possible injury to others and that unavoidable damage will be amply justified by net gains. Checks and balances help ensure us a good equation of resource development.

Coordinated multiple use

The Multiple Surface Use Act of 1955 reserves for the Federal

**Surface
and
subterranean
or
submarine**

government surface rights to nonpatented mineral claims on public land and charges the Bureau of Land Management with the
conservation of nonmineral resources on such claims. The claim-
ant must confine himself to mining, without damaging surface
resources unduly. Similar federal authority should be extended
to patents under the mining laws to stop abusive practices, even
though a patent conveys title to the land as private property
under the General Mining Law of 1872. Through the issuance
of patents, permits, and licenses, and the negotiation of leases,
the Bureau of Land Management governs all mining on public
lands and lands in the outer continental shelf. From these lands
come substantial contributions to our mineral production, especially of gas and oil, phosphate, potash, salt, and sulfur.[22] The
adjudication of surface and subsurface values, the constant surveillance over authorized operations, and the prohibition of
trespass are monumental tasks for our national custodial agency,
especially since federal resource management often sets a standard
to which state, corporate, and private interests must conform.

All the land classes and patterns aforementioned have their
places in our national conservation of natural resources. Some
are less conspicuous on the land than others; but each has its
niche in the total landscape. The conservator observes them when
he travels and takes patriotic pride in every view that evinces
competent resource stewardship.

11

Wildlife: Functions and Abuses

we have often maligned and abused the fellow creatures that render our environment tenable

Broadly interpreted, "wildlife" embraces all native life forms, both plant and animal, which are not domesticated or cultivated but survive in their wild state.[1] Plants grown as crops and animals raised for market or to produce a marketable commodity fall outside the pale. The term *wildlife* connotes freedom and not captivity, independence rather than helplessness.

Wildlife resources are renewable, or perpetual, because, being alive, they renew themselves as long as they can reproduce. The powerful instincts of survival and regeneration place wildlife resources in a unique category. Given half a chance, they multiply and retain their respective positions in the total landscape. However, those which have been exterminated are more completely expended than an oil pool pumped dry, and those which have lost the capacity to survive without special attention or care have also lost the most distinctive characteristic of wildlife, namely *wildness*. Herds of game fed like cattle lose their wildlife status much as soil loses its true character when its upper horizon washes away. Prairie grasses lost their durability when the plow turned them upside down, and remnants of the rich plant community that was once true tall-grass prairie are now a rare sight. Thus some wildlife resources have already been expended, some have lost their natural character, and still others stand in

Broadly
interpreted,
"wildlife"
embraces
all native plants
and animals

271

imminent danger of one of these fates. Let us say that wildlife resources *should* be perpetual, and would be so, but for our inept or abusive treatment.

This chapter, and the next as well, treats wildlife in accordance with a somewhat restricted and popular definition: "fishes, birds, mammals, and the related association of fields, forests, and waters." [2] Emphasis will be on animals rather than on plants, although the two primary divisions of life cannot be divorced. We shall further limit our discussion by excluding the biota which support our commercial fisheries; those will be treated in Chapter 14. Thus the two chapters now at hand deal primarily with land animals and the animals of little inland waters, with attention also to the plants upon which the animals depend. And let us remember that all live in a competitive world. More than any other resource, wildlife depends upon natural balance and adjustment to persistent cyclic change. The conservator treads lightly where fools rush in with hobnailed boots!

Animals are both part and product of the basic resource complex: water; land; soil; vegetation. Their category is high man on the environmental totem pole—an integral constituent of the landscape. Animals assist with the formation of soil, which produces plant growth, upon which animal life depends. Therein lies a fundamental natural cycle that must be respected in wildlife conservation. We are here concerned mainly with the higher animal forms—the vertebrates, especially mammals, fishes, and fowls.

Animal resources are part and product of the basic resources

For the first time in this volume we are dealing with resources capable, within certain limits, of adjusting to a changing environment or moving to one more suitable. For the first time we deal with resources that participate actively in their own conservation—now cooperative, now reticent, but always responsive to the skillful conservator. Animals are often more helpful by instinct than are their would-be benefactors by artificial means.

As the product of other resources, animals are often best conserved by conserving those resources upon which they depend. *A healthy combination of water, soil, and vegetative cover is our most positive assurance of a healthy wildlife community.* Herbivorous species thrive when their favored plant association remains intact, carnivora thrive on fat vegetarians, and omnivorous kinds, who take meat with their potatoes, do well when either flesh or vegetable foods are readily available. Mutuality permeates the good biotic community, and if one constituent be lost the others suffer.

By the same token, one of the basic resources cannot alone sustain a healthy wildlife; all must be in as good balance as possible. Being farther up the resource scale, wildlife demonstrates more positively than any other the interdependence of renewable resources and the unity that must pervade their conservation. Wastage of other resources is usually inimical to wildlife; conservation of other resources is generally beneficial.

During many centuries preceding the advent of Europeans, Indians and wild animals lived in ecological harmony on the North American continent. Animals supplied many needs for food, clothing, and shelter, and the red men usually killed no more than they could use. There were few Indians and many animals; so, neither jeopardized the other's existence. Wildlife habitats remained almost undisturbed, and natural increase kept pace with the kill.[3]

A rich fauna inhabited the American wilderness

To this savage serenity came predaceous white men with lethal firearms and burning ambitions—and the scene changed. They found wildlife of such variety and abundance as they had never imagined, and could not possibly foresee the decimation that would result from three centuries of "civilized" settlement on the land. Old men now living have seen in their youth such numbers of fish, fowl, and grazing herds that their assertions lend credence to earlier records of flocks that darkened the skies, herds that dotted the plains, and fishes so crowded in shallow creeks that one could catch them with his bare hands. The land in many areas fairly crawled with life, and it is almost incredible that civilization could so quickly threaten the survival of many species.

The rich fauna of the forty-eight contiguous states numbers 2,368 vertebrate species, including 670 mammals, 811 birds, 149 reptiles, 138 amphibians, and 600 fresh-water fishes. Among the mammals are 116 fur bearers.[4] A score or two of species endemical to Alaska and Hawaii were added when those territories became states in 1959. Species classed as "game" constitute only about 10 per cent of the total; species of commercial use only about 7 per cent.[5] Most of the others are beneficial to us, or at least harmless.

Without abundant wildlife the sturdy pioneer would have been hard put to it for meat as he pushed back frontiers. Powder and shot were his shopping money; with them he got food and clothing when no other source availed. They provided him with roast fowl, steaks, moccasins, jerked venison, candles, robes, window panes, buckskin shirts and breeches, and grease with which to keep his musket oiled. More as provider than protector he treasured his trusty musket above all other possessions. Neither

His musket meant food and clothing to the sturdy pioneer

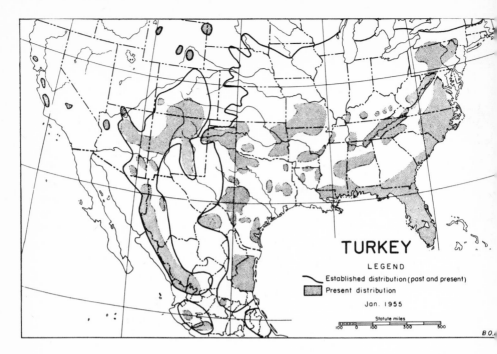

Fig. 11.1 *Clearing of forest and woodland evicted the turkey, America's contribution to the poultry line. The distribution of this magnificent game bird has been extended considerably since the map above was prepared. Habitat: Chiefly forested country varying in type with the geographical area and race of turkey: Eastern races chiefly deciduous forest or southern pines; Rio Grande race chiefly scrub mesquite and live-oak woodland, or cottonwood borders of streams in grassland areas; Rocky Mountain and Mexican races chiefly mountain pine-oak forest. Range: Native to eastern and southwestern United States, much of Mexico, and extreme southern tip of Ontario, Canada. Now extirpated over much of its original range, particularly in the eastern United States and in Mexico. Established after introduction outside original range in Wyoming, South Dakota, and California. (Figs. 11.1, 11.2, and 11.4 from Circular 34, Fish and Wildlife Service. Maps by Bess MacMaugh.)*

plow nor ax surpassed the muzzle loader as an implement for taming the wilderness. Its rank is well symbolized in our cherished tradition of Thanksgiving turkey (Fig. 11.1).

It was most fortunate that our frontiersmen could live "off the land," but it is tragic that they unwittingly instituted a "scorched-earth policy." Quite innocently and to good purpose they initiated many of the problems we are here concerned with solving, but some things that they had in untold numbers have now vanished from the land.

Fur bearers lured trapper and trader across the continent

Food and raiment for its conquerors were not the only contributions of wildlife to formative American history. The fur bearers lured trapper and trader across the continent in quest of the pelts that constituted one of America's first great export commodities. The demand for furs made Indians commercial trappers. Trading posts for gathering in the pelts became vanguards of civilization and the basis for political claim to territory. Beavers probably did more than statesmanship to secure our hold on the great Northwest. Astor and other Americans outmaneuvered the Hudson's Bay Company before the 49th Parallel became an established boundary. American fortunes famed to this day were built on the lucrative fur trade. St. Louis became renowned as a fur market long before the birth of the "blues."

Fine furs gave the United States prestige in world trade, but trappers took the skins faster than the animals could multiply and produce them. Men overtrapped the fur resources in much the same manner as other men overcropped, overgrazed, overfished, and overlogged other assets that also could have been self-perpetuating.

The fur business swept across the country far ahead of systematic land utilization. Fur bearers felt the sting of civilization long before the main force of mankind arrived. Then, with the advance of settlement, wildlife generally shrank and retreated. Man was the master. He converted the land to his own use without regard for those creatures he dispossessed. He felled the forest, broke the sod, drained the marshes, and flooded the stream bottoms, so that he might raise cultivated plants and domesticated animals. It was well and good that he should adapt to his purposes the land suitable for them, but tragedy it was, indeed, that he cleared and burned, plowed and drained many areas that would have served him much better in their natural state and as homes for wildlife. By drainage alone he ruined the wildlife habitat and water-storage capacities of some hundred million acres.[6] Perhaps our greatest attrition of wildlife has been passive and unintentional—by usurping or ruining every sort of natural habitat (Fig. 11.2).

Wildlife shrank with the advance of settlement

But much of our destruction was willful; some of it so shameful that one hesitates to mention it. We became killers by ignorance, without qualms or conscience. We killed as if impelled by some diabolical obsession to destroy every wild thing. We killed for sale and we killed for sport, just to see the fur or feathers fly. We killed on suspicion and on prejudice, and we killed without pretext or provocation; there are those who continue the wanton slaughter even now.

We became killers through ignorance

Being conspicuous by their size and often too bold for their own good, the ungulata—hooved mammals such as antelope, elk, and bison—were primary targets in the war of destruction. In the Eastern forests they had some concealment, even after farmers

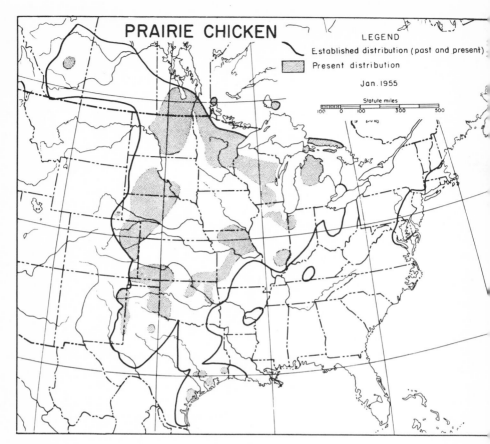

Fig. 11.2 *The prairie chicken retreated when clearing, drainage, and cultivation destroyed its habitat. Most of its range has been appropriated by the exotic ring-necked pheasant, now one of the leading "American" game birds. Habitat. Natural grasslands, particularly of the savannah type with mixed grassland and groves of trees or brushy growth. The extinct eastern race (heath hen) lived in semiopen mixed scrub oak and low bushy heath of the sandy coastal plain. The southwestern race (lesser prairie chicken) lives in mixed shinnery oak and grassland. The Gulf-coast race (Atwater's prairie chicken) inhabits the moist, open coastal prairie. The central race (greater prairie chicken) lives in a variety of natural grassland types from extensively open to quite brushy; also man-made openings in the Great Lakes region. Range. Open parts of the central and eastern United States and southern Canada. Formerly present, now extirpated on northern Atlantic seaboard. Much restricted in other parts of its former range. Northern populations at least partially migratory.*

moved in, but on the prairie plains, with no place to hide, the wild beasts stood little chance against armed men on fleet horses.

On the open grasslands one of the most shameful atrocities in American history was perpetrated against the magnificent bison. His very usefulness condemned him. Pony-riding Indians of the plains put up a formidable defense of their heritage against designing white men until the white men decimated the animals upon which the Indians depended. Cut off from their "base" of supplies, the Indians were soon routed, and the land was secured for settlement. Hunters and soldiers killed the bison and ousted the Indian to appropriate for crops much land that plowing and cultivation exposed to ruin. The abuse of land discussed in Chapter 7 began with the passing of the emblematic beast of our grasslands. Of an estimated 75 million bison that roamed in great herds when colonists first saw them on the Atlantic slope, only a few hundred survived the carnage.[7] Doubly tragic was the fact that Indians themselves sold for a pittance the hides of animals upon which their very lives depended.

Predators—such as wolves and foxes, owls and hawks—have been pursued relentlessly to protect domesticated animals. Men have indicted them on suspicion, convicted them on circumstantial evidence, even put a price on their heads (bounty) when, in fact, few have been "guilty as charged," and many should have been awarded medals for outstanding service. Figure 11.3 indicates how badly certain hawks have been maligned.

Killing of wildfowl for food markets flourished after the Civil War, probably reaching its peak in the 1880's and continuing past the turn of the century. Shooting and snaring went on most of the year, and markets were almost constantly glutted. The business was badly organized, refrigeration was elemental, handling so slow and crude that much of the game spoiled in transit. Birds that did arrive in good condition sold for a few cents a pair. Such was the ignominious fate of millions upon millions of passenger pigeons, prairie chickens, grouse, ducks, geese, upland plover, snipe, woodcock, quail, and other equally desirable game species.[8] Market shooting brought nobody much profit or benefit, but it brought disaster to wildfowl. Although now forbidden it is still practiced by many unscrupulous people.

Some creatures were killed because they looked menacing or because they seemed too numerous. Bears and wildcats that never invaded man's province were killed in their own haunts because men feared they might become hostile. Fish by the tub were fed to swine or spread on fields—away from the captor's domicile to spare him the annoyance of their stench. Untold numbers of pike and other species prized both for sport and flavor were so disgraced.

Wholesale slaughter, coupled with destruction and constriction of habitats, must inevitably lead to extirpation. And so it has. For a few species it is an accomplished fact. The passenger pigeons that once darkened the skies have vanished. So have the heath hen and the Labrador duck. The Carolina paroquet, the

Some species have vanished; others may go

DIET OF HAWKS (%)

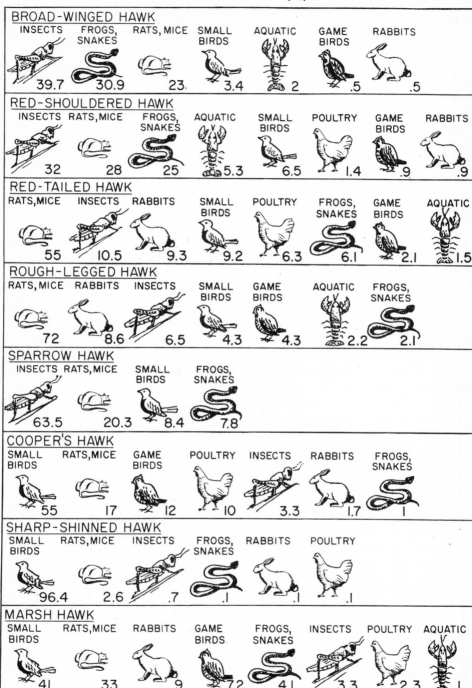

Fig. 11.3 *Evidence such as this helps exonerate those wrongly blamed. The numbers are percentages of diet. (From Circular 25, National Audubon Society.)*

only species of parrot once at home in the United States, has gone. The Cape Sable sparrow probably went with the 1937 hurricane. The whooping crane, the trumpeter swan, the bald eagle (national emblem), the California condor (largest American bird), the ivory-billed woodpecker, the everglade kite, the prairie chicken, the Nene goose, and others are so near extermination that their survival is in doubt. Once extinct, they are lost forever.

Human depredation has been no kinder to the mammals. The Maine mink, the Gull Island meadow mouse, the Eastern puma, the big-plains wolf, the Arizona elk, the Dakota bighorn sheep, and several types of grizzly bears have gone the way of dinosaurs and mastodons. The Arctic walrus appeared doomed by the very equipment with which he digs for a living until he was protected by federal law. His ivory tusks are worth $125 a pair; his skin as much as $150, if one inch or more thick. King Islanders derive half their income from the hunting and carving of ivory. Survival of the polar bear is threatened by trophy hunters. The Florida Key deer, the Florida manatee and crocodile, the fisher, the martin, the wolverine, the black-footed ferret, and the kit fox have three feet in the grave. Many of them will probably disappear despite our belated efforts to save them. Their pathetic remnants are not likely to survive the natural hazards of a biotic community in which they were once numerous or dominant. Even brutes are overwhelmed by the social persecution visited upon minorities. We have exhausted living resources that might have survived indefinitely; perhaps as long as man himself.

Extermination is not the only consequence of killing and encroachment. Abuses have reduced many remaining species to a pitiable state of dependence upon the human society that maligned them. Tame game, planted fish, and domesticated fur bearers are not our preference. They are substitutes; self-imposed penalties for waste and transgression. While it is rarely possible to restore a wilderness as we might wish to do, it is often possible to restore erstwhile wilderness residents so they can simulate normal functions or behavior, or preserve in a semiwild state a few specimens for our curious grandchildren.

Results of abuse: tame game, planted fish, synthetic habitats, and domestication

Big-game animals, herded and fed like so many cattle, have lost their true wildlife character and acquired closer kinship with a pet goat or the old brindled cow. Their dependence upon man, especially for winter feeding, has almost tamed the elk in Jackson Hole, Wyoming.

Because we ruined our lakes and streams or fished them dry, a substantial percentage of game fish are now hatched and reared from incubators and brooders like so many chicks. A few years ago it was customary to stock waters with fingerlings (minnow-size fish) and let them mature on their own. However, so many of them died soon after liberation that for such species as trout it was found more economical to rear them to legal size and then plant them where they would get caught before succumbing to natural causes. Perhaps the fly caster with fancy gear takes more pride in catching really wild trout, but if he does his angling near any populous area he is likely to catch only those reared and planted for him. But he seems to find it quite easy to flavor his pride with pan-fried trout and swallow the two together.

Hand feeding of big game, artificial propagation of fish and fowl, artificial defense against natural enemies and diseases are tacit admissions that the natural habitat has deteriorated so badly that the only apparent expedient is artificial correction. Wildlife

Table 1

Wild Fur Catch in the United States,* 1961

Numerical rank	Fur bearer	Number pelted (U.S.)	Leading State
1	Muskrat	4,421,338	Louisiana
2	Raccoon	1,099,699	Michigan
3	Nutria	730,912	Louisiana
4	Mink	297,216	Minnesota
5	Beaver	218,324	Alaska
6	Opossum	186,988	Missouri
7	Fox (Gray, Red, Cross, Silver, Blue, and White)	114,272	Wisconsin
8	Fur Seal	95,974	Pribilof Islands
9	Ringtail Cat	65,297	Texas
10	Skunk and Civet Cat	55,515	Minnesota
11	Weasel	24,070	Minnesota
12	Otter	15,353	Louisiana
13	Bobcat	10,477	Montana
14	Coyote	8,553	Wisconsin
15	Badger	6,518	South Dakota
16	Marten	6,490	Alaska
17	Lynx (Canadian)	1,120	Alaska
18	Fisher	858	Maine
19	Timber Wolf	828	Alaska
20	Wolverine	300	Alaska

* No data from Arizona, Georgia, Illinois, and Nevada. Beaver *only* reported by Connecticut, New Jersey, and Vermont; only beaver and fisher by Maine, fisher and otter by New York. In Hawaii no wild fur is harvested. Fox bountied (1961): Michigan—29,241; Minnesota—21,419.

Source: *Wildlife Leaflet 444*, Fish and Wildlife Service (Washington, D.C., 1962).

so pampered and protected has about as much wildness left in it as a caged canary in his old age.

Wild fur bearers contribute most of our annual fur crop, but the composition of the crop has changed greatly since the days when trappers and traders scoured the country for beaver, otter, martin, and other hairy aristocrats. The lowly muskrat has dethroned furred royalty and become far and away the most important American fur species. As may be noted in Table 1, muskrats contribute more than one-half of the wild fur catch numerically, and one in four or five of the muskrat skins comes from Louisiana. Center of American fur trapping has shifted from Northern forests to Southeastern coastal marshes, where now the exotic nutria contests the muskrat's sovereignty.

The lowly muskrat dethroned furred royalty

Commoners tolerant of man have gained prominence as others less sociable quit his presence. The ubiquitous cottontail rabbit, the odoriferous skunk, and the slovenly opossum accepted the human newcomers and found them to be fairly decent neighbors. Men planted whole fields of food where there was little before. They raised flocks of gullible chickens and trained them to roost regularly in the same place for easy stealing. They laid culverts in the ground like prefabricated dens, and they built barns and sheds under which families could be reared. They provided places of concealment under piles of brush, stone, or wood, and they erected barriers that stopped or confounded the canines. Except for their guns and traps they were most neighborly.

Commoners tolerant of man have gained prominence

Undaunted by human occupancy of the land, the cottontail has multiplied in the time-honored tradition of rabbits and risen to top position among American game animals. He attracts more hunters than any other species and provides our children one of their earliest contacts with wild creatures. Unless he disappoints us, he will still be the first game stalked by farm boys when they carry ray guns instead of air rifles.

We saw in Chapter 7 that grassland rodents prosper under abusive land utilization. On the other hand many upland species, both mammals and birds, are benefited by good land use. Productive, cultivated fields provide certain kinds of wildlife much more food than did the same areas in their natural state. Land abuse invites vermin, but good land use enriches desirable wildlife when the creatures are given an opportunity to live and raise families. Upon that singular land-life relationship we must base most of our plans and projects for wildlife conservation (Fig. 11.4).

Attempts to conserve selectively and eradicate those thought inimical to the chosen ones have complicated our wildlife prob-

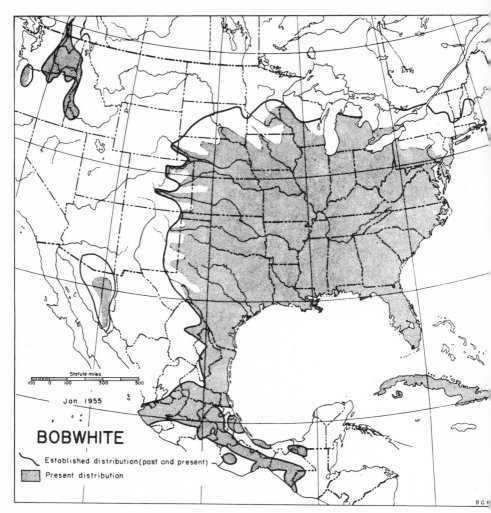

Statute miles
100   0   100   300   500

Jan. 1955

BOBWHITE

Established distribution (past and present)

Present distribution

Fig. 11.4 *Although the birds have retreated somewhat from the boundaries of their native range, the Bobwhite habitat generally has probably been improved more than it has been damaged. Range: Native to United States east of the Rocky Mountains and extreme southern Ontario, Canada; also in Cuba and a large part of Mexico. Established after introduction beyond its native range in eastern Washington and the Snake River valley of eastern Oregon and western Idaho. Habitat: Mixed brush and grassland types broken up into small areas of each. Open woodland, brushy and weedy fallow fields most characteristic of eastern races; brushy areas along stream courses on the western plains; brushy scrub oak or mesquite-cactus pastures for southwestern races. Usually mixed, disturbed habitats are best. The numerous Mexican races in the aggregate occupy nearly any type of open country from short grass prairie of Jalisco and mesquite-grasslands of Sonora, to savannahs in Chiapas.*

lems. People have been prone to classify all wild things as either desirable or undesirable, without qualification or compromise. They have branded whole groups as good or bad without determining the innocence or guilt of individual species (Fig. 11.3, Chapter 11). To protect domestic livestock against predators, states have voted large sums of money for bounties when it would have been much cheaper and more practical to pay for all the losses. In many states, the bounty system has, in fact, been abolished. Most naive of all our *selection* blunders has been our habit of denouncing a given predator wherever found, although the stigma might not be applicable away from the region that attached it. We do not display much brilliance when we kill predators where their prey does more damage than they do. The coyote has long been persecuted for killing lambs, but more recently he has also gained favor as a killer of rodents that ruin the range on which the lambs feed.

> "Judge not,
> that ye
> be not judged"

Animals, like men, are neither wholly good nor wholly bad. One may be more inclined to be good than another, but the best is liable to sin if the temptation is strong enough. None has immunity to the forces of circumstance. A fox in a steer pasture may be as innocent as a freshman at his fraternity initiation, but the same fox in a sheep fold and the same freshman at a sorority dance may be "wolves" as fierce as any. A vixen with a family is a menace in a poultry-raising community, but unless rabid, she is only a curiosity on a cattle ranch. Circumstance makes the difference.

Animals are partly good and partly bad by human standards. Probably none is entirely undesirable, but very few are without fault in relation to man's economy. The apparently harmless cottontail can be ruinous to fruit trees and berry bushes. When snow covers other food and orchards stand in deep drifts, the rabbit girdles the branches where they protrude through the snow. After the ladder he climbed has melted away the damage is so high on the tree that a novice would never identify the criminal. He is not a predator, yet he may prey on fruit growers who disdain repellent sprays.

Mistaken identity has been a costly error. Many useful species have suffered because they resemble destructive ones. Owls and hawks are excellent examples (Fig. 11.3). Because one or two of their kind affect man's interest negatively he has condemned all of them. Had Kipling meted out similar justice, the entire regiment would have hanged for Danny Deever's crime. The great horned owl and the Cooper's hawk are notorious killers of domestic fowl and small game, but most of their relatives are strictly honorable and have value for the control of mice and other rodents. Screech owls are such diligent mousers that they have been referred to as "self-setting mousetraps." [9] Other owls and several hawks have comparable merit.[10] Their worth as destroyers of vermin is, indeed, gaining recognition, as evinced by state legislation. Connecticut passed a law in 1951 protecting *all* raptors (owls, hawks, and others), and before 1960 fifteen other states had followed the example. Half of the states have laws that protect some raptors but specifically exclude certain species.[11] A score of states blacklist accipiters, and an equal number the great horned owl, the magnificent silent marauder. Seven hold a public grudge against the peregrine (duck hawk), and two were bountying the golden eagle when Congress voted its protection in 1962. Six states protect neither hawks nor owls of any kind,[12] and they might be well advised to consider timely legislation. To kill a raptor caught in the act of attacking a domestic animal must be permissible, of course, but the killing of innocent birds should not be condoned. Where protective laws have been enacted, their enforcement needs improvement generally.

Foxes and other wild predators have often been convicted of crimes committed by house cats, which, when abandoned, become feral, and destroyers of birds and upland wildfowl. The fox was the bird hunter's "public enemy number 1" until it was discovered that he may prefer mice to quail. The house cat on the prowl hunts birds both on the ground and in trees, and her mousing services may be inadequate payment. In the "Deep South" where tenant farmers move frequently and carry with them more superstitions than furnishings, it is a "bad sign" to move a cat. So the cat stays behind, often becoming a menace to wildlife. (Stray dogs, and dogs permitted to roam at will, are also destructive of small game and ground-nesting wildfowl.) Foxes have probably done less damage in most places than cats; yet, the fox has had a price on his head while the cat goes scot-free. The conscientious nimrod of today shoots stray cats on sight, as a sort of community service in appreciation of hunting privileges.

In the event that a given species becomes intolerably destructive in a certain situation, as might be anticipated in our "civilized" environment, the menace should be destroyed without hesitation; however, let it not be attempted by offering a bounty for killing the villain. Bounty systems for the control of predators have failed generally, except as they have profited bounty hunters. Yet, as recently as 1959 thirty-one states variously bountied one or more of twenty-five bird and animal species and disbursed in bounty payments almost 2 million dollars annually without significant results.[13] (North Dakota discontinued all bounties in 1961.) Some of the most bountied animals—foxes and coyotes—appear to thrive better under a bounty than without, as do also several less infamous. Bounty laws should be repealed, and the funds diverted to more constructive use.

Bountied Animals in Various Parts of the United States

Blackbird	Ground squirrel	Fox
Crow	Jack rabbit	Bobcat
Great horned owl	Pocket gopher	Coyote
Raven	Porcupine	Wolf
Rattlesnake	Weasel	Mountain lion
Copperhead	Wild Belgian hare	Wolverine
Hair seal	Wild German hare	Lynx
	Woodchuck	Bear

From *Sports Afield*, July 1959, and Bureau of Sport Fisheries and Wildlife, January 1963.

When predators are exterminated their prey often multiplies so rapidly that starvation finally checks its number. We abhor scavengers like turkey buzzards who clean up the remains, and we foolishly bounty the predators that would obviate most of our need for the clean-up service. Since the weak and sick are most easily killed, "survival of the fittest" tends to improve the stock upon which predators feed. Eluded by the more vigorous survivors, the killers raise smaller families to stay within the budget. With less carrion about, the scavengers also thin their ranks, and a balanced ratio of all becomes more or less stabilized. The human hunter might well ponder more deliberately his hostile attitude toward brute competitors. His may be the choice between sharing a few live deer and quail with other predators or consigning many dead ones to scavengers. Errors of human judgment have created many wildlife problems that the animals themselves might have solved. Passive tolerance can accomplish more, in many cases, than the most determined attempt to regiment. Nature has its own system of selection,[14] and nature's system has been working a long, long time.

All creatures have some function in the complex operation of natural biotic equilibrium, though many, such as reptiles and rodents, are repulsive and despicable in the eyes of some humans. Snakes give some people goose pimples, and rodents are known to carry dread diseases transmissible to humans, i.e., bubonic plague and tularemia. But our contempt for these groups has been no more discriminating than our hostility toward predators.

Kill the snake, and avenge Mother Eve!

We have permitted individual species and isolated misdemeanors to incriminate a whole genus or family without weighing the merits of an individual member in particular circumstances.

We are not snake haters by instinct, nor snake killers by religious conviction; but, most of us have been taught to kill a snake on sight. Our acquired aversion is certainly impractical, if not sacrilegious, because many snakes and other reptiles are, indeed, not enemies, but servants of man, living in mortal fear of their master.

Snakes are active destroyers of rodents, and many a Southern farmer keeps a pet blacksnake about his place or a pair of rat snakes in his corn crib to discourage vermin. This is not a plea for the protection of snakes, which most of us abhor, but merely to illustrate that even our most despised creatures do have merit and fit into the scheme of things somehow.

Mice bother men when men invite them

Rodents and other little mammals have been broadly maligned because a few here and there have become a local nuisance. In most such cases man's own abuse of the biotic community invited the trouble. In this and preceding chapters we have mentioned several instances: eviction of predators from fields and orchards; depletion of the range; disruption of forest society by clear cutting the timber. In each case certain rodents multiply beyond their normal abundance and become destructive pests; mice become menacing under poorly laid plans of men. Prairie dogs mutilate the range when it has been overgrazed and cleared of coyotes; rabbits girdle fruit trees and mice injure the roots when hawks, owls, foxes, and weasels have been routed from the orchard; squirrels, chipmunks, and mice devour the seeds and seedlings that would make them a new home when natural enemies quit the scene and normal food supplies fail. In a deranged environment the little fellows can be extremely detrimental to the basic resources upon which they and all higher animals depend.

A gardener sees little virtue in moles and shrews when they furrow his beautiful lawn or when one of the busy little beasts tunnels the length of a newly sprouted row, leaving the young plants suspended in air. A farmer condemns the pocket gopher for every mound that dulls his mower sickle, and he has equal contempt for ground squirrels that steal his seed corn right out of the hills as if schooled in geometry. An apple grower loses patience with mice when they accept the mulch about his trees as an invitation to set up housekeeping among the roots. And the keeper of chickens maligns the mouse-killing weasel when that sly hunter trespasses in the hen house. Yet all these industrious culprits have hidden virtues that may exceed their vices.

Our field-mouse population has been estimated at 21 billion, which is quite reasonable when one considers that a female mouse will breed at the age of four weeks and may have seventeen litters a year, with five or six babies in each litter.[15] A few happy families in a field of grain can destroy 20 per cent of the crop, which should be ample reason for a farmer to encourage both feathered and furred predators that might reduce his loss.

The insectivorous mole in his ceaseless toil to satiate a voracious appetite consumes vast numbers of grubs and worms that might otherwise plague the gardener. All burrowers—be they moles, gophers, ground squirrels, mice, rats, or prairie dogs— perform a unique and valuable function in soil development and maintenance. While they live, their nests and mounds add vegetable matter, and after they die their bodies make further addition to organic content. Their burrows improve aeration, facilitate the infiltration of water, and increase the capacity for water storage. Any country schoolboy who has enjoyed the sport knows that it takes considerable water to "drown" a ground squirrel out of his hole. However, unless he be taught, the boy might overlook the implication that ground squirrels improve water reception and increase water storage. To see the good in some of our fellows one must look beneath the surface, and he may have to look twice to establish the guilt of a suspect. Many a mole has been wrongfully accused of eating holes in roots or tubers, when in fact a mouse got into his run and did the damage. The poor, blind mole was merely an accessory before the fact, or so hungry for meat that, when he found no grubs, he reluctantly settled for potatoes.

Even the mammalian "underground" has virtue

Birds are not all song and plumage, not all purity and innocence. Many have neither beauty nor musical talent. Some serve us with distinction, and others are apparently useless, if not actually harmful. Birds have caused many people to die in airplane crashes. Blackbirds, and starlings, in great, noisy flocks, often wreak havoc on fields and farmsteads, devouring crops and feed stores or soiling them so badly that livestock will not eat what is left. Roosting areas in which the flocks congregate at night become mutilated and mired with filth—the *unlovely* work of birds. Dozens of winter roosts in southeastern United States, some with millions of birds concentrated in one place, have become objects of special study by Fish and Wildlife Service biologists seeking effective means of curbing the depredations.[16]

Birds are not all song and plumage

Excepting those listed below, virtually all birds in the United States are protected by acts of Congress.

Some Common Birds Not Protected by Federal Law

Ibises	Crows, ravens, jays
Pelicans	Starlings
Cormorants	English sparrows
Anhingas	All hawks and owls

Source: *Wildlife Leaflet 432*, Fish and Wildlife Service (Washington, D.C., 1961).

Purely aesthetic and sentimental values place birds high on our wildlife list. Their intangible enrichment of our lives would be sufficient reason for protecting them were more concrete justification entirely lacking. The cheering song of the cardinal on a balmy morning in spring, the reassurance of the robin after a rainstorm, the liquid notes of the meadow lark from far across the pasture on a bright summer day, the excited scolding of the catbird when an intruder approaches its nest and the angry chatter of the saucy little wren under similar circumstances, the demonic scream of the mischievous bluejay, the haunting staccato of an owl, or the brave call of a whippoorwill in the stillness of night—mere sounds, but sounds associated with a thousand cherished memories—these would be reason enough for counting songbirds among our natural resources.

Nor must they make noise to be esteemed. Who would discount the worth of the swallows who plastered their mud nests on the great hewn beam in the old barn, of the robins who reared a brood in the box elder by the kitchen window, or of the wrens who appropriated grandma's clothespin bag for half a summer. Such values defy auditing, and enviable is the man who has known them.

While most of us view a pretty bird with admiration, others see in handsome plumage a marketable commodity. In the past many nongame species died that their feathers might decorate millinery. Many egrets, herons, grebes, terns, and gulls gave their lives to "feather merchants" who supplied ornament for ingenious contraptions worn on ladies' heads. Egrets and terns were almost extirpated for the purpose before laws restricted feather traffic and forbade the killing of the birds.[17] Recovery of plumage birds under legal protection first demonstrated the effectiveness of such measures. In the case of gulls protection appears to have been overdone.[18]

Birds have considerable functional significance, and the value of a given species is reflected mainly in its choice of foods. Insect eaters, such as bluebirds, swallows, wrens, titmice, and meadow larks are definitely useful, as are also the seed eaters, such as sparrows, finches, and red-winged blackbirds.

A bird
in the bush
is worth two
in the hand

Considering that birds are heavy eaters, one must acknowledge their unique service in combating weed and insect pests. Examination of stomach contents has revealed that birds consume prodigious quantities of insects and seeds, much of their diet noxious. However, there is less evidence to prove that birds actually prevent infestations of weeds or mass invasions of harmful insects. The bird enthusiast may be prone to give our avian folk more credit than they deserve. Here again arises the pertinent question of biologic balance and environmental unity to which an adequate answer still lies beyond our poor powers of perception. As with predator control, the most obvious interpretation may be the one utterly wrong.

From the standpoint of direct economic liability many of our fine-feathered friends often provoke persecution more than they elicit praise—always according to the circumstances. Bobolinks in a rice field, linnets in an orchard, or robins in a strawberry patch can be intolerably destructive. Crows in a young corn field pulling out the sprouts, or mallards in a ripe field of grain can ruin the crop and cause heavy loss to the farmer. This, despite the fact that the same birds may have rendered yeoman service in another season or in another place.[19] Broad generalizations do not fit birds any better than they fit quadrupeds or men. The insect eaters destroy good insects along with the bad ones. A main course of weevils may be followed with ladybirds for dessert. The seed eaters frequently fill up on cultivated crops and ignore the weeds. Furthermore, while destroying some seeds they spread others by voiding them undigested and while combating plant parasites they also carry plant diseases. The sapsuckers, maligned members of the woodpecker family, may cause some injury to trees, but who can say positively that their taste for hickory sap has no desirable influence in the long train of forest succession? Certain it is that their cousins, the woodpeckers, combat destructive forest insects.

One need not exaggerate their virtues to accord songbirds resource status. No other resource is more universally appreciated. In city, town, and country their company is enjoyed. Their services to land use are invaluable, probably indispensable. As noted, sportsmen are beginning to learn that there can be no game without conservation of the fundamental resources—water, soil, forest, and grassland. If game can sell the idea to sportsmen, perhaps songbirds should be employed to sell nonsportsmen the critical concepts of conservation. Birds take wing when soils and water fail. Their songs are evidence of a tenable environment.

Even the least of our fellow creatures have their places in nature's plan. Insects, worms, and spiders serve unique purposes in the total environment, although an adequate explanation of their virtues would go far beyond the scope of this volume. Neither can we attempt an objective appraisal of handsome butterflies, musical cicadas, or fascinating lightning bugs except to observe that their advertisements may be deceiving. The butterflies lay eggs that hatch into worms, the musicians have voracious appetites, and, though they set nothing afire, the torch bearers have destructive propensities. To say that grubs are mole food, earthworms are robin food, and spiders are humming-bird food would be pointless, except that those tidbits furnish energy for more useful functions—to the mole for soil working, to the robin for bug catching, and to the humming bird for pollen distribution.

Most important, perhaps, is the function of one in control of another, so that all together maintain a healthy, balanced environment. The prey-predator concept holds for large and small alike, right down to the spider and the fly. That is one reason for the controversy in scientific circles provoked by our increasing use of selective toxic sprays to kill injurious organisms, inevitably killing some good ones along with the bad. It is conceivable that we may initiate a biotic chain reaction fraught with danger.[20] If by killing one pest we encourage another until that one must also be eradicated, and we then eradicate each one in turn as it becomes a threat, we should finally have no life at all, but a sterile void instead.

More practical than theoretical is the work of ants and earthworms in soil development, the work of bees, moths, and wasps in plant fertilization, and the work of other legions in converting organic matter into humus and plant nutrients. It would seem only fair that ants should pasture their aphids on plants grown from soil the ants helped to build. They become enemies only when they herd their "cows" to the wrong pastures, such as chrysanthemums, roses, and fruit trees. The best have some evil in them; the worst, some good. Conflict and contradiction run the gamut of wildlife behavior, from bears and birds to bugs and bees. Human regulation demands extreme caution. Patience, tolerance, and careful research can more surely conserve wildlife than hasty interference and regimentation. One group of creatures cannot be modified without influencing another.

12

Wildlife Conservation

by better behavior as a member of the animal community man improves his own estate

In wildlife conservation we have the advantage of dealing with resources that live and move, with a certain capacity for adaptation to environmental change, and a strong, instinctive faculty to fend for themselves. Being mobile, animals can seek and select new habitats when old ones become untenable—a power denied forest and grass resources and bestowed on fish less liberally than on land creatures. Only the living resources can react to a situation; only the animal kinds can cooperate actively. Given a modicum of habitable space, with food, water, and shelter, wild things take care of themselves. All that need be done to have desirable populations of them is to allow them necessary space (some require very little), to spare enough of them to breed, and to prevent their increase beyond the capacity of the allotted habitat.

We cannot pretend to restore the wildlife environment that was the American wilderness. Only a few scattered remnants remain essentially intact, mainly high among our Western mountains; even their wildness is not everywhere "primitive," but rather a matter of degree. We cannot hope to restore to its original abundance the wildlife our country once knew; nor would we wish to do so if we could. We do not intend to consign much land to the sole occupance of wild things, though some

Can we regain a favorable balance and truly conserve our wildlife resources?

291

portions might better be so utilized. Neither do we intend to regain or retain, except in a few "wild" areas, the *natural* biotic balance that once prevailed.

Wildlife conservation need not conflict with other more productive resource developments. It should be a part of them. It must impose no obstacle to economic gain or cultural progress but should enhance both. It must not interfere with the use of land for crops, pasture, and forest, though it can materially enrich all three.[1] In general, wildlife production must be incidental to agriculture, grazing, and forestry; a by-product of good land management and conservation.[2] The establishment of balance compatible with human occupancy of the land becomes a fundamental object of the wildlife manager. His is the problem of adjusting wildlife to a habitat dominated by man and to an environment radically modified by human enterprise. Basic requirements for food and fiber have first claim on space. Wildlife must be secondary—now favored, now handicapped by the primary land function.

Wildlife management reconciles animals and people in joint tenancy

The procedures whereby men rebuild and stabilize wild populations in harmony with human socio-economic patterns have become known, collectively, as *wildlife management,* a major phase of resource conservation with guiding principles only recently evolved. Its development has been impeded by our failure to comprehend the involved organization of animal societies, our tardy acknowledgment of their disruption and constriction by civilization, and our reluctance to interfere further with groups already jeopardized by inept interference in the past.

Our wildlife manager of today builds on many trials and errors, accepting his raw materials as he finds them, however deplorable their state. He knows he may appropriate very little land exclusively for wildlife. He knows that one species may depend upon a chain of others and that blunders in selection can break vital links in the chain. He also knows painfully well that broken links cannot always be quickly or easily mended and that many gaps may never be repaired. Where predators have lost their normal function he must initiate substitute measures. Where predators, including man, become too destructive he must take steps to control them. For the most part, he deals with public property on privately owned land, and he must please the public without infringing upon private rights. Quite often he is obliged to get quick results to satisfy an ignorant clientele when he knows that the hasty expedient demanded is absolutely incompatible with sound long-range development. His problems are often more complex and infinitely more delicate than those confronting conservers of land and water, yet his labors produce much less than theirs from a materialistic point of view.

Loss or threatened loss of indigenous species has prompted the importation of exotics to fill their places, and the importations of wildlife are subject to the same challenge as the importations of foreign grasses to reclothe the plains. Are the ones introduced so much better that we wish them to replace completely the native ones? Should we hazard permanent loss of a native species by introducing an alien species that may not succeed, or may succeed too well?

Exotics are
a sorry solution

We brought ring-necked pheasants from China and Hungarian partridges from Europe to make up our loss of prairie chickens, and thus far the newcomers have pleased us. Both have become splendid "American" game birds. However, our sorry experience with English sparrows and European starlings prompted legislation to exclude such opportunists in the future.

Indigenous species ask very small favors to stay with us. All they ask is their elemental needs for food, water, and living space. Many have quickly repopulated places from which they once departed and occupied places not previously inhabited when those three simple requirements were available. However, all three conditions must be present—one or two will not suffice. And all three must be within reasonable distance of each other and safely attainable.

Indigenous
species ask only
food, water, and
cover to stay
with us

Requirements differ widely according to size and habits of individual species.[3] The ungulata need more space and food than songbirds. Aquatic mammals and waterfowl make demands quite different from those of their upland counterparts. Resident species need only one set of facilities, while the migratory kinds need several.

A multiple function is also commonplace. Racoons find food where deer come only to drink. Fish live permanently where ducks stay only briefly. A single bush may contribute to both food and cover for deer, birds, and small mammals. A permanent home for muskrats may be a winter resort for geese, affording both the resident and the visitor his special choice of food and cover. But, if animals shall thrive the three essentials must be present. Those three together constitute wildlife habitat, and since habitat is the most important consideration in wildlife conservation, let us take it apart and look at it right here.

Cover is to wildlife as housing is to people, and wild creatures do no better in slums than do humans. While we have degraded

Cover takes
top priority

Fig. 12.1 *Muskrat habitat in Horicon Refuge, Wisconsin. Drainage has ruined many similar communities. Muskrat "houses" have special meaning for some weather prophets. If the muskrats build low in the water, the coming winter will be severe, they say. However, muskrat architecture is probably styled by the availability of materials and the work force. (Fish and Wildlife Service photo.)*

many of our citizens to slum living we have literally razed the living quarters of wildlife. The greatest single need for the conservation of wildlife is the provision of places to live.[4]

Habitat requirements differ as widely as do the inhabitants. Deer need a forest, but robins ask only one leafy tree—safe from cats. Canada geese need one marsh in the south for winter vacation and another in the north for rearing a family in summer. Bobwhites need only a neglected field corner on an annual basis to produce many more children than the geese can boast. Some live better by the square rod than others by the square mile. A tuft of grass, a thorny bush, a tangle of vines, a clump of trees, or a patch of briars may be the home of a family.

Some forms of wildlife demand standard design; others accept a variety of architecture. If he loses his den tree, a raccoon can be expected to quit the neighborhood and remove to another suitable tree somewhere else. Gray squirrels and bluebirds are almost equally set in their ways, desiring hollows with a small entrance to exclude uninvited company. A mink will not live far from water, nor will a trout live in water that is not cool and clean. Others are less exacting. A woodchuck is equally at home anywhere, be his "summer cottage" a stone wall in New England, a rockpile in Iowa, or a hollow tree in West Virginia. When he digs in for the winter it bothers the chuck not in the least if a cottontail moves into his attic while he sleeps in the basement. The cottontail borrows any burrow at hand unless the owner objects, and if no hole is handy a brush pile or briar patch serves him quite as well. Muskrats are also adaptable, tunnelling into the bank to supplement their huts in the water (Fig. 12.1).

Cover is not adequate unless it gives a fair degree of protective concealment for all essential activities of the tenant. The best rock pile fails a woodchuck if all about it stretches bare ground or close-cropped meadow. The touted weather prophet is safer to vacate the premises than to expose himself dangerously each time he goes for food or water. Lacking speed, he must live where cover screens his travel between home and the grocery store. A rabbit could more safely occupy the isolated rock pile, and for a skunk, who sleeps by day and digs his grubs at night, the rock pile could be highly desirable. A safe place to live and to rear a family, a safe place to feed, a safe place to hide from enemies, a safe place to play and to sleep, and a place for shelter against severe storms, or cold—all these are necessary. But they cannot attain full value unless passage between them is also guarded.

Connecting cover is the vital link often overlooked by the would-be conservator. He can learn its importance by observing how consistently wildlife uses it. Another kind, also neglected, is the haven of retreat from danger—*escape cover*. In this category is the clump of briars that saves a rabbit from the pursuing fox, the matted grass under which a mouse escapes the hawk, the thorny bush or tangled vine that spares a bird from violent death, and the bushes or trees that come between a hunter and his quarry. Nature endowed some with protective coloration, but its value is often negated by environmental change. It is never entirely adequate without the help of protective vegetation. Color loses effect when the creature moves, and it is no defense against the elements.

A house without food and drink has only the semblance of a home, and shelter devoid of food and water makes no habitat for wildlife. However, vegetation that provides shelter may also produce food for its tenants.[5] Therein reposes a natural nicety that simplifies the rehabilitation of wildlife areas. The hollow oak in which a squirrel resides may also yield a store of acorns. The mulberry or dogwood tree in which a robin builds contributes berries to his diet. The leafy shrubs that best hide a deer are also his browse. The weed patch to which quail escape may also be a good seed producer. Thus it is that by selection of shrubs, forbs,

Food and drink make the home tenable

or grasses, either by sparing the desirable volunteers or by planting those of proved worth, the two prime essentials of wildlife
habitat—food and cover—can be developed simultaneously.[6] In
the humid East natural revegetation is often quite satisfactory
without artificial improvement.

Animal tastes differ exceedingly, and many species vary their
diets with the seasonal availability of food. Some prefer seeds or
insects, others prefer forage or browse, and still others prefer
flesh and not much else. Whatever their preference, it comes
directly or indirectly from the plant cover, for meat is plant tissue transformed. Vegetable-eating insects become food for birds
in summer, but plant parts become their mainstay in winter when
the insects are gone. Green foliage and forage keep deer in summer, but bark, buds, and twigs must suffice when the plants are
dormant. Seeds, berries, nuts, buds, flowers, leaves, stems, and even
roots contribute to the dietary requirements of wildlife.

Food supply to be satisfactory must always be sufficient, *within
the foraging radius* of a species, to keep that species alive and
capable of reproducing. An abundance in summer may be much
less important than the smaller, more critical supply during winter shortage. The least bountiful season fixes wildlife populations
in exactly the same manner as drought years limit range carrying
capacity. If artificial feeding must be resorted to in any but the
most unusual season the natural food supply is not sufficient for
the population dependent upon it. Supplements doled out regularly to keep animals alive are futile attempts to offset deficiency of habitat or to maintain an abnormal population. They
are dangerous palliatives in either case. Doubly blessed are those
creatures that fatten when food is plentiful and hibernate during
the slack season. Commendable are those that lay up stores to
tide them over, or migrate with the sun. Our chief concern here
is for those that remain in permanent residence, lay nothing by,
and seek their food needs within a narrow orbit instinctively
defined. Research has shown the lifetime cruising radius of bobwhite quail to be less than half a mile.[7]

Water supply is often the only limiting factor of wildlife habitat. However, its importance in the total picture evinces many
gradations as between different species and different climatic
regions. Fish live in it, ducks live on it, and other birds bathe in
it and drink of it, while certain upland species are virtually
"camels," taking only what they get in their food.[8] Mallards need
an area of standing water, trout need it running, deer need it
clean and in quantity, and quail can get by on dew. Water must
be available in one form or another if wildlife shall inhabit an

area. In its absence food and cover lose their value. Furthermore, it must be near at hand and attainable by a covered approach.

Our waste and abuse of surface waters by drainage, pollution, accelerated run-off, and siltation have imposed a major obstacle to wildlife conservation. Conversely, good management of water resources will probably contribute more to the enrichment of wildlife than any other measure. When water and land are properly conserved, wildlife benefits inevitably.

Habitat is the approved solution of wildlife problems. A combination of cover, food, and water to equal or approximate the natural arrangement favorable to a given animal society goes further toward perpetuating its component species than any number of more specific devices to increase them. Without reasonable habitat other measures are futile; with good habitat conditions many of them may be quite unnecessary. Biologists tried many direct methods of increasing desired species before they learned that none does much good unless it is coupled with suitable habitat. They tried protective measures against excessive capture by humans, they persecuted predators, they established special reservations and refuges, they introduced exotics, they propagated and planted, hatched and released what was wanted. Finally they discovered that the objective hinges upon habitats, and these not in a few isolated places, but throughout the country—maintained or restored on farms, ranches, and forest areas, on lands both public and private. They adopted nature's method and now they get real results.

Habitat is the approved solution

In typical American fashion, we have often overdone our beneficence to wildlife. We have killed with kindness. In a favorable habitat some species are capable of such rapid increase that they eat themselves right out of house and home unless they are checked by natural enemies or their human guardians. Too many can be worse than too few, a fact amply proved by the gross overpopulation of deer in the Upper Lakes states and throughout much of the West. (In the upper peninsula of Michigan alone 11,200 deer starved to death in 1960.) Whether we blame the problem on faulty favoritism or limitation of space makes little difference. The fact remains that the quickest way to readjust a manipulated environment is to manipulate it some more, as by controlling the number of its inhabitants. We could breed and plant cougars or import packs of wolves to reduce certain game populations, but it is much easier to kill any surplus by encouraging, or even hiring, hunters to do so. Common stumbling blocks in wildlife conservation have been regulations based on inadequate knowledge or on prejudice and public ig-

Too few are better than too many

norance of a problem. Once established, protection has often become too strict and been continued too long.

Big game is not the only wildlife that needs harvesting to prevent excessive increase. Many other types, similarly favored, need similar control. Waterfowl, upland game birds, and small mammals can become too numerous for their own good unless countermeasures be applied. An unfished lake may provide poor fishing because fish cannot grow large when too many compete for a limited food supply. Too many ducks in a crowded winter resort become a menace to each other through infection and disease. *Increase of numbers is only one facet of wildlife conservation. Control of numbers at a conservative level can be even more pertinent.*

Suitable habitat is one thing, suitable population another. A population greater than the habitat can support brings disaster to itself and damage to the habitat. Starving animals can so severely overtax their food supply during a season of drought or cold as to curtail its normal replenishment when favorable weather returns. Such depletion during bad times indicates overpopulation, which, unless promptly cut down, leads to progressive degradation of the environment. In some places carefully restored to wildlife we have permitted the process to frustrate our efforts. Unless we harvest the wildlife crops we produce with proper regard for their habitat limitations, we lose not only the crops but also the facilities with which to produce them.[9] If the population controls shown in Fig. 12.2 become inoperative or inadequate, direct measures should be applied accordingly.

Gunning is better than killing with kindness

Hunters have been much maligned as butchers of wildlife by foolishly sentimental nature lovers; killing with lethal weapons is, in fact, more commendable than killing with kindness. Guns and rifles can be the best tools with which to ensure compatibility between wild populations and that of humans. Harvest of a game species outgrowing its habitat becomes a necessity; failure to harvest a thriving game species within a safe margin of reproductive capacity simply wastes the resource. Unless hunters take the annual surplus of wildfowl, for instance, the birds will die in other ways; unless fishermen pull out the hungry fish in a pond, none may grow big enough to be worth angling for. It is not conservation to deny sportsmen the pleasure of taking fish and fowl that would otherwise be lost!

The most hunted bird in the United States, and perhaps also the one whose killing provokes the most ardent objections, is the mourning dove. This controversial bird is numerous in all our contiguous States; few venture into Alaska, and Hawaii has none.

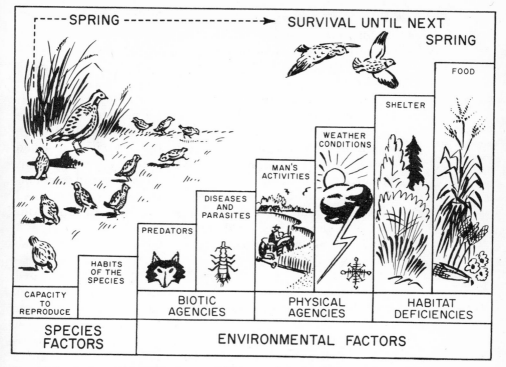

Fig. 12.2 *Factors that hold down wildlife populations. (Redrawn from Farmers' Bulletin 2035, U.S.D.A. Original by Felix Summers.)*

It is classed as a game bird in the migratory bird treaties with Canada and Mexico, and it is hunted, subject to federal and state regulations, in thirty states comprising more than half the area of the forty-eight. In the other eighteen, northeastern and north-central states, it is classed as a protected songbird.

Although about 20 million mourning doves were taken by North American hunters annually between 1953 and 1961, a harvest numerically greater than that of all waterfowl species combined, the continental dove population increased steadily during the same period. Even more to the point, biologic investigations revealed that mortality rates of the mourning dove were the same in areas where it was protected as in areas where it was legally hunted. More than 50 per cent of the annual production disappears whether hunting of the bird is permitted or prohibited.[10]

Studies of bobwhite quail, another popular game bird, have also shown that considerable hunting pressure can be sustained without altering normal population trends. On a longleaf-pine range investigated in Louisiana there was no significant difference in quail production between an area protected against hunting for fourteen years and the circumjacent territory on which the birds had been hunted every year. Obviously, the birds immune to gunning died at the same rate as those hunted.[11] Similar cases might be cited for other upland game birds.

We have already mentioned the futility of propagating game, fish, or other wildlife without providing a habitat for the incubated, hand-reared product of hatchery or breeding station. We have wasted much money, time, and energy to produce game and sport fish for release in places where they could not long survive, much less assume natural functions of food getting and reproduction. Animals born and bred in captivity, grown with medicated water and vitaminized feeds, are at best ill-equipped to fend for themselves in the cruel world outside. If their first adversary is a licensed hunter or fisherman they serve some purpose; otherwise they die to no avail.

Artificial propagation fails when habitat is lacking

Released in a hospitable environment, pen- or pond-reared stock has been the means of re-establishing wildlife in areas whence it had been expelled and of introducing it to new areas made habitable in advance. The population distribution of fowl and fish has been remarkably extended by brood stocks transplanted by live trapping or reared for the purpose. Demographic recovery of the historic wild turkey to game-bird status has been aided by the release of a few captured specimens in places that had become depopulated. In 1961 the wild turkey was taken legally in twenty-three of the forty-eight contiguous states. Hunters bagged 75,400 of the birds, more than half of them in Florida and Pennsylvania.[12] With mammals, including big game, phenomenal results have been achieved by capturing them in the wild and planting them where desired. To this method we owe the return of beavers to forest streams—deserted since Astor salted away his first million—and deer to places where none lived for many years. To it we can trace much of our annual deer harvest of almost 2 million. In many cases man's use and alteration of the land has materially improved it as a home for repatriated species. Some repatriations have succeeded so well that the animals have become a destructive nuisance. The planting of beaver along the upper Mississippi, for instance, led to so much damage to farmland and crops that beaver control has become a necessary and difficult undertaking.

Desirable stocking of fish habitats, whether rehabilitated or newly created by artificial impoundment, would be quite impossible without hatcheries to propagate the species desired. Only when properly stocked will farm ponds, reservoirs, and tail waters below dams afford the fisheries for which they may be suited.

Only by timely restocking have desirable fish populations been maintained in natural waters that sustain heavy fishing pressure year after year.

The Bureau of Sport Fisheries and Wildlife operates 100 fish propagation stations about the United States, and the states operate almost five-hundred additional units. Minnesota, land of 10,000 lakes, had forty-three hatcheries in 1958, the largest number in any state. Annual cost of all public fish-cultural operations has been about 18 million dollars, with an annual fish distribution of almost 1 billion (fry, fingerlings, and legal size). Most propagated have been walleye pike, chinook salmon, rainbow trout, bluegill sunfish, and largemouth bass.[13]

All other measures prove inadequate for maintaining wildlife populations unless men exercise judicious restraint against killing a species faster than it reproduces itself. Extinct and vanishing forms bear mute witness to the result of unbridled destruction. To avert recurrent disaster and to regain and retain a desirable abundance, we have imposed many legal restrictions conceived to protect wildlife against ourselves. Most familiar of these are the state game laws, but there are also federal prohibitions, including many rules to safeguard nongame species. Enforcement is costly and difficult, and violations numerous despite the penalties imposed on persons found guilty of infringement. Punitive measures often provoke more resentment than cooperation because the offender is either too ignorant to understand or too selfish to appreciate the bio-social purposes of the law he has violated. Protective regulations would be infinitely more effective if all our citizens understood their implications.

Our laws are to protect wildlife against ourselves

Our self-imposed restrictions are intended to save rare species from extinction and to reserve from the annual increase of those more numerous a breeding stock estimated to make maximum use of available habitat and produce the largest possible surplus for capture each succeeding year. The laws are intended to save from each *crop* enough *seed* to ensure a *harvest* the following year. Abiding by such laws, we treat wildlife much as we handle any other crop produced by the land.

Fixed bag and creel limits, daily and seasonal, are arrived at by gauging surplus game and fish against the anticipated numbers of hunters and fishermen who will pursue them. It is often desirable to make the rules adjustable on short notice to suit an available crop rather than to fix them far in advance of the harvest season. While a crop is growing it may be difficult to estimate how much it will yield.

Restrictions on weapons and gear have been imposed to prevent wholesale slaughter of wild creatures and to give them a "sporting" chance instead, as well as to afford sportsmen more equalized opportunity. The taking of sport fish with a net or the shooting of game with a machine gun cannot be condoned by an informed citizenry. The public has registered its collective objection to carnage by imposing statutory prohibitions. Implements of war and military tactics are not generally approved for use against wildlife.

A most fruitful device, the "closed season," has divers uses in the conservation of wildlife resources. Its most obvious application, of ancient origin, is for the safety of creatures during periods of reproduction or regeneration. It gives creatures a sort of diplomatic immunity while they rear their families or, if inadvertently decimated, until they regain a desirable population. The logic is very simple. He who shoots a duck when she is incubating a clutch of eggs or while the brood needs her care causes the family to die. He who takes a fish full of roe or a muskrat full of kits kills the unborn generation. He who kills a doe from her fawn, a she-bear from her cub, or a whale from her suckling calf causes the helpless offspring to die of hunger. The closed season means sanctity of the home and safety of the family while the young grow up. Since offspring are more dependent upon the mother, she is ordinarily given more protection than her mate. It is often permissible to kill buck deer, bull seals, or cock pheasants when similar treatment of the females would curtail reproductive capabilities.

The mobility of wildlife poses peculiar conservation problems. Other appurtenances of land remain in place unless man abuses them and causes their removal, but animals move from place to place of their own volition and cannot be conserved unless their travels be taken into account. The conservator must consider their itineraries as a whole, not in detached segments. This unique characteristic of wildlife requires for its conservation community interest of local, regional, or even continental scope. No other resource, with the possible exception of ocean fishes, is so reliant upon regional cooperation between places remotely distant from each other as well as between contiguous areas. A farmer cannot conserve quail if his neighbor shoots them whenever they run across the property line. Wisconsin cannot conserve deer if they stray across the state boundary and get killed in Minnesota. Canada cannot conserve geese without the cooperation of Louisiana and the other southerly regions to which they flock in winter.

Mobility poses problems peculiar to wildlife

On the basis of travel or stay-at-home habits, wildlife may be separated into two categories, *resident* and *migratory*. Permanent residents may "round out" their existence within a very limited radius, living and dying where they were born, while the most adventurous migrants make an annual circuit the length of the Americas.

The mammals, including big game, the reptiles, inland fish, upland game fowl, and several species of birds remain in their respective vicinities throughout the year. Pressed for food, they move indeed, as when deer and elk quit snow-covered mountain slopes to seek food lower down, or when grouse and quail scour the countryside for meager winter fare. But the ruminants return to the slopes in spring, and the feathered beggars starve to death unless they find enough to live on within a few miles of home.

Most of our feathered folk are seasonal migrants. With few exceptions, waterfowl, shore birds, songbirds, and birds of prey make long seasonal journeys, and like "rich folks" summer in the north and winter in the south. The rich migrate for comfort, the birds, probably, for food and survival. Some birds migrate within the confines of the United States only. Others spend summer in the United States and winter in Latin America. Still others spend winter in the United States and summer in Canada. The last category includes the greater number of our ducks and geese. To a few rugged individualists, such as the arctic tern and golden plover, the United States is simply a transit area between northern and southern residence.[14]

Migratory species need special provisions

From the above it is apparent that many birds and wildfowl are in fact international resources, requiring for their effective conservation the cooperation of all nations they frequent. Toward that end we have signed Migratory Bird Treaties with both Canada and Mexico and have given the migrants federal protection within our own country. Several other American republics have registered interest in the joint program, which should ideally be hemispheric in scope.[15]

The migrants fly many different routes and make their flights on many different schedules, but all move northward with the advance of spring and return southward after their summer breeding season. Some turn southward early, while others delay until snow or cold drives them. Ornithologists have not yet determined whether light, temperature, food, sex, or some hidden instinct is the strongest stimulus to seasonal migration; but they have deduced from banding records that species and individuals tend to follow the same route and to maintain the same schedule year after year. Consider the amazing punctuality with which the swallows are reputed to return to Capistrano.

The great flocks of ducks and geese that pass twice each year

Fig. 12.3 *The Mississippi flyway, reputedly the world's busiest natural airway. (Drawing by R. H. Hines, Fish and Wildlife Service.)*

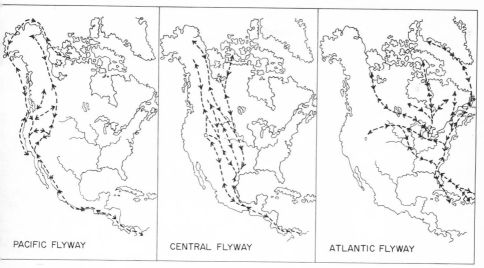

Fig. 12.4 *Other principal North American routes traversed by migratory birds. (After Circular 16, Fish and Wildlife Service.)*

between breeding grounds in Canada and the northern United States and wintering grounds southward as far as the Caribbean follow four main routes called *flyways*: the Pacific; the Central (High Plains); the Mississippi; and the Atlantic; as shown on accompanying maps (Figs. 12.3 and 12.4). Most traveled of these, the Mississippi flyway, is probably the world's busiest aerial highway, carrying the greatest variety of feathered traffic—birds of land, shore, and water.[16] (The Pacific flyway has a larger waterfowl population, but many of the birds migrate shorter distances.) Well wooded and watered, flat and free of obstruction, the broad Mississippi Valley affords easy, direct passage between northern and southern habitats (Fig. 12.3). From a bird's-eye view its only serious handicaps are the shrinking terminal habitats and the army of hunters that intercepts the autumn traffic. But for the tightening of general restrictions and imposing of special ones to protect dwindling species, the gunners would soon still the cackling V-formations that forewarn us of winter and in good time herald the return of spring. (Pity him whose sensitivities are so elemental that he would rather gorge himself on roast goose than listen to an excited parade of honkers winging their way far overhead on a clear, calm evening in spring!)

More than 29 million American waterfowl remained on the wintering grounds after the 1960-1961 hunting season; but although the next year's kill in the United States was about one-third less than that of 1960-1961, the subsequent winter flocks numbered 3.5 million fewer birds. The decline would probably continue even if shooting were entirely prohibited. Maintenance of desirable populations depends upon recovery and improvement of wetland habitats, about which more will be said in the next chapter pertaining to recreation.

Refuges, preserves, and sanctuaries

The establishment of refuges, preserves, and sanctuaries, public and private, has greatly advanced our conservation of wildlife. Governments on all levels, many private agencies, and uncounted individuals have become participants in a program of reserving for wild creatures enough suitable space to ensure their self-perpetuation. Asylum from human persecution, legal or otherwise, appears to be the most promising means of carrying certain species through the era of public ignorance and apathy that must give way to better understanding and more considerate treatment. Had the sanctuary program been instituted earlier we might have saved several species from oblivion.

Our great Federal Wildlife Refuge system, begun in 1903, has grown until we now have more than three hundred land units,

Fig. 12.5 *National Migratory Bird Refuge Areas (as of June 1962). Many have been added, and many more will be added under projected plans. (Fish and Wildlife Service, Bureau of Sport Fisheries and Wildlife map.)*

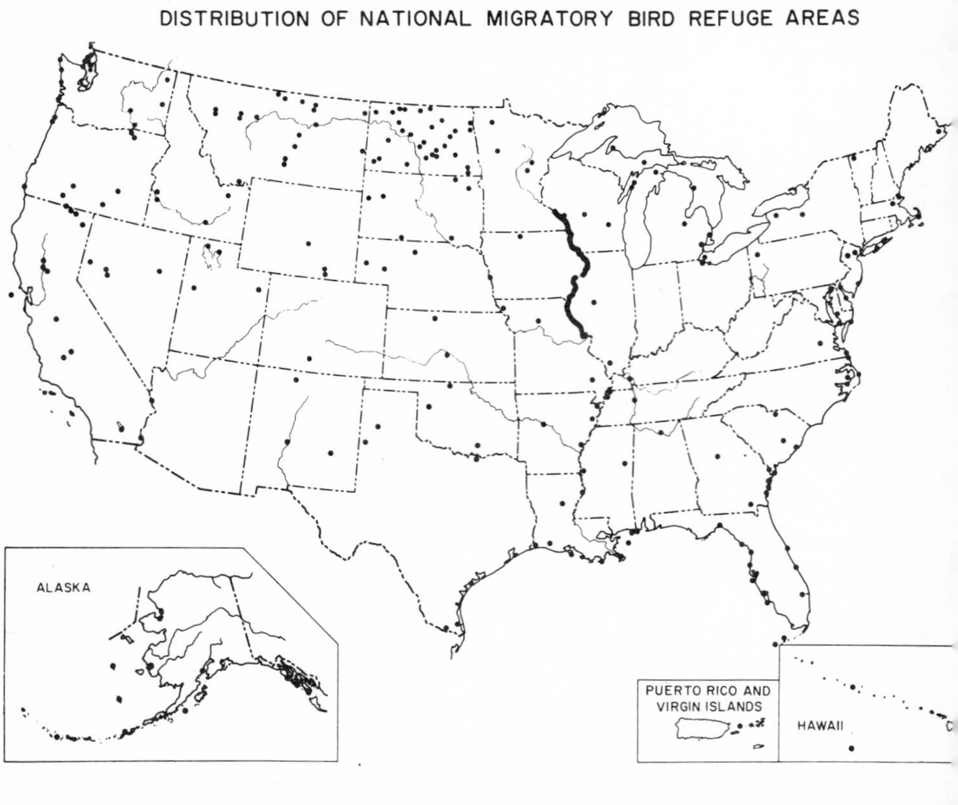

DISTRIBUTION OF NATIONAL MIGRATORY BIRD REFUGE AREAS

approximating a total of 28.5 million acres. More than two-thirds of these federal refuges (3.5 million acres in 1961) were created specifically for waterfowl—summer nesting grounds, wintering areas, and places between at which migrants may rest and feed unmolested when they traverse the country (Fig. 12.5).

The Bureau of Sports Fisheries and Wildlife supplements the refuges with many nonrefuge areas under its administration closed to the hunting of migratory birds. As of mid-1961 there were twenty-six such areas containing almost 200,000 acres in eighteen states. Lakes and marshes from which hunters are entirely or partly excluded become the certified tourist courts of flyway travelers. Other federal refuges are mainly for big game, though less exclusive than those for waterfowl. The survival of bison, elk, and several other large animals may be attributed to their timely management on reservations. National Parks and Monuments are inviolate sanctuaries except as the pampered ranks may require artificial thinning.

The states have made tremendous contributions to the total refuge system by setting aside parks and preserves in which wildlife may not be molested. The states have also acquired more than 2 million acres of waterfowl refuge areas. The entire District of Columbia is by act of Congress a wildlife preserve.

Cities, towns, and minor civil units have provided further sanctuary and retreat for wildlife. The confines of entire cities have been designated bird sanctuaries, and since cities generally prohibit the use of firearms except to maintain law and order, urban areas can be excellent homes for birds and other wildlife.

Nature lovers and independent wildlife conservators have devoted a very considerable aggregate of land and water area exclusively to wildlife defense. A grove of trees, a pond or slough, even a vacant city lot can be converted into a refuge. Any habitat area becomes a sanctuary when man denies his own kind the privilege of disturbing it.

It will probably be impossible to appropriate for the sole use of wildlife sufficient area to maintain desirable animal populations. Wildlife production must therefore be a part of other land uses. Refuges must be regarded as preventives of exhaustion rather than producers of abundance. Overflow of animals from reservations to circumjacent areas will occur, but 1 acre cannot be expected to populate 100 acres about it. Furthermore, the spread of wildlife to private land, as when elk invade farms or ranches, is frequently so destructive that it cannot be tolerated. It means that the refuge is too small for its population. If wildlife production were made the primary function of all publicly owned land (more than a quarter of our total area) we might still lack desirable variety, abundance, and distribution of species. The multiple use of land discussed in Chapter 10 will be increasingly productive of wildlife, but it does not portend the reservation of expansive areas for wildlife exclusively. Indeed, exclusive assignment of public land to wildlife production, excepting limited areas specially selected or developed, cannot be justified either biologically or economically. Rather must wildlife be a secondary product of land, whether it is owned and used publicly or privately. It is estimated, however, that there are in this country 100 million acres inherently unsuited to any use other than wildlife production. Much of this is too poorly drained for agricultural or pastoral use but is ideal for water storage and wildlife. As population pressure increases land-use competition and refines our land selection, we may expect that 5 per cent of our total space shall be used primarily for wildlife; but we cannot expect so small a fraction to populate the remainder.

The users of our land are also the keepers of our wildlife

Wildlife conservation devolves upon the users of our land—the farmers, graziers, and timber growers. Most reassuring is the plain fact that good farming, good forestry, and good range management are also most productive of desirable wildlife, that wildlife becomes, as it were, an unearned dividend from conservation of soil, water, forest, and grassland. Conversely, wildlife suffers from the wastage of other resources. Land mutilation and inept manipulation of water handicap both human and animal residents. Overgrazing, or burning that ruins forest or range, spells disaster to useful wildlife. Since the primary land uses occupy most of our space, it is logical that their production of wildlife as a supplemental crop is our only sure way to abundance.

The farmer surpasses everyone else as keeper of our wildlife. Ask him, and he will tell you that he feeds not only cattle, swine, and poultry, but also the multitudes that fly, swim, or crawl. It is estimated that farmers produce 80 per cent of our wildlife.[17] As keeper of wildlife the farmer produces public wealth on his private property. He raises animals over which he has no legal jurisdiction (in the case of protected game) on land for the use of which he pays a tax to the owner-administrator of the animal wealth. He becomes a unique public custodian, and we must learn to respect him as such.

Odds and ends of land—a home for wildlife

Every farm is a potential home for wildlife, and almost every consideration for wildlife can make it a better farm on which to live. Somewhere on almost every farm is space better relegated to wildlife than employed for other use—a rock outcrop or a

POOR MANAGEMENT

GOOD MANAGEMENT

Fig. 12.6 *Odds and ends of farmland can be choice "subdivisions" for wildlife. On a well-managed farm, problem areas such as rock exposures, gullies, and eroding stream banks become, through conservation, habitats for wildlife and assets to the human tenants.*

stony knoll that costs more in wear and tear on machinery than it can possibly repay in crop yield, a washed slope or gully in need of healing, a woods corner or slough too small or too inconveniently situated for more profitable use, or a steep declivity or stream bank that sloughs and crumbles under cattle hooves. Odds and ends, big and small, grassy, weedy, brushy, or wooded become good wildlife habitats when machinery and livestock are kept off.[18] Sheer economy commends them to wildlife; often, as from fur bearers or fish, yielding a tangible return. See in Fig. 12.6 how good farm management can accommodate wildlife.

Waste patches need not be the only farm areas productive of wildlife. A farm so uniformly fertile that it includes no wasteland can, consistent with superior management, afford ideal habitat for a rich variety of wild creatures. Any farm anywhere can produce an abundance of wildlife without curtailment, but rather with increase, of its major products. This is an idea on which American thinking must be revised; herein may lie our greatest future promise for wildlife.

No farm is without boundaries, which are often precise lines between it and adjoining lands. Such property lines are customarily secured by permanent fences jointly built and maintained by the two owners whose farms meet along the common demarcation. On most farms is also a fence or two, permanently separating from the fields a woodlot or barnyard or both, frequently a fence along a road or a stream, and likely as not an enclosure about the farmstead (home, barns, garden, lawn, and so forth). It may be safe to estimate that a square quarter-section farm (160 acres) has or might have at least 2 miles of permanent fence.

Clean wire fences are ugly, barren sentinels

The primary function of a farm fence is the confinement or exclusion of livestock, with the concomitant function of making good neighbors or providing grouchy ones with something to quarrel about. Fences are no barrier to good will or gossip but serve well as a prop for both. They are objects of grave concern to the breeder of fine cattle. They climax the adventure of boys stealing melons. They are to birds a perch on which to sit and to the hired man a nuisance to be repaired on rainy days. They can be, by slight modification, splendid homes for wildlife. The New England stone wall and the old-fashioned snake fence (rails) of Eastern forest regions have some value to wildlife for concealment and escape if nothing else; but the straight, clean, wire fence that we have accepted as an indication of good farming is a barren symbol of backwardness. The electric fence is no better, because its proper functioning requires that it be kept clear of growing vegetation capable of short-circuiting the current.

The living fence, guardian of wildlife, has until recently found little favor in America. Grassland settlers made considerable use of it initially, as many overgrown hedgerows of Osage orange attest, but when wire and steel posts became available, most of the troublesome hedges got the ax (a laborious task). The trees grew so tall that they shaded adjacent field borders, and they spread so vigorously that they were difficult to control. Most farmers were happy to root them out and replace them with conventional fencing. With their removal went miles upon miles of wildlife cover in the kind of open country where it is particularly critical.

With the soil conservation era came a reappraisal of farm practices generally, including those standard, bleak fixtures—fences. Americans rediscovered the merits of the hedgerows and fence rows so prominent in European landscapes, and concluded that clean fences, permanent ones in particular, represent a waste of energy and a practical error in farm management. Farmers pondered the unconventional idea that a fence grown up with bushes, briars, and vines confers multiple benefits without detracting from its primary function. Whereas a naked wire fence stops only animals, a densely vegetated fence row serves as a barrier to wind and a trap for snow, thus conserving soil and water. Best of all, it makes an ideal home for desirable wildlife, and lends rustic beauty to a landscape otherwise dull and monotonous.

Living fences are homes for wildlife

Contour farming brings added merit to living fences because it demands that field divisions follow curves instead of straight lines. To swing a taut wire fence about a curve calls for an interminable amount of bracing to hold the posts upright, but the planted fence grows equally well curved, crooked, or straight. A thick hedge along a slope retards run-off, catches silt, and combats erosion generally. It need not be so wide as to use much land (6 to 8 feet), and it need not be so tall as to deprive adjacent crops of sunshine. Plants available for the purpose live indefinitely and, once established, require neither care nor control.[19] Contour hedges are gaining favor, and with each one planted, wildlife gains a residential subdivision.

We have disproved the fallacious idea that clean, straight fences evince the diligence and proficiency of a farmer. We have learned that the density and uniformity of hedgerows are more valid criteria. As that truth gains wider acceptance and applica-

Fig. 12.7 *The most prolific life zone is the marginal edge, or ecotone, where one kind of community environment meets another. The richest edge is the shore or the amphibious zone between land and water, such as this swamp-marsh margin in the Grand Prairie area, Okefenokee Refuge, Georgia. (Fish and Wildlife Service photo.)*

tion our countryside will be more beautiful, more prolific, more hospitable to wildlife, and more satisfying to people.[20] The transformation is well under way, but its consummation will take many years. The convenience of electric fencing discourages the erection of barriers that are more costly and less easily removed as desirable. The multiflora rose that makes excellent fence and wildlife cover in moderate climates will not grow satisfactorily in areas subject to severe winter cold as in the northern Middle West. Living fences or hedgerows are difficult to justify on superior farmland intensively cultivated. A Corn Belt farmer is not easily convinced that one row of bushes equals several rows of corn and that a mile of luxurious hedge is worth a hundred bushels of grain per year. And who but a fool would argue with him!

Wildlife chooses the edge or border to escape "marginal" living

Fence rows and hedgerows exemplify the principle of "edge" in wildlife management. Being long in proportion to their width, they present much edge and little depth, an arrangement favoring wildlife. Edge is the periphery or border, the boundary or transition between different kinds of area—between woods and crops, water and land, forest and grassland. It is the meeting place of contrasting environments; a zone which nature endows most abundantly with life, both in variety and in numbers. See the marsh-woodland edge shown in Fig. 12.7.

The border environment, or *marginal edge,* has many interesting ramifications. Men who work in town often prefer to live in the suburbs. Skunks that dig grubs in the pasture at night retire to the woods by day. Skunks and men seek their daily bread in one environment and their shelter in another. Deer find little browse in a dense forest devoid of understory. They must seek the brush and saplings that grow at the edge of the forest or in openings that admit the sunshine. Birds may feed in the fields, but they take refuge in bushes or trees.

Aquatic life responds to edge no less than do landlubbers. Waterfowl and aquatic mammals prefer the shallow margins to deep, open water. Their food and shelter are where land and water intermingle or overlap and fixed vegetation flourishes, though they may take to deep water when danger threatens. Shore birds, the stilted waders, personify the principle of edge. Fish, too, lead a marginal existence, being most abundant near shore. Few of the commercial species we shall discuss in Chapter 14 inhabit the deep sea; they prefer the shoal waters on the continental shelf. The sea coast, the transitional zone from land to ocean, is perhaps the very epitome of marginal edge.

Discussion of borders and edges takes us back to the farm, where the most intricate pattern of wildlife environment results from good, diversified land use. Field borders (Fig. 12.8) and

Wildlife and farm economics fit well together

Fig. 12.8 *A row of brush and weeds around a field may be as good a marginal edge as any. Indeed, a hedgerow separating fields has a simulation of ecotone on both sides. A quail food strip was sown along the edge pictured here, originally barren turning space for this field in Alabama. (A. M. Rearson, Fish and Wildlife Service photo.)*

woods borders, stream banks and drainage ditches, marsh, pond, and slough margins, hedges, shelter belts, and brushy fence rows, protected waste areas and ungrazed farm woods opened by selective cutting—all these details of cultural landscape lend the *proximate variety and interspersion* that can sustain a thriving biotic community.

Most of these farm features suit wildlife best when they are well arranged and managed for good conservation farming. The farmer need not take special pains to attract wildlife, although there is many a one who does. Ditch banks covered by grass serve wildlife admirably, at the same time keeping the ditch clear of obstruction that would interfere with drainage. Turning space at the ends of a field (Fig. 12.8), wider now for big machines than when horses and mules did the work, becomes wildlife border when sown down against erosion, its quality as habitat dependent upon the choice of cover crop. The sown border conserves both soil and wildlife.[21] A farm woodland selectively cut for sustained yield admits enough sun for undergrowth to shelter animals. Its protection against burning and grazing enhances its value as wildlife habitat, while also magnifying its forestry values.[22] A farmer need not deviate from good land management to produce abundant wildlife. Figure 12.8 shows how easily he can entice and retain wild tenants.

Wildlife and social relations have lacked harmony

Farm wildlife is a free crop, requiring no outlay of money or labor except as the farmer may be inclined. He who would have an abundance may invest in fences and planting to improve habitats or leave patches of grain for winter feed, but even such concessions need not be costly. Wildlife on the farm is no luxury, though game or sport fish can cause a farmer such inconvenience as to discourage him from harboring them. Inconsiderate hunters and fishermen have caused much antagonism against the objects of their pursuit by leaving farm gates open, damaging fences, starting fires, trampling crops, or by outright vandalism. In self-defense the farmer either posts his land against trespass or destroys the game that attracts the miscreants. This social conflict has retarded wildlife conservation in many places, and true sportsmen, who respect the rights of fellow men (including farmers), are endeavoring to relieve the tension. The respectable sportsman takes no game on private land without permission, and no game anywhere out of season. Instead, he helps the farmer produce game and pays for the privilege of taking it. Sportsmen's organizations have in many places become active participants in farm improvement and wildlife management. For a little game they do much good, lending assistance with habitat and landscape problems far beyond their immediate interests. Many sportsmen are conservators, not poachers. They acknowledge and demonstrate the inseparable relationship between wildlife as a land attribute and wildlife as a recreational resource.

Wildlife belongs to everyone, benefits everyone, and can be conserved by everyone. In many ways we have made it a public trust, but its conservation depends upon our personal responsibility. Laws fail unless they be coupled with understanding.

Everyone benefits from wildlife, and everyone can help conserve it

That everyone has a stake in wildlife is well evinced by our public concern for its welfare and by our public investment in it. Every level of government contributes toward its protection and propagation, and every taxpayer supports the program.

But public action cannot succeed unless it is scientifically sound. Thus far we have acted too much on hearsay and snap judgment. Sportsmen have counted themselves conservationists when they propagated game artificially and captured it immediately upon release. In fact, their contributions to conservation in the form of licenses, fees, and so forth have been, and are, extremely important. Politicians have initiated programs known by biologists to be entirely wrong. We have spent public funds to satisfy notions and whims more harmful than helpful.

The scene is in transition. With the efficient leadership of the Fish and Wildlife Service at the national level and many competent state agencies the prospect looks good. People are learning that wildlife legislation must be based upon scientific knowledge and that the politician must be advised by the natural scientist. The trend is toward more biologists and fewer campaign managers in fish and wildlife work—a very good departure.

There remains a great need for informing everyone of his stock in wildlife and his personal responsibility for its conservation. With better understanding will come necessary individual participation. Everyone can help, and everyone will profit. When *values* and *needs* of wildlife are more universally recognized its conservation may be assured.

13

Resources
for
Recreation,
Inspiration,
and
Instruction

*above material wealth let us
treasure and preserve the gifts
of nature which exalt man's
inner self*

This chapter treats a subject that draws from all the material resources but proceeds beyond them; a subject which invites both levity and gravity of treatment. Here we deal with human happiness, with occasions when people shed their cares and quit for a time the stress and strain of making a living. We deal with the surge of reverence and awful humility with which we view God's handiwork manifest in natural wonders. We deal with escape from toil and care. We deal with pleasure and beauty, with love and romance, with science and art, with health, inspiration, and faith. We extol American pride, American confidence, American energy and drive, American democratic freedom.

We shall not attempt any strict differentiation of resources that please, inspire, or instruct, because a single resource group or area often serves all three purposes. Every one of our national parks, for example, is endowed with recreational, inspirational, and educational properties, all wrapped up in a single area or even in a single natural feature. We are further discouraged from cataloguing these resources by the fact that they serve different people in different ways. Some people get their recreation from viewing beautiful scenery, from nature study, or from exploring wilderness; others see nothing recreational in such activities. A singular experience can impart physical refreshment, intellectual stimulation, and spiritual uplift. How, then, can we segregate these sources?

Man cannot live by bread alone, and in this chapter we consider the natural resources whence come the wine and diversion to flavor the bread. We shall not elaborate upon man-made facilities and social institutions, since they do not qualify under the term *natural*. Neither shall we quarrel with definition lest thereby we sour the wine. Let us strike no discord for him who hears music sifting through pine trees, nor admit obstructions to him who sees the beauty of cathedral spires in mountain peaks. Let each be inspired in his own way; but let him furnish his own church or choir, since such are not of nature.

"Life, liberty, and the pursuit of happiness"

There is no denying that a theater supplies recreation, that there may be inspiration in a good sermon, and a modicum of learning in a classroom; but we are here concerned only with such properties in their rudimentary state, transmissible to man directly from natural sources. The quickening of the pulse when a hunter squeezes the trigger, the quiet serenity transmitted from placid water through a line and a bamboo pole, the fresh, earthy smell of wet woods when sun follows shower, the startling whirr of a frightened grouse, the invigoration of swimming, hiking, or skiing, and the satisfying rest earned by the exertion, the intimacy with creation in forest solitude, the chastening of false vanities in the presence of majestic mountains, cascading streams, or ancient canyons, the glimpse of infinity in a flaming sunset, the inspiring beauty of autumn foliage or the forbidding aspect of winter wilderness, the communion with God and Nature through intimacy with sun, wind, rain, and snow away from the frail edifices and the confused strife of men—these are a few of the priceless gifts we would cherish in our time and transmit to posterity undefiled.

Are we to presume that abstractions may be conserved, like quick-freezing faith, hope, or love? Perhaps not. But we *can* conserve those material attributes of environment whence the abstractions "emanate." This chapter is perforce one of idealism and altruism, quite in contrast to all the others, but even so, as we shall see presently, it has its materialistic and pecuniary aspects.

Among the inalienable human rights espoused by our founding fathers are "life, liberty, and the pursuit of happiness," and our conservation of recreational resources is peculiarly pertinent to the last of these. The espousal of rights would mean little were it not implemented, but American wealth and enterprise have brought it to rare fruition. From our fabulous natural resources

Not by bread alone . . .

we have, by diligence and ingenuity, achieved a high standard of living. With production and efficiency have come progressively higher wages and shorter working hours until most of our people have both time and money for fun and travel. The 40-hour week, long weekends, and paid vacations afford the leisure with which to explore the rich aesthetic resources of our expansive and varied national landscape.

The pursuit of happiness has been further aided by the increasing speed and comfort of carriers—streamlined trains, air-conditioned buses, and luxurious skyliners—to say nothing of the comfort and convenience of traveling by private automobile on paved highways with facilities and conveniences available almost everywhere. We have so effectively shortened distance that scenes utterly remote by horse and buggy are now a few hours distant.

All these cultural advances—higher incomes, faster travel, and more leisure time—have given us unsurpassed capabilities for using natural resources that refresh, inspire, and instruct. Let us hope that our capacity to utilize has been paralleled by a growing appreciation of their worth and a stronger determination to conserve them. What was once for a chosen few is now enjoyed by many, and the more numerous clientele should assert a proportionately stronger influence. The more there are who enjoy a resource, the more champions ought there be to defend it.

Improvement of body, mind, and soul

The promotion of human well-being is an object of all conservation, and the "athletic-aesthetic" resources contribute very directly to the program. They are not essential in the same sense as water and soil, but they enrich even further a people possessed of abundant water and fertile soil. They make of men better conservators by strengthening their bodies, sharpening their wits, and refining their sense of values. Outdoor recreational resources improve the bodies of persons who enjoy them, thereby fitting such persons for greater application to their work and more constructive citizenship generally. The same healthful relaxation promotes mental alertness as well, soothes frayed nerves, and makes of the participant a more agreeable associate.

A clear mind may be counted a physical quality, improved by contact with nature, but the great outdoors also bestows intellectual and psychological benefits of a higher order. Wild areas afford opportunities to study our environment as it was before we disturbed it. To him who can hear, they whisper hints on how we may mend our abuses. They have incomparable scientific value. On a mental plane still higher they challenge, and extend, our limited powers of comprehension. If we but see, they show the inescapable unity of earth and life. They breach the flimsy barrier between instinct and intellect and test the veneer we call culture. They bring our thinking down to earth on solid footing.

Perhaps the greatest of all human benefits from outdoor experience are spiritual, though such defy measurement and may reach the recipient without his conscious knowledge. Many a believer feels closer to his Creator amid His handiwork—trees, cliffs, or wide and windy spaces—than in the best appointed and solemnly dedicated chapel. In nature one can pray and meditate without distraction. Nature assists man with the conservation of his immortal soul. Could any earthly resource have nobler purpose?

Following recommendations of the Outdoor Recreation Resources Review Commission,[1] there was established in the Department of the Interior in 1962 the Bureau of Outdoor Recreation, which is responsible for the nation's recreation requirements. The Bureau was given six main functions: to coordinate the recreation programs of all federal agencies (about twenty) that deal with public land; to sponsor and conduct research; to conduct recreation resource surveys; to stimulate and provide recreation assistance to the states; to encourage interstate and regional cooperative recreation projects; and to formulate a national recreation plan on the basis of state, regional, and federal plans. The Bureau will neither own nor manage any land, but its central surveillance over all recreational land use in the nation is a gratifying departure from the disconnected hodgepodge that long prevailed.

Choice of outdoor recreation and taste in scenic beauty differ as widely as temperament and social heritage, but none can be indulged without the requisite land area. Space allocation for recreation may be based upon needs rather than upon any particular attribute of the land, as when a city *develops* a park or playground; but an area of special scenic or scientific interest must be reserved where it happens to be, no matter how remote its location. The conservator should distinguish between natural resources and artificial developments, because the latter concern him only as they occupy space. Many parks developed to meet the recreational needs of a city, community, or metropolitan area have nothing natural about them except their location, the land upon which they are situated, and the elements that impinge on the surface. Selection of site is dictated by population density, accessibility to users, and availability of sufficient space. If a site suitably located has natural beauty or interest as well, so much

Not all recreation areas are natural

the better, but proximity is more important than natural attributes. Playgrounds, amusement parks, golf courses, swimming pools, athletic fields, and other *constructed* recreational facilities lie so near the fringe of our subject that we shall say little about them. *Recreational* they are, yes; *resources* they are too—but they can scarcely be called *natural*.

Monopoly of space is not necessarily a requisite for recreation, since many outdoor activities are compatible with, or even favored by, other uses of the land. If farmland produces most of our small game and logging increases browse for deer, it follows that farmers and lumbermen are patrons of hunting, unless they deny the hunter access to the game. To hunters, game is the thing, although the enjoyment of space may be their most important gain. The sport would be exclusive, indeed, were it limited to public lands and others retained exclusively for shooting.

**Monopoly
of space is not
an absolute
criterion**

Hunting, fishing, skiing, camping, picnicking, and many other forms of outdoor recreation may be enjoyed wherever conditions favor them, on private land or public, if the participants behave decently and respect the rights of others. Unfortunately, some of our fellow citizens are so retarded socially that they may not enjoy themselves except on public land or on land operated expressly for pleasure. Their slovenliness will not be tolerated on private property. Thus a crude minority has prejudiced the decent majority.

Recreational activities that require exclusive and extensive area, or the provision of considerable facilities, must be either publicly or commercially sponsored. Not many individuals could bear the cost of a water supply for a roadside camp, nor even of a fireplace or latrine, and only by a public agency can such a stopping place be properly policed and maintained. No individual, however wealthy, can adequately conserve a wilderness, because one lifetime is too short! Thus, it does devolve upon the public, through government, to conserve natural resources for citizens to enjoy. Public ownership is a strategic advantage; public maintenance a necessity—one of our worst failures has been the inadequate financing of supervision and maintenance.

Does public ownership mean space monopoly by one exclusive use? By no means. Our National Forests are also national playgrounds. In them are many of our best hunting and fishing lands; yet the same areas yield valuable timber harvests. The public range is for grazing of cattle and sheep, but a pack trip need do the grass no harm. Dude ranching might even be supplemental to stock raising. However, the dude ranch is ordinarily a business enterprise, a recreational land-use specialty. It serves paying guests and shows a profit from land that might be marginal or submarginal for other purposes. It is thus a form of private conservation. Our attention must be focused on public recreation areas and private land with recreational aspects supplemental to its primary use.

The accompanying graph (Fig. 13.1) shows the comparative rank of major outdoor recreation activities in which American adults participate. Their most popular relaxation is simply driving about seeing the sights and enjoying the country; a form of pleasure obtainable without any special provision of space or land reservation. It discredits the fallacious idea that recreation opportunity can be gauged by the acreage of land devoted to it.

Fig. 13.1 *Per cent of American adult population participating in outdoor activities most popular. Adapted from "Outdoor Recreation for America."*

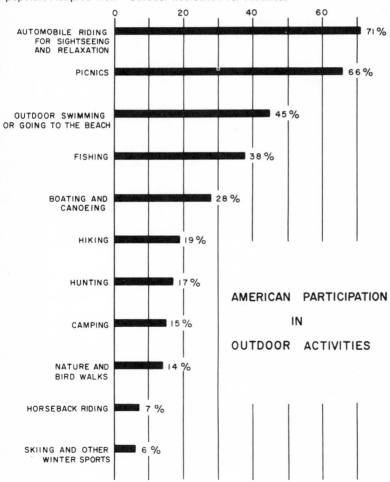

Except as it strains the capacity of roads and highways, it requires no shift in the ownership of land; neither does it interfere with prevailing land uses. Indeed, only two of the activities represented in the graph, swimming and boating, depend upon the exclusion of other land uses from suitable shores and beaches. Such forms of recreation as walking, bicycling, mountain climbing, and others are certainly not competitive with any land use; but shoreline recreation areas cannot be developed satisfactorily unless all other land uses are kept out. Many kinds of recreation may be enjoyed without infringing upon property rights, and many others require only the privilege of access.

As our population has grown, as more and more people have been able to travel and enjoy themselves, and as our land has become more thoroughly utilized, it has become necessary to guard private rights in land more jealously, and therefore incumbent upon us to reserve for public enjoyment areas desirable and available for the purpose. Increasing population pressure proves the wisdom of such public-land acquisition, and it demands also that governments at the various levels promote supplemental recreational use of private land consistent with both private and public interests. The latter is probably the larger task and certainly the one least advanced.

Development of facilities and promotion of recreation on public lands have been in progress since colonial times, but it was only recently that public sponsorship of recreation on private lands became a function of government (at first under stringent rules against selfish, landowner motives). Then, in the Food and Agriculture Act of 1962, Congress (replacing the barrier with a bonus) extended cost-sharing privileges to farmers, ranchers, and other private landowners for practices specifically and primarily beneficial to wildlife and authorized long-term loans for development of recreation areas and facilities on lands privately owned. Now the profit motive is no deterrent! We are subsidizing recreation on private lands, either as a primary enterprise or as a complementary, income-earning land use, and for good purpose: our increasingly urbanite population cannot have adequate recreation unless available rural spaces become sufficiently numerous. The aggregate of nonurban, public-designated outdoor recreation areas in the forty-eight contiguous states in 1960 was about one-eighth of the total land and water area in more than twenty-four thousand separate tracts. Units of 100,000 acres or more each, although in number little more than 1 per cent, contained 88 per cent of the total acreage. Tracts of less than 40 acres each numbered about 15,000, of which 11,000 were highway and roadside picnic and rest areas (state owned) that averaged less than 2 acres in size.[2] Two-thirds of the wayside areas were in the north-Central states and the South.[3] The entire nonurban recreation acreage publicly owned and managed was 86 per cent federal, 13 per cent state, and 1 per cent local.[4] (Although neither Alaska nor Hawaii is incorporated in the area statistics above, both of those states play unique roles in American recreation that will be increasingly important in the future.)

While we would exclude from our discussion artificial arrangements for physical exercise, group games, and other amusements contrived to meet purely recreational needs, we may not ignore them as conventional adjuncts to areas of genuine natural merit. We have often mixed the facilities for brute animation with natural resources for spiritual uplift—an incongruous formulation of secular and sacred ingredients. In many places we have constructed recreational facilities amid splendid natural scenery, and their incompatibility has provoked controversy; perhaps we have violated good conservation practice by such mixing. There are combinations we can endorse, such as a golf course or tennis court, camp ground or picnic area in a rich natural setting. A golfer's exercise need be no less invigorating because he admires the landscape between tees, and picnic gossip need be no less sensational if it is punctuated with praises of a beautiful view. However, we shall not attempt any justification for combining recreational and aesthetic resources except incidentally. Each function is probably best realized by separating the two.

The vulgar corrupts the sacred

. The plain, rustic picnic spot familiar to the average American is the smallest, albeit not the least important, recreational unit of the type we wish to conserve. With some such spot, somewhere in the United States, are associated treasured memories of friends and events that have enriched our lives. The lake shore or beach, the deep, cool woods or the bright, sunny glade, the mountain side or stream bank, the roadside park or the quiet, secluded place off a little country lane—each gave its share to our social heritage. Who can forget the last family picnic grandpa attended? Which grandmother has forgotten the time little Annie fell into the river, or the time little Willie strayed off and got lost? Who can recount his happy experiences without including the glow of a campfire on familiar faces?

The picnic area a natural resource?

Indeed, sandwiches, hot dogs, and marshmallows are symbols of an institution that Americans could ill afford to lose; one they can foster by reserving and maintaining for public use attractive nooks and corners here and there and affording access to them without trespassing. We need more picnic areas even now, and many more for the future. They are the least imposing of all the recreational resources, but even they will not be adequately conserved without our public help.

To go from picnic areas to National Parks may seem like jumping from the ridiculous to the sublime, but let us assume that editorial liberty. Our National Parks embody the ultimate in natural resources for refreshment, inspiration, and instruction.

Our National Parks—nature's masterpieces in public trust

In them one may know the magnificence of natural scenery, the ordered association of native plants and animals, and the marvels wrought by natural forces. In them we would hold inviolate certain segments of pristine America as a legacy from one generation to another.

We wrote our will a little late, after some prizes had been lost to us and all posterity; but we have salvaged enough outstanding areas to compose a National Park system of unique quality and variety. That system is the pride and property of every American, and every loyal citizen should defend it against compromise. Any unit diverted to another use would be lost forever as a natural exhibit, exactly as certain of our wildlife species have been lost. A natural area is not truly renewable; it must be preserved as it is.

In 1872 a few wise, unselfish men persuaded Congress to withdraw from entry and preserve for the use and enjoyment of all the people that wonderful part of public domain known as the "Yellowstone"—our first national park. Since then we have added other distinctive areas until we now have thirty-eight, comprising more than 8 million acres.[5] The map of National Parks and National Nature Monuments shows where they are located (Fig. 13.2). Unfortunately, few are in the East where most of our people live, not only because the natural grandeur of the western United States is more spectacular, but because the eastern lands were largely either privately owned or commercially used before the park movement began. However, every advance in transportation and ease of travel counters the regional disparity.

Under the Antiquities Act passed by Congress in 1906 we have reserved thirty-seven National Nature Monuments—areas of unique scenic or scientific interest, most of them in the Western states. The same map shows their locations, and their names indicate in most cases the features or properties to be preserved. Their focal interests virtually run the gamut of earth sciences, challenging the scholar and fascinating the casual visitor.

In 1916 the National Park Service was established to administer the entire system of national parks and monuments; and an excellent job the Service has done, often with a scant budget.

NATIONAL PARKS AND NATURE MONUMENTS

Fig. 13.2 *National Parks, Nature Monuments, etc. The National Park Service administers numerous other areas of scenic and scientific interest. The Blue Ridge Parkway has had more visitors per year (6½ million in 1962) than any other area in the system. Total of all National Park visitations in 1962 was more than 88 million.*

Under the Service come numerous national historical parks and historic sites, military parks and battlefields, memorials, cemeteries, parkways, and recreational areas,[6] most of which lack the *natural* quality of a natural resource except as they preempt land area.

Our main interest is in those federal reservations more definitively referred to as *National Primeval Parks*[7] in which we condone a minimum of artificial meddling, for the safety and convenience of visitors. These are our great, natural wonderlands, to be enjoyed in our time and conveyed to posterity unspoiled. Their aggregate area takes less than 1 per cent of our total land surface, a trifle we can well afford to dedicate to so high a purpose.

Every one of them is a wildlife sanctuary. Hunting and trapping are prohibited, as is the gathering or mutilation of native plants. Many are final retreats for remnants of big game and rare species.[8] They are living laboratories for the study of geography, geology, botany, zoology, and ecology. The geographer finds in them a wide sampling of climates, land forms, vegetation types, and environmental composites. Tropical to subpolar climates,

Fig. 13.3 *Among living things thousands of years old the egotist sheds his cloak of vanity. (Oldest yet discovered are bristlecone pines high on the Sierras of California— as old as 4,600 years.) Shown above is the Garden Club of America Grove in Humboldt Redwoods State Park, California. (Photo courtesy Save-the-Redwoods League.)*

coastal marsh to alpine meadow, desert to temperate rain forest, highest (Mt. McKinley) to lowest (Death Valley), wettest to driest, flattest to steepest—the Parks present variety. In the walls of deep canyons they show the geologist a complete rock sequence from most ancient formations to recent. They hold remnants of Pleistocene ice and great scars of severe glaciation. They display the gigantic upheaval of volcanoes and reveal the herculean powers of moving water. In them the geologist reads earth history through hundreds of millions of years. They afford the botanist, the zoologist, and the ecologist unequaled opportunity to observe and study indigenous plants and animals, including the oldest living and the most ancient dead. Such scholars may examine, on the ground, zonal distributions and regional associations nowhere else observable. For scientific values alone our National

Parks would be worth many times the cost of preserving them.

Perhaps the greatest educational value of the parks is to those numerous visitors who get their first taste of nature study from a ranger-naturalist. That first true glimpse of nature can stir the imagination more profoundly than systematic research and leave an indelible, sobering impression. Who can look at the Grand Canyon and trace its physiographic history without pondering immortality? Who can gape up at the "big trees" and feel himself terribly important (Fig. 13.3)? Who can view any of the natural wonders we guard without becoming a bit more tolerant of his fellows and a shade less satisfied with himself? Even the least thoughtful and impressionable park visitor is bound to gain higher national pride and some respect for resource conservation. The Parks are veritable classrooms for resource education, a function which, in the long run, may be their most valuable contribution. Common amusement does not become them. In 1950 almost 14 million visitors attested the aesthetic importance of Primeval Parks; in 1951 they numbered more than 15 million. All areas under jurisdiction of the National Park Service attracted 72 million in 1960.

Supplemental to the National Parks are the several state park systems. The states own more than 2,664 separate tracts of land, with a total area of about 5.6 million acres.[9] (Eighty-one new areas (156,485 acres) were added in 1961 alone.) State park standards vary in some degree between one state and another and are generally less exacting than those laid down by the National Park Service. Not all the state parks are natural, many of them being artificially developed, with more emphasis on active recreation than on aesthetic values. However, many compare favorably with the national ones in scenic beauty or scientific interest. Many, such as Itasca in Minnesota, headwaters of the Mississippi, the Adirondacks and Catskills in New York, several "Groves" of big trees in California, and a few beaches in Oregon have national interest. As game refuges or nature preserves, most of the state parks contribute to our national program for wildlife conservation.

State park systems complement the national

By their greater number and wider geographic distribution, state parks are accessible to many people unable to visit a national one. (State park attendance in 1960 reached 259 million.) In the populous Northeast they make up for the dearth of national areas and get heavy wear from city folk in search of fresh air. In the South, national forest areas supplement them, but in the south-central plains they serve without benefit of federal space. In the Mountain states they supplement the elaborate national system, and on the Pacific Slope they are generously interspersed with it. The combined pattern of state and national areas makes available to almost everyone a place to relax tensions and regain perspective away from the dull routine or strenuous hustle of making a living. No land has a higher yield.

Much could be said here about the lesser lights of parkdom—the numerous county or community reserves, the metropolitan or suburban parks and playgrounds—but, as previously suggested, few such areas qualify as natural resources. They interest the conservator, however, as *special land uses*. Those in rural communities are generally conservative of land, often putting to good use spaces poorly suited to other employment. Many areas otherwise wasted serve both for recreation and wildlife habitat. Those in urban vicinities are generally spaces appropriated for recreation in competition with intensive land uses. Patches of trees and grass where land sells by the foot instead of by the acre are concrete evidence that open space is almost as essential to health as safe drinking water. Their scarcity evinces poor conservation of space exactly where space is most precious.

The colonists transplanted to the New World the idea of a town common or village green, but the idea was apparently lost in the rush of westward expansion and the erection of vertical cities. We neglected to reserve adequate space for escape from jostling crowds, incessant noises, and gasoline fumes. We built skyscrapers without reserving enough horizontal distance between them to refresh their occupants. We ignored the object lessons taught by such great and ancient cities as London, where spacious parks, "greenbelts," and open squares have been strictly maintained for the people's enjoyment.[10] Our errors are costing us dearly in condemnation of properties, clearing, rebuilding, and landscaping. The states of New York and New Jersey, under long-range programs recently begun, have expended vast sums of money to acquire and develop open spaces for their metropolitan populations.

The vulnerability of tall buildings and compact city blocks to aerial weapons has encouraged horizontal expansion of cities. The same dispersal that renders them less remunerative as targets automatically leaves more open space. The same adjustment that promotes passive defense also promotes the welfare of urban residents when no attack threatens. Under the lash of danger urban uses occupy more land, but land devoted to health and security may be adjudged well used. It is, indeed, an ill wind that blows no good; fear sometimes provides needed recreational space where deliberate choice failed to do so.

We need more
roof gardens
on the ground

In Chapter 10 we mentioned recreation among the multiple services of forests. Now we are ready to elucidate the idea. Forests are, indeed, among our most valuable recreational resources, their intangible benefits rivaling their value for wood production. More often than not, our outdoor experiences are associated with trees, whether in a picnic grove, a thicket with birds and berries, a farm woodland where squirrels and rabbits live, or a real forest of tall timber, with deep shade by day and heavy silence at night. Neither area nor ownership is a reliable criterion for evaluation, because a mere clump of trees favorably situated, though privately owned, can be enjoyed by more people than square miles of forest fastness, publicly owned but out of reach. The eternal problem of access, which hinges upon public decency, is the main deterrent to recreational use of private land, forested or otherwise. Since right of access remains highly subjective, we shall devote most of our discussion to public forests wherein we, through government, determine our own privileges.

Forests are important recreational resources

National, state, and community forests afford exceptional opportunity for a variety of outdoor activities. The Forest Service administers 84 per cent of our federal recreation land; lesser forest agencies administer 58 per cent of our state and 81 per cent of the local, recreation lands.[11] In the National Forests many thousands of camping and picnicking areas have been equipped with tables and benches, fireplaces, safe water supplies, latrines, and garbage-disposal facilities. Hundreds of swimming places have been improved, and hundreds of winter sports areas developed. In the National Forests are numerous organization camps, with dormitories or cabins, mess halls, and other appurtenances for group outings, and more than 250,000 miles of scenic roads and trails. They contain 81,000 miles of streams and 3 million acres of lakes and impoundments—for fishing, boating, or canoeing. Game is abundant in most of them and may be hunted in accordance with regulations laid down by the state within which the particular area happens to lie, excepting areas designated federal or state wildlife refuges. More than 2 million hunters used the National Forests in 1960. They bagged 659,000 big-game animals, or one-third the total number taken in the entire country. For those who shoot with cameras the forests excel as hunting grounds.

The number of recreational visits to National Forests had grown to 92.5 million annually in 1960, about one-fourth of them by hunters or fishermen. In addition, perhaps an equal number of motorists enjoyed the forest scenery just driving through. Provision for sundry sports and other activities is more consistent with National Forest policy than our National Park standards. Rules of behavior can be somewhat more lenient in the forests, excepting, of course, a strict fire discipline. Sports that would deface natural exhibits or alter biotic communities may not be detrimental to forestry.

One should be reminded that in neither the forests nor the parks do artificial developments and construction occupy more than a minute part of total acreage. Service areas and camp sites are simply bases of operation, as it were. The parks excel in scenic grandeur and scientific interest; the forests, our greatest playgrounds, also include areas that rival the parks in aesthetic aspects.

State, county, and other public forests are in most cases desirable and useful for recreation. Many were reserved or acquired to fill specific recreational needs, and are maintained primarily for recreation. Some combine forestry with recreation, producing valuable timber crops coincidental with their service as playgrounds. Some contribute materially to our forest resources and relatively less to the recreational ones, but very few lack entirely those attributes desirable in a recreation area. They lie within easy reach of many more people than the National Forests and, within their limitations of size, afford similar opportunities for sports and other outdoor activities. Many units, or parts of units, are distinguishable from parks in name only.

Our evaluation of forests as recreational resources would be badly distorted if we failed to mention farm woodlands and other privately owned forests. They are much more numerous than public forests, and almost every one of them has recreational potential. Whether as places to observe wildlife or places to indulge in more active recreation, they are resources of more than economic significance. Many affluent sportsmen who underwrite private hunting or fishing grounds today shot their first game in a farm woodlot and caught their first fish in the creek that ran through it when they were barefoot boys without money and without business problems.

Forest industry lands attract each year more than 6 million visitors in quest of outdoor recreation, and several times that many people might enjoy them if the public were better aware of the privilege. Almost all such lands are open for picnicking, hiking, camping, and berry picking, without any charge or formality, as a quiet public service. More than 92 per cent of their area may be hunted, and more than 97 per cent of their lakes and streams may be fished. On some properties are attractive parks, with picnic and camping accommodations. Industrial forest owners are pleased to invite recreational use of their land, but they are deterred from advertising the privilege except in a few states with owner liability laws that absolve them of risk. Liability laws that encourage public recreational use of privately owned land were enacted in Maine, New Hampshire, New York, and Pennsylvania before 1963, and a few others have followed their example.[12]

The importance of small woods as wildlife habitats was pointed out in Chapter 12. The preponderance of small holdings in the total forest picture was indicated in Chapter 8. Their proportionate contribution to recreation is probably even greater than their contribution to timber supply. Those that occupy land too poor for more intensive use, or land that needs their protective covering, require no other justification for being. Almost without exception, they add charm and interest to the landscape. They have aesthetic and recreational values that merit greater recognition than is ordinarily accorded them. Many are business assets to their owners.

Shores and beaches stand almost as high as forests and mountains on the preferred list of scenic and recreational attractions; yet they have been almost ignored in public conservation programs. (A survey completed by the National Park Service in 1954 revealed that public recreation areas owned nationally or by the states comprised only 6.5 per cent of the Atlantic and Gulf shorelines.)

Shores and beaches have special appeal

In the zone of contact between land and water, man himself responds to the principle of edge that influences so strongly the distribution of wildlife (Chapters 11 and 12). A modified response it is, perhaps, but most of our water recreation depends upon "edge," be it active pleasure such as fishing, swimming, and boating, or passive enjoyment of amphibious scenery. Gunning for waterfowl adheres closely to the land-water edge, and even deep-sea sports fishing depends upon it. Boat docks, bath houses, and other shore facilities for recreation are exploitations of edge. Whoever owns the edge controls the recreational use of the water. That is a fact we have almost missed in public conservation of recreational resources. However, our neglect is moderated by many desirable commercial developments.

Except on public reservations such as parks, forests, and refuges, our use of stream banks, lake shores, and ocean beaches has been largely private or commercial, without public intervention on behalf of the resources. The public domain included no ocean beach that might have been set aside as a national park, but the deficiency has been partially corrected by acquisition of such coastal areas as the Cape Hatteras dunes; outer Cape Cod; Point Reyes, California; the Channel Islands off Los Angeles; Padres Island, Texas; the Everglades of Florida; and Acadia National Park on the coast of Maine. The last is a nature area of "stern and rock-bound coast." The Islands have beaches from which human swimmers might wish to evict the sea lions if park policy permitted. The Park Service is not an amusement agency; beach development for swimming and other sports has been incidental. On the Cape Hatteras tract recreation and nature sanctuary occupy separate areas. The National Seashore Parks were not established for water sports.

We have made substantial contributions to lake-shore recreation on the national level in connection with reservoir construction for such purposes as flood "control," power, and irrigation, as is shown briefly in Table 1. Federal planning and supervision

Table 1

Federal Reservoir Recreation

Agency	Number of Reservoirs	Shoreline Mileage	Water Surface Acreage	Millions of Visitors in 1960
Corps of Engineers	250	23,000	3 million	109
T.V.A.	29	10,000	600,000	42.5
Bureau of Reclamation	174	7,000	1½ million	24.3

Source: *Study Report No. 10*, Outdoor Recreation Resources Review Commission (Washington D.C., 1962).

assures recreational benefit from man-made lakes (Fig. 13.4), as when the Park Service manages the shore around waters impounded by the Reclamation Service for irrigation and other uses.

Pollution of streams, lake shores, and ocean beaches has become so extremely detrimental to recreation that it constitutes a major conservation problem. Waters too toxic for fish and too filthy to swim in have obviously lost their recreational value and become a menace to health instead of the boon they should be. Most of our streams (some 3.5 million miles in all size categories) have been more or less degraded for recreation use by pollution. Many cities on the Great Lakes have surrendered to pollution the recreational advantage of shoreline location. Several have closed their once pleasurable beaches, indefinitely. Many of our recreational resources are completely dependent upon water conservation. They illustrate once again the inescapable unity of natural assets.

Fig. 13.4 *Impoundment of water for flood prevention, power generation, and other purposes also creates new recreational opportunities for the people. On public sites, such as this one in Kentucky, good planning and high standards of maintenance have been the rule. (TVA photo.)*

States well endowed with lakes and beaches have generally neglected to conserve them. They have permitted private purchase of shore properties until public access to the water has been blocked, and they have condoned such conglomerations of nondescript architecture as would cause every ripple to cringe if it could see them. Homes and cottages, two and three deep, line the best places around beautiful glacial lakes, and a nonowner can barely see the water without trespassing. Shacks, "joints," and dilapidated firetraps degrade many of our finest beaches on the Atlantic Coast and Gulf Coast into a revolting clutter of trash. Such blighting of natural beauty by cheap commercialization has created many problems for the planner and the conservator.

All beaches have not been divested of natural charm and diverted from wholesome public use. A few of our coastal states have reserved and maintained for the public choice stretches of shoreline. Facilities and services are either state operated or state supervised in the public interest. Many commercial beach developments are also examples of good conservation, protecting the natural resource and catering to "solid" citizens who come to enjoy the beach environment.

The highest type of recreational or scenic resource is the primeval wilderness, though we have only recently acknowledged the

Primeval wilderness is our highest type of recreational resource

333

fact. Its conservation is first of all a matter of preservation. Any idea of direct profit or common amusement defeats its purpose. Its conservation demands an immunity from cultural modification even more absolute than that prescribed for the National Parks as a whole, and a longer vision and greater altruism than for any other class of resource, though some of our best wildernesses are actually within National Parks. The value of wilderness as a natural resource depends, not upon development, but upon strict prohibition of development—retention exactly as nature made it. To have genuine wilderness one must begin with a "mature, balanced community of plant and animal life" as it was before man arrived on the scene, and protect it, consistent with its recreational use, against every sort of human intervention.[13] Some areas, such as the Adirondack Forest Preserves, have reverted to wilderness after serving other useful purposes.

A person who has done field nature study as student, teacher, or researcher can readily subscribe to wilderness conservation, but the average "materialistic" American, seeing no practical advantage in it, is more inclined to ignore it than to support it. Public apathy born of ignorance, private selfishness, and greed constitute the major problems. The conservator must instruct the public, and the public must restrain obstructive private motives.

Why save wilderness? For its unique recreational, aesthetic, and scientific values. The last one mentioned is probably the most important, although wilderness affords the only complete escape from civilization and the only opportunity to commune with nature in her own ageless solitude. The scientific values have many ramifications, both academic and practical. Their importance is probably best evinced by the fact that naturalist groups have most actively and effectively spread the wilderness concept. The wilderness is, obviously, a complete field laboratory for the study of earth sciences. It shows what the environment was before man intervened and reveals the wisdom (or lack of it) with which he adapted it to his use. Wilderness serves as a point of departure for determining our use and abuse of durable resources. If we save it now, it can do the same for future generations. If we delay, or admit compromise, some future geographer will be unnecessarily handicapped in his interpretation of environmental influences and adaptations. If we disclaim all interest in posterity, the immediate, practical value of wilderness to land science is in itself more than adequate justification for conserving it.[14]

Federal agencies charged with the administration of public lands have responded favorably to the wilderness movement and reserved under various designations many areas of wilderness quality. The Forest Service, our greatest guardian of wilderness, first established two major categories: (1) Wilderness—single tract of 100,000 acres or more; (2) Wild Area—single tract between 5,000 and 100,000 acres in area.[15] As of 1961, the National Forests contained eighty-three units in four categories, as tabulated in Table 2.

Table 2

Wilderness-Type Areas in National Forests
February 24, 1961

Kind of Area	Number	Acreage
Wilderness	14	4,888,173
Wild	28	979,154
Primitive	40	7,907,416
Canoe	1	886,673
Total	83	14,661,416

Source: Committee on Interior and Insular Affairs, *House Report No. 2521*, 87th Cong., 2d sess., October 3, 1962, p. 88.

Many of the National Parks, several of the National Nature Monuments and Federal Wildlife Refuges, and a few state reservations qualify for designation as wilderness or wild areas, or include large portions that do.

The ideal wilderness system would include a suitable unit to represent every physiographic region and every ecologic association in the country before settlement. But we cannot attain the ideal. Particularly in the East, representative areas of sufficient size are difficult to find. The Linville Gorge Wild Area, established in 1952, was the first area so designated by the Forest Service east of the Mississippi, although the Boundary Waters Canoe Area in northern Minnesota is indeed National Forest wilderness. In nonforested regions a type unit should probably be at least 500,000 acres in area.[16] Such a block of unmodified grassland is a thing of the past, so we may have to be content with smaller units. (Fig. 13.5 shows one proposal for a National Wilderness Preservation system.)

Recognition of *wildness* as a resource has encouraged the preservation of many lesser "nature" areas. Michigan, Wisconsin, Iowa, and others have reserved primeval ecological remnants on a statewide basis. Numerous other agencies, institutions, and citizen groups are protecting an untold number of natural areas, every one of which has some scientific value (Fig. 13.3). We have

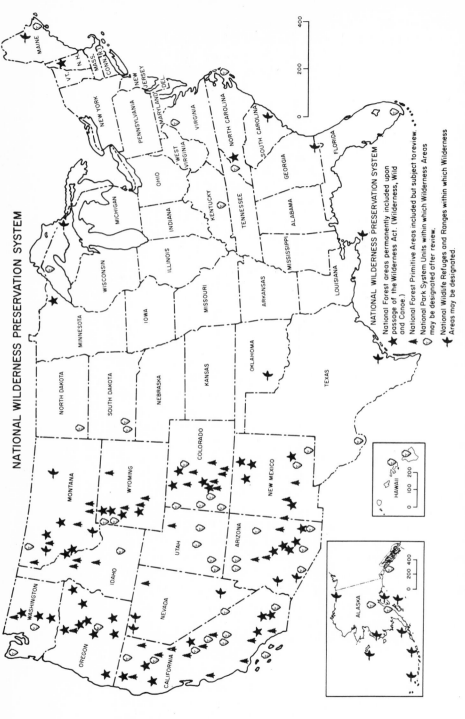

Fig. 13.5 Areas to be considered for, or included in the National Wilderness System as provided in the Wilderness Act, S. 174. Areas comprise selected National Park areas, National Forest Reserved Areas, and National Refuge units. These and additional tracts have been recommended

NATIONAL WILDERNESS PRESERVATION SYSTEM

NATIONAL WILDERNESS PRESERVATION SYSTEM

National Forest areas permanently included upon passage of the Wilderness Act. (Wilderness, Wild and Canoe.)

National Forest Primitive Areas included but subject to review.

National Park System Units within which Wilderness Areas may be designated after review.

National Wildlife Refuges and Ranges within which Wilderness Areas may be designated.

many hundreds of Nature Sanctuaries officially reserved. Every state has at least one. California alone has several score. It is too late to secure a complete set of museum pieces, but let us make sure that we do not lose any remaining exhibits that should be added.

Resources such as scenery, wilderness, and natural wonders, which have intangible values, are extremely difficult to defend against selfishness and vandalism because they cannot be appraised in materialistic terms. They might be likened to a family heirloom that lacks intrinsic worth and is nonetheless a prized possession.

Intangible values are difficult to defend against selfish pressure groups

If we assume that a resource is secure when it is publicly owned we are deceiving ourselves. Not even the national parks, reserved and dedicated by Congress, are inviolate. On the contrary, they are threatened recurrently, if not continuously, by groups and agencies with special axes to grind—axes that would chop our parks to pieces if we did not parry their blows.

To the engineer a deep, narrow canyon is a sculptured invitation to build a dam; to the lumberman a forest is something to be cut down and sold, at a profit; to a stockman grass is the stuff from which cattle and sheep make money. They see these things from a limited perspective, and when bureaucracy or sectional politics supports their aims they become a menace to national interests. Only by constant vigilance will the American people prevent wasteful appropriation for the temporary benefit of a few certain natural treasures that should be the permanent property of all. Only by national referendum should it be permissible to dam the Grand Canyon and fill it up with silt.

Timber and grass above ground and minerals underneath are as dangerous to public lands as potential dam sites. Selfish interests ferret out every statutory loophole through which they may work, and our statutes have many loopholes. No public area is secure, be it park, forest, or wilderness. Lumbermen would cut the "big trees," stockmen would overgraze the last remnants of native meadow, and miners would tear up both earth and vegetation for the purpose (or even pretence) of recovering critical minerals. Certain laws for the encouragement of mineral exploration and recovery on public lands have jeopardized other values.

If we were desperate for material resources, we might condone their procurement at the expense of the intangibles, but while we revel in abundance we have no reason for such sacrifice. If ever we permit ourselves to become so destitute that we must scrape every vestige of wealth off the land in order to prolong our survival, we may find that it would have been preferable to have per-

338   *Resources for Recreation, Inspiration, and Instruction*

ished a bit sooner amid more pleasant surroundings. For the interim we should exclude from our nature preserves every common use, such as logging, mining, or grazing, that detracts from their higher purpose. We should not permit sectional or bureaucratic pressure groups to make spoils of our rarest public possessions.

More disconcerting than selfishness is the wanton abuse of public property and public privileges without *any* apparent motive. Perverse vandalism and human slothfulness curtail public enjoyment of aesthetic and recreational resources by defacing and befouling them, and even destroying them outright. Here we face the embarrassing fact that places for public enjoyment need protection against the very public that frequents them. The United States has its share of people who lack respect for public property, perhaps because they have little of their own to care for or have got what they have too easily. These inconsiderate, unprincipled persons are the bane of a conservator's existence. They leave camp sites and picnic areas littered with garbage. They start destructive fires by leaving camp fires smoldering or by tossing lighted cigarettes away. They shoot holes in signs and markers. They collect forbidden souvenirs—a crime called larceny. They soil and mutilate public structures and facilities until decent people cannot use them. They are like a scourge of human locusts that ruin, not crops and meadows, but priceless public possessions and costly public conveniences.

Vandalism is very difficult to curb by punitive means, because the guilty person is often of the strain that resents suggestion or correction and takes pride in breaking the law. The apparent need is for education that will reform the vandals. Education and information are important to the conservation of any resource, but for conserving those with intangible values they are the primary tools. We must teach our citizens the value of natural beauty and wildness, and the very areas we wish to protect may be the best classrooms for the instruction. Well-conducted field trips and group outings for our youngsters will ensure better and easier conservation in the future.

Several times we have alluded to selfish interests inimical to the conservation of aesthetic or recreational resources, but we have said very little about circumstances under which private interests are desirable. The fact is that opportunities for outdoor recreation would be sadly inadequate without those provided by private enterprises operated for profit. Private capital exploits scenic and recreational resources just as legitimately as it exploits soils and forests, with comparable degrees of care and abuse. We mentioned

Public property gets public abuse

Commercial conservation of recreational resources

the case of beaches; some disgraceful and others commendable. The same holds for swimming pools, ski slides, tourist courts and hotels, lodges and rental cabins, and a variety of other facilities, including exclusive resorts for seasonal residence. Many represent desirable resource development and conservation. They are valuable additions to the American scene. We are improving their quality by granting to private companies the recreational and tourist facilities on public reservations under a franchise or concession contract with provisos written in to ensure high standards of operation (Fig. 13.4). Tourist accommodations in our National Parks and in such recreation areas as those on the "Great Lakes of the South" are privately operated, subject to governmental supervision and inspection. The half-and-half arrangement is advantageous both to the entrepreneur and his patrons, producing private profit and public economy. Condemnation of commercial development of aesthetic or recreational resources on general principles would be quite wrong, because many such resources would be wasted had not private enterprise grasped an opportunity. The conservator applauds those operators who maintain standards commensurate with the quality of the resource they utilize.

Commercial development can also be commercial desecration (recall the beaches again). Juke joints and hot-dog stands that cheapen a grand view are to aesthetic resources as gullies are to soils. They are wasteful abuses of natural beauty. Such commercial blights the conservator cannot condone. He counts them a form of vandalism—crimes against both nature and the American public. When planners "zone" them out of the scene they conserve aesthetic resources, hand in glove with conservators.

Hunting and fishing pay their own way

The popular outdoor sports of hunting and fishing have risen to singular commercial stature despite the precarious conditions of certain game resources and the shrinkage of land areas on which to hunt or fish. We mentioned the sportsman's dilemma before but refrained from analyzing it, because much game and many game lands have become so distinctly recreational and commercial as to be almost divorced from ordinary wildlife conservation. Especially is this true insofar as wildlife conservation pertains to migratory waterfowl. The maintenance of duck populations depends partly upon our control of hunting pressure, although genuine conservation of waterfowl remains a matter of suitable habitat and favorable biotic balance. Evicted by drainage and drought from many of their breeding grounds, highly esteemed by gunners, and subjected to mass murder the length of their seasonal flights, migratory waterfowl became a special conservation problem. Cognizant of this, the Congress placed them under federal jurisdiction in 1916 (Migratory Bird Treaty with Canada) to check their threatened extinction by killing, assumed responsibility for their protection under federal law in the Migratory Bird Treaty Act of 1918, authorized acquisition of land and water areas as "inviolate sanctuaries" by enactment of the Migratory Bird Conservation Act of 1929, and began in 1934 under the Migratory Bird Hunting Stamp Act the collection of money with which to recover and rehabilitate nesting and wintering grounds. Every licensed hunter of ducks, geese, or brant became a patron of the program by compulsory purchase of a "duck stamp" each hunting season. Price of the stamp began at $1.00 but had risen to $3.00 in 1959. During the first twenty-five years of issue, 32,592,841 of the stamps were sold, many of them to people who never hunt.

Duck stamp revenue pays for wet real estate

Duck stamp proceeds were initially expendable for "purchase, development, administration, and maintenance of waterfowl refuges throughout the country." In 1960 Congress directed that *all* revenues from the sale of duck stamps, except operational expenses reimbursable to the Post Office Department, should be used only to *acquire* land for migratory bird refuges; but, it was apparent that even this acceleration of habitat procurement would be inadequate and that waterfowl *production* areas, as well as refuges, would have to be secured by the government. Congress implemented the public production idea in 1961 by authorizing a Treasury loan of 105 million dollars against anticipated duck-stamp revenue, with a seven-year moratorium on repayment. With emergency funds thus available, the Bureau of Sport Fisheries and Wildlife expanded its program of wetlands acquisition. Its ultimate goal is the addition of 4.5 million acres of choice waterfowl habitats to the federally owned system, and the purchase of 2.5 million acres more by the states represented in the four Flyway Councils.

The wetlands produce our wild waterfowl

To deter further conversion of wetlands to farming even while they were being selected for purchase or lease, the Congress, late in 1962, suspended the federal subsidization of drainage in such crucial areas as the glacial-slough country of the Dakotas and western Minnesota, an important nesting ground for ducks. Considering that about one-half of all wetlands in the United States have been artificially drained and that many, such as Horicon Marsh in Wisconsin and Willow Slough in Indiana, proved so undesirable for agriculture that they have been *reflooded* for wildlife purposes, we may predict that public subsidy of drainage projects will be severely and indefinitely curtailed.

No matter how many unspoiled wetlands we reserve in the

United States, Canada will probably remain our major producer of the waterfowl hunted by Americans. Most of the nesting grounds are Canadian; most of the wintering grounds American. The vast Prairie Pothole Region of Canada and the United States has about 5 million small marshes that produce more than one-half of the continental duck population; but the American portion (Dakotas, Montana, Nebraska, and Minnesota) has produced only about 14 per cent of the total in recent years, the other 86 per cent being largely of Canadian origin.[17] The meager and erratic precipitation characteristic of the prairies (Chapter 7) complicates waterfowl conservation in both Canada and the United States.

Most important waterfowl wintering grounds in the United States are the coastal marshes of Louisiana and Texas and the swampy flood plains of the lower Mississippi. The flood-plain habitats have been severely constricted by drainage and other hydraulic modifications and have been reduced in carrying capacity by logging of mast-bearing hardwoods. The coastal habitats have been damaged by industrial pollution and canalization, and the suitability for waterfowl has been impaired by the fantastic spread of two exotic plants, alligator weed and water hyacinth, that crowd out desirable species.[18] Melioration of these adverse developments should keep pace with other facets of the waterfowl program; nesting grounds remain vacant unless prospective parents survive the winter. Provision of adequate wintering grounds was a major factor in the recovery of our Canada goose flocks—a signal achievement in game-bird management.

Even after we complete the most ambitious program of public wetland acquisition that can be envisioned, the private landowners, mainly farmers, will produce most of the wild waterfowl. For this the farmers will have to be better compensated than heretofore or they will, of economic necessity, continue the eradication of ducks by drainage and other means to spare themselves the nuisance of hunters and the depredations of ducks to their crops. They cannot produce a crop of ducks instead of grain unless they receive equivalent income by doing so from hunting fees, land rental, or liberal indemnity for damages.

More mallards
to shoot
or more wheat
to store

Most numerous of our waterfowl, and highly favored as game birds, are mallards and pintails; both of these duck species are field feeders, notoriously destructive of grain crops. Farmers in Canada and northern United States suffer annual depredations by these birds amounting to many millions of dollars, for which they have been poorly indemnified, if at all; and the increasing prominence of mallards magnifies the problem.

Mallards are so versatile in their habitat requirements and so adaptable to new or changed conditions that their numerical superiority among the duck populations is expected to become progressively greater. They are the pioneers among ducks, the first to explore and inhabit new water bodies, whether created by structural impoundment or by blasting holes in the prairie. They may nest a mile from water and lead their fledgling broods far afield for feeding. Most of them grow up in wheat country and might be evaluated in terms of bushels. While we have a surplus of wheat and a shortage of ducks, a shift of crop emphasis might be advantageous to all—farmers, sportsmen, taxpayers, and ducks.

Most comprehensive and permanently constructive of all schemes, whereby hunters and fishermen pay their own way and benefit countless other people as well, are two national programs of incomparable worth to wildlife conservation: Federal Aid in Wildlife Restoration (Pittman-Robertson Act, 1937); Federal Aid in Fish Restoration (Dingell-Johnson Act, 1950).

Both of these acts provide for federal-state cooperation in the rehabilitation of wildlife habitats of genuine merit and usefulness to the public. The latter was modeled after the former, and the programs are similar in concept, operation, and administration; one for sport fisheries, the other for game birds and mammals that may be hunted or trapped. Projects combining fish and wildlife restoration in one area have also been authorized and many such have been developed. For all practical purposes, work under the two acts constitute a single program, although the funds must be kept separate. The wildlife restoration is financed with a manufacturers' excise tax of 11 per cent on sporting arms and ammunition; the fish restoration with a similar tax of 10 per cent on fishing rods, creels, reels, and artificial lures, baits, and flies. (In fiscal year 1960, these excise taxes amounted to 21 million dollars, and sportsmen paid an additional 115 million dollars for state license fees.) The Federal government may pay up to 75 per cent of costs on approved projects. A state is eligible to participate if it has passed laws for the conservation of wildlife (or fish) and uses all license fees collected from hunters (or fishermen) for administration of a state fish and game department. All have participated. In fiscal 1961 almost 5.5 million dollars were apportioned to the states for fish restoration and almost 14.25 million dollars for wildlife restoration. Monies may be used for purchase and development of land and water habitats, acquisition of access lands, maintenance and management, investigations and surveys, and coordination of the projects. All lands acquired, structures erected, and equipment procured with the cooperative funds become state property. As of June 30, 1961, 165

MAJOR FEDERAL AID FISH AND WILDLIFE DEVELOPMENT AND LAND ACQUISITION AREAS

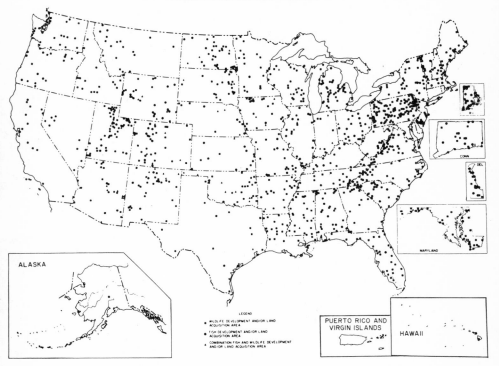

Fig. 13.6 *Restoration of fish and wildlife habitats under the programs of federal aid to the states progresses so well that numerous areas have been added since this map was compiled. (From Bureau of Sport Fisheries and Wildlife, January 1961.)*

public fishing lakes totaling about 21,300 acres had been completed and 384 public access areas had been purchased and developed, making available to public fishing 800 miles of streams and 40,000 acres of lakes; lands purchased for wildlife projects totaled 2,403,684 acres. Figure 13.6 indicates the dimension and distribution of the successful cooperative programs.

Hunting and fishing are not only recreational, but also very important to our national economy. Many landowners are realizing a supplemental income from hunting leases or permits. Farmers are becoming conservators of game for direct profit and benefactors of other wildlife inadvertently. We said earlier that this chapter has its materialistic aspects. This is one of them.

Annual consumer spending for outdoor recreation in America was estimated in 1962 to be about 20 billion dollars.[19] Ninety per cent of the population participated more or less, in one way or another. In 1960 American fishermen spent 3 billion dollars in the pursuit of fish for sport, and American hunters spent 1 billion dollars in pursuit of game. About 21.7 million persons fished in fresh water and almost 6.3 million in salt water. Some 12 million hunted (upland) small game, almost 6.3 million hunted big game, and 2 million hunted waterfowl. Many participated in more than one of the sports.[20] Not only do fishing and hunting contribute about one-fifth of the national recreation income, but they also bring much meat to the American dinner table. In 1959 fresh-water anglers caught more than 858 million pounds of sport fish and salt-water anglers caught more than 319 million pounds of fish. The total tonnage taken for sport was more than 45 per cent as large as the catch of food fish by commercial fishermen.[21] (The quantities of game eaten can only be conjectured, but the total would be tremendous.)

Hunters who sight through binoculars and shoot with cameras far outnumber those who employ lethal weapons. Each of the viewers spends perhaps half as much money as the killer and takes none of his quarry away with him. This admirable breed of hunter contributes substantially to the national economy without the least detraction from our natural resources. He is the unsung hero of wildlife conservation. He gives much, takes nothing, and makes no noise about it.

Tourism has attained the rank of a major industry

The enjoyment of our great scenic and recreational resources, in the highest sense invaluable to us, may nonetheless be accounted a major American industry with a tremendous money value. Touring to "See America First" has attained full commercial status and assumed a prominent place in American business. Color-page advertisements in a score of national magazines indicate how important it is to state finances. *Tourist farming* and the *tourist crop* have become definitive phrases in economic geography. Many "depressed" areas have become prosperous by developing and exploiting their recreational resources. The opportunity awaits many more.

Of course all recreational travel is not directly related to natural resources, but a very substantial part of it is. Comparatively few people spend their vacations in cities; most of them seek open country with beautiful scenery. Scenery has become an exploitable resource, and tourism has attained first, second, or third rank as an income-yielding industry in a score of our states. Would anyone deny that scenic and recreational resources have material values? Would he question the wisdom of conserving them when they can by intelligent management yield a big crop of dollars every year indefinitely without impairment? If one must stoop to dollars and cents in order to conserve aesthetic and recreational resources, he can stoop with confidence.

The growth of vacation travel in recent years has profound implications for conservation generally. Travel acquaints our people with their great country better than any other medium could possibly do it. They see for themselves the scars of abusive exploitation and the demonstrated methods of healing them. They see how good the land can be when it is cared for and how ill it can get when mistreated. They must inevitably gain some impression of our prodigious waste of natural wealth, and the urgent need for conservation. Certainly they cannot miss entirely the striking contrast between healthy communities on well-kept land and the cadaverous neighborhoods whose resource base has withered or worn away. Even the least observant traveler must be somewhat annoyed by stinking streams and roadside slums, and the most casual observer must surely sense the human competence and security reflected in a clean, harmonious landscape. In the long run, public consciousness thus aroused may be worth much more to our nation than the sum of money travelers spend each year. (In 1960, 40 billion dollars or almost one-twelfth the gross national product.)

If travel is so valuable as a source of revenue and so potent a medium for shaping constructive public opinion and if much of the traveling is in search of beauty, it should be an incentive for all of us, collectively and individually, to make our own surroundings more attractive and wholesome. Beauty, which is its own excuse for being, has resource status and can be conserved. At this form of conservation America is a complete novice compared with older and more crowded countries, such as England. Thus far, Americans have exploited and commercialized almost without regard for the ugliness that unbridled materialism can create. They have obliterated much natural beauty unnecessarily, and much more will be spoiled unless they recognize its value. Sparing it might be termed "passive" conservation. Our biggest task, that of restoring lost beauty and enhancing that which remains, might be termed active beautification. Both are needed if we shall have the kind of nation and communities we like to envisage. Conservation of beauty may seem fanciful, but in practice it has real economic significance. No one can live on it, but none can live in dignity and contentment without it. Its conservation can be achieved without deviating from good management of other resources and will, indeed, improve the physical ones.

Conservation of beauty deserves attention

Beauty conservation may well begin with the roadsides since

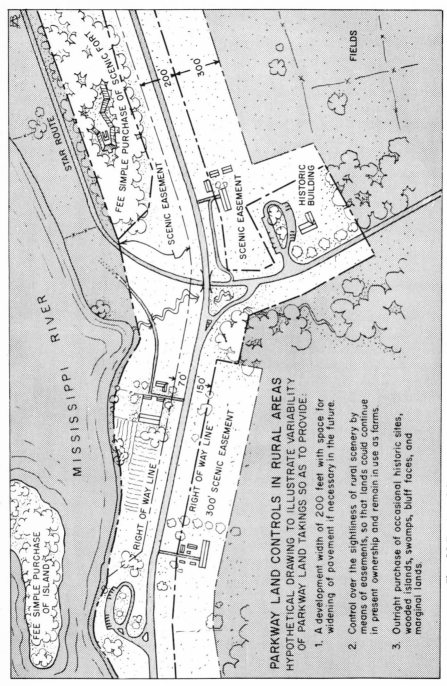

Fig. 13.7 A mobile, prosperous society can refresh itself with pleasant routes of passage. Conservation of scenic routes necessitates public jurisdiction over sufficient wayside space. (From Bureau of Roads and National Park Service, Parkway for the Mississippi, 1951.)

The following text appears within the figure:

MISSISSIPPI RIVER

FEE SIMPLE PURCHASE OF ISLAND

FEE SIMPLE PURCHASE OF SCENIC FORT

STAR ROUTE

SCENIC EASEMENT

SCENIC EASEMENT

HISTORIC BUILDING

FIELDS

200

300

70'

150'

RIGHT OF WAY LINE

RIGHT OF WAY LINE

300' SCENIC EASEMENT

PARKWAY LAND CONTROLS IN RURAL AREAS
HYPOTHETICAL DRAWING TO ILLUSTRATE VARIABILITY
OF PARKWAY LAND TAKINGS SO AS TO PROVIDE:

1. A development width of 200 feet with space for widening of pavement if necessary in the future.

2. Control over the sightliness of rural scenery by means of easements, so that lands could continue in present ownership and remain in use as farms.

3. Outright purchase of occasional historic sites, wooded islands, swamps, bluff faces, and marginal lands.

they are constantly on exhibit to our millions of travelers. Our roadsides could be attractive to the eye, or at least inoffensive; strewn with rubbish or cluttered with signboards and claptrap establishments, they lose their eye appeal. The modern "freeways," parkways, and turnpikes along which advertising and vending are prohibited have demonstrated the desirability of roadside sanitation. Zoning regulations by local government have proved another approach to the problem. Control must extend beyond the public right-of-way unless access be restricted as along the super highways, or construction be eliminated from a zone of specified width paralleling the road. The latter (called set-back) may have to be accepted in many places because we cannot make all our roads into thoroughfares with widely spaced entrances— too much of our traffic is local. Neither can we convert them all into elaborate parkways such as the one suggested in Fig. 13.7.

Gaudy signs and claptrap buildings along the edge of a road are not only unsightly in themselves, but they also block or corrupt a beautiful view. They are also traffic hazards inasmuch as they crowd the roadside, restrict visibility, and distract one's attention from his driving. In the interest of both beauty and safety, roadside advertising should be prohibited and roadside business places set back from the right-of-way a safer distance. Both these correctives are under way despite the resistance of vested interests. Many states prohibit billboard advertising adjacent to their "superhighways," but the set-back rules are often circumvented by outdoor advertisers. To offset the set-back they simply make signs more monstrous. Prohibition by zoning works better. Prohibition by taxing or licensing, *at exorbitant rates,* might be most effective.

Control of outdoor advertising became a national issue in 1958 when Congress, in response to public demand, amended the Federal-Aid Highway Act of 1956 thus: "To promote the safety, convenience, and enjoyment of public travel and the free flow of interstate commerce and to protect the public investment in the National System of Interstate and Defense Highways, it is declared to be in the public interest to encourage and assist the States to control the use of and to improve areas adjacent to the Interstate System by controlling the erection and maintenance of outdoor advertising signs, displays, and devices adjacent to that system." (23 U.S. Code 131.) The law provided as incentive an increase of one-half of 1 per cent in the federal share of project cost in those states that would meet prescribed national standards of control. The Bureau of Public Roads, responsible for the 41,000-mile interstate system, prepared a set of standards specifying not

Figs. 13.8 and 13.9   *Advertising that endangers the traveler and spoils the view generates sales resistance in the conservator. Photo above courtesy Minnesota Highway Department; photo below courtesy National Roadside Council. Both photos from "Roadside Protection," published by the American Automobile Association, 1951.*

only that advertising signs must be 660 feet away from the right-of-way (of controlled portions) but that *no* outdoor advertising must be *visible* from those portions of the interstate system. Retroactive features of the law were repealed in 1959, so it applies only to stretches of the highway built on new locations, hence "controlled portions," which will comprise about 75 per cent of the total mileage.[22] The standards permit four classes of signs: official signs; signs within 12 miles of advertising activities; on-premise signs; signs in the specific interest of the traveling public, but limited in their size, spacing, etc.[23] As of December, 1962, seventeen state-highway departments had signed agreements with the Secretary of Commerce to comply.

Americans who boycott goods and services advertised at the expense of beauty are conservators just as surely as are conservers of soil or water. A sufficient number of them could possibly stop the vulgar abuse. Let us submit that if all available media, other than outdoor advertising, fail to sell a product, its quality should be improved. The American consumer might choose between the scenes shown in Figs. 13.8 and 13.9.

Someday we may also get rid of all telephone and power transmission lines that parallel our roads, the better to enjoy both the scenery and the automobile radio. Perhaps we shall bury all the lines, thus preventing storm damage and obviating the need for pole replacement. This burial is in process. Where once a maze of parallel lines were strung overhead, they are now often contained in underground cables. Communications engineers have turned landscape beautifiers for practical reasons. They have also outmoded certain trunk lines with microwave transmission, thus conserving both material and aesthetic resources.

Another objectionable practice is the clearing and burning of roadsides and other rights-of-way to control vegetation, particularly in wooded areas. If, instead of repeated burning or spraying to check undesirable growth we used the money thus spent for planting desirable species, we might have our roadsides bordered with demonstration areas for resource management. That trend too, along with billboard eradication, is well established. If all highways had their borders thus improved, we might easily provide adequate stopping places for the enjoyment of travelers. Several states have wayside park systems that fit into the general beautification scheme. Roadside protection is definitely a national conservation issue.

Let us not suppose that roadside improvement alone can adequately conserve the beauty of our environment. Highways are mere ribbons traced across the country, and their sanitation is

The cultural landscape has conservable beauty of tone and design

only a beginning. Prevention of water littering by many millions of pleasure boaters is urgently necessary, but the waters are also mere ribbons that compose only a small part of our total estate. The cultural landscape as a whole has conservable beauty of tone and design. The countrysides in which men work and live can be beautiful as well as productive. Good land use enhances outward beauty and generates an atmosphere of peace and stability that only the "inward eye" can see. It has the subtle power of conveying a sense of tranquility and well-being. To him who loves the land it reflects harmony between natural attributes and human adaptation as well as correct matching of physical and cultural qualities. He feels the sensory beauty of green woods, flourishing fields, and lush pastures patterned in accord with the terrain they occupy, because he knows that they contribute to human comfort and security. He feels the stark ugliness of ghost towns and abandoned farmsteads because he knows that human failure and suffering attended them. Indeed, the good *cultural* landscape has a deeper beauty than that which meets the untrained eye—a beauty more profound than virgin wilderness could ever boast. It shows human competence, decency, and dignity as clearly as if those qualities were done in oil and framed under glass.

Beauty of cultural landscape is commensurate with the prevailing conservation of land resources. Clear, perennial streams, the alternate curves of strip cropping, the hedgerows, living fences, and habitat islands for wildlife, green fields interspersed with green groves—every evidence of conservational land use adds charming tone and design. Beauty, the by-product of competent land management, becomes a free bonus for good work and an incentive to do even better. Indeed, the man who works to beautify his place will, almost invariably, also conserve its natural resources.

Cleanliness and tidiness add the finishing touches to our landscape portrait, but we show a sad lack of artistic training. The most picturesque landscape loses its charm when it is cheapened by junk piles or trash heaps and littered with tin cans, bottles, paper cartons, old shoes, and other discarded rubbish. The law forbids our printing an adequate indictment of the contemptible people who strew our roadsides with waste, or dump their accumulations of refuse on the property of another. The vile practices are punishable under the law, but we have been lax in its enforcement. Furthermore, the "sneak thief" who soils the landscape is probably more difficult to apprehend than the one who takes something away with him. Once again, our recourse must be to education, such that stimulates personal pride and elevates human dignity. Everyone can be a conservator of beauty by properly disposing of his own trash, and, with example and suggestion, by dissuading others from scattering theirs about the countryside. Every American has an obligation to the form of conservation that might be called *landscape housekeeping,* and at this moment the "house" could stand a thorough scrubbing. It would be easy to keep if all our citizens were housebroken. Meanwhile, the contemptible persons who soil the environment should be pursued, punished, and publicly denounced as common criminals.

Splendid scenery, enchanting wilderness, and the varied beauty of cultural landscape may be esteemed the classical offerings in our resource repertoire. Conservation of their recreational and inspirational values might be likened to the fine arts in a college curriculum. How dull the graduate who lacks acquaintance with the arts; how crass the gain from conservation that neglects the finest gifts of nature—intellectual stimulation and spiritual assurance!

Keep the "fine arts" in our conservation curriculum!

A great wealth of these resources is in our possession—all of them vulnerable to erosion and pollution by the humans they benefit. They serve everyone, they can be abused by anyone, and their permanence depends more upon the intellectual idealist than upon the practical realist. They are therefore peculiarly vulnerable to selfish argument supported by dollar statistics. Selfish design and malicious abuse are their greatest threats, and public reservation is only a fair defense against either.

If we would have the prized possessions mentioned in this chapter, we must educate our fellow citizens to a fuller appreciation and respect for them. We cannot conserve all of them by public or group ownership, and without public understanding and cooperation we cannot conserve any of them under any form of ownership. Scenic beauty belongs to him who admires it, regardless of title or property line; but, if he trespasses in order to admire, he denies himself the privilege. Genuine respect for the rights of others would solve most problems pertinent to the conservation of aesthetic and recreational resources.

Our material progress has so far outstripped our cultural refinement that we stand in greater need of mental and spiritual nourishment than of food for our bodies. We have the wherewithal to conserve the resources that enrich our lives and strengthen our spiritual convictions, and we must meet the challenge! As our nation grows and matures we shall draw increasing benefit from intangibles that renew and define perspective. Those intangibles nurture the high ideals that will aggrandize our national destiny.

14

Resources of Our Bordering Seas

the wealth of the sea beckons the conservator to explore a vast resource frontier

In several chapters before this we have examined those renewable resources which in the main attach to the emerged land masses of the United States—waters, soils, forests, grasslands, wildlife, recreational and scenic properties. We have developed the treatment in a sequence that parallels the progressive dependence of resources one upon another, the worth of each in turn commensurate with the composite quality of others. We have trod solid ground with fixed locations, definitive geographic boundaries, and specific ownership.

Advisedly, we deferred our discussion of the resources in seas and bordering oceans because, directly or indirectly, those resources are products of the land whence running water, returning to its source, carries with it the minerals dispersed in sea water and organics that become food for sea creatures. The sea that nurtured elemental life forms until they evolved sufficiently to emerge from the water and inhabit the land now receives from the land it populated the substance that sustains those species which remained in their aquatic habitats. (Not for us here to inquire whether such sea mammals as the whale, the porpoise, and the sea lion once came onto the land and were evicted from high society, or whether they remained behind and flourished as competing neighbors departed.) If the seas be enriched by the

The land returns in kind the gifts bestowed by the sea

352

land, it is appropriate that marine resources be viewed against a background of the terrestrial ones, because the abundance and distribution of the former are conditioned by the latter. The quality of its watershed determines the wealth of sea life beyond a river's mouth, and soil erosion and stream pollution spoil marine habitats.

The resources of our bordering seas are so rich and varied that, were they exploited fully, they might yield more wealth than all those on the land. But men have only begun to explore them, let alone exploit them to any extent. The oceans remain a major frontier for modern scientific development. It is not beyond the realm of possibility that scientists will someday economically extract from sea water a long list of scarce minerals, including precious metals and fissionable materials. The present commercial recovery of magnesium and iodine is certainly a mere beginning. One may be confident that clarified and desalted sea water will greatly enlarge the usable water reserves now available, that ocean tides and currents will be harnessed for power, and that many marine flora and fauna now unknown or neglected will be put to valuable use. But thus far the seas have served mainly as a great highway system and as a source of rain and fish. We cannot presume to alter their role as rain givers. We can improve and protect their usefulness as highways, much as we construct and maintain overland transport facilities, mainly by clearing or preventing any obstruction of terminals by stream or shore sediments. If permitted to become polluted with wastes or overloaded with silt, the very stream by which ships gain the hinterland blocks the threshold. Harbor improvement may be regarded as a form of marine conservation; however, let us limit this discourse to the conservation of material aquatic resources—animal, vegetable, and mineral.

The oceans roll in wealth— animal, vegetable, and mineral

The minerals in sea water remain largely unappraised and neglected—resources the magnitude of which is largely speculative. Analyses of sea water indicate that most known elements are present and that several of our most useful minerals may be more abundant in the oceans than on the continents. Certain industries now recover bromides, magnesium, salt, and a few others commercially, and they anticipate profitable recovery of many more in the future. Each must wait until improved techniques or scarcity on the land render its exploitation economically feasible.

Mineral and vegetable assets remain largely undeveloped

The floor of the sea contains, in places, low-grade deposits of cobalt, nickel, copper, iron, and especially manganese in the form of nodules precipitated from sea water.[1] They are known to be abundant under parts of the Atlantic and Pacific, and they contain sufficient manganese to warrant speculation about submarine mining.

The vegetable contents of the sea also remain largely unexploited, although the mass of marine vegetation is several times that of all terrestrial floras. Kelp forests off California "stand" 80 feet tall and spread a floating canopy on the water in "beds" so dense that they create a twilight gloom below and subdue the agitation of the surface by wave or swell. The myriad phytoplankton with photosynthetic equipment swarm and function in the sea to depths of several hundred feet where the water is moderately clear and open to sunlight. Large and small, attached or adrift, the vast volume of vegetation in the oceans lies in the realm of conjecture rather than mensuration.

Until recently only one notable American enterprise exploited the vegetal wealth of the sea, and that on a modest scale; New England Yankees have an age-old industry (since about 1835), the gathering of Irish Moss, a red alga that yields a gelatinous substance called *carageenin*. The extract is used to stabilize ice cream, confections, and other foods, to demulcify cough remedies, and to make dental-impression compounds and other pharmaceutical preparations. Annual harvest of Irish Moss off our Northeastern coast amounts to several thousand tons.[2]

During World War I Americans harvested kelp, the giant brown alga, on both the Pacific and Atlantic Coasts for the extraction of potash (bromine and iodine were valuable by-products). After the war only a few plants continued to operate, switching to the preparation of fertilizer and cattle feed from dried seaweed. When it was discovered that kelp contains alginic acid which can be used to make algin, the industry flourished once again; algin also serves primarily as stabilizer in ice cream and other dairy products, but its uses are extremely varied. Figures 14.1 and 14.2 picture Irish moss and kelp at a certain stage in their harvest.

Only from certain red seaweeds comes the gum called agar, most prized for making bacteria-growing media in hospitals, and essential in several manufactures. Previously it came largely from the Orient, but World War II compelled us to search our own coasts for a supply.[3] On the California coast were found beds of Gelidium sufficient to meet our bacteriological and medical needs. On the South Atlantic and Gulf coasts, Gracilaria was discovered; this yields a substitute for agar in many of its uses, though it is undesirable for bacteriological purposes. By 1945 our extraction of gums or agars from marine algae reached a value of 3 million dollars.[4] Under stress of war, Americans learned about the value

Fig. 14.1 *Irish moss spread to dry on Peggoty Beach, Massachusetts. The gathering of marine vegetation is an old industry with tremendous possibilities for future development. (Fish and Wildlife Service photo.)*

of marine vegetation, and peacetime exploitation has remained very considerable.

The harvest of giant kelp in California reached 150,000 tons a year by about 1952—a volume equaled only by Japan, whose seaweed industry is the largest in the world.[5]

The conservator feels reassured by the possibility that the sea might spare enough vegetation to maintain a desirable humus

Fig. 14.2 *Kelp (giant brown alga) on drying racks of Kelp Laboratories, Inc., San Diego, California. From such seaweeds come extracts for medicinal and other purposes. (V. J. Samson, Fish and Wildlife Service photo.)*

content in our soils if other sources of organic material were exhausted. The use of seaweeds for soil maintenance is an established practice in certain maritime cultures, as on the Orkneys and the Channel Islands.

The animals of seas and ocean margins have been taken and used by man throughout his history. For most primitive folk, fish remains to this day a major item of food, and to peoples culturally advanced it contributes a wholesome, pleasant, and often economical variation of diet. (Had Midwesterners eaten more sea foods they might have spared themselves the scourge of goiter, for the prevention of which most table salt is now iodized.)

Animal life is the one aquatic resource that has been exploited extensively, albeit unwisely. Whatever may have been man's first profession, fishing was among the most ancient of his occupations —hunting, fishing, and gathering—for food, shelter, and raiment.

Europeans came west to fish long before they came to settle the land, and soon after they settled fishing became a leading commercial enterprise. In New England the small, stony fields played second fiddle to the rich fishing grounds on the broad continental shelf. Fishing was more attractive than farming, materials for sturdy ships were readily available from the splendid mixed-wood forests, and the demand for fish was strong, especially in Catholic Europe. From fishing (and whaling) came fame and fortune to young America and historic character to many of her settlements (Gloucester, Wellfleet, New London, and a score of others). The whole business was lucrative but highly competitive, and its successful pursuit required superior shipbuilding and seamanship. Those proficiencies, gained for catching and marketing fish, helped America win her independence and bolstered her economic security thereafter. From that point of view the Northeastern fisheries have been invaluable.

Fishing is primarily a quest for food, but men also capture sea animals for many other products; among them ivory, whalebone (baleen), sponges, pearls, furs, vitamins, buttons, oils, leather, tortoise shell, stock feed, glue, paint, perfume, and fertilizer.

Baleen from the mouth of the "right" whale (literally the right kind to catch) supplied the corset staves with which the stylish ladies of the Victorian era molded their hourglass figures. Oil from right and sperm whales illuminated the streets so swishing skirts, high-wheeled velocipedes, and horse-drawn carriages might safely mingle. By the middle of the nineteenth century whales had become the greatest marine resource. America dominated the industry. American whaling fleets numbered 735 boats and employed

Aquatic animals have been food for man since remote antiquity

Our colonial fisheries helped us gain independence

We fish for many goods other than food

40,000 people.[6] However, the fabulous whaling era was short-lived. The discovery of petroleum at Titusville, Pennsylvania in 1859 took the gilt edge off the industry. The increasing cost of hunting down the monsters that survived in remote ocean areas could not be met with a declining market. Whaling went, faster than it had come, and has never regained importance as an American industry. After many years of dormancy, United States whaling resumed, modestly, in 1956. In 1960, American whalers took 271 whales with five harpoon vessels operating from two stations in San Francisco Bay. The catch yielded almost 3 million pounds of meal, 4 million pounds of meat, some 3 million pounds of whale oil, and 170,000 pounds of sperm oil—all worth about $672,000.[7] Both companies operated mainly to produce whale meat, which they ground and froze for sale to mink ranchers or sold for use in canned pet foods. Demand and price were good, and an additional station was ready (1960) to operate at the mouth of the Columbia River.[8] Most of the American catch was taken within a 100-mile radius of the stations. More than half of the whales caught were fin whales.

The great factory ships and whaling fleets of our present era operate mainly in the Antarctic Ocean. Blue and fin whales make up most of the catch, since right and sperm whales have been literally chased right out of the oceans. The industry was headed for suicide by sheer extermination of the largest surviving animal when in 1937 the International Conference for the Regulation of Whaling at London drew up protective measures that were signed by all interested nations. The international agreement has provisions in it that may save a valuable marine resource. It fixes a minimum legal size for each species, prohibits the killing of females accompanied by calves, protects completely all right, gray, and humpback whales, excludes factory ships from calving grounds, and requires the fullest possible use of the whale carcass. Furthermore, the signatory nations enforce the regulations by licensing whaling vessels, supervising factory ship operations, and reporting the weekly catch against seasonal quotas. Figure 14.3 shows the ocean regions on the basis of which regulations have been formulated.

For bone and oil— and profit— we have almost destroyed the whale

Conservation of whales illustrates the requirements of international cooperation in the maintenance of certain fisheries. Scientific equipment and methods have become so effective that unless their employment be restricted the capture of a desirable species may far exceed its reproduction. Petroleum did not jeopardize whaling so much by initial competition as by later power-

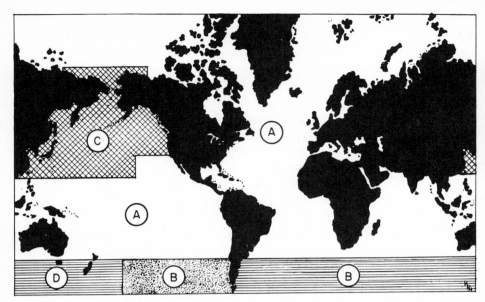

Fig. 14.3 *World whaling regulations instituted by the International Whaling Commission. The United States was one of 17 signatories. (Fish and Wildlife Service map.)*

Map Legend—Key to zones established by convention:

A. Factory ships prohibited from taking baleen whales.
B. Proposed sanctuary for baleen and humpback whales.
C. Factory ships permitted for taking baleen whales.
D. Factory ships for taking baleen whales permitted, but the same ships may not be operated elsewhere less than a year after closure of the season. Humpback whales may not be taken.

ing of modern whaling vessels. Whether international agreement and policing can save the great mammals from extinction remains to be seen.

We "sponge" for animal skeletons

Skeletons in the cupboard may be a nuisance, but the skeletons called *sponges* are a convenience in the bathtub or sink. These useful skeletons come from the bottom of the sea. A colony of Greeks has made sponging a legitimate business in west Florida. They began more than three-quarters of a century ago, and the business became centered about Tarpon Springs. In a single year they sponged 2.5 million dollars' worth.[9] The industry prospered, despite many artificial substitutes, until a disease decimated the sponges. Annual production, which reached a peak of 655,000 pounds in 1934, was less than 16,000 pounds in 1951. The Greeks then turned to "tourist" fishing as a means of livelihood.

The sponge, a simple form of animal life, neither sows nor reaps but sits like a puffball, attached to the ocean floor. It produces eggs—fertilized and developed within its own body and released as larvae that drift for a while—which settle down to the slow, monotonous task of growing into big sponges. There is no excitement, no travel, no romance, neither pain nor pleasure in the life of a sponge.

Foam rubber and other substitutes do much of our wiping now-adays, but for special purposes, as in the manufacture of certain hygienic and surgical preparations, natural sponges are still required. They remain valuable, but unless the biologists discover some means of combating sponge diseases, the animal may be lost. A minimum-size law (5-inch diameter) passed by Congress in 1914 and also enforced by the state of Florida in waters under State jurisdiction was the only significant conservation measure while the industry flourished. British experiments in the Bahamas and Honduras have demonstrated the practicability of artificial propagation from small cuttings, like potatoes, but if Americans devote a fair amount of biologic research to the Florida sponging grounds, they may spare themselves the "farming" costs.

From the sea come several luxuries, such as pearls and mother-of-pearl for the ornament of milady, ambergris (the spew from sick whales) for the base of fine perfumes, and furs for vanity, if not always for comfort. Genuine pearls come from certain species of oysters (salt water) and from river mussels (fresh water). The latter are taken primarily for their shells, from which pearl buttons may be made. (Since most buttons are now plastic, most of the mussel shell is exported to Japan, where fragments of it serve as nuclei for cultured pearls). The hope of finding a pearl adds a touch of glamor to the dull work of "musseling" for the mollusks. During recent decades enterprising Yankees have developed a flourishing industry in the manufacture of artificial pearls. Still based on a natural resource, the manufactured pearls are made of the scales from certain marine fish, dissolved by secret formula into pearl essence resembling a hand lotion. Only an expert can distinguish artificial pearls from the rarely perfect real gem. While comparable in appearance, they cost less.

From the sea come pearls, genuine and artificial

By ownership of the Pribilof Islands off Alaska, the United States controls the world's largest herd of fur seals (80 per cent of the total). When Alaska was claimed by Russia the herd probably numbered about 2.5 million, but the animals were so ruthlessly killed for their fine pelts that by 1910 only about 150,000 remained.[10] Seeing the threat to a valuable resource, the American government intervened in that year and in 1911 signed, with Great

Furs worn in the Arctic Sea must be warm and waterproof

Britain (for Canada), Japan, and Russia, the North Pacific Fur Seal Convention. The agreement outlawed *pelagic* sealing (killing them in the water), which had previously taken a heavy toll of pups by the killing of their mothers.

The international agreement, reviewed in 1957, together with the polygamous habits of the seals, had completely re-established the herd, bringing it back to approximately 1.5 million in only thirty-five years of protection.[11] *The fur seal is a splendid example of the recovery a biotic resource can make if given a fair chance.* Since each old bull seal keeps a harem of as many as forty to sixty cows, male offspring become a social liability, good for nothing except to eat fish. From frustrated two- and three-year-old bachelors comes our annual crop of skins. The bachelors have nothing to look forward to, and their removal leaves more food for parents and babies. Sometime, when more is known about the fishery resource of the "high seas," it may be discovered that the voracious seal eats more fish than he is worth, but until then any guilt attached to the giving or wearing of seal should be laid to something other than the killing of the original owner. For a quarter of a century the Alaska fur-seal herd has sustained an annual harvest of about 69,000 skins.[12] Almost 96,000 skins were taken in 1961.

From the sea come most of our health-protective vitamins. Cod-liver oil was a household remedy long before the vitamin-capsule era which now sustains a major pharmaceutical industry that began with fish livers. Once a by-product of cod and halibut fisheries, fish-liver oil—notably that of the despised sharks—became a prime object of certain fisheries.

From the sea comes our major supply of natural vitamins

In 1927 the Fishery Research Board of Canada discovered that the liver of a certain small shark, the dogfish, has as much as ten times the vitamin-A potency of ordinary cod-liver oil. Sharks became popular almost as suddenly as a homely coed when she gets a shiny new convertible. Vast numbers of dogfish, soupfin, and other sharks were taken only for their livers, the remainder of the carcass thrown back into the sea, until California passed a law requiring that the entire fish be delivered to port. Shark steak, smoked shark, fish meal, and leather became by-products of the liver fishery. The industry flourished the length of our Pacific Coast, until less expensive synthetic vitamins intervened. The cost of transporting dead sharks a long distance to make meal out of them raised the cost of the natural vitamins too high. It would have been more conservative to pitch them overboard for their vitamin-making friends to eat! In 1960 only three American plants (two on the Pacific Coast) processed shark livers and viscera, extracting from them 30,474 gallons of the vitamin-rich oil.[13]

The sharp stench of a fish cannery, of a fish wharf at low tide, or of an ill-kept fish market suggests the value of dead fish and fish wastes as fertilizer. The practice of fertilizing soil with fish antedates American history; the Indians, we are told, showed the Pilgrims how to plant a fish under each hill of corn in order to ensure higher yield and more cause for "Thanksgiving."

Since those early beginnings fertilizer has become an important product and by-product of our expanding fisheries. A major trend in our conservation of fishery resources is the salvage of wastes by legal compulsion. As mentioned before, California ruled that a shark taken for his liver must be landed and used, and international agreement places similar requirements upon whaling. The Antarctic whaler would be pleased to take home only oil and meat, were he allowed to do so, but in compliance with the law, he gets from an average whale, besides the *oil,* about 3 tons of *meal* for stock feed and 1 ton, more or less, of a potent fertilizer.[14]

From fish comes fertilizer for our soils

The salvage of waste parts of fish in canneries and other fish-processing plants has far to go, but its accomplishment, like the utilization of sawmill wastes, must await such demand for the products and such complementary factory arrangements as will make it profitable. Perhaps legal prohibition of wastes can hasten their economical salvage, but rules too stringent can also injure the industry producing the wastes. Rarely can one justify plant closure to prevent waste, because some waste may be an inevitable part of production. Waste prevention that places undue strain upon a productive enterprise is dubious conservation.

Whether applied as dried scraps ground into meal or as liquid concentrate, the fertilization of soil with fish completes a cycle that portends new horizons in conservation. Wash from the land feeds the diatoms and other plankton (minute sea life); little ones feed on the tiny ones; bigger ones feed on the little ones; man catches the big ones and with them enriches the soil—whence the wash to feed the minute ones! Is man in this case a cog in the natural round, or is he the intellectual member who wittingly completes the cycle and thereby improves his total environment? Perhaps he is both master and servant when he improves the land with waste from the sea.

From fish come especially nutritious feed for our land animals. Fish meal and fish oil increase our production of meat and eggs, and in a roundabout way enrich the soil as well. So desirable are these by-products that a major fishery has developed to supply them (Fig. 14.4). Menhaden, a herring-like fish that ranges the

From fish comes feed for beast and fowl

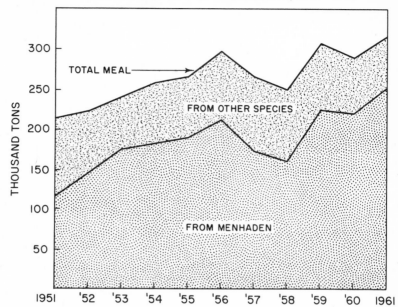

U.S. PRODUCTION OF FISH MEAL, 1951-1961

Fig. 14.4 *Several species of schooling fishes comprise the main industrial catch, which about equals in tonnage the combined landings of food fisheries. (From C.F.S. No. 2885, Annual Summary.)*

Gulf of Mexico and our Atlantic Coast, ranks far above others in the volume of catch, and fifth in value among all our fisheries; it has held first rank in tonnage ever since 1946.[15] (See in Table 1 the relative importance of our major commercial fisheries.) In 1960 the lowly menhaden was pursued by 4,353 fishermen with 183 purse-seine vessels, and they accounted for 41 per cent of the total commercial landings in the United States. Forty-two per cent of the menhaden tonnage was landed on the Gulf Coast and 33 per cent on the Middle Atlantic. Leading menhaden ports were Pascagoula, Mississippi, Lewes, Delaware, and Empire and Cameron, Louisiana.[16] Menhaden are taken for industrial products (fish meal and marine-animal oil), and although the catch has exceeded 2 billion pounds a year the stocks appear undiminished. Annual catch has been limited because of a saturated market and not because the fish were less available. The menhaden fishery yielded nine-tenths of all our fish oils and eight-tenths of all our fish meal produced in 1961.[17]

Food outranks all other fishing products

Many other marine products, many other fishery by-products, might be mentioned, but let us turn to a consideration of fish

Table 1

United States Catch
-(Certain Species, 1961-62)

Species	1961		1962[1]		Record production	
Fish	Thousand pounds	Thousand dollars	Thousand pounds	Thousand dollars	Year	Thousand pounds
Anchovies, California	7,712	110	2,800	40	1953	85,836
Bluefish	3,736	512	5,800	700	1897	20,000+
Bonito	8,653	235	2,300	100	1947	13,918
Cod, Atlantic	46,591	2,995	46,000	3,800	1880	294,351
Croaker	5,175	762	3,200	400	1945	64,668
Cusk	1,905	101	1,800	100	1937	10,263
Flounders, Atlantic and Gulf	85,388	9,523	104,300	10,800	1962	104,300
Haddock	133,597	9,907	134,200	10,900	1929	293,810
Hake, white	5,214	217	5,100	200	1898	39,900
Halibut, Pacific	53,238	8,408	53,100	11,900	1915	66,696
Herring, sea:						
Alaska	49,465	559	32,000	400	1937	261,400
Maine	54,463	1,036	156,700	2,400	1950	185,481
Mackerel: (California)						
Jack	97,606	2,025	90,000	1,900	1952	146,522
Pacific	44,110	956	48,600	1,000	1935	146,427
Menhaden	2,314,677	25,579	2,249,100	25,500	1961	2,314,677
Mullet	42,813	2,548	42,200	2,300	1902	43,385
Ocean perch, Atlantic	132,062	5,114	124,000	5,200	1951	258,320
Pollock	21,406	795	16,300	400	1938	40,694
Salmon, Pacific	310,398	52,027	317,400	48,100	1936	790,884
Sardine, Pacific	43,170	1,146	15,400	500	1936	1,502,299
Scup or porgy	46,584	2,931	45,400	3,000	1960	49,229
Sea trout	10,287	1,719	9,800	1,500	1908	49,869
Snapper, red	12,688	3,266	12,300	3,200	1902	23,457
Striped bass	9,495	1,270	7,700	1,200	1961	9,495
Tuna:[2]						
Albacore	32,844	5,867	43,100	7,200	1950	72,514
Bluefin[3]	24,288	3,346	39,400	5,300	1962	39,400
Little	5	[4]	[4]	[4]	—	—
Skipjack	76,354	8,526	102,100	13,200	1954	167,777
Yellowfin	192,313	24,607	124,500	18,800	1948	207,420
Total tuna	325,804	42,346	309,100	44,500	1950	391,454
Whiting	100,729	2,245	105,300	2,300	1957	133,041
Shellfish						
Clams (meats)	50,330	11,661	53,600	11,800	1962	53,600
Crabs:						
Blue	152,758	8,149	147,000	8,400	1960	154,697
Dungeness	32,699	4,977	22,100	3,400	1948	45,823
King	43,412	3,914	52,000	5,200	1962	52,000
Lobsters:						
Northern	27,998	14,572	28,200	14,300	1960	31,168
Spiny	3,235	1,263	3,600	1,400	1957	4,687
Oysters (meats)	62,305	33,204	55,500	28,000	1908[5]	152,046
Scallops, sea (meats)	27,461	10,404	23,500	9,500	1961	27,461
Shrimp: (heads-on)						
South Atlantic and Gulf						
States	153,544	50,589	167,800	71,500	1954	265,799
Alaska	15,980	639	17,000	680	1962	17,000
Washington	1,463	131	1,400	120	1958	6,730
Oregon	1,464	119	2,000	170	1959	2,734
California	2,005	190	1,800	170	1899	6,495
Other	74	20	400	60	—	—
Total shrimp	174,530	51,688	190,400	72,700	1954	268,316
Squid, California	10,286	231	9,400	200	1946	38,024
Other fish, shellfish, etc.	634,729	43,815	714,500	43,960	—	—
Grand total	5,186,709	362,210	5,239,700	381,200	1956	5,268,246

[1] Preliminary.
[2] Does not include landings of tuna by United States vessels in Puerto Rico.
[3] Includes data on the catch of bigeye tuna in Hawaii.
[4] Less than 500 pounds or $500.
[5] First year in which an oyster survey was made in all regions.
Source: *Current Fishery Statistics* (Washington, D.C., 1963).

taken primarily for food, since they constitute the most valuable and most exploited aquatic resource. No less than *180* different edible species contribute to our annual commercial catch of some 5 billion pounds. They range in size from the little sardine and anchovy to the giant tuna and swordfish. Large or small, they are excellent food, supplying protein of superior quality, calcium, magnesium, phosphorus, iron, copper, vitamins A and D, and iodine in natural form.[18] No other meat comes nearer being a complete food in itself than does fish—a fact not adequately appreciated in America. Another century of wholesale land abuse might have *made* fish eaters out of us; conservation will permit us to eat fish by choice, in itself an act of conserving both natural and cultural resources. Wartime meat rationing awakened Americans to the merits of fish, and many retained their taste for fish after the emergency. Even so, we consume only about 11 pounds of marketed fish per capita annually, which is less than a tenth of our consumption of "red" meat and only half our consumption of chicken. (Recreational and subsistence fishing contribute several additional pounds of fish food per person.) We could improve our health, save money, and conserve natural resources by eating twice, or three times, as much sea food as we now consume. We should not have to be prodded by high meat prices or war to do so; the increase would raise our standard of living and extend our longevity, because fish fat is a cholesterol depressant.

Perhaps none of our great natural resources equals in variety the choice of species offered by our food fisheries, unless it be the forests. However, less than fifty species make up the main catch. Most of these are *fin fish,* the kind of creatures that come to mind at the mention of "fish," with fins, bones, and usually scales. The others, often lumped together under the term "shellfish," bear no resemblance to the fin fish. They belong to two major zoological groups, namely *mollusks* and *crustaceans.* (We are omitting frogs, turtles, and other reptiles, because they are relatively unimportant.) The mollusks include oysters, clams, mussels and scallops (bivalves), and the abalone with only one shell. The crustaceans include the scorpion-like lobsters and shrimps, and the spider-like crabs. The three classes have little in common except that they all live under water, get caught by fishermen, and become food for humans. Their habits, their modes of capture, and the problems of conserving them differ as greatly as they do in appearance.

The big three: fin fish, mollusks, and crustaceans

Here are *Six Leading Food Fisheries:*

Salmon (5 species)—northern Pacific Coast
Shrimp—Gulf Coast and elsewhere
Tuna (5 species)—southern Pacific Coast

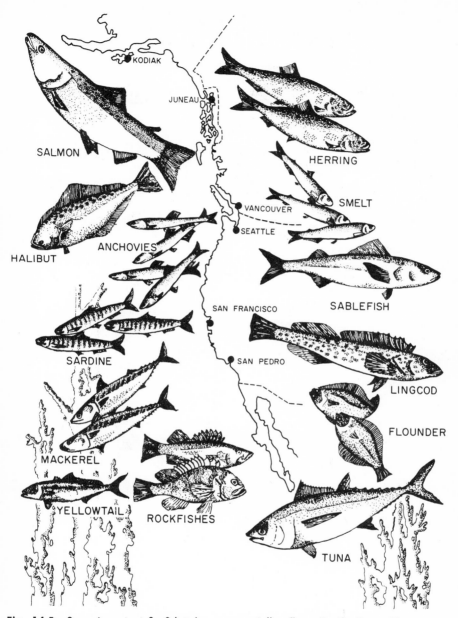

KODIAK

JUNEAU

SALMON

HERRING

SMELT

VANCOUVER

SEATTLE

HALIBUT

ANCHOVIES

SABLEFISH

SAN FRANCISCO

SAN PEDRO

LINGCOD

SARDINE

FLOUNDER

MACKEREL

YELLOWTAIL

ROCKFISHES

TUNA

Fig. 14.5 *Some important fin fish taken commercially off our Pacific Coast. (Sizes not proportional.)*

Oysters—Middle-Atlantic Coast and elsewhere
Northern Lobsters
Blue Crabs—Atlantic Coast

The upper four have changed position year to year.
Fishes and fisheries show considerable regional specialization

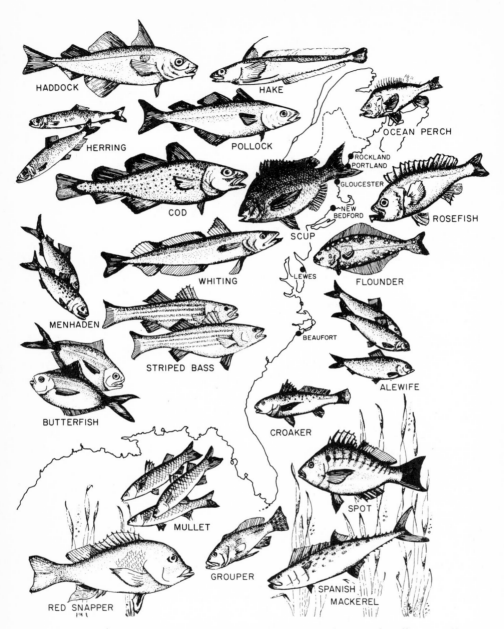

Fig. 14.6 *Some important fin fish taken off our Atlantic and Gulf coasts. (Sizes not proportional.)*

much as do game and hunting, timber and lumbering, soils and agriculture. Species differ widely from one region to another, and only in general respects do fishing methods and conservation problems of one region resemble those of another. Maine lobsters, Chesapeake "blue points" (oysters), Gulf shrimp, California albacore (tuna), and Alaska salmon are well-known regional fish specialties that support regional fisheries, almost without any similarity. Figures 14.5 through 14.9 merely suggest the variety of species and their approximate regional distribution. Fishing gear differs about as much as the fishes: *pots* (box traps) for lobsters, *dredges* for oysters, *trawls* for shrimp, *hooks* for tuna, *traps, seines* and *nets* for salmon. Several types are shown in Fig. 14.10. Purse seines take most of our fish, and otter trawls rank second.

The trawler who puts out from New England and spends weeks in cold and fog to capture cod or haddock on the Great Bank has little in common with the shrimper who makes a daily run from Houma, Louisiana in the warm waters of the Gulf. There is as much difference between the adventure of a tuna cruise and the monotony of oyster dredging as there is between fly casting for trout and trolling for marlin. Yet, each of the commercial fisheries mentioned holds high national rank and attains pre-eminence in its own locale. Each employs many people and flavors the regional culture.

Until quite recently our highly perishable fish foods were limited in use and distribution by inadequate packaging and transportation facilities. Except in winter, fresh fish was only for those who lived near the water, each species in its season. A quarter-century ago off-season fish was either cured or canned. The herring barrel and anchovy keg vied with great wheels of cheese to dominate the pungent odors in country stores. The infant canning industry supplied a few items, such as salmon and sardines. To farm folk in the Midwest oyster stew was a rare treat. They had never seen a shrimp, much less eaten one.

Modern facilities and packaging revolutionize market distribution

Then came improved refrigeration, improved canning, and, most recent and revolutionary, quick freezing. Fresh fish—packaged, labeled, and frozen—became available anywhere in the country, as did also a wide variety safely preserved in cans. The deep freeze replaced the grimy herring barrel. Dakota farmers learned to eat shrimp cocktails, fried oysters, fillet of Pacific halibut, Gulf flounder, New England sole or codfish balls whenever they chose, without fear of food poisoning. Housewives who never saw the ocean tried new sea-food recipes and served their unwary husbands dishes they could not pronounce. Now they buy New England cooked fish dinners, ready to heat and serve.

Modern preparation and packaging, transport and storage have all but erased the old deterrents of seasonality, climate, and distance. Similar species from Atlantic and Pacific waters lie side by side in refrigerated display cases—the one most attractively wrapped getting the buyer's nod. But for innovations such as

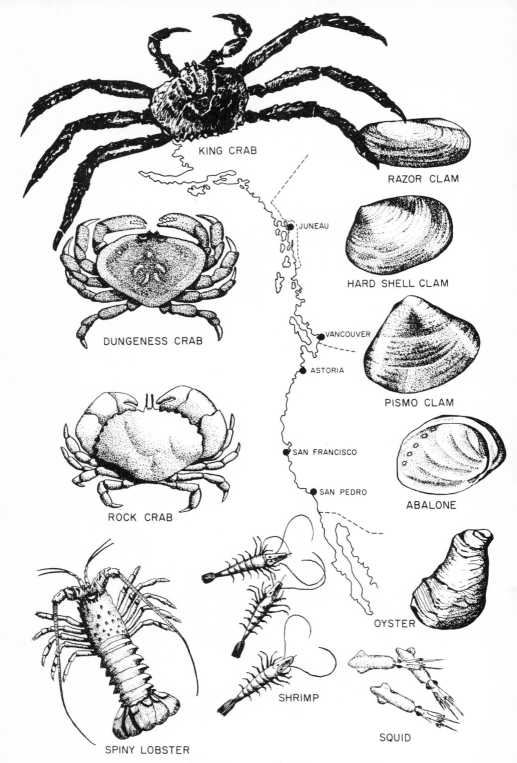

Labels within image:
KING CRAB
RAZOR CLAM
HARD SHELL CLAM
DUNGENESS CRAB
PISMO CLAM
ROCK CRAB
ABALONE
JUNEAU
VANCOUVER
ASTORIA
SAN FRANCISCO
SAN PEDRO
OYSTER
SPINY LOBSTER
SHRIMP
SQUID

Fig. 14.7 *Some important West Coast shellfish. (Not drawn to scale.) Giant among them is the king crab.*

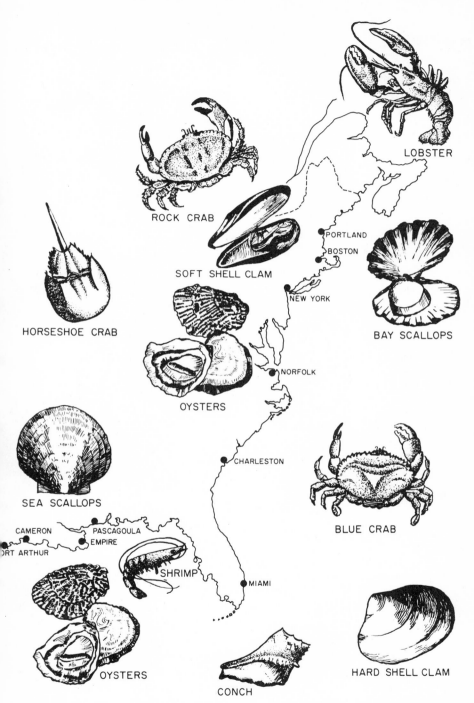

ROCK CRAB

LOBSTER

SOFT SHELL CLAM

HORSESHOE CRAB

BAY SCALLOPS

PORTLAND

BOSTON

NEW YORK

OYSTERS

NORFOLK

SEA SCALLOPS

CHARLESTON

BLUE CRAB

CAMERON   PASCAGOULA

RT ARTHUR   EMPIRE

SHRIMP

MIAMI

OYSTERS

CONCH

HARD SHELL CLAM

Fig. 14.8 *Some important East Coast shellfish. (Not drawn to scale.) The archaic horseshoe crab and the conch contribute more to the artistic balance of the page than to value of total catch. The conch is destructive of oysters, particularly on the Gulf Coast.*

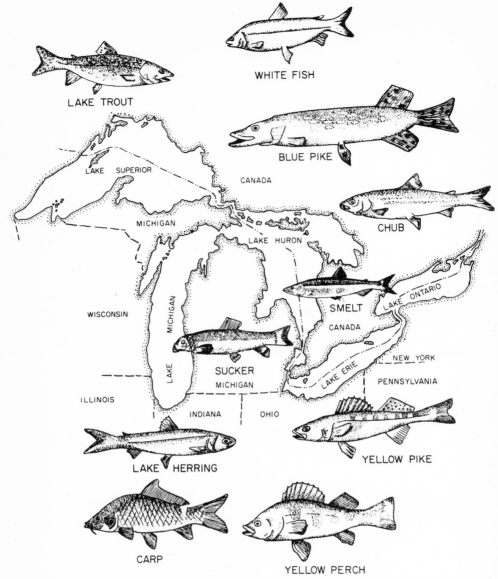

Fig. 14.9 *Traditional food fishes of the Great Lakes may be displaced by industrial species.*

quick freezing and refrigeration in transit, our valuable Gulf Coast fisheries could not have emerged, nor could our fishery resources as a whole have attained the status and potential that commend them to our most careful study and conservation.

While space does not permit us to describe all the freaks of "fishdom," and their idiosyncrasies, it is necessary that we identify a few major groups, or classes, on the basis of habits and habitats by way of introducing our main thesis, for fishing tech-

SMALL OTTER TRAWLER

LINE TRAWLER

MEDIUM SIZED OTTER TRAWLER

BEAM TRAWLER

PURSE SEINER

SHRIMP TRAWLER

HALIBUT SCHOONER

PURSE SEINE

TUNA CLIPPER

FYKE OR HOOPNETS

LOBSTER POT

GREAT LAKES TRAP NETS

TRAWL

SET LINES

GILL NET

Fig. 14.10 *Commercial fishermen employ many kinds of craft and gear, of which only a sampling is shown here. (After Fish and Wildlife Service.)*

niques and conservation measures must be adapted to the behavior of the fish. The problem must be defined before its solution can be approached intelligently.

No military commander would engage the enemy without more "intelligence" than we have about our fishes. We know that certain fishes, such as the hardtail, squid, bluefish, and herring, live near the top of the water. We call those *pelagic*. We know that others, such as flounder, halibut, sole, cod, pollock, haddock, hake, and rosefish live on or near the bottom. We call those ground fishes *demersal*. We know that several species, such as the salmon, shad, and smelt live and mature in the sea but come up the rivers to spawn. Ichthyologists call them *anadromous*. We know that snappers, groupers, and cod live on "banks," that pilchards, porgies, pompanos, and mullets live near shore, and that tuna and swordfish roam the high seas. We know that mackerels, anchovies, and weakfish migrate considerable distances, that crabs and shrimps stay nearer home, and that oysters sit tight in one place.

But we have used our knowledge almost entirely for catching the fish—hardly at all for conserving them. We have applied our information in devising efficient methods of exploitation and neglected its application toward perpetuating the resource. We have in some cases maintained our catch of a declining species by improving fishing techniques, thereby obscuring the real problem. The same "intelligence" that makes us expert fishermen must also be directed toward making us better conservators.

Anadromous species fall easy prey to nets and traps when they crowd into the rivers to lay their eggs. If they be denied access to their spawning grounds, or the rivers be so polluted that the young cannot survive, the species will decline, and eventually vanish. Filth has driven shad from certain Eastern streams; engineering and pollution have virtually exterminated salmon in certain Western ones. Pelagic fishes that migrate in dense schools are also easily caught during their seasonal "runs" when the sea fairly foams with them, but if they be seined out indiscriminately year after year, from one end of their migration to the other, attrition will decimate them. These are the hosts that convey the idea of marine inexhaustibility, but if in a given season a million mackerel eggs produce only three or four fingerlings, mother mackerel's fantastic fecundity may be a poor guarantee of profitable fishing. Ground fishes, mollusks, and crustaceans are obviously influenced by conditions of the bottom on which they live. Trawling or dredging to harvest them can easily reduce their numbers more by damage to the habitat than by capture. Here, also, as with anadromous species, man's behavior on the land helps or hinders marine resources. Oysters and other shellfish that are either fixed in place or capable of very limited movement succumb when men befoul their "beds" with sewage or bury them in silt.

Does conservation hang together? Indeed it does. Forested watersheds, soil held in place, and clear streams with uniform flow insure the health of marine life in coastal waters. Reverse the picture and havoc runs the length of the sequence. Cutover slopes, eroded soils, dirty streams, and floods produce dead fish. Kill the little shore fishes, and larger ones farther out die of hunger. The tunas that roam the high seas depend upon farmers in Iowa and Illinois, though less directly than do corn-fed swine. Conservation on the land promotes conservation in the sea. Abuse of the land abuses the sea.

The unity of land and sea resources

Fish killed by stream pollution float down the Potomac right through our capital city, and in many less dignified streams they float even faster, and just as dead. The hardy ones that survive in poisoned water are dangerous to eat, a hazard to human life instead of the food resource they ought to be. Scores of streams in our metropolitan Northeast and elsewhere have been so corrupted with sewage, industrial refuse, and mining wastes that they have lost their natural function as homes and spawning grounds for fish. Pollution of shellfish-growing areas in bays and estuaries, if not in every case fatal to the fish, renders them dangerous to eat. This menace requires constant surveillance by the Public Health Service and necessitates the prohibition of fishing in many areas each year. Hepatitis has been traced to the surreptitious capture and illicit sale of shellfish contaminated by sewage.

Pollution, erosion, and drainage have ruined fish habitats

Any manipulation of water on the land has a direct bearing on fishery resources, near and far. Insofar as such manipulation accelerates run-off it is generally detrimental. Insofar as it impedes run-off, it is generally beneficial unless detention, as for irrigation, causes excessive loss by evaporation and a consequent reduction in the volume delivered to the sea and other water bodies inhabited by fish. Theoretically, if we were to use all the rain that falls and to expend our surface waters before any could reach the sea our fishes would be starved by evaporation.

But thus far our fault lies mainly in the other direction. By poor water and soil conservation, including drainage, we run our rain toward the sea so fast that fish have no social security in any phase of the process. Drainage of inland marshes and swamps, canalization for transport or local flood "control," restricts or destroys fish habitats adjacent to the project and damages all those downstream from the site. Lakes and streams in some seasons shrunken to mere puddles and trickles and at other times full of muddy water are poor homes for respectable fish. When we prevent floods by proper *management of headwaters* and refrain from meddling with *natural water storage* we will increase, simultaneously, both water and fishery resources. In the conservation of renewable resources a little integration of the various phases works infinitely more good than the most fastidious attention to any single phase. Let no one, least of all the conservator, attempt to sever the natural tie that binds them all together.

Salmon, shad, herring, and other anadromous species (also the catadromous eel, which reverses the sequence) have no doubt heaped fishy curses upon the builders of dams across rivers. While creating new homes for fresh-water fishes above them and reducing the hazards of flood and silting that beset the bottom dwellers of bays and estuaries below, dams across certain streams on the Atlantic Slope barred shad and herring from their spawning grounds in the headwaters. If one concedes that the barriers serve other purposes more valuable than the fisheries they curtail, he may also challenge the necessity for sacrificing one resource in order to conserve others. River fisheries may in fact be enhanced by impounding the waters. Fresh-water fishes must also be considered in connection with engineering that affects salt-water species.

Engineering works create special fishery problems

In some of our great dams, such as on the Pacific Slope, the engineers have built "ladders" whereby salmon might "climb" over the obstruction and gain their upstream spawning areas. (See Fig. 14.11.) The ladders have been at least partially successful, but even if they served their purpose completely they would solve only half the problem. When mother salmon has laid her eggs she dies, but her innocent young face the stupendous task of clearing the dam before they can go to sea and grow up. How to get the baby salmon past the dam alive and then safely to the ocean is the second half of the problem. Many are killed in flumes and turbines, and many get lost in irrigation ditches. (Grand Coulee and other dams too big for ladders require capture and stripping of the prospective parents below the dam, and artificial planting of the fertilized eggs in suitable streams above.)

Several other kinds of construction have impaired our fishery resources. Causeways across bays that kill oyster beds by blocking the tides, jetties or breakwaters that stop or deflect shore currents, have ruined local enterprises and reduced the total gain from fishing. In future engineering projects on our streams, lakes,

Fig. 14.11 *Fish ladder, Bonneville Dam, Columbia River. The dam was too high for fish to leap, so the engineers devised this stairway by which salmon can clear the obstruction and reach headwaters in which to spawn. (H. B. Carr, Fish and Wildlife Service photo.)*

and coasts we can very profitably pay more attention to the protection of fish and other aquatic resources than we have in the past. The structures can be only temporary, whereas the biotic resources should be permanent.

We have fished just as we once hunted and trapped, as if our quarry were utterly inexhaustible. And well we might think our fisheries inexhaustible, considering the prodigious populations and amazing fecundity of certain species. A shoal (consolidated schools) of herring may run into the billions, and a female ling can lay 30 million eggs. But "Old Devil Sea" harbors a vicious, competitive society, its infant mortality alone often exceeding 99 per cent.

Overfishing, often the consequence of other handicaps, has reduced many favored commercial species to a fraction of their former importance. California had our first salmon fishery, but it lasted only about a quarter-century. The Chinook salmon in the Sacramento River was virtually exterminated, apparently by intensive fishing, between 1864 and 1882.[19] However, during the same period hydraulic mining also damaged the salmon streams. When the fishery had declined to negligible proportions, dams built across the river for water projects barred the salmon from their spawning grounds and possible recovery.[20]

Half a century ago, shad ranked third among our commercial fishes, outclassed only by New England cod and Pacific salmon, but by 1945 shad had fallen to thirtieth place among our choice food species (partly because competing species had gained favor). In 1940 the shad fishery produced less than one-fifth the catch taken in 1896.[21]

In the case of salmon and shad, major anadromous food fishes, stream pollution and engineering works have been extremely destructive, but excessive fishing through the years has probably reduced them quite as much as the other handicaps. Ground fishes on the New England Banks, far from the influence of stream pollution and engineering, show downward trends more obviously attributable to overfishing. Halibut and haddock have been severely reduced; rosefish and certain flounders, more moderately. Many favorite fresh-water species once important in our valuable Great Lake fisheries have been reduced to insignificance, largely by excessive fishing. Lake Erie cisco, land-locked sturgeon, blackfin of Lakes Huron and Michigan, and bluefin of Lake Superior are almost gone. One—the Lake Ontario bloater—is extinct. Production of whitefish, trout, and perch (Fig. 14.9) has declined in spite of intensified fishing. Lamprey depredations, mentioned later, have accelerated this decline. Our most desirable mollusks and crustaceans, helpless against power trawls and dredges, have also suffered.

Overfishing of any species has several negative consequences: (1) reduction in total number of fish in the stock, producing smaller yields for given amounts of fishing effort; (2) reduction in average size of fish in the stock, necessitating catching more fish to sustain the tonnage; (3) decimation of spawning stock below the number necessary to maintain the population—all factors leading to progressively smaller annual catches.[22] In short, overfishing does to fisheries what overcutting does to lumbering, what overcropping does to agriculture, and what overgrazing does to range cattle raising—it exhausts the resource upon which the enterprise is based. However, fishermen deal in transient property without title, and unless they take it when it is available, they lose it to someone else. Only when regulations become standardized on a regional basis can fishermen subscribe to the sustained-yield idea already widely accepted in forestry, agriculture, and grazing.

Fishermen seek new fishing grounds

As their catches decline, fishermen seek new fishing grounds, usually more remote than those they have overexploited. When more intensive fishing—more and better gear employed for longer periods—fails to yield a profitable volume, they extend their spheres of operation. They go farther and farther from home and bring in fish costing more and more. Their maximum distance is that beyond which the cost of catching and bringing in the fish comes too near the market price to leave a profit from the venture. In bygone days the gallant men of Gloucester took cod and haddock on Georges Bank, a day's run by schooner with a following wind. Today their grandsons sail diesel-powered trawlers to far-off Bankereau, 800 miles "east by north" for the same kinds of fish (Fig. 14.17). Some *shifting* of fish stocks may be attributed to the rising temperature of northerly ocean waters during recent decades.

The banks fisheries of our Northeast, probably because they are oldest, show best how scarcity extends operations, but the search for new fishing grounds grows wider in other regions too. Many fishing runs are now so long that freezing or processing must be done at sea. Cannery ships will quite surely become a major means of harvesting the high seas, of bringing in many species not yet found on our store shelves. Treaties delineating international boundaries in mid-ocean will then be more than mere words—they will indeed have meat in them.

Substitutes are often indications of scarcity, accepted only when the preferred article becomes difficult to procure. Weed trees found a market when better woods grew scarce. "Trash" fish will gain acceptance when the "fancy" ones become hard to get. In the Great Lakes catch, suckers, carp, sheepshead, and burbot are replacing more desirable species that have been depleted, and housewives are learning to accept the substitutes. Better preparation for market (fillets, steaks, fish sticks, and so on) and more attractive packaging are selling many species previously rejected, thereby promoting conservation in two directions, both by sparing depleted stocks so they may recover and by employing stocks that were previously wasted by neglect. Similar circumstances have evolved comparable, two-way conservation in certain marine fisheries.

Housewives accept substitute species

Thus far, restrictions on gear, season, and catch have been the major conservation measures, because too little has been known about the private lives of the fish to aid many of them more constructively. Research by marine and fresh-water biologists is the most urgent need in fishery conservation, but while sufficient basic facts are being accumulated for developing a suitable program, curtailment of capture may be the means whereby enough of the fish will remain to render the program applicable. From

Biologic research is the first step toward fishery conservation

plankton, the minute forms, to tuna and other big ones, fishes are food for other fish, and if either those that get eaten or those that eat them become too scarce, the lost balance can be difficult to re-establish. In many cases balance of aquatic life is so delicate and complex that it cannot be regained or maintained without thorough scientific understanding of all relationships involved. For none of our resources is knowledge complete, but for our fisheries it is clearly inadequate. For most species such fundamental information as that shown in Fig. 14.12 is lacking. Certainly no resource can be well conserved unless its location is known, and for migratory fishes the correlation of location with life cycles and growth stages can be exceedingly complex.

We have noted how salmon and shad are caught en route to their spawning grounds, exactly when they are bent on perpetuating the species. To the commercial fisherman whose family depends upon his catch, the time to take fish is when they are "running," fat and full of roe, without qualms about the fact that caviar never hatches. Only when his annual catch dwindles can he be convinced that he has been taking each year not only that year's run but those of years to come. Only then does he respect

Fig. 14.12 *Map of Gulf shrimp. Until we know the location of a resource we can neither fully exploit nor intelligently conserve it. Information compiled here came from research conducted by the Fish and Wildlife Service. (Redrawn from Commercial Fisheries Review, Vol. 14, No. 7, July 1952).*

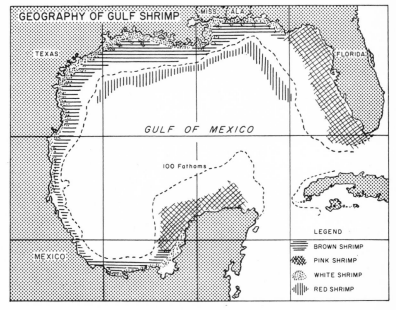

the spawning season and treat more discreetly the parents of his future hauls.

Many species with which we are sufficiently well acquainted are protected during critical periods such as the spawning season in much the same manner as game on the land. However, the protection fails unless it is provided at the right time and in the right place. For species about which our knowledge is too vague for the formulation of protective measures, the first requisite is biologic research to discover their life habits. When we learn where all the important species spawn and where the young grow up, we shall know where and when to spare them, and when and where we can fish them most intensively without depleting the resource. Let the biologist inform, let the lawmaker legislate, let the police enforce, and let the fisherman conform to safeguard his own fortune, whether he likes it or not. Until he cooperates he is a menace to his own vocation.

The development of fishing gear and fishing techniques compares favorably with our mechanization of farming and lumbering, but unlike farming and logging machinery, the scientific fishing equipment that facilitates fish exploitation has not yet been equally applied in fish conservation. Good plows and big tractors aid in both soil use and soil defense, but bigger nets and faster boats simply catch more fish. Thus, our progress in fishing has been essentially one-sided, and it is imperative that research be accelerated to take up the slack.

So ruthlessly effective have our gear and craft become that fish survival is almost more amazing than the phenomenal hauls brought in. With purse seines as much as 1,200 feet long, fishermen can encircle and capture a whole school with one setting. With otter trawls—bag-like nets with wide mouths—they can follow and overtake their quarry, be it pelagic or demersal, crab or shrimp; the nets are towed behind "draggers" and "trawlers" that can outrun the fish. With dredges several feet wide, they can scrape oysters off their beds and dig clams right out of the mud in broad swaths across the bottom. These three specialized types, *purse seine, trawl,* and *dredge,* take most of our fish, but other devices are also important, among them haul seines, gill nets, pound nets, trot lines, traps, weirs, and many more. Even this partial list puts an edge on the casual expression, "poor fish." We even find them and track them with electrical devices such as graphically illustrated in Fig. 14.13, or herd them to their doom with air-bubble curtains (Fig. 14.14).

Restriction of gear and limitation of catch became mandatory

We have mentioned overfishing of favored species as a major fishery problem—a problem intensified by every improvement of

Fig. 14.13 *Fishing becomes progressively more scientific and technical. The airplane is used to spot fish feeding on the surface. The electronic fish-finder locates fish feeding in deep water. The "finder" sends out sound waves which bounce back to the ship from large schools. (Drawing after Fish and Wildlife Service.)*

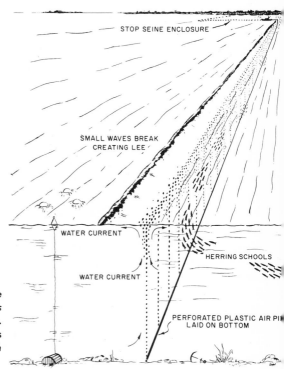

Fig. 14.14 *The air-bubble curtain diverts herring schools into a stop-seine enclosure. (From Commercial Fisheries Review, Vol. 23. No. 3, March 1961.)*

equipment and methods. Positive measures to alleviate it have been mainly in the form of legal restrictions on the use of certain "implements of mass destruction," and limitation of the catch, especially of young fish that should be spared for breeding stock. Minimum-size limits and maximum quotas may often be the answer, and fishermen are beginning to see that such discretions pay off in the long run. Nets and seines of larger mesh to permit

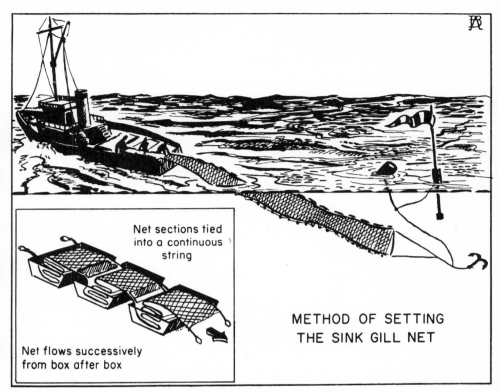

Net sections tied into a continuous string

Net flows successively from box after box

METHOD OF SETTING
THE SINK GILL NET

Figs. 14.15 and 14.16 *The gill net remains an important type of fishing gear. Floats at the top and sinkers at the bottom hold the net vertical in the water. A large mesh makes the net selective, capturing only the "big ones" and permitting the young, growing stock to escape. This may be compared with the selective cutting of mature trees as a facet of sustained-yield management. (Drawings after Fish and Wildlife Service.)*

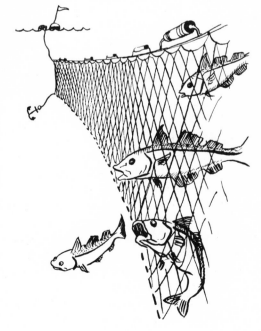

the escape of immature fish bring to fishing a conservation feature that parallels selective logging for stand improvement and sustained yield of timber. Selection by mesh size of a sink gill net is shown in Figs. 14.15 and 14.16. Sparing a fair portion of a run compares with leaving seed blocks instead of clear cutting. Many fish are so highly migratory, and their seasonal runs so extremely erratic, that fishermen cannot adopt a sustained-yield program with the same readiness as a timber grower; but wisdom compelled by mandate need only prove its merit to gain acceptance and voluntary application. It has been suggested that economics will save a declining fishery before the species fails biologically,[23] and there is certainly logic in the idea. Whenever a fisherman can no longer pursue a particular species profitably, he will, of necessity, either turn to another species or quit the business entirely. Thus, for reasons purely economic, he gives a declining species the respite it needs for recovery. Biologically the idea may be sound, and it is certainly operative; but, economically it would seem to place undue strain on the fishing industry. Its negation may well be one of our objectives in fishery conservation; in international waters American fishermen would lose the game to other nationals with lower wage standards.

We have practiced fishery conservation enough to know that it can be highly successful, that depleted species can be restored to abundance, and that a fishery like a forest can be utilized on a sustained-yield basis. Fish respond admirably to fair treatment. Given a reasonably good environment, they will maintain their populations unless the rate of capture exceeds their capacity to reproduce.

Concrete examples indicate the future capabilities of fishery conservation. Good management of the river and the fish saved the shad fishery of the Hudson. Runs had sunk so low that they yielded only 40,000 pounds of fish in 1916, but by 1944 they had made such spectacular recovery that 5 million pounds were taken.[24] Study and control of the Pacific halibut fishery under an International Commission (the United States and Canada) rebuilt and stabilized a resource that was in grave danger of destruction. In places the annual catch had fallen to one-third of its previous volume, despite much more intensive fishing; on many banks halibut were being removed more rapidly than they could replace themselves. Under a treaty signed in 1930 the Commission defined four geographic divisions of the fishery and fixed an annual quota for each. When the quota was taken the season was closed. Two areas in which small specimens predominated were closed entirely. Limitations of catch and season were the

Fishing can be placed on a sustained-yield basis

only conservation measures applied, all based upon careful scientific study. The results have convinced even the fishermen that conservation pays high dividends. One hundred per cent increase of catch per unit of gear over somewhat more than one decade of time should be convincing.[25]

Conservation of Pacific halibut demonstrates the effectiveness of regulation when it is wisely applied to an entire fishery throughout its life range. The best conceived controls cannot accomplish much if they be applied to scattered segments of a fishery, because *a fishery is a biologic unit* and must be treated as such. Until quite recently the lawmakers neglected that fundamental fact and tried vainly to protect a resource common to several states with unrelated, even conflicting, laws passed and enforced independently by the various states concerned. Fish have no respect for politics or political boundaries—neither should laws for their protection follow political lines. Only recently has acknowledgment of that peculiarity found expression in the interstate fishery commissions which now include all our coastal states in three regional groups: Atlantic, Pacific, and Gulf. The Great Lakes fishery has been similarly unified by agreement among the bordering states and Canadian provinces.

Species that migrate the length of our Atlantic Coast cannot be conserved by New Jersey or Maryland or South Carolina individually, but only by all the states of the Eastern seaboard cooperating in a unified program. It was impossible to restore the Great Lakes fisheries before the bordering states and provinces standardized their regulatory measures and formed an international alliance against the lamprey. Lack of uniformity over the entire range of a species renders a fishery regulation ineffective. Comprehensive regional scope and standardization of regulatory measures are essential. Fisheries, more than any other resource except perhaps migratory waterfowl, depend upon interstate or international agreement and cooperation for their conservation. The need is obvious, the trend well established, and many more species will be written into treaties and coordinated state codes. The United States government is already a party to nine international agreements for the conservation of fisheries in which Americans are interested. Additional treaties will be necessary as we realize more fully the value of fishery resources and extend the range of our fishing operations. Competitive fishing of international waters foreshadows cooperative conservation by the competing nations. Figure 14.17 shows some historic fishing grounds affected by an international agreement drawn up in 1951.

Protection should be comprehensive and standardized

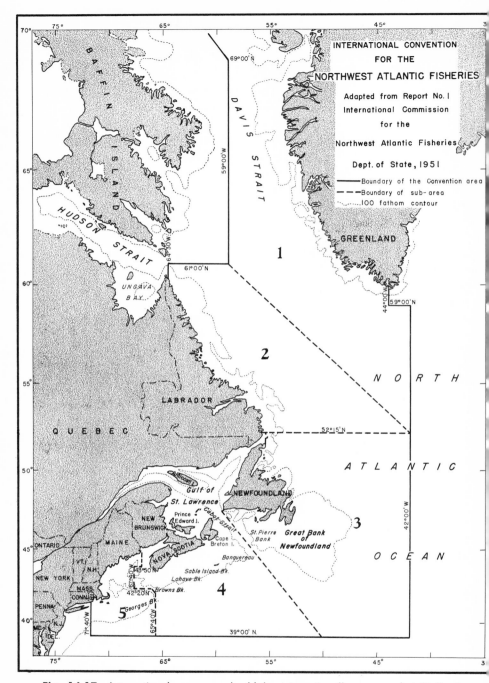

Fig. 14.17 *International resources should be internationally conserved. Initially, ten signatories ratified the conventions pertaining to the region outlined on the map: Canada, Denmark, Norway, Spain, Italy, Portugal, Iceland, United Kingdom, United States, and France. West Germany adhered in 1957, the U.S.S.R. in 1958, and Poland in 1961. Regulations are promulgated on the basis of the areal units bounded and numbered on the map. (Redrawn after Department of State.)*

Favored species of fish need protection against natural enemies other than man, allowing that for fisheries as for other resources conservation is largely a matter of correcting man's own abuses. Since man is only one among many creatures that feed on fish, including fishes themselves, he can increase his share of supply by restraining or destroying his rivals. However, in asserting his superiority he must exercise caution lest he set up a biotic chain reaction that ultimately defeats his purpose. The killing of one rival may multiply another; the killing of all might increase their prey beyond its food supply and cause it to starve. The biotic balance in water is sensitive to disturbance much the same as that on land.

Favored species need protection against natural enemies

The oyster, leading American mollusk, spends its quiet life in constant danger of being eaten by any one of a dozen mortal enemies. Perhaps that is why one oyster can produce as many as 500 million eggs in a single spawning season. Perhaps that is why an oyster can change sex, apparently at will. One of the worst oyster destroyers, the starfish, has long been the object of costly combat with suction dredges and rope "mops." The discovery that it is fatally allergic to lime has offered a possible solution. Chemical barriers have also been used against oyster drills as well as against starfish.

Predators are, however, only partially accountable for the rapid decline of our oyster fishery during recent years—from first to fourth place in value of catch. The 1960 catch was the smallest in more than 100 years.[26] Poisoned by pollution, smothered by siltation, and mutilated by dredging, the immobile oyster has also fallen victim to epidemics of such diseases as Dermocystidium, and the parasitic MSX that literally killed oystering in Delaware Bay in 1960 and has since spread to other Atlantic oyster grounds. Such was the sorry plight of the oyster fishery in 1961 that the Congress voted special appropriations for expansion of shell-fisheries research facilities to improve artificial propagation, to control predators, and to train personnel in advanced methods of shellfish culture.

Predators of many other kinds infest our fishing grounds, sometimes causing serious depredation before detection, and often continuing their inroads despite our best efforts to eradicate or control them. The lamprey (Fig. 14.18), scourge of the Great Lakes, is one such invader.[27] Overfishing of decent aquatic folk may give pirates their opportunity. Wherever man changes or soils the habitat he is liable to aggravate problems otherwise naturally subdued.

When the sea lamprey abandoned his anadromous habits and

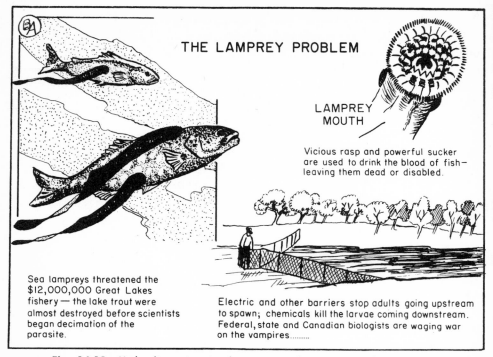

THE LAMPREY PROBLEM

LAMPREY MOUTH

Vicious rasp and powerful sucker are used to drink the blood of fish — leaving them dead or disabled.

Sea lampreys threatened the $12,000,000 Great Lakes fishery — the lake trout were almost destroyed before scientists began decimation of the parasite.

Electric and other barriers stop adults going upstream to spawn; chemicals kill the larvae coming downstream. Federal, state and Canadian biologists are waging war on the vampires.........

Fig. 14.18 *Hydraulic engineering for purposes of navigation and biotic imbalance due to over-fishing and pollution invited the invasion. The erstwhile anadromous parasite discarded its migratory habits and became a life-long fresh-water resident. (Adapted from Fish and Wildlife Service.)*

took up continuous residence in fresh water, his depredations on favored food fishes soon threatened the valuable Great Lakes fisheries. It was only by intensive, cooperative attack, joined by Americans and Canadians, that the vicious invader came under control. The adult monsters can be denied access to spawning grounds by electric barriers across stream entrances, and the young of those that pass the barrier, the larvae coming downstream, can be killed with selective toxicants introduced into streams. Both of these tactics have been used in a campaign first completed on Lake Superior and then projected for each of the other Lakes in turn.

Meanwhile the Great Lakes have been restocked with millions of hatchery-reared lake trout, the worst lamprey casualty. Adaptation of alewife, smelt, and other species has been so successful that stocks of fish have become enormous, albeit less desirable than the native species decimated by the lamprey. On advice from the Bureau of Commercial Fisheries, Great Lakes fishermen have been replacing former methods with otter trawling. Their catch is becoming mainly industrial, sold for animal food, with lesser quantities suitable for human consumption.[28] Michigan has the largest Lake fishery.

While popular species are being overfished, others of known merit and abundance are being neglected or underutilized.[29] Neglect here, as the failure to cut a ripe forest tree, entails positive and avoidable waste. Even more overtly wasteful, like slash and slab left from lumbering, is any failure to use completely the fish that are caught.

Neglected species and wasted parts challenge the conservator

The myriads of anchovies along the length of our Pacific Coast went almost untouched while the pilchard population showed definite signs of shrinking due to fishing. The Pacific sardine, or pilchard, supported the largest fishery in the Western Hemisphere in 1945,[30] and the somewhat smaller anchovy found little use except as live bait for chumming tunas.[31] The 1952-1953 sardine season was the worst in history, the entire season yielding only "one fair day's catch" (3,320 tons). In its peak year, 1936-1937, it amounted to 700,000 tons. In 1952-1953, the pilchard fleet turned to anchovies as a substitute,[32] thus demonstrating how economic necessity may, in fact, afford opportunity for biologic recovery of a fishery.

At least four Pacific fishes remain underutilized. Bonito, black sheep of the tuna family and only slightly inferior to other tunas, makes only a small fraction of its potential contribution to the total catch.[33] Sablefish, or black cod, is a superior food fish neglected by fishermen because housewives have not gained its acquaintance. Pacific cod resembles in quality its East Coast counterpart, but few are taken. Lingcod is excellent for food and yields a liver oil exceptionally high in vitamin A. Its catch remains incidental to the halibut fishery.[34] Only recently has canned bonita made its debut on market shelves.

The burbot in the Great Lakes, the carp in rivers and lakes almost everywhere, the ocean pout of New England, and the squid on both our Atlantic Coast and Pacific Coast are other valuable food resources largely wasted at present. Education and attractive marketing might make them commercially profitable. The ugly burbot gained acceptance during World War II but fell into disrepute again thereafter. The lamprey relished it without camouflage. The carp, ubiquitous problem fish, becomes, by smoke curing, almost equal to smoked salmon—a delicacy.

Our fisheries present many opportunities for conservation through the salvage of fish parts largely wasted, such as the carcasses of fishes taken for their livers, the oil-rich heads of salmon, the bones, viscera, and other parts thrown away when fish are filleted, and so forth. Salmon canning wastes only a third of the fish, and salvage of that waste is improving. (Halibut fishermen use salmon heads for bait.) Improved technology and a growing demand for low-grade fishery by-products can affect a tremendous saving of fish.

A most constructive phase of fishery conservation must be the reconditioning and improvement of fish habitats. Insofar as man has impaired or destroyed the habitats by pollution, silting, drainage, flooding, or other malfunction, it behooves him to set them aright by every means compatible with other resource uses. Perhaps fishery conservation should not be permitted to interfere with more essential projects, such as multiple-purpose stream developments, but, by the same token, high-priority undertakings of the future should not be planned without regard for the aquatic life they may disturb. A good fish habitat and a healthy fish population may more often enhance other values than detract from them.

Fish habitats will be much benefited by our improved use of water and land resources generally. Many already spoiled may never be recovered, but many damaged ones can be returned to their natural state without exorbitant expense. Those habitats which remain in good condition can usually be kept so by treating them with common sense. Unfortunately, men who fish for fun are often better conservators than those who fish for a living. Commercial fishermen must learn to fish without tearing the bottom out of the sea.

Artificial propagation of commercial fishes becomes increasingly feasible as our requirements increase and natural sources decline. In certain Gulf and Middle Atlantic localities oysters have been "domesticated," their beds cared for much as one tends cultivated fields, and their young stock (spat) transplanted to better feeding grounds much as cattle are driven to good grazing. The oyster farmer gathers seed, sows it on leased sea-bottom land, protects the growing crop against poachers and other enemies as best he can, and harvests the crop when it is ripe. With good management, and a little luck, he gets 100 to 150 bushels per acre annually, worth more than a bumper yield of any but the most intensively cultivated farm crops.[35] Those oystermen who persist in scraping public lands do well to gather a few bushels per acre.

Admittedly oysters and other mollusks, being more or less sedentary, lend themselves better to farming than fishes that range considerable areas of water. However, the hatching and rearing of commercial fin fish as we now propagate many of our anglers' prizes is a possible method of marine-fishery conservation.[36] Pond-fish culture, long important in the Orient, has distinct com-

Habitats must be improved rather than spoiled

Artificial propagation of commercial species becomes increasingly feasible

mercial possibilities in the United States, incidental to its valuable contribution to water and soil conservation. However, while one may expect an increase in the controlled production of market fish, he need not anticipate any revolutionary developments while glutted fish markets persist.

The diminishing value of the fisheries to the nation's economy, culture, and security became a matter of public concern almost a century ago (1871) when Congress authorized the appointment of a Commissioner of Fish and Fisheries to study the "decrease of the food fishes of the seacoasts and lakes of the United States, and to suggest remedial measures." [37] In 1903 the Commission was renamed the Bureau of Fisheries and placed in the Department of Commerce and Labor. In 1913 it was removed to the Department of Commerce, where it remained until 1939, largely preoccupied with administration and enforcement of federal laws protecting various marine species. In 1940 the Bureau was merged with the Bureau of Biological Survey (Department of Agriculture) to form the Fish and Wildlife Service, Department of the Interior. The new Service received larger appropriations and greater authority; conservation of our fish and wildlife resources at the national level began in earnest. But the organization was faulty, as was soon apparent, and in 1956 the Congress called for reorganization and elevation in stature of the Fish and Wildlife Service. Most gratifying to conservators was the creation of two separate agencies within the Service: the Bureau of Sport Fisheries and Wildlife, mentioned in previous chapters; the Bureau of Commercial Fisheries, whence much of the information in this one. The reorganization was completed in 1959. Since then, as never before, the United States has, at the top level of government, promoted the conservation of marine resources. The BCF now operates some 177 laboratories and field, or experimental, stations[38] and a growing fleet of research vessels—all to improve our knowledge, capture, and utilization of resources in our bordering seas. The coastal states have greatly expanded their respective facilities and activities for similar purposes. Marine biologists "tag" fishes by the millions—the marine counterpart of bird-banding.

Even as the public programs gained momentum, our fishermen and their erratic vocation remained quite forgotten. Handicapped by domestic restrictions, beaten by foreign competition, their income inadequate to keep a home, and their boats rotting and sinking for lack of repair, American fishermen stood aloof from public assistance until their plight became a matter of national concern. Worst depressed, because it fishes most, was his-

Public support of commercial fisheries

toric New England. It is noteworthy that our first federal provision for improving the fishing industry itself, the Saltonstall-Kennedy Act of 1954, bears the names of venerable Yankees. The act authorized financial implementation of the program with a certain portion of monies from imposts on foreign fishery products—an ingenious scheme! The program and its funding were made permanent by the Fish and Wildlife Act of 1956.

The 1956 act also established a loan fund to help fishermen directly, just as farmers were helped many years before. Fishermen may now borrow from the government for the financing or refinancing of operations, maintenance, repairs, replacement, and equipment of fishing vessels and fishing gear, and, under certain conditions, for research into basic fishery problems. By the end of 1961, 1,066 applications had been filed and 560 (for 13.7 million dollars) had been approved.[39] Subsidy funds have been augmented by a mortgage insurance guarantee, also administered by the Bureau of Commercial Fisheries. The first vessel completed under federal subsidy is the 73-foot wooden otter trawler *Venus,* documented for fishing at New Bedford, Massachusetts on October 10, 1962. In due course our fishing fleets will be seaworthy and efficient and profitable, making us proud instead of causing us shame.

We cannot quit the sea without comment on one additional idea; namely, the possibility of alleviating human hunger wherever it prevails by furnishing adequate supplies of whole fish flour. The United States has produced such flour that is palatable and of tested nutritional excellence. It is the cheapest high-protein food material known; but for aesthetic objections, it could satisfy world hunger. Assuming that population growth must be increasingly sustained by food from the sea, acceptance of fish flour could be a good beginning. As the nations cooperate in the conservation of marine resources, so may they all also share the wealth thus conserved.

None of our natural resources has been more neglected than our fisheries; none has greater possibilities for conservation and future productivity. Commercial fisheries of the United States employ about 500,000 people—fishermen, transporters, shore workers, makers of gear or processing equipment, salesmen, boat builders, and other allied tradesmen. The 1960 catch was taken by some 130,400 fishermen, of whom about 42,000 worked on fishing vessels. The fishing fleets numbered more than 12,000 vessels (5 net tons and over), almost 57,000 motor boats, and 8,150 other craft engaged in fishing. More than 2,000 persons operated 1,094 transporting craft. Some 4,200 wholesaling and manufacturing plants employed 93,625 persons.[40] The annual catch of our commercial fisheries approximates 5 billion pounds, and its retail value is more than a billion dollars. It is marketed as shown in Fig. 14.19. On the basis of the value of fishery products New England remains our leading fishing region. California ranks first among all our tidewater states, and Alaska ranks second.

DISTRIBUTION OF
5.2 BILLION POUND CATCH OF COMMERCIAL FISHERIES
1962

ROUND WEIGHT   MARKETED WEIGHT

713,354,000 lbs.__MARKETED FRESH_____606,000,000 lbs.
486,134,000 lbs.__FILLETS (FRESH AND FROZEN)__170,000,000 lbs.
374,512,000 lbs.__FROZEN (NOT FILLETS)_____286,000,000 lbs.
80,000,000 lbs.__CURED_____56,500,000 lbs.
1,136,118,000 lbs.__CANNED_____888,000,000 lbs.

MEAL
597,000,000 lbs.

2,450,000,000 lbs.   BY-PRODUCTS   OIL
246,000,000 lbs.

CONDENSED
FISH SOLUBLES
214,000,000 lbs.

WASTE FROM FRESH AND
548,000,000 lbs.   PROCESSED FISH USED   HOMOGENIZED
FOR BY-PRODUCTS   CONDENSED FISH
22,000,000 lbs.

Note: Round and marketed weights shown above do not include imported items processed in the United States. The marketed weights listed do not include fresh bait, or animal food prepared from waste, shell products, or other miscellaneous by-products.

Fig. 14.19 *A graphic summary of the American fishing industry, reflected in end-product volumes. How many market categories does each of us patronize? (From C.F.S. No. 3200, Bureau of Commercial Fisheries, April 1963.)*

Among the great fishing nations of the world, the United States has fallen from second to fifth place since 1956 and is now surpassed not only by Japan, for many years the world leader, but also by mainland China, Peru, and the U.S.S.R. Peru came up overnight, by phenomenal development of a whole fish-meal industry based on the swarming anchovies that previously became sea-bird guano on her desertic offshore islands. The industry has successfully and profitably short-circuited a natural food cycle.

Our importation of fishery products has become progressively greater despite considerable import duty on several such products. In 1961 about 1.1 billion pounds, or substantially more than one-sixth our total consumption, entered the United States from countries all over the world. Nonedible products comprised a value of 61 million dollars; edible ones almost 336 million dollars, of which half came from Canada and Japan. Duties collected amounted to about 16 million dollars.[41] Our fishery exports in that year amounted to less than 45 million dollars, about one-eighth the value of the imports.

The wealth of the sea—mineral, vegetable, and animal—presents a major challenge to technology and conservation and a unique opportunity for international cooperation. The nations will be increasingly jealous of their ocean boundaries as marine resources attain greater importance.

It has been estimated that the oceans might yield 500 million tons of food per year indefinitely.[42] Thus far, however, mainly due to ignorance and neglect, men have realized only a minute part of that potential.[43]

15

Mineral Fuels and Major Metals

mineral materials and machines, mineral energy and motive power: facilities of our accelerated, transient mechanical age

Having surveyed the land and scanned the seas that border it, we are now ready to examine the mineral resources deposited by nature within the earth. We shall not delve deeply into the subject, but without a cursory examination of minerals and their conservation a discussion of natural wealth would lack the broad practical perspective that is paramount to its rational development.

A comprehensive treatment of minerals would fill several volumes much larger than this one, but such treatment does not suit our context. It is more fitting that we examine only those minerals which dominate our mechanized age, and especially those in imminent danger of exhaustion.

Unlike our renewable resources, which become permanent and perpetual under conservation, minerals are fixed endowments, expendable once and then gone for our time. In this age, they hold a commanding position, but that position they cannot retain indefinitely. They are a legacy given like cash, and we are spending it rapidly. Unlike the renewable resources we have discussed, which resemble permanent trust funds, the minerals are ours to spend once only, without accrued interest to cushion their exhaustion. They are expendable. Their rate of accumulation does not approach even remotely the rate at which we are ex-

**Tools that
forge our
mechanical age:
destructive
and
constructive**

tracting them. There is no evidence that those stores we deplete
will be significantly replenished during the age of mankind. In
fact, the very culture built with those we extract in some cases
interferes with the accumulation of new stocks for future use,
as when we drain and burn peat bogs that might have become
coal in the far, distant future had they been left undisturbed.

Minerals are the tools of our mechanical Atomic Age, as they
have been the tools of civilization ever since prehistoric men
threw rocks at each other. Stone, bronze, iron, and steel have,
in their turn, dominated the affairs of men and gauged the progress of human culture. From Stone Age to Atomic Age minerals
have provided implements of war and peace—the spears and
plowshares by which tribes and nations have risen or fallen. They
remain the decisive factor in war and an essential element of
pacific progress. Our national prestige hinges on the comparative
abundance of minerals available to us.[1]

Certain minerals are as necessary to life and health as are air
and water. We cannot live without them. Common salt, for example, is so vital to the human organism that it has been an
article of commerce throughout the history of man. It has
emerged from its rudimentary role as a component of blood and
tissue to a prominent place among industrial raw materials. It
is indispensable and invaluable; yet it is so cheap and abundant
that we shall say no more about it. The earth's crust and the
seas that lap it contain so much salt that we shall have plenty
without conserving it. There are solid sections in the ground
more than 1,000 feet thick.

For the giants of our technological age—the metals for machines and the mineral fuels to drive them—the prospect is quite
different. Some of these are neither abundant nor cheap, and we
are consuming our reserves at accelerating rates.[2] They have
brought us our high material standards, our superior producing
capacity, our leadership in world affairs, and the leisure time to
enjoy life and contemplate our bounteous natural wealth. They
have been the means of ruthlessly exploiting renewable resources
and are now the most efficient means of conserving them. With
machines made of minerals and powered by mineral fuels, men
till the soil, log the forest, fish the sea, process and distribute the
products, and apply conservation measures to ensure a permanent supply of renewable resources. So intimately related are
the *renewable organics* and the *nonrenewable minerals* in our
complex culture that the two groups require some degree of
correlation in a treatise on resource conservation. Their relative

prominence in the American economy of the distant future will inevitably change.

The great variety of mineral materials and the versatility with which they serve us every day of our lives are suggestive of their importance as natural resources. Minerals compose the earth's crust, the solid foundation of our world environment. Contained therein are all the elements known to chemistry and perhaps many more not yet isolated. Every kind of common rock is a compound or combination of minerals—be it simple, as the calcium carbonate of limestone, or more complex, as the mixture of silicon dioxide and other minerals in granite.

In variety and versatility, minerals challenge the whole array of renewable resources

Since the main body of soil is disintegrated, decomposed rock, and soil is the main support of life, one might conclude that the vegetable and animal resources spring from the mineral ones. One might contend that minerals are the primal category. Have we put the cart before the horse? Are minerals the egg or the hen among resources?

Perhaps the most valuable contribution of minerals is their function as soil materials and not in the forms normally classed as mineral. Perhaps our most important mineral resources have been discussed in earlier chapters under soils. Be that as it may, we are here concerned with minerals of specific kinds, and of these we shall discuss only the functional groups most essential to our continued prosperity. Let us take a quick look at the field and make our selections.

Stone, clay, and other earth materials have almost countless uses, and, but for their superabundance, we might discuss their conservation. However, since we may have more stone than we shall ever quarry for construction, flux, road material, statuary and monuments, more sand than we can ever make into bifocals, mirrors, window panes, store fronts, and other glass products, and more clay than we can mold into pots, crocks, bricks, tiles, and other ceramics, we shall not devote space to them here. They may be used more and more as other materials grow scarce, but one cannot foresee any shortage even so, excepting special glass sand and clays in limited supply.

One orthodox classification divides the minerals proper into three groups—*metals, nonmetals,* and *fuels*—each of which may be variously subdivided. For our purposes it might be desirable to consider minerals according to their functional uses: (1) those which are converted into finished goods, such as aluminum; (2) those used mainly for processing or manufacturing *other* materials, such as sulfur; (3) those which furnish energy for industry,

Major functional groups

commerce, and domestic convenience, such as coal and petroleum; (4) those which contribute to soil fertility, such as potash
and phosphate. However, since many play a dual or even a
triple role, we shall take a more deliberate approach.

Iron stands unique among the metals and sets the pace for
the others. To date, steel has no substitute, and iron is the bulk

**Energy
and steel
dominate our age
of mechanization**

component of steel. Other metals are in some degree interchangeable, as for instance aluminum for copper in electrical
transmission, but iron has no satisfactory stand-in. We may therefore appraise our metal situation in terms of iron, since the others
could not be put to work without the steel produced with iron.
When we discuss prospects in Chapter 17 we shall make some
long-range predictions about replacements for iron, but for the
present and the foreseeable future it is our most essential metal.[3]

From iron and the ferro-alloys come the machines and tools
for making other metals into useful articles—the rotors for generating electricity to be converted and distributed by copper, the
cans to be coated with tin, and the sheet metal to be galvanized
with zinc. Indeed, iron is the prime mover among the metals, if
not in the entire mineral field.

Between the metals and the fuels there is almost complete
interdependence and reciprocity. The fuels would not be available as we know them if metal machines did not extract and
distribute them; neither would there be the machines and vehicles for the fuels to drive if the metals were lacking. In the
absence of iron and steel, most of our oil and coal would languish
in the earth. The little trickles and lumps we might recover
would be used to heat and illuminate our homes, in competition
with tallow candles and firewood. In the absence of oil and coal
we could neither produce nor operate our machines and vehicles.
We should revert to hand tools, animal power, and sailing ships.
Metals would have little value without the mineral fuels, and the
mineral fuels would be largely wasted without the metals to
extract and employ them.

Since the metals and fuels are indispensable to each other in
functional use, it is logical that the two groups should be conserved jointly rather than independently. Both must be put to
optimum use by maintaining their reciprocity as long as possible.
Considering our abundance of coal in the United States, any
expenditure of coal to prolong the life of iron reserves may be
good conservation.

Nature provided us with iron ore by separating and accumulat-
ing in certain places the iron compounds contained in rock
materials of various kinds. Iron is present in rocks and soils al-

most everywhere, contributing to them the reddish hue of rust. In places, as in our Southeastern states, iron hardpan layers have been precipitated in the soil; but our commercial ore deposits are of ancient geologic origin, produced by several different earth processes.[4]

Coal, petroleum, and natural gas *are* organic products—a fact that strengthens the proposition that biotic resources are those upon which man is actually most dependent. The whole story is too long to relate here, but let us sketch it for coal and oil, in order to illustrate once again the interminable kinship between minerals and organisms. In the case of mineral fuels, that which we choose to call "mineral" is in fact "organic" in origin. Through long, slow processes living resources have given us our expendable fossil fuels.

The fossil fuels have biotic origins

Long after Marco Polo returned from a trip and reported that the amazing Chinese were burning rocks, scientists learned that those rocks were the concentrated carbon residues from ancient forests that flourished in fresh-water swamps at least a million years before the advent of man.

Long after petroleum was used by men as a cure for mange on their camels, we learned that the oily fluid derives from myriads of salt-water organisms that inhabited the shallow margins of ancient seas and became entombed within layers of sedimentary rock.

Somewhere in the dark, distant past both the fresh-water plant remains and the salt-water plankton remains were buried deep under marine sediments, were compressed and concentrated into "seams" of coal and "pools" of oil as we know them today, and lay almost unused until men of the industrial age put them to work. We have made them our servants and become dependent upon them, but they cannot serve us always. When they expire others must take their places, else we should lose the civilization they gained us.

The mineral fuels—coal, oil, and gas—are the prime movers of our modern industry, having displaced almost entirely both wood and muscle power in little more than a century. As recently as 1850 wood and muscles powered most of America's industry and transportation, wood heated almost all homes and other buildings in which people worked, and wood charcoal smelted more than half of such iron as was then produced in crude furnaces.[5]

After the Civil War wood gave way to coal at a rapid pace, accompanying the building of railroads and the use of steam locomotives. Then came the automobile propelled by gasoline, bringing petroleum into prominence since the turn of the century much as coal had gained importance previously. Both coal and oil became major energy sources in connection with motive power for transportation. Although gas was associated with oil from the beginning, it was largely wasted until men learned how to ship and distribute it through pipes, a later development.[6] Then it became important, not for propulsion, but as a space heating and process fuel, for which purposes it has surpassed coal and oil. The rank of all three as primary contributors to our total energy consumption is represented in Table 1.[7] Coal held

Table 1

Sources of Energy

Energy Source	Per cent of Total 1960	1980
Coal	23.1	26
Gas	31.4	28
Oil	41.4	41
Hydropower	4.1	2.5
Nuclear Power	Nil	2.5 or more

first place until 1953, when oil took the lead; gas took second place even more recently. Note that the three conventional mineral sources are expected to furnish 95 per cent of energy requirements in 1980 as they did in 1960, although their total consumption will almost double (82,000 trillion Btu in 1980). Hydropower will decline relatively as we run out of good dam sites; coal will regain its lost supremacy as the other fossil fuels become depleted.

The consolidated origin and disposition of all energy used in the United States may be fairly comprehended by studying the accompanying diagrammatic flow chart (Fig. 15.1). The prodigious consumption of energy in the United States, which is far greater than that of any other country in the world, has attained fantastic proportions. In 1960, for instance, Americans produced about 434 million short tons of coal, 12.5 billion cubic feet of natural gas, and 2.6 billion (42 gallon) barrels of oil. As of about the same time (1960-1961) our estimated available reserves remaining in the ground amounted to some 830 billion short tons of coal, 270 trillion cubic feet of gas, and 40 billion barrels of oil. If all exploration, technology, and conservation stopped right now and our rates of consumption remained constant, we would have enough gas for less than two decades, enough oil to last a decade and a half, and enough coal to last two millennia. We

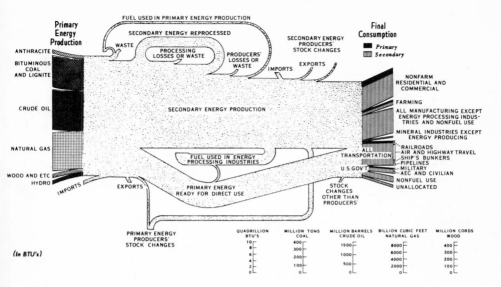

Fig. 15.1 *Origin and disposition of all energy in the United States, 1954.* Primary Energy: *This includes fuels or energy materials in their natural form or as produced from the earth: Anthracite, bituminous coal, lignite, crude petroleum, unprocessed (virgin) natural gas, and fuelwood. It also includes wood wastes and bagasse since both are essentially primary to the energy economy. Finally, it includes hydroelectric energy because of the relatively minor importance of mechanical waterpower in applications other than for generating electric energy. Secondary Energy: A fuel or energy form derived through a conversion process is defined as secondary energy. It would include distillation or refining from one of the foregoing primary energies, such as coke from coal, gasoline from crude petroleum, LP-gas and natural gasoline from unprocessed natural gas, or electric energy from coal. Some secondary energy forms are also derived from other secondary energy forms as (for example) manufactured and blast furnace gases from coke, or electric energy from distillate or residual fuel oil. (Chart and explanatory notes from* Energy Production and Consumption in the United States: An Analytical Study Based on 1954 Data, *by Perry D. Teitelbaum, Bureau of Mines, with cooperation of Resources for the Future, Inc.)*

shall see, however, that such calculated predictions have little validity, being subject to many variables that change with time. The useful life of our fuel resources may be considerably extended by measures such as will be described in Chapter 16; since all are hydrocarbons, and largely interchangeable in use, the exhaustion of one will shift the load to another without any catastrophe. Even while they remain naturally available in three forms—solid, liquid, and vapor—their uses are not only complementary, but they are even more largely competitive in the same market place. All three compete in the markets for generating electricity, for space heating, and for process heat. The consumer's preference of one or another is based on convenience, adequacy and reliability of supply, and price. Two of the fuels, and even all three, are used interchangeably in many electric

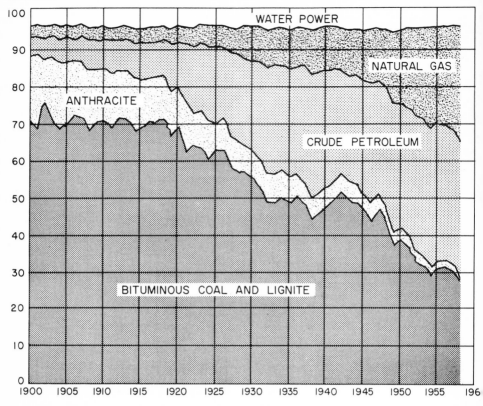

Fig. 15.2 *Per cent of total production of British thermal units equivalent of mineral energy fuels and energy from waterpower in continental United States, 1900-58. (From Bureau of Mines.)*

generating stations equipped with dual or three-way facilities. Only about 35 per cent of our energy demand, mainly that for motive power, is exclusive, requiring liquid fuel.[8] Be it gasoline for automobiles and trucks, jet fuel for aircraft, or diesel oil for locomotives and tugboats, it comes from petroleum. (There is searing irony in this! The railroads and coal attained preeminence under conditions of mutual dependence; but now, although coal still comprises a major item of railway freight, it no longer pulls the trains.) Coal, in the form of coke, retains quite exclusively the metallurgical market, unchallenged as a reducer of iron. Oil took the space-heating market away from coal, and since then oil has lost most of that market to gas (Fig. 15.2). One could only guess how many and how momentous will be the future fuel changes, but he may be sure they will come.

Energy is a cheap commodity in the United States whether purchased by household consumers, factory entrepreneurs, or any other group. However lavishly we use energy in the American home, it takes only a small part of the family budget. In most of our industrial production energy is a minor item of cost, excepting, of course, such energy-intensive manufactures as aluminum, cement, and iron and steel. It is for these very reasons of abundance and low price that the public gives little thought to the eventual depletion of mineral fuels. The following cursory examination of their production and use will help us better to understand and appreciate them. Since coal is our oldest major energy source and the one destined to serve the longest, it is appropriate that it be considered first.

Fig. 15.3 *Heat values compared with proximate analyses. (From U.S.G.S., Bulletin 1136.)*

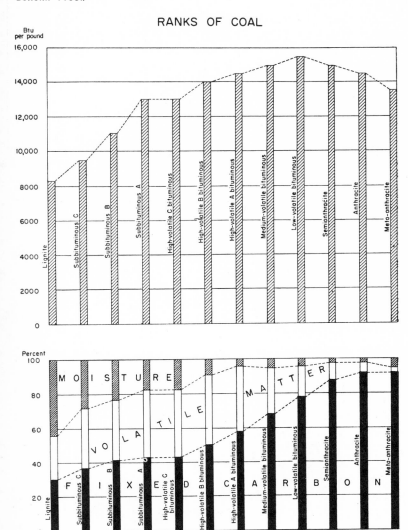

The collective term *coal* pertains to several "coals" in four major classes and twelve ranks (excluding unconsolidated brown coal), as shown in Fig. 15.3. They are ranked on the basis of fixed carbon content, which ranges from more than 90 per cent in anthracite to about 33 per cent in lignite. Highest energy-mass ratio is in the low-volatile bituminous rank. Anthracite has declined to minor importance as a fuel because of increasing mine depths, mine water problems, and growing competition from other fuels. Peak production came in 1917 (94 million tons); since then it has declined steadily, amounting to only about 17.5 million tons in 1960.[9] It retains a considerable market for space heating in New England and the metropolitan Northeast and is shipped from mines in near-by eastern Pennsylvania. Lignite, the lowest ranked coal, remains negligible as an energy source. Some 2 million tons were mined in 1960, mostly in North Dakota.[10] Thus, we may concern ourselves mainly with bituminous, of which annual consumption remained at about 375 million tons in 1961; it has declined rapidly since World War II, from a peak of more than 630.6 million tons in 1947.[11] (Exports of American bituminous reached a record of 76.5 million tons in 1957, but they had fallen to 35 million tons in 1961, largely due to foreign restrictions.)[12]

Fig. 15.4 *Coal fields of contiguous United States. (U.S.G.S. map.)*

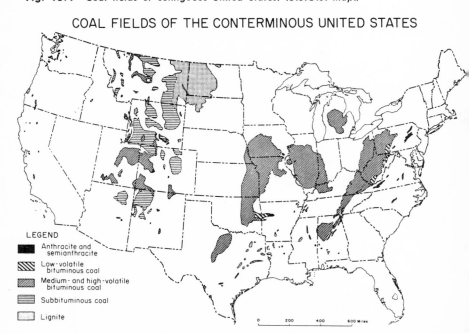

COAL FIELDS OF THE CONTERMINOUS UNITED STATES

LEGEND

Anthracite and semianthracite

Low-volatile bituminous coal

Medium- and high-volatile bituminous coal

Subbituminous coal

Lignite

COAL FIELDS OF ALASKA

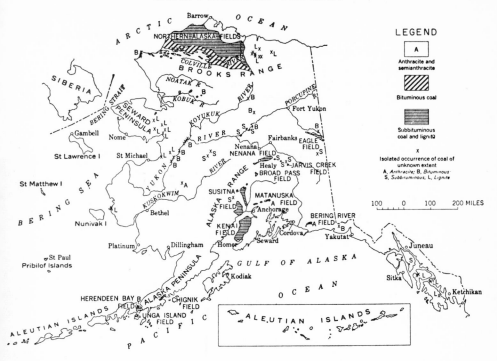

Fig. 15.5 *(After F. F. Barnes, 1959, from U.S.G.S., Bulletin 1136.)*

The location of American coal fields and types of coal by major classes may be seen in Figs. 15.4 and 15.5. Six states produce most of the bituminous now in use—West Virginia, Kentucky, Pennsylvania, Illinois, Ohio, and Virginia in descending order of tonnage. Two-thirds of the output is mined underground[13] and most of the remainder by surface stripping. Operational in 1960 were 5,989 underground mines, 1,530 strip mines, and 346 augur mines that produced 8 million tons of coal.[14] Mining has become so highly mechanized that man-day production in 1961 averaged almost 14 tons.[15] (Here is another paradox in coal: many coal-mining machines are oil driven!)

Almost one-half of domestic consumption is used for generating electricity, and about one-fifth of it is made into metallurgical coke for iron smelting. This metallurgical use is the unique capability of special coals that coke (or cake) when highly heated (2000°F) under controlled conditions, as in coking ovens. Although coking quality is not a direct function of other properties, it is limited to certain anthracite and low-volatile bituminous coals. Unfortunately, coking coals have become scarce, constituting only about 1 per cent of our total coal reserves.[16] The Ap-

palachian (Eastern Province) coal field that extends from northern Pennsylvania to west-central Alabama has been the main
source of supply.

Most of the bituminous coal produced in 1960 was disposed
of as shown in Table 2.

Table 2

Disposal of Bituminous Coal, 1960
(In round figures)

	Million tons
Electric power utilities	180
Other manufacturing and mining	77
Coking	74
Export	35
Retail delivery to consumers	28
Cement mills	8
Steel and rolling mills	7

Source: *Bituminous Coal Facts*, National Coal
Association (Washington, D.C., 1962).

Important by-products from carbonization of coal to produce
coke are heating gas, coal tar, and light oils. The tar and oils
are raw material for organic chemicals and may also be made into
wood preservatives, disinfectants, and other products. The impending shortage of coking coals can be deferred by conservation.

**Gas and oil:
the fluid-fuel
complex**

The extraction of "coal oil" (kerosene) from coal and the
escape of dangerous methane gas from coal diggings had shown
the chemical similarity between coal and the other fossil fuels
long before the discovery of petroleum in commercial quantities
in 1859. But coal was coal, whatever its possible derivatives. Such
clear distinction has never been possible for oil and gas because
they are genetically associated and often come from the same
well. Indeed, the proportion of gas and oil coming from an oil
well—the *gas/oil ratio*—has become a useful index to production
efficiency and conservation: the less the gas released the better
the oil recovery. In the event that the gas/oil ratio becomes extreme, the well loses its identity as an oil well and is considered
a gas well.[17] About 30 per cent of our natural gas is produced
in association with oil; 70 per cent comes from dry holes.[18]
Maryland produces natural gas but no oil.

The category, natural-gas liquids—neither gas nor oil, but
in between—epitomizes the inherent association of the fluid
fuels. These liquids are identified as *condensate, natural gasoline*

and *liquefied petroleum gases.* All are derived from natural gas at wellheads, but are diverted, processed, and used as petroleum products. Thus we have, not merely two materials, natural (dry) gas and crude oil, but also a third one, liquid gas, obtained from oil and gas fields. The crude oil and gas liquids are identified collectively as the liquid hydrocarbons. At points of common origin and production, crude oil and natural gas are intricately related; in transmission to market they become segregated and move through separate pipe systems; in areas of consumption their distinctive features belie genetic affinity and often set them against each other as monopolizers of certain markets and contenders in some.

The location and extent of producing oil and gas fields in the United States, as well as the vast area whence future production may come, are shown on the accompanying maps (Figs. 15.6 and 15.7). Oil pools in commercial production vary in size from a few acres to more than 200 square miles.[19] As of December 31, 1960 the United States had almost 600,000 wells producing oil and an estimated 84,570 producing "dry" gas.[20] Remaining unexplored by drilling are more than 2 million square miles of the United States and fringing continental shelves underlain by rock potentially favorable for the discovery of oil.[21] Exploration of this extensive area would require the drilling of a million wells to an average depth of about 8,000 feet, at a cost of $12.00 to $15.00 per foot. Average depth to which wells were drilled in 1960 was 4,079 feet, and 46,751 wells were completed that year.[22] The Drake well at Titusville, Pennsylvania (1859) was only 69.5-feet deep; commencing in 1958, several wells in Texas have been drilled to a depth of 25,340 feet.[23]

Most productive oil and gas fields are those about the western Gulf Coast and in the southern plains (mid-continent) region. Texas has been the leading crude petroleum–producing state since 1927,[24] and, although her share of total domestic output has decreased steadily for many years, it was still about 36 per cent in 1960.[25] Second-ranking Louisiana produced more than 15 per cent of the total that year and third-ranking California slightly less than 12. Other important producers, in order of rank, were Oklahoma, Wyoming, Kansas, New Mexico, Illinois, Mississippi, Colorado, Montana, and Arkansas (1+ per cent).

About 45 per cent of the crude oil becomes gasoline, 22 per cent distillate fuel oil, and 11 per cent residual fuel oil. Other refinery products include kerosene, still gas, asphalt, jet fuel, liquefied gases, lubricating oil, coke, wax, road oil and petrochemicals.[26]

OIL AND GAS FIELDS AND AREAS OF PROBABILITY OF CONTIGUOUS UNITED STATES

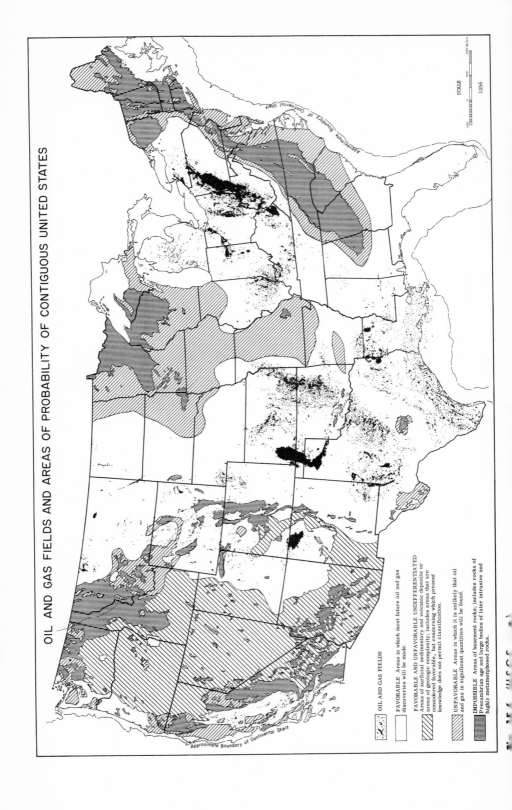

OIL AND GAS FIELDS

FAVORABLE Areas in which most future oil and gas discoveries will be made.

FAVORABLE AND UNFAVORABLE UNDIFFERENTIATED Areas of surficial sedimentary and volcanic deposits or areas of geologic complexity; includes areas that are considered favorable, but concerning which present knowledge does not permit classification.

UNFAVORABLE Areas in which it is unlikely that oil and gas in significant quantities will be found.

IMPOSSIBLE Areas of basement rocks; includes rocks of Precambrian age and large bodies of later intrusive and highly metamorphosed rocks.

SCALE

100   0   100   200   300   200 Miles

1956

Approximate Boundary of Continental Shelf

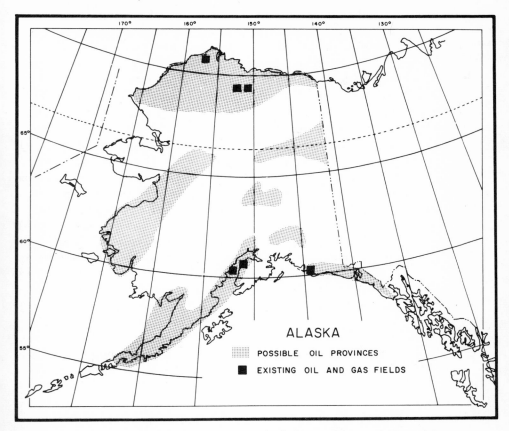

Fig. 15.7 *(Adapted from maps by U.S.G.S. and Alaska Department of Natural Resources in Report for the Year 1962 by Division of Mines and Minerals, Juneau.)*

Texas, Louisiana, Oklahoma, and New Mexico produced 80 per cent of the natural-gas output in 1960; Kansas and California contributed an additional 10 per cent; the remaining 10 per cent came from twenty-three other states. Forty-seven states burned the gas, all except Hawaii, Maine, and Vermont.[27]

About one-half of the natural gas marketed is used as industrial fuel; more than one-third is used in homes (31.1 million residential customers in 1961); about one-tenth is used in commercial establishments.[28] A minor, but very special use of natural gas, also served by quantities of liquid hydrocarbons, is in the manufacture of carbon black. For that purpose, more than 151.1 billion cubic feet of natural gas and more than 313 million gallons of liquids were reduced in 1960,[29] mainly in Texas and Louisiana.

**Extravagant
consumption**

Carbon black is compounded with both natural and synthetic rubber at a rate of about 857 pounds per long ton of virgin rubber,[30] predominantly for automobile tires. If the rubber be synthetic, carbon black becomes formed with two other petrochemicals, butadiene and styrene. The three, as tires, lend the traction whereby engines made of metal propel vehicles made largely of metal, with mineral fuel (gasoline) laced with a petrochemical, ethylene, and a metallic salt, dibromide, so that another metal additive, lead, gives the engine "zip" and the vehicle "scratch-off" without gumming up the works. In cold weather yet another mineral derivative, ethylene glycol, serves as "permanent" antifreeze so that the elaborate dissipation can be kept going. Energy applied between tire and pavement is a ridiculously small part of that in the petroleum source originally. All the lead and most of the other fuel components are wasted to the air as pollutants. Small quantities of carbon black become ink with which to record the whole business and keep us informed about resource use, wastage, and conservation, among other important matters.

The large and growing variety of petrochemicals is too great for discussion here. They originated about 1919-1920 and have since grown to a yearly production of many millions of tons. They may be defined as "chemical compounds made with a petroleum hydrocarbon as one of their basic components."[31] They range in character from ammonia to acetone, including carbon black and several others mentioned above; there are a score of major types from which thousands of minor products are made. The liquid hydrocarbons are a remarkably versatile resource and one, therefore, whose accelerating consumption and eventual exhaustion should concern all intelligent people.

**Vast
fluid assets,
gradually
expendable**

This raises a conservation issue that generates much controversial friction despite frequent "lubrication" with theory and opinion—the matter of oil and gas reserves and how long they will last. We cannot resolve the issue, but we shall examine it well enough to realize that any prediction of terminal exhaustion must remain subjective, if not entirely arbitrary. Only this can be said with certainty about reserves and their future production: deposits remaining in the earth have fixed quantity, quality, and availability and must eventually become progressively more scarce and difficult to remove. How *far* we shall deplete them cannot be forecast any more confidently than we can predict changes in population, material culture, technology, and other mutable factors *in combination,* which must be highly speculative. How *long* we shall maintain or accelerate production rates in the face of progressive scarcity may be somewhat better conjectured because it has immediate implications and should be postulated against a shorter span of time.

Since it is solid and fixed, a coal seam can be measured in place quite accurately; oil and gas, being fluid, cannot, because they are constant in neither volume nor place. They expand or contract in response to pressure and temperature change; they can move through the rock containing them and may escape from it. Without this fluidity they would not be extractable by conventional methods; however, the same characteristic renders their volume difficult to ascertain.

As noted earlier, quantitative estimates of oil and gas reserves are, in fact, available; but, they are not indices to the useful life of the resources, nor were they compiled with that intent. Proved reserves, economicably recoverable with technology now known, can be counted on with some certainty; they will sustain the production we shall require for, perhaps, two decades. Any estimate of "ultimate" recoverable reserves can be little better than guesswork and may be more confusing than illuminating.

In recent years the discovery rate has been greater than extraction, thus enlarging the margin between reserves and production. This could not, of course, continue indefinitely, but it still remains a continuing capability. Until our exploratory efforts become much less successful than they are at present, the ultimate exhaustion of oil and gas is difficult to foresee. Whether the peak of American petroleum production has passed or is imminent, one consolation remains: production that has grown for one century may take another to taper off. Depletion will be gradual—best discernible, perhaps, in decline curves for producing wells and reservoirs. Meanwhile, such conservation measures as we shall mention in Chapter 16 will take up the slack for a long time.

The fossil fuels generate more than four-fifths of our electricity, a secondary energy source so convenient and desirable that its production had become twenty times greater in 1961 than it was in 1920. Installed generating capacity increased one-third between 1956 and 1961. Production in 1961 was 635.6 billion kilowatthours by steam plants, 151.8 billion by hydroplants, and 4.6 billion by internal-combustion plants.[32] As of January 1, 1962 the hydroelectric potential in the United States was estimated to be 148.9 million kilowatts of generating capacity, capable of producing 641 billion kilowatthours of electric energy annually. Only about 36.2 million kilowatts, or one-fourth of the ultimate potential had been developed at that time.[33]

Fossil fuels generate most of our electricity

DEVELOPED AND UNDEVELOPED HYDROELECTRIC POWER
BY MAJOR DRAINAGES
JANUARY 1, 1962

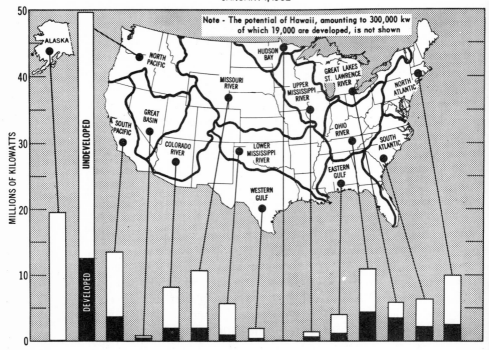

Note - The potential of Hawaii, amounting to 300,000 kw of which 19,000 are developed, is not shown

Fig. 15.8 *See how this correlates with several other maps! (Federal Power Commission map.)*

Fig. 15.9 *Federal and nonfederal hydroelectric capacity. (From Committee Print No. 15: Floods and Flood Control, Senate Select Committee on National Water Resources, 86th Cong. Basic sources: Department of Commerce and Federal Power Commission.)*

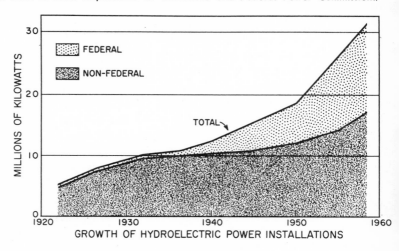

GROWTH OF HYDROELECTRIC POWER INSTALLATIONS

Figure 15.8 shows by major drainage divisions the developed and undeveloped hydropower available. Federal projects accounted for considerably less than half the installed hydropower capacity as recently as 1959,[34] despite rapid public construction since 1950 that appeared imminently destined to exceed nonfederal generating capacity (Fig. 15.9).

Some thirty-six hundred electric utility systems, supplied by 3,411 generating plants, public and private, comprise the power network that reaches almost every inhabited place in the United States.[35] And we may proudly submit that this capitalistic "juice" is furnished to us profitably and democratically: investor-owned utilities transmitted 77 per cent of the electricity sold in 1960.[36] Average use per home during 1961 was 4,000 kilowatthours,[37] representing a 27 per cent increase in the use of electric power by residential consumers in only five years. Air conditioning and electric home heating have increased rapidly, displacing gas and fuel oil. However, industries have used almost one-half of the electric energy sold in recent years, while residential use has taken considerably less than one-third; commercial establishments have used only about one-fifth.[38] Many industrial plants have self-contained generating equipment, which produced almost one-fifth of the electric power used by industry in 1960.[39] However, a strong trend toward greater dependence on purchased power was clearly evident. The large generating plants produce electric power most efficiently.

Having thus appraised all the major energy sources, both primary and secondary, it is appropriate that we also examine briefly the further requisite to their functional utility—delivery where and when they are needed. Conveyance from points of origin to areas of consumption enhances the usefulness of fuels and energy, and thereby, in a very practical sense, conserves them. Each of the energy industries—gas, oil, coal, and electric —has, by the very nature of its commodity, peculiar problems of transport or storage, or both, that affect its present and potential market.

Gas goes to market through a veritable spider web of pipelines, aggregating at the end of 1961, 659,000 miles of "main" (56,730 miles of field and gathering mains to collect the gas; 191,840 miles of transmission facilities; 410,390 miles of distribution mains to consumers).[40] Transportation and distribution costs represent almost three-fourths of the average value of natural gas where it is consumed.[41] Most facets of the gas industry are closely controlled and regulated by the Federal Power Commission in the interest of "public convenience and necessity" as

Does efficient delivery conserve anything?

prescribed by the Natural Gas Act of 1938 and subsequent federal law. Among other responsibilities, the Commission licenses interstate transmission lines and determines "just and reasonable prices."

A most perplexing problem in the natural-gas industry arises from two simple facts: pipe lines have a fixed capacity and operate most efficiently at full capacity; consumer requirements vary so much seasonally that peak consumption (usually in January) may be twice that of a slack month (July, August, or September). Gas companies have attempted to "fill the summer valley" by selling to industries on an interruptible basis at rates sufficiently attractive to warrant the maintenance of gas-burning equipment for use only in summer. Peak winter demands have in the past been met with surplus summer pumpage stored near the market, and by supplementing natural gas supplies with manufactured gas. Gas manufacture, from coal and oil, has, however, declined to minor importance; terminal storage of gas has increased rapidly, accelerated by the recent advent of underground storage. This innovation is of special interest to conservators.

Underground storage of natural gas in the United States began in the Zoar field near Buffalo, New York in 1916 [42] and has been developed in many places and on a large scale since about 1940. By the end of 1961 there were 229 storage pools in twenty-one states, with an estimated ultimate capacity of more than 3.1 billion cubic feet.[43] Almost three-fourths of the storage was in California, Michigan, Ohio, Oklahoma, Pennsylvania, and West Virginia. Most of the storage capacity is in depleted gas and oil fields, but where such are not available near markets, aquifers and other geologic structures are coming into use. Abandoned mines may have possibilities. Underground reservoirs afford immense storage capacity at a unit cost that is minute by comparison with conventional tanks and pipes aboveground. Balancing supply and demand wherever possible reduces the cost of gas and also relieves the necessity for interruptible contracts that often replace coal for generating electricity. Unfortunately, underground storage entails great physical waste; much of the gas injected cannot be recovered.

The oil industry also uses pipe lines, some 200,000 miles of them; but they are by no means the sole transport medium for oil as they are for gas. Quite the contrary, oil transportation is both various and flexible, employing all conventional methods as shown in Table 3. More than three-fourths of the crude oil moves by pipe

Table 3

Per Cent of Total Petroleum Transported in the United States by Method of Transportation

	Pipe Lines	Water Carriers	Trucks	Railroads
Crude oil	76.25	17.00	6.39	0.36
Refined Petroleum Products	21.19	36.77	37.10	4.94
Crude and Refined	43.22	28.86	24.82	3.10

Source: *Petroleum Facts and Figures*, American Petroleum Institute (New York, 1961).

line, but only about one-fifth of the refined products moves this way. It should be remembered in this connection that there are essentially two pipe-line systems for oil; one that delivers crude oil to refineries and another for transmission of refinery products. Refineries are transport terminals, as it were.

Although the pipeline is the cheapest method of *overland* shipment, water transport by tank barge or seagoing tanker is much cheaper still. Tank trucks and trailers have the unique advantage of enabling direct delivery to the greatest number of consumers. Water-borne oil moves mainly from west Gulf ports to refineries and storage areas at ports on the Atlantic Coast and the Pacific Coast.

Oil pipe lines operate as common carriers, and about three-fourths of their total mileage comes under the jurisdiction of the Interstate Commerce Commission. A single pipe line may convey a variety of products in successive "slugs," without significant mixing. Gasoline may be followed by kerosene or distillate fuel oil, for instance. This versatility, together with the other kinds of carriers available, makes possible the equation of supply with demand. Furthermore, consumption of gasoline, the principal petroleum product, is only about one-fourth greater in the peak month (August) than in the lowest month (February) —a seasonal disparity nicely offset by requirements for heating oil.

One may conclude that our efficient, independent petroleum industry has so effectively resolved its transportation problems that another fuel industry, less adaptable or less inventive, might fail in open competition. Coal has been such a victim.

Gas and oil might have made inroads on the heating market once filled by coal for reasons of convenience alone, but their lesser bulk and more economical transportation are the advantages that have more decisively usurped the market, with disastrous consequences to the coal industry. We need not recount the events and degrees by which the once flourishing industry has been stifled. Its plight had become so grave that in 1960 the Congress established an Office of Coal Research charged with investigating the situation and seeking possible means of relief and recovery.

Meanwhile the coal and related industries have launched an aggressive campaign that may regain status for the black fuel. This has thus far taken two main avenues of approach, both bent on negating the transport handicaps that have frustrated other coal modernizations. One is the coal pipe line; the other, long-distance transmission of coal-generated electricity by "extra-high" voltage lines. Each has revolutionary possibilities and warrants our examination. Both pursuits appear justified by the tabulation in Table 4.

Table 4

Comparative Cost of Transporting Fuels and Electricity

	Cents per 1 million Btu per 100 miles
Electricity (conventional voltage)	.23- .88*
Coal by railroad	3.0 -7.6
Coal by pipeline, claimed in due course	1.0 -2.0
Oil pipeline	-1.0
Natural gas at high load factor	1.5 -2.0
Crude oil by tanker	.2 - .7

* Calculated at 3,415 Btu per kwhr.
Source: Senate Committee on Interior and Insular Affairs, *An Assessment of Available Information on Energy in the United States*, The National Fuels and Energy Group, Senate Document No. 159, 87th Cong., 2d sess., 1962, p. 168.

A pipe line carrying pulverized coal in a water slurry has been in operation between Cadiz and Cleveland, Ohio (108 miles) since 1957. The line has a diameter of only 10 inches, but it can move 1.5 million tons of coal a year, at a cost of about 1 cent per ton-mile. In the future, with larger lines, costs as low as three-tenths of a cent per ton-mile may be possible.[44] The economic advantages of coal pipe lines are so considerable that extensive construction may be anticipated, including such major trunk lines that will connect Appalachian coal mines with the Eastern seaboard and the coal fields of Utah with the port cities of California. The projects might be greatly facilitated by timely state legislation granting right of eminent domain to coal pipe lines, which has long since been done by some for facilities handling other commodities. Some states have shown reluctance. Natural-gas pipe lines have right of eminent domain by an act of Congress, and similar authority may be forthcoming in aid of coal.

Of the total bituminous coal mined in 1960, 73.1 per cent went to market by rail, 12.7 per cent by motor vehicle, and 11.3 per cent by water. (At the mines, 2.9 per cent was used.)[45] Water transport has gained because large thermal-electric stations must be adjacent to a water supply sufficient for cooling and boiler feed. Many suitable water sources are also navigable.

As coal pipe-lining progresses, it will divert from the railroads a major item of freight and revenue; as another innovation, extra-high voltage transmission, comes into practice electrification of railroads may also become general. Then coal, in disguised form, will once again haul the freight! The "integral train," miles in length and running at passenger-train speed between mines and distant markets, may only temporarily forestall the loss of coal traffic by the railroads. Eventually, "coal by wire" will probably relieve the solid fuel of its ordinary transportation handicap and shock the entire energy industry. The idea is akin to that which is said to have started moonshining: corn in a jug has greater market radius than corn in a bushel. Coal concentrated into kilowatts can go farther to market by high-voltage wire than when sold by the ton raw. In general, the higher the voltage at which electricity is put on a line the greater the amount of power that can be transmitted and the longer the distance it can be sent.

At less than 60,000 volts (60 kilovolts or kv) electric current is said to be low voltage; at 60 to 230 kv, high voltage; greater than 230 kv, extra-high voltage (EHV). It is this EHV that has propensities for rejuvenating the coal industry.

Although the United States has more than 350,000 miles of circuits of 22 kv or greater, there were only about 4,000 miles with voltage greater than 220 kv in 1962.[46] The average distance between terminals is only about 50 miles,[47] and most of our electricity goes less than 200 miles from the generators. Much coal is hauled to generating stations from points more distant than can be served by the current it generates, a rather obvious demonstration of inefficiency. The waste of effort in such crude utilization of coal might be largely eliminated by employing EHV transmission—installing generators at the coal mines instead of locating them amidst electric service areas, as has been customary.

A 500-kilovolt line can move a given quantity of power more than twice as far as can a 345-kilovolt line and five or more times as far as can a 230-kilovolt line. A 150-mile 230-kilovolt line and a 500-mile 345-kilovolt line have about the same transmission capacity. Thus for a given capacity, increasing the voltage increases the distance more than proportionately, by far. For a given distance, increasing the voltage increases the capacity also more than proportionately.[48]

Even greater efficiency could be achieved by transmitting electricity as direct, rather than alternating, current.

The National Power Survey commenced by the Federal Power Commission in 1962 encouraged experiment and research with voltages as high as 750,000. A 345,000-volt circuit became operational in the Bonneville hydropower system in 1954. A pioneer commercial project based on coal was under construction in 1962 for transmitting electricity generated at a mine mouth near Elkins, West Virginia by 500-kilovolt lines to Richmond, Virginia and Washington, D.C. (350 miles).[49]

It should be remembered that EHV and/or d.c. transmission affects, not coal alone, but all sources of electric energy. It renders economically feasible hydropower projects on sites otherwise useless, and it reduces the need or opportunity for installing nuclear-power facilities in areas remote from conventional energy sources.

Larger generators, higher voltages, bigger pipes, and other elaborations reduce the cost of energy, improve its usefulness, and increase its consumption. Such innovations help keep our industry vigorous and growing. However, the use of energy depends upon the employment of metals, and the metals in turn depend upon energy for refinement and fabrication. Metal is, in effect, the tool with which energy works; one would be of little value without the other. It is, therefore, essential that we look also to the metals and other nonfuel minerals, without which the fuels might languish in the ground. We can discuss only a few major ones and merely mention several others in this and the next chapter.

A perusal of Table 5 [50] convinces one that Americans use prodigious quantities of all important minerals—metallic, nonmetallic, and others, as well as fuels—and should suggest that the maintenance of supplies equal to requirements will, for some materials, wax more difficult as consumption continues and demands increase. The need for others hinges on the availability of a half-dozen metals, and on those six we shall now focus our attention.

Table 5

Estimated per Capita Consumption of Mineral Materials in the United States, 1960*

Energy (in terms of bituminous coal)	9.6 tons
(oil equivalent—1,675 gallons)	
Major metals:	
Steel	794.0 lbs.
(Estimated steel in use—8.4 tons per person)	
Copper	15.1 lbs.
Lead	11.4 lbs.
Zinc	9.8 lbs.
Aluminum	22.5 lbs.
Chromium	7.4 lbs.
Manganese	5.8 lbs.
Nickel	1.2 lbs.
Tin	1.1 lbs.
Nonmetallic minerals:	
Stone, sand, and gravel	14,771 lbs.
Cement	652 lbs.
Clays	541 lbs.
Gypsum	261 lbs.
Common salt	291 lbs.
Phosphate rock	152 lbs.
Lime (other than for cement)	144 lbs.
Sulphur	79 lbs.
Potassium salts	26 lbs.

Among metals consumed in smaller amounts are antimony, magnesium, molybdenum, cadmium, cobalt, tungsten, beryllium, vanadium, niobium, and bismuth.

* Based on estimates of total consumption by the United States Bureau of Mines and United States population figures of the United States Bureau of the Census.

Source: Adapted from Hubert E. Risser, "Illinois-Missouri Mineral Resource Complex—A Base for Industrial Development," *Circular 337*, Illinois State Geological Survey (Urbana, Ill., 1962), p. 14.

Iron, (Fe), the kingpin of metals, stands unchallenged as the foundation of modern industry, and, as the principal component of steel, subordinates other metals alloyed with it for special quality or durability. Steel, a material by which men gauge the physical strength of nations, though preponderantly of iron, incorporates in its various formulations or employs as protectors against corrosion more than a score of metals that are not iron. A dozen of the principals and their special functions can be seen in Table 6. The value of some (manganese, for instance)

Table 6

Principal Metals Used by the Steel Industry

Metal	*Function*	*Products and Uses*
Aluminum	Removes gases and impurities; aids surface hardness.	Seldom more than a trace remains, except in nitrided steel.
Chromium	Small amounts improve hardening qualities; more than 10 per cent prevents rust.	Tools; machinery parts; stainless and heat- and acid-resisting steels.
Cobalt	Holds cutting edge at high temperatures. Improves electrical qualities.	High-speed cutting tools; permanent magnet steel.
Copper	Retards rust.	Roofing and siding sheets; plates.
Lead	When mixed with tin, forms a rust-resisting coating for steel. Small amounts alloyed with steel improve machinability.	Sheet steel for roofing; auto gasoline tanks, etc.; machinery parts.
Manganese	Small amounts remove gases from steel; 1 to 2 per cent increases strength and toughness; 12 per cent imparts great toughness and resistance to abrasion.	Small amounts present in all steels; 1 to 2 per cent used in rails; 12 per cent or more for frogs and switches and dredge bucket teeth.
Molybdenum	Increases strength, ductility, and resistance to shock.	Tools; machinery parts; tubing for airplane fuselage.
Nickel	Increases toughness, stiffness, strength, and ductility. In large amounts resists heat and acids.	Tools; machinery parts; stainless steels; heat- and acid-resisting steels.
Tin	Forms corrosion-resisting coating on steel.	Sanitary cans; kitchenware.
Tungsten	Retains hardness and toughness at high temperature.	High-speed cutting tools; magnets.
Vanadium	Increases strength, ductility, and resiliency.	Tools; springs; machinery parts.
Zinc	Forms corrosion-resisting coating on steel.	Galvanized roofing and siding sheets; wire fence; pails, etc.

Source: Adapted from *Steel Facts*, American Iron and Steel Institute, February 1947.

derives mainly from their use in, or with, steel; others, such as aluminum and copper, rank as major metals independently, their use in steel a minor part of total service and utilization.

The American steel industry in which we take justifiable pride, and to which we owe, in large degree, both our productivity in peace and our invincibility in war, began its main growth toward world leadership only about three-quarters of a century ago, after the discovery of rich iron-ore deposits about the head of Lake Superior.

During the Gay Nineties, a bustling iron-mining industry developed in northeastern Minnesota, destined to be our chief supplier of iron ore from that era onward.[51] In 1897 the United States assumed world leadership in the production of pig iron.[52] The famed Mesabi Range became the greatest source of iron in the world; its fund of rich, red ore (hematite) is one of the largest ever found and the one most exploited to date. These Pre-Cambrian deposits lie horizontally disposed and so near the surface that their extraction has been primarily by open-pit methods, leaving gigantic holes in the earth. The Mesabi has consistently yielded a lion's share of Minnesota's iron output, and Minnesota has been the pre-eminent producer.

Iron— kingpin of industrial might

Iron minerals are of several kinds—hematite, magnetite, turgite, geothite, limonite (brown ore), xanthosiderite, siderite, and fayalite. Known deposits of important ones in the United States are distributed about as shown in Fig. 15.10. Most valuable, both for their high grade (metallic iron content) and their abundance,

Fig. 15.10 *Iron ore has extensive distribution, but the bulk of production has been from the "Iron Range" of Minnesota. Several iron deposits have been found in Alaska. (After U.S.G.S. maps.)*

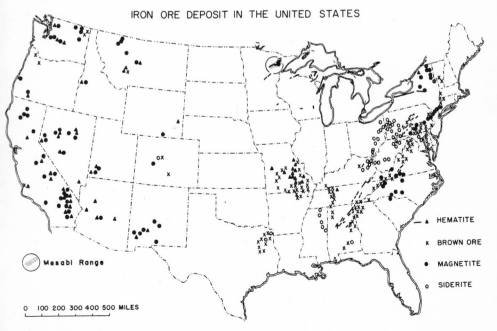

IRON ORE DEPOSIT IN THE UNITED STATES

Mesabi Range

▲ HEMATITE

x BROWN ORE

● MAGNETITE

o SIDERITE

0 100 200 300 400 500 MILES

are the hematites and magnetites; of relatively minor importance are the limonites, siderites, and others. Each kind has its characteristic chemical composition, but with several variants separable into subclasses. By-product iron ore is obtained when titanium is extracted from ilmenite and when pyrites and pyrrhotite are roasted to make sulfuric acid—convenient conservation.

Of about 155 million long tons of crude iron ore mined in the United States in 1960, almost 98 million were hematite, 51 million magnetite, and the remainder brown ore.[53] The ore came from 246 mines, of which 107 that were in Minnesota accounted for almost 110 million long tons. Other important producing states in descending order of rank were Michigan, New York, Alabama, Utah, New Jersey, Wisconsin, Nevada, and Missouri. Thirteen additional states had at least one operational iron mine each. Almost seven-eighths of the total crude ore produced came from open-pit mines.

Almost all iron ore mined becomes utilized in steel after first being smelted into pig iron. The processes utilize great quantities of material other than iron ore, as shown in the diagram of furnace charges below (Fig. 15.11). Since raw iron ore comprises only about one-half the bulk charged into a blast furnace and since most pig iron goes directly to a steel furnace, the location of steel plants (smelters integrated with them) is affected less by the distance from sources of iron ore than by the combined availability of other raw materials *and* accessibility to markets for the heavy products. Indeed, plant location involves the resolution of many economic and geographic factors, but transportation is the only one with which we shall concern ourselves.

The Great Lakes— highway for iron
By geologic providence in placing iron near the upper extremity of the Great Lakes and coals adjacent to other parts of the gigantic basin, the American steel industry became deliberately oriented on the Lakes and developed an "inland empire" so disposed about them as to avail itself the advantages of water transport they afford. The arrangement was duly systematized as the industry matured; iron ore became long-distance freight hauled to smelters less distant from sources of coking coal. The singular fact that most iron moves to coal and little coal moves to iron has special implications for the conservation of iron and the estimation of reserves, because the quality (degree of purity) of an ore generally determines the distance it may be transported profitably. (The fortuitous juxtaposition of coal and iron in the Birmingham, Alabama steel complex renders the rule inapplicable, but it is nowise abrogated.)

Largely by benefit of the Great Lakes and water transporta-

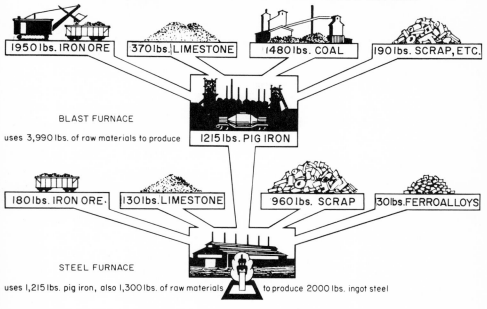

A TOTAL OF 5,290 POUNDS OF RAW MATERIALS USED TO MAKE ONE TON OF INGOT STEEL

| 1950 lbs. IRON ORE | 370 lbs. LIMESTONE | 1480 lbs. COAL | 190 lbs. SCRAP, ETC. |

BLAST FURNACE
uses 3,990 lbs. of raw materials to produce | 1215 lbs. PIG IRON |

| 180 lbs. IRON ORE· | 130 lbs. LIMESTONE | 960 lbs. SCRAP | 30 lbs. FERROALLOYS |

STEEL FURNACE
uses 1,215 lbs. pig iron, also 1,300 lbs. of raw materials to produce 2000 lbs. ingot steel

Fig. 15.11 *Furnace charges for a ton of steel. Note the relative volumes of primary and secondary metal. (From Steel Facts, courtesy American Iron and Steel Institute.)*

tion, iron ore mined in Minnesota becomes pig iron and steel in Pennsylvania, Ohio, Indiana, and Illinois, the four leading producers, ranked in the order named. Almost all ore shipments go by water, down from Lake Superior to terminals serving steel mills on or near the other Lakes. Representative freight charges on ore moved by the rail-water-rail system from the Mesabi to Pittsburgh in a recent year totaled $6.70 per long ton, of which $4.70 went for the rail hauls (from Mesabi to Duluth and from Lake Erie to Pittsburgh) and for transferring the ore from one conveyance to another. The long haul by lake carrier from Duluth to the docks on Lake Erie was at a rate of only $2.00 per long ton. (How much per ton-mile?) Freight rates for shipping ore by rail all the way from Mesabi mines to Pittsburgh were quoted at $10.23 per long ton.[54] When these rates prevailed the average value of Minnesota hematite at the mines was $7.70 per long ton for "direct-shipping ore" (meaning untreated), and $8.11 for iron-ore concentrates. Iron content of the natural ore was more than 54 per cent;[55] yet a long ton of it at the mine was worth only a dollar more than the cost of shipping it to Pittsburgh, where its price became $14.40. A low-grade ore could not pay its way that far and compete with better foreign ones imported via the St. Lawrence Seaway in oceangoing vessels!

Minnesota iron mining has prospered with the aid of the Great Lakes; but the Lakes also facilitate the importation of foreign ores in competition with the domestic iron-mining industry. The St. Lawrence Seaway improves the prospects for our inland steel manufacture while, incidentally, imposing new standards of quality and efficiency on domestic iron-ore production. In 1960 the United States imported about 33.5 million long tons of iron ore, almost one-third coming from eastern Canada. This was five times the average annual volume of imports during the period 1951-1955.[56] As importation increases it tends to shrink domestic reserves of ore by relegating to the "potential" class those of lower grade than the imports. It also stimulates the application of techniques and practices whereby the degraded domestic materials regain, and may retain, commercial quality. Beneficiation and other conservation measures that help accomplish this will be considered in Chapter 16.

Signs of iron-ore depletion

One may properly conclude from the foregoing that any estimation of iron-ore reserves that can be mined must be subjective, allowing for several variables and possibilities. Change in the world iron market, opening or closure of a mine overseas, change in volume of imports—any of these, and others, can alter the economic classification of iron-bearing material in the United States. Reduction or elimination of the coke requirement in iron smelting, and the construction of new steel plants near the known iron deposits would greatly increase the reserves of exploitable ore. To what degree we shall ultimately extract iron from material containing less and less metal one cannot even guess. How long the present rate of production can be sustained might only be conjectured. Increasing procurement from foreign sources would seem to indicate that we have skimmed the cream off the reserves at home and that depletion will become progressively more apparent. Exhaustion will never be complete, because extraction will cease when it becomes uneconomical; in which year or which decade no one can predict with certainty. Iron will be scarce, probably within the reader's lifetime. Total iron (refined metal) content of reserves now workable exceeds 3 billion tons, obtainable from direct-shipping ore and concentrates (mainly of magnetic taconite), whereas the annual extraction is about 54 million tons.[57] Potential ores with iron content ranging from 22 per cent to 50 per cent contain more than 20 billion tons of metal (about three-fourths of it in taconite). The magnitude of leaner iron-bearing materials has not been investigated, nor can we now envision their possible future use. Our outlook for iron has been summarized most aptly as follows:

Production cannot be maintained through the rest of the century at the present level without the discovery of new reserves or the creation of reserves out of presently potential ore beyond what has already been accomplished. Self-sufficiency in iron ore would require the addition of new reserves in the next 40 years more than equal in quantity to present reserves.[58]

Obviously, our iron resources should be conserved by all means practicable.

Besides iron, only five other metals may be regarded as "major," based not only on tonnage but also on the peculiarity of their functional uses. They are aluminum, copper, lead, manganese, and zinc,[59] with which we shall deal only summarily. Table 7 saves both space and reading time, and although it might provoke considerable discussion, we shall limit ourselves to a few elucidative remarks.

Obviously, adequate supply of all these major metals is essential to our industry and economy; else their continuous availability would concern us less than it does. They are vital to our national defense, and have been stockpiled to avert shortage in event of a shooting war. Search for them has been federally supported with a cost-sharing program (up to 50 per cent), administered by the Office of Minerals Exploration, Bureau of Mines.

Most important nonferrous metal both in quantity and value is copper, surpassed only by iron. The venerable, soft, red metal has fostered human progress since ancient times, and especially after the discovery of bronze, a hard material made by alloying nine parts of copper with one part of tin. Its excellent conductivity, resistance to corrosion, ductility, malleability, and strength made it the modern medium for electrification. The electrical industry uses about one-half of the copper produced;[60] only aluminum can be substituted in any applications that take large quantities of metal. To maintain domestic production, from ores containing less than 1 per cent metal, we dig more for copper than for any other mineral, excepting sand and gravel and stone. Even greater than the vast tonnage moved in iron mining is the earth material handled to win copper. That the winnings usually contain some gold and silver seems a nicety of nature's providence in deference to human perseverance.

Copper

Lead, the soft, heavy metal with which men have killed each other since the invention of firearms, now protects men against radiation as no other material can. By its density it prevents penetration by gamma rays; and, unlike other shielding materials, lead remains uncontaminated even under continuous use.[61] In many applications it serves as protector of other, less durable,

Lead

Table 7

Major Nonferrous Metals—United States

Metal	Uses	Annual Primary Production (short tons)	From Foreign Sources	Rank of States in Domestic Ore Production	Domestic Reserves of the Metal
Copper	Electrical, brass, bronze, and other alloys	1.5 million	1/4	Arizona 50%, Utah 20%, Montana 9%, Nevada, New Mexico, Michigan, Tennessee, and 22 others	32.5 million short tons
Lead	Storage batteries, tetraethyl lead, cable covering, paint pigments, construction, ammunition, solder, bearing metals, type metals, radiation shield	382,000	2/5	Missouri 45%, Idaho, Utah, Colorado, and more than 16 others	5 million tons (shortage impending)
Zinc	Galvanizing iron and steel products, chemicals, die castings, brass, pigments, porcelain enamels	800,000	4/7	Tennessee, Idaho, New York, Colorado, Utah, and 19 others	25 million tons Potential: 20 million additional
Aluminum	Military, building materials, transportation, communications, machinery and appliances, containers, packaging, chemicals, high voltage transmission, die castings (extremely versatile)	2 million	4/5	Arkansas 97%, Alabama, Georgia	13 million short tons Potential: 25 million short tons additional
Manganese Ore	"Scavenger" of sulfur and oxygen in steel making (flux), chemicals, dry-cell batteries, alloys and metals	2 million (35% Mn content, or better)	99/100	Nevada 54%, Montana, Arizona, Tennessee, and 10 others	900,000 tons Potential: 77 million tons additional

Source: Assembled from: *Statistics*, Bureau of Mines: "Mineral Facts and Problems," *Bulletin 556*, Bureau of Mines (Washington, D.C., 1962): Bruce C. Netschert and Hans H. Landsberg, *The Future Supply of the Major Metals (A Reconnaissance Survey)*, Resources for the Future, Inc. (Washington, D.C., 1961): "Metals and Minerals (Except Fuels)," *1960 Minerals Yearbook*, I, Bureau of Mines (Washington, D.C., 1961).

materials. In liquid form as tetraethyl lead 1.5 to 3.0 cc per gallon of gasoline improves the performance and efficiency of automobile engines. Although the supply of lead became excessive under the stimulus of bounty and requisition for the atomic-energy industry, it will probably be the first of the base metals to become scarce. Galena crystals may be curios a few generations hence.

Zinc is commonly associated with lead in nature; with either or both may also be copper, silver, and gold. Once extracted

Zinc

from the magma and separated from each other, lead and zinc remain largely distinctive in use. Each serves as protector or container, but in ways the other cannot entirely simulate, as in dry-cell and storage-battery cases, for instance. Biggest uses of zinc are in die casting and galvanizing; biggest use for lead is in storage batteries. Each is useful as pigment in paints. In its second greatest use zinc is alloyed with copper to make brass, a hard material with multifarious applications. No shortage of zinc can be foreseen; but temporary oversupply should not be taken to indicate inexhaustibility.

Aluminum has but recently attained major rank among the commercial metals and the rapid increase in use that brought it into prominence still continues. Being a versatile newcomer, much of its growth has come by replacing the older metals in their accustomed uses. Its light weight, heat reflectivity, corrosion resistance, electrical and thermal conductivity (greater per weight than in copper), strength when alloyed with other metals, excellent workability, and lower cost have given it competitive advantage in many applications. Almost all aluminum comes from the ore, bauxite, whence alumina is extracted by selective leaching and precipitation of Al_2O_3 as a gray powder. The alumina is then electrolytically reduced to metal, a process that consumes some 17,000 kilowatthours of electricity to produce one ton of virgin aluminum from almost twice that weight of the powder.[62] A short ton of the metal represents about 4 long dry tons of bauxite.[63] Current commercial standards for bauxite are: no less than 32 per cent recoverable alumina content; no more than 15 per cent reactive silica content. Any relaxation of quality standards made permissible by technologic innovation or other means would immediately enlarge ore reserves. Aluminum comprises about 8 per cent of the earth's crust, but anyone who would wager on a cut-off point at which its use will stop ought to pick a number nearer 32 than 8, and then consult a fortune teller!

Manganese would not qualify as a major metal on the basis of its use in refined form; but manganese metal, ore, or concentrate is indispensable in the manufacture of steel, hence its importance. A mere 13 or 14 pounds of manganese (mostly ferro-manganese) suffice for each ton of finished steel; yet that handful of material must be in the furnace charge, and it has no substitute. Three grades of manganese ore—metallurgical, battery, and chemical—are recognized commercially and stockpiled for strategic reasons. The metallurgical grade, suitable for steel flux, must merely contain 35 per cent or more manganese; the other grades have more exacting specifications. The paucity of domestic man-

Aluminum

Bauxite

Manganese

ganese ore is considerably relieved by vast deposits of manganiferous iron ore and other, low-grade manganiferous materials. Large quantities of manganiferous iron ore (5 per cent or more manganese) are mined in Minnesota and Michigan. The smelter product from such ore is manganiferous pig iron, which saves on manganese additives in the steel process. Synthetic manganese ore remains too expensive for metallurgical use. In high-manganese steels the manganese is alloyed with iron and remains a component of the product; otherwise most of it is wasted in the furnace slag.

Ferroalloys

Manganese is only one of several elements which, when added to iron or steel, perform special functions or impart certain qualities; but no other equals manganese as an agent that can work several improvements simultaneously. It is *the* ferroalloy most nearly self-sufficient. Some others in common use are listed with it below, grouped according to their singular or several transmutative attributes. It should be noted that a number of them have similar capabilities and may be used more or less interchangeably; thus the supply of one may be supplemented by another. The effectiveness of one may depend upon the presence of another, or several others. They may be employed in multiple combinations and various proportions to produce steel with many different specifications.

(Much of the following was introduced by a previous listing but in quite another context.)

Some ferroalloys and their functions as cited by the Bureau of Mines, *Bulletin 556,* 1956, are:

> *Deoxidizers:* Aluminum, calcium, manganese, silicon, titanium, zirconium.
> *Agents to improve hardenability:* Boron, chromium, manganese, molybdenum, nickel, silicon, tungsten, and vanadium.
> *Agents to improve resistance to corrosion:* Chromium, columbium, nickel, phosphorus, silicon, titanium.
> *Agents to provide special magnetic and electrical properties:* Cobalt, nickel, phosphorus, and silicon.
> *Desulfurizers and sulfur neutralizers:* Manganese, titanium, zirconium.
> *Agents much used to provide properties desired in alloys for use at high temperatures:* Chromium, cobalt, columbium, molybdenum, nickel, titanium, tungsten, and vanadium.

Many of the ferroalloys are classed as strategic or critical materials because domestic supplies are inadequate or lacking, and procurement must be from distant sources in other countries. They become, in effect, articles of commerce rather than fund resources amenable to conservation by Americans. They raise perplexing questions that conservators should ponder. How, for instance, may one conserve that which he does not possess? Does one conserve a material by bidding for it successfully in the world market? Can we employ or conserve any exhaustible resource without taking into account world reserves as well as our own? Does American conservation transcend foreign policy and international trade or must it be subservient to them? The first two questions are naively academic and need not be debated here; the latter two have practical implications of which the American conservator should be cognizant.

Importation of a mineral may be indicative of its domestic deficiency, either in quantity or quality, but it is often hastily misinterpreted. If not unduly opposed by regulation, imported raw materials enter the country when those available from domestic sources would be more expensive to produce and less profitable to manufacture. Unless they are admitted, the cost of finished products goes higher and they become less competitive; instead of importing the raw materials, we then tend to import the finished products. If we were to protect our mining interests with exclusive tariffs, we should have to protect our manufacturers the same way. The full cycle would bring commercial failure because our manufactures would be priced off the world market.

Importation of any raw mineral stops whenever a domestic supply of equal quality at comparable price becomes sufficiently available; potential domestic reserves become exploitable when foreign sources of better quality have been depleted. During any such transition affecting an American resource, the industry involved must be kept solvent and vigorous; else it would be incapable of exploiting the potential reserves in the United States when they attain commercial grade. The importation of any mineral should be neither restrained nor promoted to conserve a domestic reserve without judicious evaluation of all attendant circumstances. Conservation would be a sour prelude to bankruptcy!

This chapter might be concluded with a long list of metals and other minerals not yet mentioned. However, none of them would have much worth if we were divested of those already discussed. A variety of the contemporary subordinates will be encountered in the next chapter.

16

Mineral Conservation

being consumed by our use, minerals are conservable only as diligent search, thorough extraction, and efficient employment increase the available supplies and prolong their usefulness

Objectives are simple; methods more involved

Mineral conservation is quite simply a matter of continuous exploration, complete extraction, substitution, maximum use, and minimum waste insofar as economic circumstances permit or national security demands. Private interests in open competition cannot apply a conservation measure that deprives them of profit; neither can the public, through mandate, compel the application of such a measure unless the government bears the cost. Excessive conservation costs imposed on private enterprise can defeat their own purposes by retarding production or suspending operation entirely. Conservation of minerals must be practical to a degree even greater than conservation of renewable resources, because minerals are strictly material, with values purely intrinsic. They have no aesthetic or subjective values in the ordinary sense. Mining attracts men and money because it pays; but, if restrictions be imposed whereby the pay be lost, the men and money must seek other employment, leaving the mineral in the ground. Since an unmined mineral is useless, its abandonment in the earth represents outright waste—the antithesis of conservation. Preservation is not the object of mineral conservation. Digging, efficiently, as fast as it pays, is more nearly the correct idea. Protection can hasten the obsolescence of a material by curtailing supply and stimulating substitution, but supply

428

and demand operating without restraint may be inducement enough to replace scarce materials. Nothing could be much more embarrassing to future conservators than to discover a century or two hence that materials lying obsolete and worthless in the ground might once have been exploited profitably. That which is good common sense is usually also good conservation.

There are many means of increasing the over-all usefulness of our expendable resources and many methods whereby we may lengthen their service. Some of these conservation methods can be applied by everyone, since everyone is a user of minerals. Some methods can be applied only by citizens and corporations who produce or process mineral materials. Other important means depend upon public policy and practice. There are many striking parallels between the conservation of expendables and the conservation of permanent resources, and a considerable interdependence as well. We cannot attempt any detailed exposition of procedures, but we shall introduce the general concepts under which they operate. It will be noted that the application of technology is, perhaps, the most important factor.[1]

The greatest physical waste of mineral resources results from our inability to extract more than a portion of the stores found in the earth. Methods and economics have permitted only partial recovery of many. Many an oil field has been "exhausted" for all practical purposes with 75 per cent of its original oil content still in the ground.[2] Such loss is physical, not economic; but, if abandonment *now* curtails recovery *later,* when improved techniques and higher prices would make it profitable, we have shortened the life of nonrenewable wealth. We have, in effect, created future waste by present inefficiency.

More complete recovery of known stores

A vast quantity of solid minerals, such as coal and ores, lie buried deep in abandoned mines where great walls and pillars were left in place to support the roof and where seams or veins were too thin to be taken out profitably. Both solid and liquid wealth has been wasted in the earth because abundance and quality available elsewhere invoked the law of diminishing returns and forbade more thorough extraction.

Perhaps the most colossal physical waste of a mineral at its source has been that of natural gas released from oil fields. Until recently most of this ideal fuel was simply blown into the air or "flared" to get rid of it. *Flaring* is the practice of venting gas through an open, upright pipe several feet tall, and burning it as it comes out at the top. Flaring was and is a perfectly logical safety measure. Unless the gas can be used or marketed profitably it is simply a hazard.

Now natural gas has come into its own as the aristocrat among fuels. It is piped increasing distances for use in industries and homes. It is estimated that by 1975 about half the homes in the nation will be heated by natural gas.[3] Thus far, consumption has been largely of dry gas, produced independently of oil, but the "wet" varieties (oil-field gas) can greatly increase and prolong the available future supply.[4]

A double resource tragedy attaches to our wasteful disposal of natural gas at wellheads. The very gas we have burned or blown away might have been used to push more oil out of the reservoir by what is known as *secondary recovery,* illustrated in Figs. 16.1 and 16.2. A pity it is that we took so long to accept a hint demonstrated by nature since the beginning of oil production. Here, as in hundreds of other ways, one resource helps to conserve another. The conservator who despairs can regain confidence through nature study.

We are becoming more and more proficient at recovering the minerals we discover, largely by improving our techniques, but

Fig. 16.1 *Natural pressures that have helped concentrate oil in the ground also help drive it out. (From American Petroleum Institute.)*

TYPES OF ENERGY DRIVES APPEARING IN OIL FIELDS

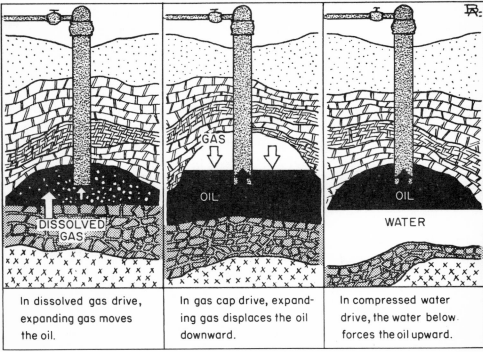

| In dissolved gas drive, expanding gas moves the oil. | In gas cap drive, expanding gas displaces the oil downward. | In compressed water drive, the water below forces the oil upward. |

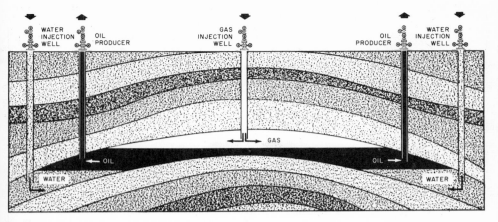

Fig. 16.2 *Gas and water are pumped into the oil-bearing formation, forcing oil toward the well. Usually the gas method is used first; later, water drive is employed. (From American Petroleum Institute.)*

also by virtue of stronger markets. As prices go up we can afford to take more pains. Flaring of gas continues in some places because arrangements for its economical use have not been possible. Increasing quantities are, however, piped to market or forced back into the reservoir to pressurize the oil and prolong economical production.

More effective than gas in the recovery of petroleum is water—another oil propellant in the natural arrangement. Water flooding, or water drive, has given an extraction rate of 85 per cent.[5] We know the techniques for good oil recovery, but their application depends upon cooperation. To be successful, pressurizing or flooding of an oil reservoir must be done on a unit basis, with all operators participating. Such "unitation" or grouping of wells has been difficult to achieve, but the Interstate Oil Compact Commission established in 1931 has achieved some coordination of necessary legislation in thirty-three states participating. Many incidental economies are implicit in such an arrangement.

Until about 1930 oil-field development was a mad scramble by competing surface proprietors to punch an oil pool full of holes. Under the archaic "rule of capture," each operator endeavored to offset with a well of his own every hole drilled by any adjacent property owner. The field became a wilderness of derricks, especially dense along property lines. Whoever could pump faster than his neighbors got the largest share of the oil. The system was grossly inefficient and wasteful.

Then came corrective measures such as wider spacing of wells, prescribed by both state and federal legislation, and prorating of output from the wells (allowable production). Pumping became slower, ultimate recovery greater, and production adjust-

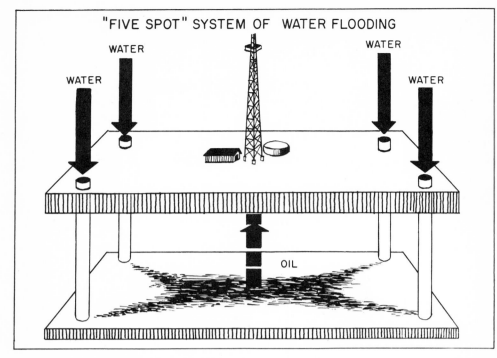

Fig. 16.3 *Oil well at the center of a square which has a water injection well on each corner. (From American Petroleum Institute.)*

able to market demand. An oil pool became acknowledged as the natural unit that it is—better extracted cooperatively than through a pumping contest among jealous producers. Conservation of oil in the ground began. By 1957 seventeen states had compulsory "pooling" laws, requiring owners of small tracts to integrate their holdings into workable drilling units and thus comply with spacing regulations.[6] Such laws conserve, not only oil, but also steel and other materials used in its capture.

> With the advent of conservation, the meaning of the phrase "producing capacity" changed. Instead of being the maximum rate at which a well could produce, it became, for many wells, the highest producing rate commensurate with maximum economic ultimate recovery. This is generally called the "maximum efficient rate," usually abbreviated "M.E.R." [7]

Secondary recovery of oil

Secondary recovery, by water flooding, gas pressurizing, and other "drives" has spurred cooperative effort because it is best accomplished by using several surrounding wells for injection to drive the oil toward one central producing well (Fig. 16.3). There were more than 5,700 injection projects operated in 1960, accounting for 29.6 per cent of our total petroleum production.[8] Production by water flooding, the principal secondary recovery method, increased from 27 million barrels in 1948 to 280 million barrels in 1959.[9] Meanwhile other secondary (and tertiary) methods for more thorough exhaustion of oil in pools, and extraction of oil from sands and rocks containing it, are in various experimental stages. *Fire drive,* that is, liquefying the oil and forcing it out with heat produced by burning some of it in place, shows special promise.

We are also making progress in the improved recovery of solid minerals, and it is indeed urgent that we do so. Our recovery of coal from underground mines has generally been only about 50 per cent of the total coal present; in some operations as low as 15 per cent[10] (Figs. 16.4 and 16.5). Backfilling, to permit removal of pillars and walls before closure of worked-out coal mines, can save 20 to 30 per cent of the original volume.[11] Better mining machinery and better mine management can work thinner seams at a profit. Strip mining, the ultimate in complete recovery (90 per cent), can now be accomplished where removal of the overburden was prohibitive a few years ago.

Many good coal seams have lain undisturbed because they are too deep for stripping and too thin and poorly "roofed" for underground mining. Now they can be mined with augers—up to 7 feet in diameter and capable of drilling horizontal holes

Complete extraction of coal

Fig. 16.4 *Whatever the type of mine, conservation is achieved when a bed or seam is mined in such a manner that a minimum of coal is abandoned in the ground. (After Bureau of Mines diagram.)*

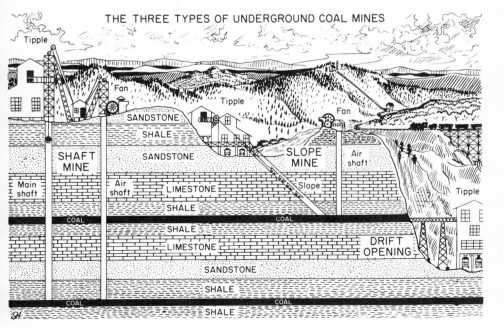

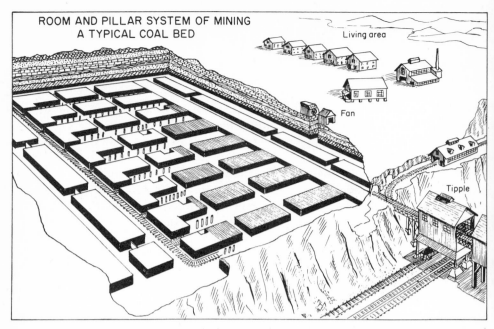

ROOM AND PILLAR SYSTEM OF MINING
A TYPICAL COAL BED

Living area

Fan

Tipple

Fig. 16.5 *Much coal lies wasted in pillars that support the roofs of abandoned mines. By back-filling the voids with slag as mining progresses, the pillars can be removed from mines now in production. (After Bureau of Mines diagram.)*

Fig. 16.6 *View from spoil bank showing complete operation of auger mining Pittsburgh coal bed and coal being loaded into truck. (Photo and caption courtesy Bureau of Mines, U.S.D.I.)*

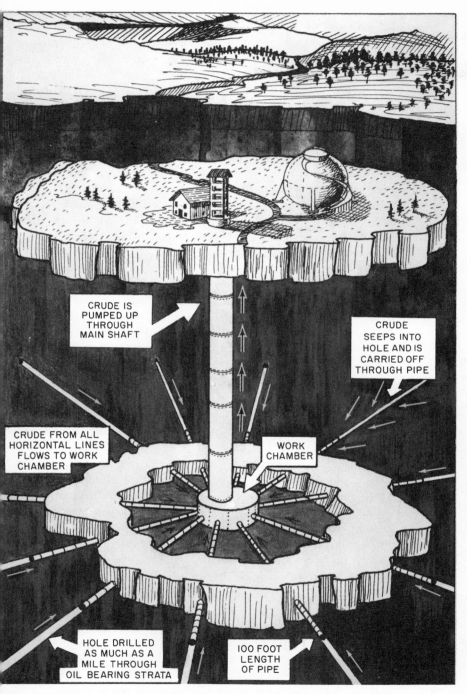

Fig. 16.7 *Proposed horizontal oil well system for draining oil sands otherwise unexploitable. (After Fortune, September 1947.)*

216 feet deep, at speeds up to 17 feet per minute, and producing as much as 25 tons of coal in the minute.[12] See in Fig. 16.6 how auger mining works. Auger mining conserves coal by making available deposits not commercially exploitable by other methods.

Especially noteworthy as means for complete removal of coal from underground workings are the *retreat-longwall* mining systems that have come into use. Retreat-longwall mining may be described as a room-and-pillar operation with only one room and no pillars left standing. The single wall may be several hundred feet in length. It is undercut from end to end by a "planer" run back and forth, gouging into the face at the bottom. As the coal tumbles onto a conveyor and is taken away the planer cuts on and on causing the wall to "retreat." As the wall being mined retreats the roof props are moved forward, and the side of the room already mined out caves in behind the operation.[13] The method is highly efficient in suitable situations, but it may cause some damage to the land above that settles down and closes the void once occupied by the coal seam. Packing the void with slag (backfilling) as mining progresses would prevent subsidence.

Other methods of mineral extraction even more remarkable and potentially more efficient, have been conceived but not yet put to work, among them such ideas as underground horizontal drilling (Fig. 16.7) to drain oil out of sands that vertical wells alone cannot reach.[14] We may be confident that engineering genius will for many minerals so vastly improve our recovery as to multiply the available supplies. We shall dig cleaner and deeper as time goes by.

More thorough search for new deposits

In the field of prospecting and exploration, the first step toward exploitation, there is less cause for pride. Excepting oil, for which intensive search has been conducted by techniques shown in Fig. 16.8, we remain delinquent in mineral exploration.

Compared with the improvement in technology of recovery, our search for deposits to work has lagged. Herein lies a major opportunity for the conservation—the increased usefulness—of mineral resources. Such costly procedures as the test drilling illustrated in Fig. 16.9 is often disappointing—a high-risk venture for private capital.

"Two kinds of maps, topographic and geologic, are essential to an adequate inventory of our mineral, fuel, and water resources. The topographic map should come first, to provide a base on which the geologic map is compiled and on which basic water-resource data are plotted." [15] Yet, as recently as early in 1963 we had topographic maps available for only 63.5 per cent

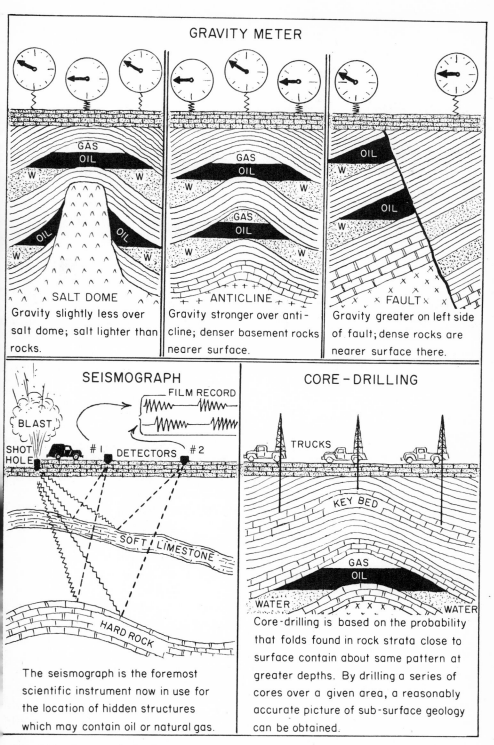

Fig. 16.8 *Some methods of search for petroleum (and other minerals). All exploratory evidence helps, but the presence of oil has only one positive proof—striking it with the drill. (After American Petroleum Institute diagrams.)*

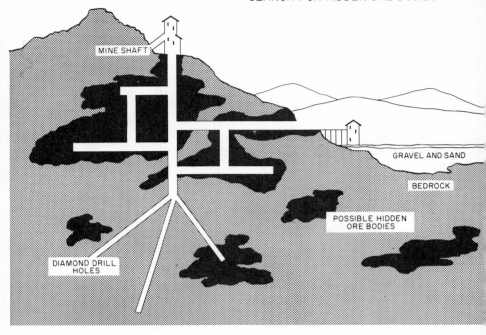

MINE SHAFT

GRAVEL AND SAND

BEDROCK

POSSIBLE HIDDEN
ORE BODIES

DIAMOND DRILL
HOLES

Fig. 16.9 *Instruments help us detect ore bodies, but only drilling proves the size and quality of a deposit. Much of our country remains unexplored geologically. (Source: Vol. I, P.M.P.C. Report.)*

of the area of the United States. Published geologic maps at scales adequate for detailed studies of mineral resources and land utilization—1 inch or more to 1 mile—were available for only 18 per cent of the contiguous states.[16] (Consider how the lack of accurate maps deters watershed development.)

Our scientific knowledge of the public lands is especially deficient. As recently as 1962 about 112 million acres of federally owned land in the public-land states (other than Alaska) remained unsurveyed—that is, it was not physically identifiable by any description of record.[17] Only 1 per cent of Alaska had been cadastrally surveyed.[18]

Only with good maps to guide us can we employ effectively all the ingenious methods of detecting minerals—geophysical, geochemical, radiometric, and others (Fig. 14.17). With aerial color photography we can get valuable clues from plant indicators and surface-rock exposures.[19] Photogeology has become a useful aid in rapid reconnaissance for minerals; and the airborne magnetometer can be carried to help locate mineral bodies while flying an area to photograph it.[20] Improved aerial photography and the technique called *photogrammetry* have greatly facilitated our mapping program.

Geologists are generally agreed that our undiscovered mineral wealth far exceeds that which we have found. We are assembling the basic map data, albeit too slowly, and perfecting new methods of discovery to ensure that we shall not starve while sitting on a loaf of bread. Possibilities for mineral discovery are tremendous.

We may very materially increase our economic mineral wealth by exploiting ores of lower metallic concentration and rock formations poorer in mineral content than those currently worked. Advancing prices, better techniques, or both, become the direct agents of conservation here as with improved recovery. Preferably we would have the low-grade deposits worked because cheaper, more efficient mining or manufacture makes them profitable, but a slight increase in the price of end products can also encourage more careful gleaning of our mineral harvest. Depletion of saw timber has compelled us to accept lumber of declining quality at steadily rising prices. The same rules apply to mineral materials.

Use of lower concentrations

A trend toward the use of lower concentrations is well under way in the metals. Most striking perhaps is the recovery of magnesium from sea water, which contains magnesium on the order of only 1,300 parts per million. In 1961 our domestic production of magnesias was almost three-fourths from brines—a fact of genuine significance, considering that the use of magnesium is increasing faster than that of any other metallic material.[21] Consumption of magnesium increased 23 per cent from 1960 to 1961 —so desirable is the new, light metal for alloying with aluminum and others. (How is magnesium extraction related to water desalinization?)

On almost every hand improved technology is elevating once worthless, lean deposits to the status of ores—a sort of promotion by human proficiency. The average grade of copper mined in the United States about 1900 was 5 per cent; in 1950 it was 0.9 per cent.[22] We *can* recover the metal from ores containing only 0.5 per cent copper.

Better than 50 per cent iron content has been the market standard for iron ore, although grades as low as 20 per cent have been mined. The Lake Superior taconite, containing only 25 to 40 per cent iron, yields, by beneficiation, concentrates of 65 per cent iron. From magnetite, or magnetic taconite, the iron is separated by crushing, grinding, and magnetic concentration. However, the concentrate is so fine and dust-like that it cannot be used in a blast furnace before it is agglomerated (formed into granules or pellets). The complex process (Fig. 16.10) remains

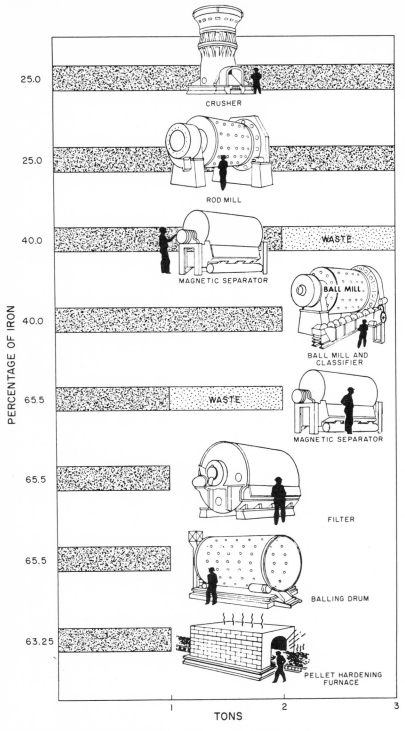

25.0   CRUSHER

25.0   ROD MILL

40.0   MAGNETIC SEPARATOR   WASTE

40.0   BALL MILL   BALL MILL AND CLASSIFIER

65.5   WASTE   MAGNETIC SEPARATOR

65.5   FILTER

65.5   BALLING DRUM

63.25   PELLET HARDENING FURNACE

PERCENTAGE OF IRON

TONS   1   2   3

Fig. 16.10 *Vast quantities of taconite are available for concentration, but only part of the ores are magnetic, and separable as shown here. Taconite will probably have a longer history than hematite as main supplier of our great inland steel industry. (Courtesy American Iron and Steel Institute.)*

expensive but our metallurgists and mining engineers have reduced processing costs sufficiently to bring taconite into prominence as a source of iron.

Before the end of 1961 the United States had seven taconite-type beneficiating plants in operation, with an annual production capacity of almost 20 million tons. These plants are enormously expensive, representing investment of as much as 300 million dollars in one installation.[23] The pelletized material has improved furnace efficiency, to which the increased use of oxygen and hydrocarbon injection has also contributed.

Beneficiation of ores

Sintering is another kind of iron-ore enrichment, illustrated in Fig. 16.11. Our annual plant capacity at the beginning of 1962 was 71.5 million tons of sinter.[24] Twenty-one plants, with about one-half the total capacity, were built since 1955. We are, indeed, capitalizing the conservation of iron!

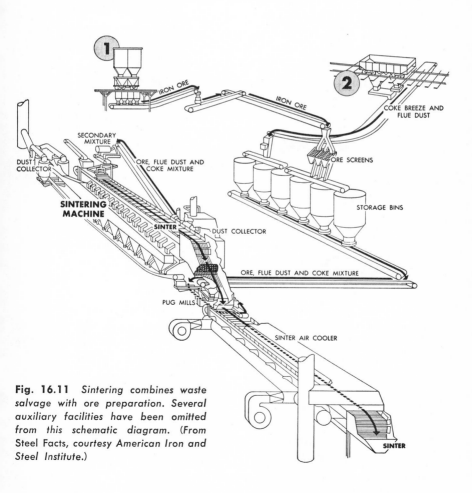

Fig. 16.11 *Sintering combines waste salvage with ore preparation. Several auxiliary facilities have been omitted from this schematic diagram. (From Steel Facts, courtesy American Iron and Steel Institute.)*

When we have exhausted all the bauxite in the world and the less abundant natural cryolite with which to process it, we may still fly airplanes and enjoy the multitude of other aluminum products now in use. Cryolite is now produced synthetically; so, the waning supplies in Greenland are no longer critical to the aluminum industry. When the economic climate of supply and demand persuades us we can extract the "second most abundant metal" from clays and rocks that are worthless under present price levels.[25] In the long run our supply of aluminum depends upon sources of energy with which to process low-grade ores. The leaner the ore, the greater the energy requirement!

Whether by flotation (Fig. 16.12), electrolysis, distillation, roasting, fuming, cracking, leaching (Figure 16.13), washing, or any other process of separation or refinement, the present and future supply of minerals can be immeasurably extended by progressively greater use of low-content material. The whole earth's crust and all the seas are ours to explore and refine before anyone can truthfully say that a single element has been completely exhausted. If it be true that man can neither create nor destroy matter but may only transform it, we shall never lack a material except as its presence eludes us.

Minerals wasted in processing and fabrication afford an opportunity for immediate and direct conservation. Many losses in the mineral industries can be reduced by improved techniques and more careful handling. Recovery and conversion of milling wastes has the same role in steel mills and machine shops as in sawmills and woodworking plants, with the added advantage that metal scraps may be reworked without the stigma that attaches to sawdust and shavings. Many losses incidental to the distribution and marketing of minerals warrant attention. Liquids and gases are particularly difficult to contain and transport without considerable loss. Fortunately, they are the very ones shipped by pipeline, which reduces leakage, spillage, and evaporation to a minimum.

Milling and shipping losses are minor compared with losses incidental to the treatment and smelting of ore, the coking of coal, and other conversions. We have made good progress along these lines, as a few examples will show, but there are many possibilities for further improvement.

By catalytic cracking we now produce gasoline of 77 octane number from the same grade of crude oil that yielded only 66 octane by thermal cracking, thus, in effect, raising the quality of crude oil.[26] Flotation has made profitable the reworking of "tailings" once dumped as waste from ore-reduction plants. Improved

Reduction of waste in processing, conversion, and fabrication

Fig. 16.12 Flotation cells used for the recovery of copper (Utah). "Flotation is a method of wet concentration of finely ground ores in which the separation of mineral from gangue is effected by surface energy, causing the mineral to float at the surface of a liquid pulp [foam] while the gangue remains submerged. Minerals with a metallic luster are preferentially wetted by oils and certain other organic agents in the presence of water, while the gangue is wetted by the water and remains in that medium." The process has considerable adaptability. (From Materials Survey—Zinc, pp. 11-25; Bureau of Mines photo.)

Fig. 16.13 Recovery of copper at Ray, Arizona, by leaching old waste dumps left from conventional mining operations. Water sprinkled over a heap of waste percolates through the material, picking up copper in solution as it goes. The solution water caught at the bottom of the heap is passed over old tin cans that have been burned and crushed for the purpose. The copper is precipitated on the cans. One waste material conserves another. (Courtesy Kennecott Copper Corporation.)

furnace design and ore preparation are reducing the quantity of coke required to smelt iron,[27] thus saving high-grade bituminous coal. One could go through a long list of minerals and point out similar conservational developments.

Another direct saving accrues from manifold improvements in the efficiency with which erstwhile wastes are being transformed into useful by-products of the mining and mineral industries. Not long ago beehive coking ovens produced the coke for charging our iron furnaces. Coke was their sole product. All the volatile contents of the coal were simply released into the air—a most wasteful practice. Modern coking plants capture the gases driven off and make from them such a variety of useful products (aromatic chemicals) that coke, once the only item saved, may be incidental. It is, conversely, regrettable that many beehive coke ovens have recurrently polluted the air with *valuable* "smoke" and "dust," because the by-products market was temporarily glutted.

By-products conservation

"Co-product" magic has been wrought in many other ways. The sulphur fumes that once poisoned the countryside around copper smelters are now converted into sulfuric acid, and the basic slag spewed by blast furnaces has become valuable in hydraulic cement. Reassuring indeed is the profitable recovery of erstwhile wastes that would otherwise pollute air and water, such as dust from coal workings and fly ash from thermal power plants. Fly ash has attained commercial importance as a complement to cement in concrete, lending notably superior strength and quality to the concrete. A major use of fly ash has been in the concrete for large dams. This kind of waste salvage will, when universally applied, greatly reduce our problems of landscape sanitation. Smoke and dust abatement does double duty as a conservation measure, and at least some part of its cost can be defrayed with the wastes that are recovered.

Application of recycling: salvage and re-use

The return of stack gases to the fire for more complete combustion illustrates an important conservation device, the *principle of recycling*—in plain words, salvage and re-use, which lengthen the useful life of minerals. Although minerals are non-renewable in character, many of them have an advantage over renewable resources in their capacity for wear. In general, an organic material serves only once and is consumed, but certain metals have such endurance that they can serve over and over again when properly salvaged and put back to work. Everyone can be a conserver of metal by selling his scrap, and there are thousands of merchants pleased to buy it.

Metal salvage has become differentiated into two branches, one handling scrap iron and steel and the other handling nonferrous scrap metal. Each recovers "secondary" metal, which, together with "primary" metal extracted from ores, comprises the "production" in any given period. Each is organized nationally and operates according to certain standards. Scrap iron and steel must be segregated and processed to meet specifications of seventy-five different grades recognized by the Federal government.[28] A practical system for classifying nonferrous scrap metals contains about 100 items, each identified by a code word and number.[29] Both industries perform a unique and essential conservation service.

Under the stress of World War II we reclaimed anything metallic, from abandoned streetcar tracks and worn-out machinery to horseshoes and tin cans. Reclaimed metal helped give us the machines that crushed Hitler's armored legions and the ships that sank Tojo's scrap-iron fleet. We became scrap conscious as never before. But we have too readily reverted to the reckless, wasteful discard of material that is typically American. We are wont to throw our worn-out tools and utensils into a gully or dump them on another's land. When a farmer's implement breaks down beyond repair he pulls it aside and leaves it in some odd corner to rot and rust away. But for that enterprising scavenger, the scrap collector, many such articles would crumble to dust instead of being returned to the furnaces or foundries as they should. A ton of iron and steel scrap, recycled, may save 2 tons of iron ore, 1 ton of coke, and half a ton of limestone. In 1961 almost 31 million tons of such scrap were salvaged.[30]

For some metals, notably iron, copper, and lead, reclaimed scrap constitutes a major source of supply. We could not maintain our great steel industry without the scrap cycle shown in Fig. 16.14. The metal charge that goes into a steel furnace is a mixture approximately 45 per cent scrap iron (or scrap steel) and 55 per cent pig iron, and 60 per cent of the scrap comes from junk,[31] mainly automobiles. During recent years scrap has contributed more than 50 per cent of our copper supply and as much as 80 per cent of our lead.[32] Moral: the battered copper kettle may one day sing in a big electric generator and the dead storage battery may be reborn to another useful lifetime.

Salvage adds more or less to many other metal reserves and could be substantially increased by making it more systematic. With the tremendous variety of alloys and mixtures now in use, it is often difficult to determine where a particular piece of scrap belongs. If necessary identification costs too much the piece is of course worthless. Experts have proposed that a standardized code system be adopted under which parts and articles might be

Metal salvage and re-use

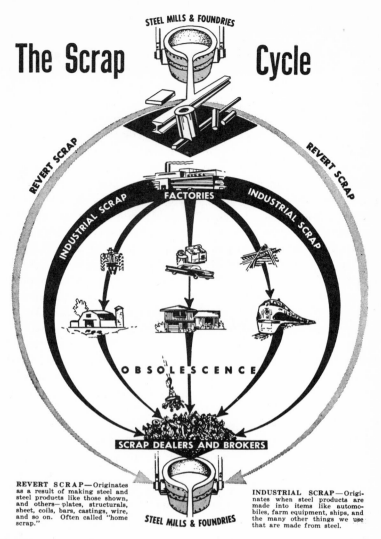

The Scrap
STEEL MILLS & FOUNDRIES
Cycle

REVERT SCRAP

REVERT SCRAP

INDUSTRIAL SCRAP

FACTORIES

INDUSTRIAL SCRAP

O B S O L E S C E N C E

SCRAP DEALERS AND BROKERS

REVERT SCRAP—Originates as a result of making steel and steel products like those shown, and others— plates, structurals, sheet, coils, bars, castings, wire, and so on. Often called "home scrap."

INDUSTRIAL SCRAP—Originates when steel products are made into items like automobiles, farm equipment, ships, and the many other things we use that are made from steel.

STEEL MILLS & FOUNDRIES

Fig. 16.14 *The scrap cycle in iron and steel. Factory leftovers, called "prompt industrial" scrap, comprise about one-third of the volume handled by the scrap industry. "Obsolescence" scrap contributes most of the remainder. An automobile yields about a ton of scrap, usually compressed as shown in Fig. 16.15. (Courtesy Institute of Scrap Iron and Steel, Inc.)*

identified at the factory by stamping on them a symbol representing the metallic formulation they contain. This would be an elaborate adaptation of the "hallmark" warranty on sterling silver, in use for centuries. Better still might be a system under which the scrap industry would be furnished by manufacturers their complete lists of parts and specifications, with alloy formulations held in confidence if desired. (The scrap industry is not for irresponsible paupers; it requires good organization and

446

heavy investment, as may be inferred from Fig. 16.15.) With appropriate regulation and enforcement, such a system would ensure maximum recycling of metals, a logical conservation development.

Substitution of abundant minerals for scarce ones is another means of extending our reserves. By shifting the load from short-winded horses to long-winded ones we can ride farther. Some such shifts are actually taking place, and many others will come.

Substitution of abundant minerals for scarce ones

The briquetting of lignite that has just begun in America may render our abundant deposits of the low-carbon material highly valuable as a source of fuel. The blending of abundant high-volatile bituminous coals with the scarce low-volatile ones, which is already practiced extensively, will immeasurably prolong the availability of metallurgical coke.

Aluminum has taken over much of the burden once borne by copper, and magnesium, in turn, has stepped in to relieve aluminum in other functions. As noted previously, aluminum is extremely abundant, and magnesium will be plentiful until the ocean dries up. The use of microwaves for transmitting low-voltage currents is releasing both copper and aluminum from work that has been almost exclusively theirs. Just how far ideas will, in effect, displace materials is anybody's guess, but a re-

Fig. 16.15 *Baler-Shear, designed to compress with high density, then shear, bulky scrap such as whole autos less engine. This hydraulic machine, shipped and installed some distance from Cordele, Georgia early in 1963, cost about $140,000. Price of some models was more than half a million dollars. Secondary production of metal is good conservation, but not without cost! (Courtesy Harris Foundry and Machine Company.)*

source optimist will look for many such discoveries in the future.

Perhaps the most momentous mineral substitution now foreseeable is the replacement of petroleum and natural gas with oil and gas derived from coal. The feat has been accomplished, both by gasification and by hydrogenation of coal, but neither process can compete commercially with natural gas or oil at prices now prevailing.[33] In due time, the coal with which we are so abundantly blessed will not only stand alone as a mineral fuel, but it will also fall heir to a host of material functions now performed by gas, petroleum, and other minerals. Its chemical derivatives will be a major source of rubber, textiles, plastics, and other synthetic products. Coal also has possibilities as a raw material for the manufacture of fertilizer. Thus, the probable future scope of mineral substitution defies prediction.

Employment of substances now idle

Useful employment of idle substances, an objective in several fields of conservation, holds special promise among mineral resources. We are using only a few of our known minerals, and the enlistment of new ones is a continuing challenge to the conservator. Every addition enlarges the aggregate wealth and prolongs the combined usefulness of the whole lot. Half a century ago aluminum was almost unknown; now it ranks second only to steel. Its consumption has multiplied ninefold during the last quarter-century.[34] So quickly can a mineral rise from obscurity to prominence! Only the fissionable materials have made a more revolutionary impact on the mineral industry.

One after another, new metals make their commercial debut. Recent introductions include boron, barium, calcium, ductile titanium, beryllium, and ductile zirconium, to mention a few interesting ones.

Zirconium and titanium belong to the family of light metals (aluminum and magnesium) and wait only for perfection of techniques to elevate them to the rank of their fellows. Titanium is especially resistant to marine corrosion and has almost the strength of steel although it weighs only 42 per cent as much. It is only fairly resistant to high temperatures.[35] Zirconium, on the other hand, has such tolerance of high temperatures that it has become important as an alloy for rockets and jets. It is exceptionally noncorrosive, and particularly promising as a construction material for nuclear reactors.[36]

Beryllium has been used primarily to harden and strengthen copper, giving it more resistance to wear and fatigue, and improving its capacity to conduct electrical current under high temperatures. Its most promising new use is as a moderator and neutron reflector in the atomic-energy industry.[37]

Boron is scarcely known except as borax or boric acid, and the metal as such has no use at present. Experiments indicate possibilities for boron as a coating material and, within certain limitations, as a structural material. It may become important in propellants and be elevated from its position as janitor to real prestige among the metals. It is relatively scarce but locally concentrated at Death Valley.

Barium and calcium interest the conservator because, although extremely abundant, they are very little used as metals. Barium is in fact the most common "getter" for vacuum tubes, in addition to other uses in electronics. Calcium serves several purposes in metallurgical processes, but in its own right remains unimportant. Both barium and calcium are too reactive to water and atmospheric moisture to serve any structural purpose without protective coating. These two metals, and the most abundant of all, *silicon,* may some day become ranking mineral materials. Their commercial destiny is a major challenge to metallurgy and conservation.

Research and investigation point clearly to our future exploitation of materials now idle to supplement or supplant our present sources of mineral fuel. We may anticipate commercial development of oil shale, lignite, and subbituminous coal to produce "synthetic liquid fuels." During recent decades the Bureau of Mines, assisted by private interests, has made gratifying progress in this direction. Low-grade coals compose the largest mineral resource we possess and will almost immeasurably enlarge our fuel reserves when we can economically gasify, liquefy, or by other process convert them into usable concentrations. Our oil-shale formations are also tremendously extensive and rich. A single geologic formation in Utah and Wyoming (the Green River) covers more than 14,000 square miles. One test revealed a section 90 feet thick, averaging 25 gallons of shale oil per ton of shale.[38] Whether we quarry the shale and extract the oil aboveground, crush the shale and extract the oil in underground mines, or by more ingenious contrivance draw off the oil without handling the rock containing it (Fig. 16.16), the exploitation will add hundreds of billions of barrels to our liquid-fuel reserves.[39] According to a USGS estimate in 1961, oil from oil shale constitutes 16 per cent, petroleum and natural gas about 16 per cent, and coal 68 per cent of the total recoverable reserves of mineral fuels in the United States. Refined, or treated, shale oil yields products nicely comparable with the counterparts obtained from petroleum, including gasoline suitable for automobiles. (Take note: we may soon be touring our scenic country

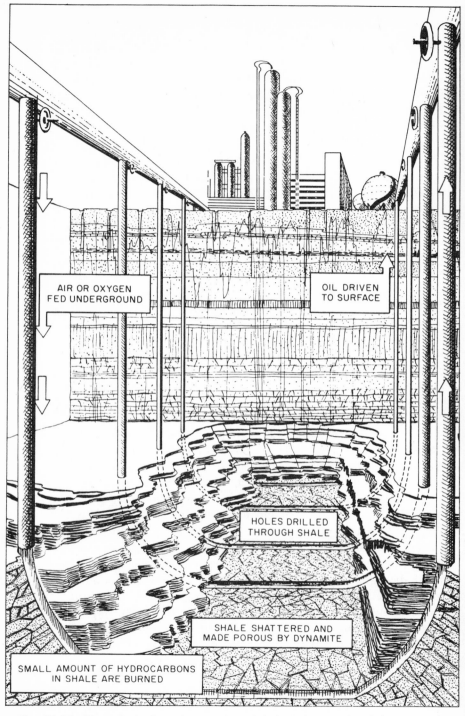

Fig. 16.16 *Theoretical scheme for retorting oil shale underground and driving out the oil, obviating the need for quarrying and crushing the rock above-ground. (After* Fortune, *September 1947.)*

with *rock* in the gas tank.) How many idle substances can be put to work? Who can tell? Many await our pleasure!

As previously mentioned in another context, importation from foreign sources is often an effective method of conserving domestic mineral supplies. In the interest of the nation as a whole, we should welcome, and even encourage, the procurement of mineral materials from other lands. Every delivery conserves the supply at home; and it is indeed a grave mistake to raise any artificial barrier against it, as has been done with tariffs on oil and copper under the pretext of stimulating domestic enterprise. Had the stimulation worked, which it did not, it should simply have stimulated us to exhaust our reserves at an earlier date. From the standpoint of conservation—and *national security*—it is utterly preposterous that we collect import duty on several critical minerals for the supply of which we are largely dependent upon foreign sources.[40] In a practical, calculating world one might see more logic in the restriction of mineral exports. If in the interest of security or self-sufficiency we wish to accelerate the discovery and production of minerals, let us do so by bounties at home rather than by excluding materials economically available from overseas. (Favorable taxation has aided the Minnesota taconite industry.) Imports conserve domestic supplies

Foreign trade in minerals has a flavor quite different from trade in reproducible materials such as cotton, lumber, meat, or grain. The organics are replaceable; the minerals are not. The world contains fixed quantities of the minerals, and the advantage goes to him into whose hands they fall. Wherever they come from, they benefit most that nation that consumes them. Collection from abroad and stockpiling at home may be a most fortuitous conservation practice, especially as national security is one of our major objectives in conserving natural resources. Wise conservators should formulate the foreign policy that embraces certain minerals classified in Table 1.

At the hazard of appearing stuffy and old-fashioned, one must submit that discretion and thrift in the end use of minerals might greatly magnify their services and that more efficient and selective employment might greatly prolong their terms of service. But with these *conservative* means of conservation, we have made little progress; just enough to indicate their potential.

At the turn of the century we burned 7 pounds of coal to generate one kilowatthour of electric energy. By 1925 we had reduced the average coal requirement to 2 pounds, and by 1952 to 1.1. Our most efficient thermal generating plants are now approaching a ratio of a half-pound of coal to 1 kilowatthour Discretion and thrift in mineral consumption

Table 1

Domestic Supply Position of Selected Mineral Materials

KNOWN ECONOMIC RESERVES ADEQUATE FOR WELL OVER 25 YEARS

Magnesium	Potash	Sand	Barite
Molybdenum	Lime	Gypsum	Feldspar
Coal	Salt	Borax	Clay
Phosphate			

KNOWN ECONOMIC RESERVES INADEQUATE

Discoveries geologically likely, though not necessarily adequate

Copper	Vanadium	Petroleum
Lead	Tungsten	Natural gas
Zinc	Antimony	Sulfur
Uranium		

Beneficiation progress expected

Iron	Beryllium	Fluorine
Aluminum	Thorium	Graphite
Titanium	Oil from shale	

Synthesis progress expected

Oil from coal	Gas from coal

LITTLE OR NO KNOWN ECONOMIC RESERVES, SIGNIFICANT DISCOVERIES NOT LIKELY

Beneficiation progress expected

Manganese

Synthesis progress expected

Industrial Diamonds	Quartz crystals
Sheet mica	Asbestos

Significant beneficiation progress or synthesis not expected

Chromium	Tin	Platinum
Nickel	Cobalt	Mercury

Source: Vol. 1. P.M.P.C. Report, 1952.

of electric energy (Fig. 16.17). The average ratio is now considerably better than 1 to 1 (0.863 lb. per kwhr in 1961). In terms of heat rates coal-electric generating efficiency improved 1.4 per cent from 1960 to 1961; the average Btu consumption per kilowatthour decreased from 10,701 to 10,552 in one year. Other fuel rates also fell to new levels in 1961: gas to 10.8 cu ft per kwhr; oil to 0.076 gal per kwhr.[41]

Selectivity of use may have advantages comparable with those accruing from efficient conversion. If we were to burn natural gas exclusively for the heating which best exploits its distinctive

Fig. 16.17 Eddystone station of Philadelphia Electric Company, Pennsylvania, our most efficient steam-electric generating plant in 1961. That year this plant had a heat rate of 8,760 Btu per kilowatthour, the best in the United States. Its fuel—coal; its installed capacity—650 million watts. (From Federal Power Commission.)

qualities, we might double the life of our gas reserves.[42] If we would use aluminum wherever it can replace sheet iron, we could save not only the iron but also its protective coating of zinc or tin. If all our minerals were put to their optimum selective use, they would serve us better for a longer period of time. They would be conserved by judicious consumption.

Thrift is a virtue that wealth and ease have almost divorced from American culture. Our sacrifice of substance to needless speed, vain display, and sheer negligence has reached prodigious proportions, and there is little evidence that we may retard or reverse the trend. Our extravagance as consumers of goods is particularly revolting when it dissipates irreplaceable mineral wealth. Would our economy suffer if we discarded our wasteful habits?

The American craze for flashy, high-speed automobiles illustrates the sorry extravagance with which we waste the end product of minerals. We insist on shiny metal trimmings. We burn leaded gasoline for more "zip" and higher speed. We drive automobiles when walking would be quicker and infinitely more beneficial, and we drive them aimlessly, without destination. We give them hard use and little care, and we trade them in, "slightly used," when a new model takes our fancy. We treat many other consumer goods in the same manner. Must the conservator condone the needless abuse of goods as a necessary accelerator of business and industrial activity?

Since almost every commercial mineral is represented in an automobile and since wear, tear, and fuel consumption are directly related to speed, it follows that a slight moderation of performance standards would be a desirable conservation measure. A little less speed on our highways would also show an incidental saving of metal that goes into coffins for crash victims. Certainly speeding and killing on the highways cannot be justified in the interest of economics!

Every American can conserve mineral resources by taking *decent* care of "things" he uses: by mending a bucket when it springs a leak; by oiling a bearing when it runs hot; by painting or housing a machine to protect it against rust or corrosion; by turning off the lights in any empty room as well as when courting his best girl; and in countless other ways. Such individual acts of conservation yield invaluable collateral in the forms of personal satisfaction, dignity, character, and self-respect. Revival of thrift might well be a conservator's crowning achievement.

Two groups of minerals—energy materials and fertilizer materials—command the special respect of conservators; the latter because soil fertility determines the reproductive capacity of organic resources, the former because energy or power is the agent of conversion whereby other resources, especially the metals, assume usable forms. Energy and soil fertility are the supporting foundation of industry and enterprise, of wealth and prestige. They are the alpha and omega among natural resources. All of our material wealth derives from them; all of it would be lost if they were consumed. It is therefore most reassuring to know that both can be maintained far into the future, from sources already discovered, by processes that our present, limited knowledge makes available to us.

The *energy mix*—that is, the proportionate share of the total contributed by various sources—will change gradually with time and circumstances, and conversion losses will increase as secondary forms, such as electricity and gasoline, gain greater prominence. Natural gas and petroleum will probably continue their present upward trend relative to coal for the remainder of the century. It appears that the mineral fuels will dominate the energy picture for an indefinite period. Coal will probably regain and retain top rank.

As mineral fuels are to energy so are the mineral fertilizers to soil maintenance. The availability of phosphorus, potash, and nitrogen with which to replenish the supply of these essential

Mark the supremacy of energy and fertilizer sources

plant foods in crop-producing soils transcends all other aspects of mineral conservation. We shall probably need food from the soil long after we have consumed or discarded all the metals and fuels mentioned in this chapter. What is more, we shall probably not hunger. Many generations of pessimists will die of ulcers before their optimistic contemporaries must begin to tighten their belts.

Of our three most *precious* minerals only one, phosphorus, gives us any cause for concern. Our nitrate supplies were precarious until we learned the secret of the legumes and began "fixing" nitrogen from the immeasurable volume contained in the atmosphere. Now we can have all the nitrogen we want as long as we have the air to take it from and enough energy to perform the task: 0.75 kilowatthour per pound of ammonia.[43] Domestic deposits of potash salts (mineral) may last the United States about 100 years; those of the world can supply all the nations for about 1,000 years.[44] When we exhaust these supplies we can take potash from the sea. Phosphate rock, our source of phosphorus, though less abundant, is sufficient to last us several hundreds of years.[45] Although the supply presents no immediate problem, it would be comforting to know that we might extract phosphorus from the sea or the atmosphere when the phosphate mines have been worked out. Perhaps the phosphorescence in the wake of a ship will show us the way. Perhaps we shall spread on the land quantities of native rock containing phosphorus when the rich phosphates have been exhausted.

From the foregoing one may conclude that our mineral resources, as now mined, smelted, and converted, will sustain our mechanical culture for a long, long time and that by the application of intelligent, profitable conservation, we can multiply their usefulness. One may predict that many transitions in use will accompany the inevitable decline of reserves and the constant advance of technology. But he *cannot* subscribe to any confounded idea that the ultimate exhaustion of one, two, or several of the commercial minerals now worked can stop, or greatly impede, the progress of civilization, and of our own nation in particular. Expired minerals will send no ghosts to haunt us. Other materials will take the places once filled by the departed ones.

New materials will take the place of expired ones

Finally, a responsibility to conserve associated resources attaches to the exploitation and utilization of minerals. Several times we have alluded to the interplay between permanent and expendable wealth. In many cases they are complementary, as when water carries ore and coal cargoes, and in other cases inimical, as when underground water interferes with anthracite min-

Guard well the permanent wealth while extracting and consuming the temporal

ing. In many instances we have extracted or processed minerals
to the extreme detriment of the land and its life. We have
mutilated the soil mantle to get at minerals lying under it; we
have killed the vegetative cover with poisonous fumes; we have
soiled our waters and choked our stream channels with mining
wastes. In short, we have often sacrificed permanent wealth in
our quest for momentary gain. Sometimes our devastation has
been greater than our gain—an error we will avoid in the future
if we apply in practice the concept of unity that should pervade
all conservation. New laws and new practices are even now correcting past mistakes.

We have seen how poisonous fumes and smokes may be profitably captured and put to use. Many other mineral wastes can be
similarly salvaged, minimizing their injury to the landscape. Even
strip mining, that most thorough extracting method that tears the
land apart, can be offset by rather inexpensive reclamation practices. At the very worst, strip-mined lands can be converted into
highly productive wildlife and recreation areas. By planting
or sowing, they can become forest or pasture rather quickly.[46]
By leveling and soil building many of them can be made suitable
for most any kind of land use. Give or take a few thousand, we
have perhaps 500,000 acres of them. Although many various minerals are mined by stripping, coal strip mining is most extensive
and has, therefore, also attracted most attention in conservation.
State legislation requiring strip mine operators to reclaim spoil
banks was first passed in West Virginia in 1939; other states
concerned have enacted comparable reclamation laws since that
time. Under conditions ordinarily encountered, satisfactory reclamation of land stripped for coal may be accomplished at a cost
of less than 1 cent per ton of coal removed.[47] It is a fair price
to pay for rehabilitating land instead of leaving it a shamble.

The raw spoil banks of strip mining, like giant furrows across
the landscape, have symbolized the destruction of permanent
wealth to recover a material of only temporary value. Their gradual erasure from the American scene will be a good sign of conservation progress. Filling and sealing of abandoned underground
mines to avert land subsidence must also be accomplished.

The eternal land, its soils, and its waters, must not be unduly
disturbed or damaged to procure any substance of relatively
minor benefit in the long run. The wise choice between surface
and subterranean resources at any given time and place is a
responsibility of the voting citizen. He must decide how well
we shall restrict the abusive treatment of public lands by further
amending our mining laws. He must determine the regulations

under which minerals will be produced. As umpire of the all-American resource game, he should learn the ground rules and keep his eye on the ball. As fans, we can insist that the plays be called accurately, but we must first know the plays ourselves. We, the people, as both fans and umpire, must abide by decisions that we ourselves pronounce. Let us resolve to make them good! Let us guard well the permanent values while extracting and consuming temporal wealth!

17

Prospect and Responsibility

by advancing our knowledge of resources and employing them accordingly we can progress and prosper through ages to come

Conservation—
the key
to future
prosperity

The future of our people and of our nation depends upon the intelligent use of natural resources. Unless it be spiritual conviction or moral fiber, nothing we can muster holds greater promise of continuing prosperity than systematic, unified conservation. We have attained economic leadership by exploiting natural wealth. We can maintain that enviable position indefinitely if we husband carefully the wealth that remains. We should certainly lose, not only our material standing, but also our democratic freedoms, if we continued the waste and abuse that attended our rise to greatness. One cannot overdraw his accounts continuously without finally exhausting them. Up to the present, withdrawals in the form of soil and water—the real capital assets—have been monstrous, and from the shrinking reserves we are still squandering more than we can afford. Worst of all, many of the losses are, for practical purposes, complete and final. Land divested of its soil, and water reservoirs caved in or filled with debris, have lost most of their usefulness for the immediate future, if not for all time.

Sick soil can be cured and filthy water can be purified, but if malignancy and contamination be permitted to spread faster than treatment or prevention, the main resource "body," the land, must grow progressively weaker and less amenable to conservation. Land morbidity leads directly to economic bankruptcy and social decay.

Conservation literature contains many stern warnings that we are riding toward starvation full tilt, with Malthus spurring our horses. (Malthus propounded the theory that population increase is ultimately checked by the limitation of food supply.) Unless we mend our ways we shall starve; pessimism and procrastination can only hasten our hunger. But if we heed the ominous warnings and take positive action to conserve our resources, we may project the curve of *population increase* and the curve of *food supply* somewhat after the manner of parallel lines that meet only in infinity.

We have given freely of American abundance that other nations might live, but the "stars in our crown" will shine with a false glitter if in their winning we waste the substance entrusted to us. Ours, the wherewithal to grow and prosper as a nation for an indefinite time to come if we but use our resources wisely. If we *must* subscribe to the Malthusian theory that man will multiply until he eats himself right off the earth, let us determine that we shall be the last to go. No other nation has natural wealth equal to ours, and if we apply conservation better than any potential adversary, who then shall prevail against us? Indeed, conservation holds the key to our future far beyond the shifting currents of international politics. Not only is conservation the guarantee of strength with which to defend our freedom against any threat, but it is also the assurance of prosperity after the threat has been dissipated. *Conserved resources are coveted resources;* but the same wealth that provokes hostile design also provides the means with which to repel hostile attack. Strength keeps us free; conservation can keep us strong.

Among our demographers (population experts) are those who oppose vigorously the defeatist attitude toward world hunger. They predict that conservation and technology can provide a century hence a more adequate diet for 7 or 8 billion people than is now available to a world population of 3 billion. If by such means the redundant peoples of the Orient are better fed and attain a higher level of living, their potential in world affairs will become more nearly commensurate with their numbers. Therein lies a real challenge to American conservation! We need not fear hunger, at least not for centuries to come; however, we must respect the competition of superior numbers. If living standards equalize, then *international competition* for *world resources* will also become more nearly equal. Other nations will require a larger share of world products.

Meanwhile, our American population is expected to continue increasing rapidly and will, according to Census Bureau projections, number about 215 million by 1970 and 261 million by 1980. Thus, a novice may predict that there will be more than 375 million Americans in the year 2000. We may also assume that our level of living and per capita requirements will rise substantially during the years intervening. Thus our natural resources will be taxed more and more heavily as years go by, and it is imperative right now that we take full advantage of techniques and procedures for magnifying their usefulness.

Emergency first aid cures no malady

We have displayed much less intelligence in conservation than in technology and exploitation. We have advanced scientific theory, economic order, and social behavior and neglected their resource base. We have recognized resource problems when they became spectacular, dangerous, or tragic—too late for preventive action. We have applied first aid to the recurrent eruption of boils and failed to treat the blood infection causing them. First aid is no cure for a chronic malady. We have taken futile emergency measures when disaster struck and failed to follow through to avert its recurrence.

Each devastating flood, each disastrous forest fire, each dust storm, each water shortage, and each passing of a wildlife species has moved us to feverish activity at the moment, but our results have been only temporary or superficial because we tackled consequences and not causes. When the waters have gathered it is too late to stem the flood. It is too late to save the forest when it goes up in smoke, too late to hold the soil when it is blowing away, too late to store water when it has reached the sea, and too late to save a species of animal when it has lost the capacity for competitive survival. Conservation must be preventive, and it must attack the causes of calamity, not the calamity itself. It must discern those causes in time to avert their consequences. It must be deliberate, continuous, and systematic, not dictated by emergencies and forgotten between times. Thus far we have administered much resource first aid without diagnosing the ailments to prescribe permanent cures.

Fragmentary and desultory attacks cannot solve the integrated problem

Neither can we conserve by attacking isolated problems or by attempting to conserve any particular resource independently. Since all natural resources together constitute the indivisible environmental composite set forth in Chapter 2, it is impossible to conserve one without regard for the others. This fundamental concept of conservation we have often failed to respect and have never fully applied. Instead, we have engaged in specialized conservation of one resource or another, apparently oblivious to others related thereto. We have made fragmentary and desultory attacks upon an integrated problem, often aggravating one phase while trying, vainly, to resolve another. Conservation cannot be accomplished in detached segments. Chapter headings in this book suggest the common error of isolating resources, but the book was so organized for the sake of simplicity. Because the division is artificial and the sequence in some places arbitrary, there have been numerous reminders that the entire subject matter is in reality intimately related.

Specialists are prone to compartmentalize resources, and it is inevitable that they should, because one technician cannot possibly master all the skills involved in the total conservation program. Hydrologists work with water, geologists with minerals, pedologists with soils, foresters with trees, zoologists with wildlife, ichthyologists with fish, agrostologists with grass, recreationists with recreation, engineers with structures, and teachers with education—ad infinitum. We need the services of all these and other experts, but we need even more the comprehensive coordination of their work. The over-all direction of conservation has evolved very slowly and remains seriously deficient. Technical conservationists might be likened to players on a football team, and any football coach will agree that the best lineup of players will lose the ball unless they combine their talents in teamwork. The conservation team might have more competent coaching if administrators were apprised of the unique qualification of geographers to perform the task. Geographers themselves should certainly be less reticent about assuming and discharging this professional responsibility.

Regional or group interests often hinder conservation by violating the general program to gain local advantage or special privileges. These handicaps are inherent in geographical differences and human weaknesses, and cannot be attributed to sectional malice or selfish ambition. Rather they are a matter of narrow perspective and short vision, neither of which fosters a comprehensive national scheme. Regionalism offers a logical framework for planning and conservation and might well have been the basis for organizing the subject matter of this book, but regional schemes are not always in the national interest. Whereas the conservator would encourage private or group interests and expressly defend them as the most practical means of achieving conservation, he cannot endorse drummed-up projects or programs sponsored by any locality or pressure group; such undertakings victimize the very people they ostensibly profit and waste public funds that could be put to good use elsewhere. He

Regional developments may hinder the national program

should evaluate from the national point of view every regional development that is federally financed. Sectional illusions of grandeur have caused extravagant waste of public funds and may actually handicap areas in which the monies were invested, as when a short-lived reclamation project becomes defunct and requires relocation of the families it attracted.

Public ignorance and apathy are the worst obstacles

Worst obstacle to conservation is the general ignorance of resource problems and public apathy toward the solution of problems that have been acknowledged. In a democracy such as ours the private citizen decides what the conservationists, planners, and administrators shall do, but at this time John Q. Public, U.S.A. is not sufficiently informed to act wisely and not sufficiently aroused to acquire the necessary information. This book is one among many written to apprise John Q. of his personal stock in conservation and thereby stir him out of his lethargy. His incompetence and detachment constitute the most perverse barrier to good resource management. In the final analysis, it is his fault that we waste scientific knowledge and technical skill incidental to poor organization and confused administration. The voter has himself to blame when conservation policies and practices fail in America. He is the American conservator, and until he backs them up more wisely and resolutely, our conservationists cannot attain the goals for which they strive on his behalf.

We must preach conservation to our fellows as a missionary preaches religion to heathens, and we need many more inspired missionaries to get a sufficient number of converts. Public education should be our most fruitful medium, and every thinking layman can help the schoolteachers. Only when a much greater number of our people recognize its full significance will conservation become a reality.

New frontiers of technology broaden conservation concepts

New frontiers of our technological age constantly broaden conservation concepts. Discovery, invention, and adaptation alter the prospect and shift the points of focus. Conservation cannot be a static proposition; it must keep pace with scientific, industrial, and commercial progress. Every change in the relative utility or availability of a resource has its impact upon others, and conservators must take account of the revised status. Conservation must be dynamic and flexible if it shall serve its purpose. The pessimistic dogma that has crept into the literature incurs a certain skepticism in view of modifications and substitutions that disprove it. It is well to warn people that certain resources upon which they now depend will one day be consumed, but in the same breath one should express some degree of confidence that means will be found to meet the eventuality. If one contemplates cultural stagnation whenever an "essential" material becomes exhausted, he lacks the confidence in scientific genius that it so well deserves. Let the conservator, rather than bemoaning future shortage, encourage timely research to circumvent or alleviate its consequences. This challenge could be elaborated through several volumes the size of this one, but let us be content with a few cursory suggestions.

Solar energy transformed into power drives the wheels of our technological age, and, as seen in Chapter 15, we derive most of our present needs from fossil fuels through indirect and inefficient application. We have done very little to harness sun power in other forms. We have converted only a fraction of the energy in water precipitated on the land. If all of it were developed, it would exceed our present consumption of electric power from all sources. We have discovered the revolutionary possibilities of atomic power, but unless we can extract fissionable material from other than rare and fugitive minerals, we cannot rely on atomic energy to satisfy our future power needs. We have almost ignored the energy manifest in the ebb and flow of ocean tides, the endless sweep of winds over the earth, and the light rays that produce sunburn. We should have ample power without any of our present sources; we need only redesign our engines. We know the scientific principles involved.

Latent energy

Modern technology, dependent upon energy released by combustion, and increasingly proficient at chemical reduction and combination, makes of the very air we breathe a conservable resource. Atmospheric pollution around industrial centers has reached dangerous proportions. We are contaminating our air much as we have contaminated our waters. We have coined a new word, *smog*, to identify the dirty pall that blankets many of our cities when there is no wind to clear it away. Smog, or drifting smoke, has long been recognized as a nuisance and inconvenience that soils and corrodes what it touches. It has caused housewives no end of grief and their husbands exorbitant expenses in the form of cleaning bills. Whether it pours out of a smudge pot in California or a chimney pot in London, smoke is disagreeable stuff with which to live.

Conservation of air

Local concentrations of smoke, dust, gases, or fumes in the atmosphere are not only unpleasant; but they have become destructive of life, both plant and animal. Notable examples include the desert around Copper Hill, Tennessee made by fumes from the smelters, and the disaster at Donora, Pennsylvania in 1948, when several people were killed by toxic smog.

Polluted air is a menace to health as a contributing cause of

**Artificial
rain**

diseases in the respiratory tract, and a direct hazard to life as an obstruction to visibility in air and surface travel. Air—the most abundant substance on earth—as water—the second most abundant—approaches resource status because men contaminate it with waste from other resources. Conservation in other fields will go far toward solving the problem. Another development of recent years, namely cloud seeding to produce rain, further substantiates the suggestion that air approaches resource status. "Free as the air" may soon be an outmoded maxim, and the conservation alarmists may ask us to refrain from deep breathing. Artificial rain making is intended to increase our water resources and equalize their distribution, but since it involves air as the carrier of moisture, the air becomes a direct medium for resource conservation.

Without entangling ourselves in technical argument, while being aware that rain can be precipitated artificially when the air is not quite ready to release it naturally, we may envisage a conservation frontier fraught with fascinating possibilities and vexing problems. If men can precipitate atmospheric moisture where they want it, when they wish, they can solve most of the problems noted in Chapter 7, the water deficiencies in Chapters 3 and 4, the fire problem in Chapter 9, and many others that now beset us. If they can turn it on, can they also turn it off at will, thus preventing floods and water erosion? *There* is a frontier *beyond* a frontier!

Unless tailor-made rain can be made to coincide with property lines, we shall have no end of damage suits. If Farmer Brown engages a rain maker to fill out his corn and the ensuing deluge falls on Farmer Smith's cotton and ruins it, who will adjudge Brown liable for Smith's loss? If moisture from the Gulf headed toward Nebraska is "stimulated" over Oklahoma and falls on Kansas, shall Kansas be required to pay Nebraska for the water precipitated by Oklahoma? These theoretical cases are not mere jokes; they presage a new body of conservation law.

**Synthetics
and substitutes
broaden the
resource base**

Most revolutionary of all technological innovations is the development of synthetics and substitutes as industrial raw materials. One discovery after another changes the status and prospect of various resources and requires the conservator to revise his estimates. New processes and new uses constantly shift the burden of dependence from one resource to another, increasing the consumption of this and reducing the consumption of that, until any prediction of shortage or inadequacy becomes largely speculative. Plastics from soybeans, gasoline from coal, textiles from coal or wood, and wool from rocks instead of sheep are a few examples. Scientific genius gives the basic resources a versatility that greatly improves the overall prospect and allows conservation a latitude rarely comprehended by conservationists themselves.

When petroleum runs out we can drive our wheels with synthetic fuels—gasoline from coal, and alcohol from wood or other vegetable sources. When we turn the wheels without petroleum, we will also lubricate the bearings without it. When the metals run out, the seas having been completely divested of them, we will probably replace them with glass, the raw material for which exists in almost unlimited quantity—silicon dioxide from plain quartz sand. If we exhaust the supply of sand, we shall all embark upon the "boundless deep" in glass boats, because the seas will then have engulfed the land. However, we shall probably find a substitute for steel which is much better than glass, and so obviate the need for undermining ourselves in quest of silicon dioxide. Besides, who can say with certainty that men will use wheels in the remote nonmetal age? Let this perverted humor suffice to ridicule the finality that some people attach to the impending exhaustion of certain expendable materials essential to industry in its twentieth-century stage. The prospect is bright and unlimited if we but view it optimistically.

As we exhaust our minerals we shall become increasingly dependent upon soils, plants, and water as the bases of cultural progress. The renewable resources will prevail after the expendables have corroded and evaporated away. It is therefore much more important to perpetuate those capable of renewal than to stretch the fugitive ones. Their relative future value may be approximated in the proportionate space devoted to them in this book. A long view indeed, but a conservator must not be shortsighted.

The renewable resources will prevail

Steel towns will be ghost towns when their supply of ore has gone, unless they anticipate their dilemma and take steps to meet it. All of those now flourishing may not boom and glow in the year 2000 as they do today. Unless they make transition while still smelting iron, they will be hard-hit when the furnace fires go out. No enterprise, no community, no culture based upon extractive exploitation can endure after the resource upon which it depends has been expended. It must either find a renewable resource to support itself or die a natural death. The alert conservator would commence the transition before the crises arrive. Crises did we say? There will be no crisis; supply and demand, through price, will make the transition. The ascendancy of renewable resources over the expendables is implicit in a new term, *chemurgy,* coined to identify the fabrication of "homemade" materials into "store-bought" articles, the conversion of products from the soil into products from the factory. Previously mentioned were plastics from soybeans, a good example; one might enumerate a long list of other useful articles made by applying technology to a vegetable material. Many plastics are wholly or partly of mineral substances at present, but they may contain fewer mineral ingredients as time goes by. The rapid growth of the plastics industry during recent years indicates almost unlimited future possibilities. It may thrive indefinitely if we reorient our mineral conservation. Instead of fretting about shrinking ore bodies and oil pools, let us pay more attention to the mineral plant nutrients and trace elements essential to high soil fertility. Without them to produce healthy plants we should really be in a quandary, and without any known substitute to make it a dilemma. In the dark and distant future, phosphate, nitrate, and potash may be the big three; not coal, iron, and oil. Our needed supplies may be won from the sea by scientific methods.

From the limited perspective we now command it appears likely that civilization will one day depend entirely upon the renewable, regenerative resources. The change will not come soon, and it will not come suddenly; but come it must, in due time. It will probably begin before the year 2000, accompanied by intensified search for expendables. Could it be that the shift has, indeed, commenced even now?

As our expendables decline, as our population grows, and as our needs increase, the planned allocation of surface space becomes increasingly urgent, the better to sustain and employ our durable wealth from land and water. Our future prosperity will be commensurate with our vision in developing surface land use, reorganizing economic structure, and rearranging industrial facilities to suit the new order. Attributes of land and water will reorient our geographic culture pattern as mineral deposits relax their magnetic grip. People and industry will gravitate ever more toward areas with a good combination of soil and water resources. Cultural stability and social security will improve in the degree to which conservation attends the process.

Planned allocation of space becomes increasingly urgent

The propitious allotment of space for various purposes will become more and more important in conservation, and early planning is our best assurance that it will be wisely brought about. Factors of surface space and pattern deserve more attention than conservators have given them. They will assert themselves with increasing force as our land fills up and the nation matures. While total population may neither crowd our space nor strain the reproductive capacity of our durable resources for some time to come, the spotted distribution of our people and the continual change of regional population densities have already created many problems for the conservator. The recurrent rerouting of highways and the constant extension of road nets lay increased claim to space in competition with other land uses. The question whether any given area shall be devoted to basic production, to facilities, or to conveniences must be faced by the planners-conservators. That question resolved, they must be further concerned with the relegation to crops, to pasture, to forest, to water storage, or to other use, according to land capability and human needs, of the space earmarked for productive management. Planning experts are well aware of these responsibilities, and their demonstrated competence to discharge them gives us added confidence in the future. Optimum employment of space is a prime objective of planning, be it national, regional, or local in scope. With this facet perhaps more than with any other, planning is indispensable to conservation, and geography indispensable to planning.

Planning calls to mind the opportunity for better regional coordination and technical integration in our conservation work. Natural resources differ from one region to another, and techniques should be adapted accordingly. Much as the people might wish it, no region can conserve resources with which it is not endowed. Attempts to do so are bound to fail, doing more ill than good. When men try to make fields out of rough timber land or land too dry for any use more intensive than open range, they handicap themselves by flaunting the natural order. They penalize other parts of the nation that must pay for the experiment. The nation fares best when each of its component parts contributes what it can most efficiently and reliably produce. This dynamic phase of regional economic geography should never be neglected by the conservator.

Regional coordination and technical integration must be achieved

Regional division of labor pertains to conservation as well as to any other activity, and it can be applied to good advantage in resource management. Regional specialization or diversification will coincide with natural resource boundaries under conditions of open and free competition. That is as it should be. That is how a farm conservation plan lays out divisions between cropland, pasture, and woodland. An enlarged farm plan could be devised for the nation. It is an ideal toward which planning and conservation project us. Planners envisage regions that complement each other much as do classes of land on one farm. They would have regions best suited to forest produce wood primarily,

those best suited to grazing, to meat and wool, and so on. Resource conservation becomes operative on a grand scale when
regional planning puts human occupance in harmony with natural attributes and when cultural emphasis is placed where it
belongs. Let us quit the folly of trying to build a regional economy that the region cannot sustain. Permanence with flexibility
constitutes a major tenet of conservation.

In areas well endowed with natural wealth, diversification of
resource use is desirable, reducing the problem of outside coor-

**The technical
work of experts
needs
coordination
by a "general
manager"** dination while at the same time multiplying technical problems
within. A general, or combination, land economy lends security
to a region much as crop diversification does to an individual
farm, but either case complicates resource management. A specialized area may need only one kind of technician, whereas a
diversified one must have several. This is where our administrative organization appears defective; it is not consistent with
the need for technical integration. Fortunately, the defects are
much less serious in practice than they appear on paper. Capable
administrators almost ignore departmental lines in their employment of technical experts from various fields. The Soil Conservation Service, for example, employs specialists in virtually every
branch of conservation, from hydrology to wildlife management.
The specialists are by training biased and prejudiced to a degree
—a forester thinks in terms of trees, an agronomist in terms of
field crops, a pedologist in terms of soil, and so on. Application
of their combined knowledge in proper proportion to solve a
given problem is a delicate function of administration. Whereas
the specialist concerns himself only with his own narrow field of
science, the administrator must view conservation in broad perspective. Whether any specialist, by virtue of seniority or appointment, is qualified to prescribe and supervise the work of
specialists in fields other than his own is a debatable question.
It is probably better to select administrators who understand
conservation generally and know what each discipline can contribute to a total program. Leading conservators, both practical
and academic, have recently recognized the unique value of
"generalists" and have elevated to professional level the university graduate trained for a general *conservation* career. Much of
the optimism expressed in this book springs from the confidence
that young men who study conservation in all its aspects and
practical ramifications will elevate it to genuine professional
status. They may have more to do with our future than all the
scientific specialists put together. Every professional conservator

should be thoroughly grounded in geography, lest he be handicapped by narrow perspective.

A unified program, incorporating all aspects of conservation and every kind of resource, must replace divergent approaches and isolated projects. Our environment is a mosaic of many parts, each of which influences every other. One resource cannot be exalted and another debased when all are so related that they rise or fall together. Experience has taught us the utter futility of guarding one resource and ignoring others upon which the chosen one depends. It has been a costly lesson, and one we cannot afford to forget. Conservators must constantly remind themselves that the unity in nature is their best guide to good resource management and that regional variety is a source of national strength.

Unity in conservation must be achieved without infringing upon democratic freedoms, because such a price would be too high to pay for any kind of material wealth. Resources would lose their worth were they to be conserved at the expense of individual dignity and free enterprise. American democracy was bought and paid for with natural resources; it can best be preserved by ensuring their permanence. That is a tenet on which the conservator should base his propositions.

There are several ways by which unification in conservation can proceed and several trends that indicate progress. Administrative reorganization is one way, geographic consolidation another, and group association of private interests, a third. All three have possibilities. At first blush one might assume that private operators in a competitive economy are too busy trying to beat the other fellow to take time out and talk with him. The facts are quite different. Competition continues, it is true, but cooperation has become remarkably important in industrial circles. "Dirty competitors" are also "worthy associates" in the common interest of the business they represent.

Some sort of association, institute, or other group organization serves virtually all the major resource users or producers—lumbermen, stockmen, coal miners, oil producers, farmers, sportsmen, fishermen, and many more. Their purpose is not monopoly, but common security, which demands a unified approach to conservation. This voluntary, practical unification has many good implications for our future prospect.

Geographic consolidation relates to the regional coordination discussed a few paragraphs ago, with certain elaborations and refinements. Along with argument for regional treatment one

A unified program must replace divergent approaches

must remember that several resources are often intermingled or interspersed in one unit of space, as, for example, soils, water, plants, and wildlife on a farm. One must remember that regional organization on paper can be a pretense, as when river basins are "developed" with attention only to water. The fanfare and noise do no good unless accompanied by intelligent action that encompasses all the resources. One should be mindful also that drainage units or watersheds, for all their inherent advantages, constitute only one kind of natural division, and that other geographic factors such as climate, topography, soil, or vegetation may also be logical bases for regional resource management. The strongest unifying factor, the most valuable resource, be it water or something else, might be the best criterion for regional definition and resource management.

Natural versus political boundaries

Assuming that natural geographic boundaries have an important bearing on conservation, how may we better employ them? Shall we erase the arbitrary lines that separate our counties and states and redraw them to coincide with natural boundaries, or shall we continue the involved process of combining numerous political segments into one superimposed conservation unit? TVA incorporates parts of seven states, but it took a big stick from Congress to unite them. Shall we proclaim that resource unity transcends politics, or shall we retain our extravagant political compartments? From a purely economic standpoint the subdivision of states into horse-and-buggy counties is preposterous. Whenever economy dictates consolidation or dissolution of delinquent counties, it affords an opportunity to reconcile political and geographic boundaries—a fertile field for the planner-conservator. A dozen "natural" counties would probably be enough for any state, including Texas, which now contains 254. The reduction would improve government, reduce graft and other costs, and facilitate conservation. Concurrent with internal unification, planners might go a step further and eliminate useless boundaries between the states. The savings from politico-geographic reorganization might pay for a unified conservation program, but the prospect for a more logical political arrangement is dubious at best. Wishful thinking may be the beginning, so let us wish.

Governmental organization will be improved

Reorganization of state and federal governments for closer coordination of conservation activities shows positive trends that augur well for the future. During recent years several mergers and transfers of administrative agencies have strengthened conservation at both state and federal levels. Several states have established under one name or another permanent departments for the conservation of natural resources. Missouri, Ohio and Wisconsin are good examples. These states, and a few others, are ahead of the Federal government in organized resource management.

Organization at the federal level has experienced some renovating, despite difficulties; cabinet members and department and bureau heads often resist changes that might deflate their little empires. This is not a slur on any of the officials, most of whom are simply demonstrating the courage of their convictions when they guard their own establishments; it is merely by way of indicating that structural alterations can rarely be expected from within. One recent exception was the merger of the Biological Survey and the Bureau of Fisheries to form the Fish and Wildlife Service, placed in the Department of the Interior. Changes at cabinet level, though rare, were also made to evolve the present Bureau of Land Management. Many more changes can be anticipated as public opinion grows strong enough to assert itself. Eventually we may have a Secretary of Conservation in Washington with his fingers on every major resource. It will not be easy to determine whether soils belong under "Agriculture" or "Resources," or whether "Interior" shall be dissolved or renamed; Americans may have to decide those issues at some future date. The prospect for a wise reorganization depends upon public enlightenment.

In the last analysis, the American citizen will determine how well we conserve our natural wealth, because every citizen in a democracy is a policy maker. The conservator can do nothing more constructive than to inform the people and to arouse citizen interest. Resource management cannot be successful and comprehensive before public consciousness decrees that it shall be so. Man, whose creature existence depends upon his use of resources, must be made to see clearly that all his worldly goods, his health, his comforts, and his happiness can be secured indefinitely for him and his children by wise conservation. Above all, he must grasp the idea that complete use of a resource for maximum benefit to mankind is, in fact, conservation. When a sufficient majority of our people have learned that fundamental concept, group action will vouchsafe for us and posterity the perpetual replenishment of natural stores that sustain life and society. Until then, education and information will remain the conservator's best tools.

Conservation is not difficult to sell if the approach is right. Sales resistance breaks down when the merchandise is honestly shown. A clever saleslady sells gowns to coeds by exclaiming

The citizen must be sold the idea of conservation

with forced enthusiasm, "it really *does* something for you." The conservator can say truthfully to everyone that conservation does much for him, directly or indirectly, sooner or later. Good soil in the country means good business in town. Good grass on the plains means good steaks in the city, today and tomorrow. Conservation is our assurance of good business and good steaks day after tomorrow, next year, and in the year 2000.

Emergent citizen interest paves the way to future prosperity

Adequately informed, the individual turns conservator for his own good, and often as not identifies himself with one group or other actively interested in some phase of conservation. Almost every resource now has its group of defenders—practical, idealistic, or otherwise—and the groups are beginning to reconcile their views and pull together. (The appendix contains a partial listing of organizations.) The manifest unity in nature and the universal interdependence of resources will inevitably assert a unifying influence on conservation activities. Education stimulates interest; interest motivates to action; and action by individuals and groups achieves the desired results. Education must come first, and the others follow. Our manifold media for disseminating information—press, radio, television, schools, churches, movies, and so on—lay the foundation for conservation by informing our self-governing public.

The public is becoming informed and concerned. What is more, the public is becoming articulate and active in conservation matters. People in all walks of life are beginning to see the real importance of natural resources and the urgency of conserving them. That fact strengthens our hope for the future, because genuine progress under democracy must come by democratic procedures.

Education of our youth secures the future

Concerted implementation of a policy can be a reality tomorrow if we instruct our youth intelligently today. On nothing else does our future so much depend; in no area of instruction can the rewards be greater. No subject lends itself better to informal presentation and practical approach, and none better to active student participation (Fig. 17.1). None has so many potential instructors, because in the teaching of applied conservation good common sense often means more than formal training and fancy words. It can be taught well under many different circumstances, in many different ways, and by many different kinds of people.

Everyone who uses a resource wisely, be he farmer, manufacturer, sportsman, fisherman, or tourist, gives object lessons in conservation. The technicians and administrators who work in conservation endeavor to teach the public how to use resources

Fig. 17.1 *The author and conservation students planting slash pine seedlings. The teacher who demonstrates and supervises the planting of forest should be mindful that impact of the experience on young minds is the main objective. Tree survival and growth are quite incidental, except as the young planters retain an interest in their project. A few inexpensive plants can generate genuine community pride. (Photo by Harold J. Price, courtesy East Tennessee University.)*

without wasting or abusing them. Professional and business people who know where their bread is buttered also spread the word. Thus, much conservation teaching is done by persons who are not regarded as teachers in the ordinary sense. They dispense practical knowledge, without classrooms or recitations.

For our schoolteachers, privileged to instruct young people, the challenge and opportunity are especially great. It is appropriate that we devote some space to the *teacher-conservators* who instill in young minds the sense of values and responsibility on which we pin our highest hopes for the future.

The work can begin in the first grade, allied with such basic personality traits as thrift, respect for property, and the Golden Rule. Conservation has a place in religious instruction and should certainly be an important part of citizenship training. The fundamental concepts of conservation and the general idea of resource consciousness can be incorporated with several areas of elementary learning, such as nature study, health, art apprecia-

From kindergarten to university, we need good teacher-conservators!

473

tion, and others. The good elementary teacher sows the seeds of conservation upon which we have based our optimistic forecast. The seeds strike root without benefit of big words like "resources" and "conservation."

Throughout the grades and high school, opportunities for teaching conservation become progressively more varied and definite, notably in the areas of natural and social sciences and especially in geography. It is vitally important that sound conservation concepts be developed at this level of instruction, lest our future conservators be only those fortunate enough to attend college. Whether conservation should be taught in elementary and secondary schools as a separate subject or integrated with others is a matter for school administrators and supervisors to determine. The objectives can probably be gained about as well under one system as under the other if administrative policy is favorable and the teachers themselves are sufficiently indoctrinated. This book should assist with the suitable indoctrination of elementary and high-school teachers and should contribute something to the understandings of those who determine what shall be taught—superintendents, board members, and parents.

A survey of natural resources and their conservation should certainly be offered in every liberal-arts college in the United States. No general education curriculum can be considered adequate without it; a teacher-training program that omits it is positively defective. It is gratifying to note that many of our teacher-training institutions offer at least one separate course in conservation of natural resources; many such institutions conduct special short courses to keep in-service teachers up to date. The conservation conference that mingles several academic specialists with their counterparts in practical work can be a most profitable experience for everyone concerned. A project such as a tree plantation can be an object lesson to students and a generator of community interest as well.

So broad is the scope of conservation that no subject-matter area or discipline can claim it entirely as its own. It combines **Many disciplines contribute to conservation education** many fields of learning and treats many kinds of material. On the one hand, it borrows from basic earth sciences such as geology, pedology, meteorology, ecology, and oceanography; on the other hand, it employs applied sciences such as agriculture, forestry, and engineering under conditions dictated by economics, sociology, history, and politics. It combines natural, physical, and social sciences in the interest of material culture.

Since conservation depends upon a unified program, it appears that successful conservation teaching should have a unified, comprehensive approach. It should not give undue attention to one resource at the expense of another, nor should it emphasize natural factors to the neglect of the cultural. Since a central theme of geography is the interpretation of man's relationship to his total earth environment—correlation of the natural with the cultural—it follows that trained geographers have a professional obligation to teach resource conservation. Other sciences such as biology, agronomy, chemistry, and economics make distinct and essential contributions to conservation, but none of them has the inclusive viewpoint of geography. Other educators may conduct a balanced conservation course by engaging an appropriate variety of scientists and practical conservationists, but continuity and perspective may be difficult to maintain. Geography bridges the gap between the physical and social sciences; that bridge is indeed the essence of conservation.

Conservation education is a task so big and so vital that there is no time to quarrel about its academic province; rather, let every instructor cooperate whenever possible in any program designed to convey to young men and women the basic concepts of resource conservation. Let the teaching be practical rather than theoretical. Let the ideas inculcated be applicable and profitable rather than academic and idealistic. Let it be emphasized that conservation must pay its own way and can pay its way when intelligently applied. Such teaching is the foundation of perpetual wealth and continuing prosperity. Schoolteachers hold the keys to America's future. Their labors will ultimately secure the concerted public action by which conservation can be fully assured. Public action is the means—action individually and collectively—but action will not come before a consciousness is aroused. Arousing that consciousness is a major challenge to our educational system.

Our prospect will be what our actions make it. If we persist in waste, abuse, pollution, and dissipation of natural wealth, we shall indeed starve. If we apply our technical knowledge with a fraction of the intelligence it took to get it, we may be twice as numerous in the year 2000 as now, and better off besides. When eroded land, burned forests, silted reservoirs, dirty waters, dispossessed wildlife, unused minerals, soiled landscapes, and abandoned spaces become acknowledged as the forms of sabotage they are, we may envisage the bright future that conservation can secure for our democracy. Let us resolve to conserve our natural wealth with the same determination that has preserved our constitutional liberties. Wise planning and diligent conservation vouchsafe for the future the great national heritage it is our good fortune to possess. Let every true American be a conservator-patriot.

The conservator-patriot

Teaching

Aids

The conservation teacher borrows from several fields of knowledge, each with its own literature and philosophy. Eight major resource classes have been discussed in this book. Each of those classes should be treated in any survey course in resource conservation. None should be neglected, but relative emphasis might be judiciously gauged to area interests and problems. All resource classes, or fields, should be reduced to the common denominator—conservation, with its central theme of "better use for better living." To incline students toward critical evaluation and deliberate acceptance of conservation as a personal responsibility, to lead them to discover its origin in natural unity, and to observe its culmination in cultural progress should be the teacher's main objectives. These cannot be achieved unless the teacher maintains a sufficiently broad perspective, reinforced with current information on developments and trends. The following suggestions and compilations are intended to help the teacher acquire or strengthen the professional competencies and practical techniques pertinent to the immense subject area of resource conservation.

This appendix contains items of interest to teachers at all levels of instruction, from the lower grades to college. It is hoped that instructors in teacher-training institutions may find it particularly valuable. The listings provided here should be helpful in presenting conservation "methods and materials" to prospective or in-service teachers. Choice and employment of the aids to suit a given situation and a particular level

476

of instruction must devolve upon the individual teacher. Although several listings appear lengthy, indicating the scope and variety of subject areas, none of the lists is exhaustive.

SECTION A   Suggestions to the Prospective Conservation Teacher

The author would not presume to tell the established teacher how to teach a course or manage a class, but on the basis of long experience, he feels privileged to offer a few suggestions that may help the inexperienced teacher conduct a course or a unit of work in resource conservation. Here are his admonitions to anyone who contemplates conservation teaching:

1. Stress resource relationships rather than treating components as detached segments.
2. Take care that the emphasis on material things does not obscure the higher spiritual and intellectual values.
3. Be mindful that, although nature study contributes to basic understandings, the objectives of conservation are social. Do not confuse the means with the ends.
4. Remember that a teacher's primary responsibility is the conservation of people and minds, and not the direct conservation of natural resources. Beware the error of pursuing a conservation project for its own sake and neglecting its educational implications.
5. Be more concerned with concepts and attitudes than with facts and figures. Wisdom begins with knowledge.
6. Do not attempt to engage student interest with a pessimistic, negative approach. A student's "so what?" may be difficult to answer adequately. The positive, optimistic approach will stimulate more interest and better participation.
7. All outdoors is a conservation study hall and laboratory. A well-planned day in the field can be more instructive than a week in the classroom.
8. In a survey course, such as this book might serve, make the work sufficiently stimulating to attract good students and sufficiently easy to attract poor ones. The dullard may be a greater menace to resources than a more intelligent person. Do not restrict enrollment in a conservation class by imposing prerequisites.
9. In conducting a unit of study on an elementary or high-school level, take special care that students understand the limitation of scope. Otherwise they may exaggerate their qualifications as conservators. A little knowledge can be dangerous in conservation as well as in other spheres.
10. Develop some kind of constructive project involving student participation, thus combining practice with theory. Let the students

choose, plan, and carry out the activity. The skillful teacher will maneuver the students into a good choice without making the decision for them.

11. Place emphasis on the practical values of conservation rather than on sentiment and idealism. Do not confuse poetry with profits. On the other hand, do not be materialistic to the exclusion of intangible, aesthetic considerations.

12. Focus on present problems, not on those that may arise in the future. Young people are not easily persuaded to worry about posterity, perhaps because they do not wish to deprive their elders of a popular pastime. Begin with vicinal problems and proceed to state, regional, and national ones.

13. Encourage individual students to submit for class discussion any resource problem of immediate concern to themselves or to their families. If a need is clearly indicated, the teacher may seek the advice of an appropriate technician or official, and possibly bring him before the class.

14. Encourage every student to become an active member of an organization concerned with conservation. Of course, the teacher should belong to at least one such group. (See sections E and F.)

15. Explore both sides of current conservation issues. Avoid snap judgment on any controversy. Debate by opposing groups of students may be a good medium of presentation.

16. Seek the advice of experienced conservationists and conservators. Establish a working arrangement with those who can best contribute to a planned program of instruction. The visiting expert adds both substance and prestige to a course.

17. Make readily available to the students a collection of conservation literature appropriate to their educational level. (Several selections may be made from sources listed in this book.)

18. Practice what you preach!

SECTION B   **Sample List of Movie Films**

Motion pictures available are so numerous and excellent that a teacher may well conduct a once-weekly film showing open to the public as well as to students and parents. Such programs have proved highly successful. The teacher should be careful not to violate any loan agreement that prohibits an admission charge. All films should be handled carefully, shown by a competent operator, and returned promptly by insured mail or express.

It is assumed that the conservation teacher will select films to present a balance from three points of view; namely, national, regional, and community interests. Unfortunately, no film now available treats the conservation of commercial fisheries nor the general subject of mineral conservation. In other resource areas there is often a considerable choice. New films are being produced so rapidly that each edition of the *Educational Film Guide* should be checked for additions. All those in the following sampling are 16 mm, sound, and color films.

Yours is the Land, 20 minutes, Encyclopaedia Britannica Films.

Man's Problems, 18 minutes, Encyclopaedia Britannica Films.

Clean Waters, 24 minutes, General Electric.

George Washington's River, 28 minutes, United States Public Health Service.

Watershed Wildfire, 20 minutes, U.S. Forest Service, Department of Agriculture.

This is TVA, 28½ minutes, Tennessee Valley Authority.

Return to the River, 20 minutes, Brandon International Films.

All Flesh is Grass, 26 minutes, American National Cattleman's Association.

A New Look at Range Management, 27½ minutes, United States Steel Corporation.

Realm of the Wild, 28 minutes, United States Department of Agriculture.

Honkers in Illinois, 40 minutes, Illinois Department of Conservation.

Bobwhite Through the Year, 55 minutes, Missouri Conservation Commission.

Ecology: The Sea, 30 minutes, Encyclopaedia Britannica Films.

Halibut, 18 minutes, U.S. Fish and Wildlife Service.

Story of Menhaden, 21 minutes, U.S. Department of the Interior.

Story of Copper, 33 minutes, U.S. Bureau of Mines.

Iron: Product of the Blast Furnace, 14 minutes, Academy Films.

Birth of an Oil Field, 30 minutes, Shell Oil Company.

SECTION C   **Some Aids Toward Building Vocabulary**

"A Glossary of Special Terms Used in the Soils Yearbook," *Soils and Men: Yearbook of Agriculture, 1938* (Washington, D.C., 1938), pp. 1162-1180.

"A Glossary of the Mining and Mineral Industry," *Bulletin 95,* U.S. Bureau of Mines (Washington, D.C., 1947).

Carpenter, J. Richard, *An Ecological Glossary* (Norman, Okla.: University of Oklahoma Press, 1938).

Dayton, W. A., *Glossary of Botanical Terms Commonly Used in Range Research, Miscellaneous Publication No. 110,* U. S. Department of Agriculture (Washington, D.C., 1950).

Five-page glossary of fishery terms at the back of John Wiley & Sons, Inc., "Fishery Science" by G. A. Rounsefell and W. H. Everhart (New York: John Wiley & Sons, Inc., 1953).

Forest Terminology, Society of American Foresters (Washington, D.C., 1950).

"Glossary of Geology and Related Sciences," *Publication 501,* American Geological Institute, National Academy of Sciences, National Research Council (Washington, D.C., 1957).

Range Conservation Glossary, Soil Conservation Service (Washington, D.C., 1944), 18 pages, mimeographed.

Soil and Water Conservation Glossary, Soil Conservation Society of America (Des Moines, Iowa, 1952).

"Some Words Woodsmen Use," *Trees: Yearbook of Agriculture, 1949* (Washington, D.C., 1949), pp. 911-916.

Alfred H. Thiessen, compiler, *Weather Glossary,* U.S. Weather Bureau (Washington, D.C., 1949).

SECTION D   **Public Source Agencies**

The following agencies (public and semipublic) should be contacted by the conservation teacher as appropriate. Several of them can furnish materials specially prepared for the teacher. Some are in position to sponsor certain activities, to participate in the school program, or to help the teacher in other ways:

1. Federal Agencies with a primary interest in resource use and conservation: (Periodicals listed under certain agencies are available from the Superintendent of Documents, Washington, D.C., for a nominal subscription fee. Most of the agencies listed have area representatives from whom a teacher may get personal advice and assistance. Several of these agencies have special educational displays, posters, and attractive reading material available to teachers for the asking. A copy of their annual reports will help keep teacher and students up to date.)

National Park Service, Department of Interior.

Office of Defense Mobilization, Executive Office of the President, Washington 25, D.C.

Tennessee Valley Authority, Knoxville, Tenn.

Our Public Lands, U.S. Bureau of Land Management, Department of Interior, Washington 25, D.C.

U.S. Bureau of Mines, Department of Interior.

U.S. Bureau of Outdoor Recreation, Department of Interior.

The Reclamation Era, U.S. Bureau of Reclamation, Department of Interior.

Wildlife Review and *Commercial Fisheries Review,* U. S. Fish and Wildlife Service, Department of Interior.

U.S. Forest Service, U.S. Department of Agriculture.

Soil Conservation, U.S. Soil Conservation Service, U.S. Department of Agriculture, Washington 25, D.C.

2. Federal agencies whose activities and publications are of special interest to the conservator, although conservation is not their special responsibility:

Economic Research Service, U.S. Department of Agriculture.

Bureau of the Census.

Federal Power Commission.

Industrial Reference Service, Department of Commerce, Bureau of Foreign and Domestic Commerce.

Interstate Commerce Commission, Department of Commerce.

Legislative Reference Service, Library of Congress.

Agricultural Stabilization and Conservation Service, U.S. Department of Agriculture.

Public Health Service.

Public Roads Administration.

U.S. Corps of Engineers (Army), Department of the Army.

U.S. Geological Survey, Department of Interior.

U.S. Office of Education.

Monthly Weather Review and *Daily Weather Map,* U.S. Weather Bureau.

3. State agencies of special interest to the teacher-conservator are variously organized and named in different states. The conservation teacher should refer to a directory of state offices or officials in order to establish desirable contacts. It makes little difference whether a particular agency is designated a department, board, commission, bureau, or something else; key words such as the following are a better guide:

Agriculture	Fisheries	Geology	Planning
Conservation	Forestry	Health	Resources
Education	Game and Fish	Mines	State Parks

The teacher should be acquainted with several state-office designations, at least. An inquiry directed to any one of them will either be answered by that office or be routed to another office better qualified to make reply. Ignorance of state government is not a valid excuse for ignorance of state resources and conservation activities. Most states publish a good conservation magazine or bulletin that the conservation teacher should read.

4. Local persons and groups may help a teacher carry out desirable school activities or projects. At the local level, civic and semiofficial agencies can be especially helpful. Local contacts can be invaluable to the conservation teacher. One or several of the following officials and organizations may give practical assistance:

Banks and Loan Associations	Community Clubs
Business, professional, and civic or commercial clubs	County Agent or Farm Advisor
	Fire Warden
Chamber of Commerce	Game Warden
College or University Departments offering work in conservation	Industrialists
	Merchants

Section E   **Helpful Organizations**

Organizations from whom the teacher may obtain periodic or timely reports dealing with particular resource and conservation developments are:

American Automobile Association, 1712 G Street, N.W., Washington 6, D.C.

American Camping Association, Bradford Woods, Martinsville, Ind.

American Congress On Surveying and Mapping, 733 15th Street, N.W., Washington 5, D.C.

American Fisheries Society, Box 483, McLean, Va.

American Forest Products Industries, 1816 N Street, N.W., Washington 6, D.C.

American Gas Association, 420 Lexington Avenue, New York 17, N.Y.

American Meteorological Society, 45 Beacon Street, Boston 8, Mass.

American National Cattlemen's Association, 801 East 17th Avenue, Denver 18, Colo.

American Nature Study Society, % Beth Schultz, Department of Biology, Western Michigan University, Kalamazoo, Mich.

American Petroleum Institute, 1271 Avenue of the Americas, New York 20, N.Y.

American Planning and Civic Association, 901 Union Trust Bldg., 15th and H Streets, N.W., Washington 5, D.C.

American Recreation Society, Inc., Bond Building, 1404 New York Avenue, N.W., Washington 5, D.C.

American Shore and Beach Preservation Association, 810 18th Street, N.W., Washington 6, D.C.

American Society of Civil Engineers, 33 West 39th Street, New York 18, N.Y.

American Society of Limnology and Oceanography, Department of Zoology, University of Michigan, Ann Arbor, Mich.

American Society of Planning Officials, 1313 East 60th St., Chicago 37, Ill.

Anthracite Institute, 237 Old Road, Wilkes-Barre, Pa.

Battelle Memorial Institute, 505 King Avenue, Columbus 1, Ohio.

Bituminous Coal Research, Inc., 121 Meyran Avenue, Pittsburgh 13, Pennsylvania.

Boy Scouts of America, New Brunswick, N.J.

Camp Fire Girls, 16 East 48th St., New York 17, N.Y.

Chamber of Commerce of the United States, 1615 H Street, N.W., Washington 6, D.C.

Charles Lathrop Pack Forestry Foundation, 1500 Massachusetts Avenue, N.W., Suite 841, Washington 5, D.C.

Citizens For Conservation, Front Royal, Va.

Conservation Education Association, % Dr. W. F. Clark, Eastern Montana College, Billings, Mont.

Conservation Foundation, 30 East 40th Street, New York 16, N.Y.

Defenders of Wildlife, 1346 Connecticut Avenue, N.W., Washington 6, D.C.

Federation of Western Outdoor Clubs, President, 201 South Ashdale Street, West Conina, Calif.

Future Farmers of America, Dept. of Health, Education, and Welfare, Washington 25, D.C.

Future Homemakers of America, Office of Education, Department of Health, Education, and Welfare, Washington 25, D.C.

Garden Club of America, 598 Madison Avenue, New York 22, N.Y.

General Federation of Women's Clubs, 1734 N Street, N.W., Washington, D.C.

Grassland Research Foundation, Box 684, Woodward, Okla.

International Oceanographic Foundation, 439 Anastasia Avenue, Coral Gables 34, Fla.

International Harvester Co., 180 North Michigan Ave., Chicago 1, Ill.

Keep America Beautiful, Inc., 99 Park Ave., New York 16, N.Y.

National Conference on State Parks, 901 Union Trust Bldg., Washington 5, D.C.

National Council of State Garden Clubs, 4401 Magnolia Avenue, St. Louis 22, Mo.

National Education Association, 1201 16th St., N.W., Washington 6, D.C.

National Fisheries Institute, Inc., 1614 20th St., N.W., Washington 9, D.C.

National Lumber Manufacturers Association, 1319 18th St. N.W., Washington 6, D.C.

National Rifle Association of America, 1600 Rhode Island Ave., N.W., Washington 6, D.C.

National Society for the Study of Education, 5835 Kimbark Ave., Chicago 37, Ill.

National Waterfowl Council, State Game Commission, Box 4136, Portland 8, Ore.

National Wildlife Federation, 1412 16th Street, N.W., Washington 6, D.C.

Natural Resources Council of America, 709 Wire Building, Washington 5, D.C.

Nature Conservancy, 2039 K Street, N.W., Washington 6, D.C.

New York Zoological Society, 30 East 40th Street, New York 16, N.Y.

North American Wildlife Foundation, 709 Wire Bldg., Washington 5, D.C.

Outdoor Education Association, 800 South Illinois Avenue, Carbondale, Ill.

Pacific Northwest Bird and Mammal Society, Route 1, Box 505, Spanaway, Wash.

Resources For The Future, 1775 Massachusetts Avenue, N.W., Washington 6, D.C.

Save-the-Redwoods League, 114 Sansome Street, San Francisco 4, Calif.

Sierra Club, 1050 Mills Tower, San Francisco 4, Calif.

Southern Pine Association, 520 National Bank of Commerce Building, New Orleans 12, La.

Southern Pulpwood Conservation Association, 900 Peachtree Street, N.E., Atlanta 9, Ga.

Sport Fishing Institute, 1404 New York Avenue, N.W., Washington 5, D.C.

Water Information Center, Inc., 44 Sintsink Drive East, Port Washington, Long Island, N.Y.

West Coast Lumbermen's Association, 1410 S.W. Morrison St., Portland 5, Ore.

Wild Flower Preservation Society, 3740 Oliver St., Washington 15, D.C.

Wildlife Management Institute, 709 Wire Bldg., Washington 5, D.C.

Wildlife Restoration, 17 West 60th Street, New York 23, N.Y.

Many leading manufacturers and several other industrial organizations have excellent teaching aids available free of charge. They may be contacted through their magazine advertisements.

SECTION F **Periodicals**

Periodicals of special interest to the teacher-conservator (obviously the organizations that publish the periodicals are concerned with resources and conservation and may provide special assistance):

American Biology Teacher, National Association of Biology Teachers, Teachers College, Temple University, Philadelphia 22, Pa.

American Economic Review, American Economics Association, Northwestern University, Evanston, Ill.

American Forests, The American Forestry Association, 919 17th St. N.W., Washington 6, D.C.

American Geophysical Union, Transactions, 1515 Massachusetts Avenue, N.W., Washington 6, D.C.

American Institute of Planners, Journal, 2400 Sixteenth Street, N.W., Washington 9, D.C.

Annals, American Academy of Political and Social Science, 3937 Chestnut Street, Philadelphia 4, Pa.

Annals and *Professional Geographer,* The Association of American Geographers, 1785 Massachusetts Avenue, N.W., Washington 6, D.C.

Audubon Magazine, The National Audubon Society, 1130 Fifth Avenue, New York 28, N.Y.

Auk, American Ornithological Union, Cornell University, Ithaca, N.Y.

Better Roads Magazine, 173 West Madison St., Chicago 2, Ill.

Chemical Week, McGraw-Hill Book Company, Inc., 330 W. 42nd St., New York 36, N.Y.

Civil Engineering, American Society of Civic Engineers, 345 East 47th Street, New York 17, N.Y.

Conservation News, Conservation Directory (Annual), *Conservation Report,* and *National Wildlife Magazine,* National Wildlife Federation, 1412 16th Street, N.W., Washington 6, D.C.

The Conservation Yearbook (annual), 26 Enterprise Bldg., 1740 K Street, N.W., Washington 6, D.C.

Ecological Monographs, Ecological Society of America, Duke University Press, Durham, N.C.

Ecology, Ecological Society of America, Duke University Press, Durham, N.C.

Economic Geography, Clark University, Graduate School of Geography, Worcester, Mass.

Economic Geology, Economic Geology Publishing Co., Natural Resources Bldg., University of Illinois, Urbana, Ill.

Engineering and Mining Journal, McGraw-Hill Book Company, Inc., 330 W. 42nd St., New York 36, N.Y.

The Farm Quarterly, The Automobile Digest Publishing Co., 22 East 12th Street, Cincinnati 10, Ohio.

The Forest Farmer, The Forest Farmers Association Cooperative, 1100 Crescent Avenue, N.E., Box 7284, Station C., Atlanta, Ga.

Geographical Review and *Focus,* American Geographical Society, Broadway at 156th St., New York 32, N.Y.

Geological News Letter, American Geological Institute, 1606 Northeast Thompson, Portland 12, Ore.

Geological Society of America, Bulletin, Mt. Royal and Guilford Avenues, Baltimore 2, Md.

The Johnson National Driller's Journal, 315 North Pierce Street, St. Paul 4, Minn.

Journal of Agricultural and Food Chemistry, American Chemical Society, 1155 16th St., N.W., Washington 6, D.C.

Journal of the American Water Works Association, 2 Park Avenue, New York 16, N.Y.

Journal of Farm Economics, American Farm Economic Association, Menasha, Wis.

Journal of Forestry, Society of American Foresters, Mills Bldg., Washington 6, D.C.

Journal of Geography, published by A. J. Nystrom & Co. for the National Council of Geography Teachers, 3333 Elston Ave., Chicago 18, Ill.

Journal of Geology, University of Chicago Press, 5750 Ellis Ave., Chicago, Ill.

Journal of Range Management, American Society of Range Management, Box 5041, Portland 13, Ore.

Journal of Soil and Water Conservation, Soil Conservation Society of America, 838 Fifth Avenue, Des Moines, Iowa.

Journal of Wildlife Management, Wildlife Society, 2000 P Street, N.W., Washington 6, D.C.

The Land, Izaak Walton League, 1326 Waukegan Road, Glenview, Ill.

Land Economics, University of Wisconsin, Madison 6, Wis.

The Living Wilderness, The Wilderness Society, 2144 P Street, N.W., Washington 7, D.C.

Mining Engineering, American Institute of Mining and Metallurgical Engineers, 345 East 47th Street, New York 17, N.Y.

Modern Metals, Modern Metals Publishing Co., 435 N. Michigan Ave., Chicago, Ill.

National 4-H News, National Committee of Boys and Girls Club Work, Inc., 59 E. Van Buren St., Chicago, Ill.

National Geographic Magazine, National Geographic Society, Washington 6, D.C.

National Parks Magazine, National Parks Association, 1300 New Hampshire Avenue, N.W., Washington 6, D.C.

Natural History and *Nature Magazine,* American Museum of Natural History, Central Park West at 79th Street, New York 24, N.Y.

Outdoor America, Izaak Walton League of America, 1326 Waukegan Road, Glenview, Ill.

Pacific Fisherman, Miller Freeman Publications, 731 Southwest Oak Street, Portland 5, Ore.

Parks and Recreation Magazine, American Institute of Park Executives, Inc., Oglebay Park, Wheeling, W. Va.

Proceedings, Soil Science Society of America, 2702 Monroe St., Madison 5, Wis.

Recreation, National Recreation Association, 8 West 8th Street, New York 11, N.Y.

Science Digest, Science Digest, Inc., 200 E. Ontario St., Chicago 11, Ill.

"Science in Review," Sunday *New York Times,* 229 West 43rd St., New York, N.Y.

Science News Letter, Science Service, Inc., 1719 N St., N.W., Washington 6, D.C.

Scientific American, Scientific American, Inc., 415 Madison Avenue, New York 17, N.Y.

Science, American Association for the Advancement of Science, 1515 Massachusetts Ave., N.W., Washington 5, D.C.

Sea Frontiers and *Sea Secrets,* The International Oceanographic Foundation, Miami 49, Fla.

Steel Facts and *Steelways,* American Iron and Steel Institute, 150 East 42nd Street, New York 17, N.Y.

Water Newsletter, Water Information Center, Inc., Port Washington, Long Island, N.Y.

Watershed, American Watershed Council, Inc., Peoples Bldg., Fairmont, W.Va.

Weatherwise (The Magazine About Weather), 45 Beacon Street, Boston 8, Mass.

What's New in Crops and Soils and *Agronomy Journal,* The American Society of Agronomy, 2702 Monroe St., Madison 5, Wis.

Excellent articles on conservation appear in farm journals and other magazines, both popular and erudite.

SECTION G   **Class Work Suggestions**

Suggested class activities and group projects: (Obviously, the choice and manner of employment will vary with locale, educational level, curriculum, and school situation.)

1. Activities:
   a. Field trips:
      (1) To study the soil profile.
      (2) To make a soil test.
      (3) To observe soil erosion or its consequences.
      (4) To observe water pollution.
      (5) To compare wildlife habitats.
      (6) To compare conditions in a healthy forest or grassland area with those resulting from burning or overgrazing.
      (7) To observe good and bad forestry practices, range management, or farming.
      (8) To trace the local water supply from source to outlet.
      (9) To observe bird banding or fish tagging, or both. (Be sure students understand the importance of returning or reporting the tags and bands.)

   b. Camping:
   The group camp is an elaboration of the field-trip technique, with the advantages of more concentrated study, experience in group liv-

ing, and better opportunity to learn good outdoor manners by actual practice. The nature camp conducted in an area removed from cultural developments affords special opportunity for children to acquire such fundamental concepts as natural unity, natural balance, and natural cycles.

Whether or not camping is incorporated with school work, children might be encouraged to participate in such youth camps as conducted by the Boy Scouts and the 4-H Clubs.

c. Visits and conducted tours (any one of the following has good educational possibilities):

  (1) Visit to a well-managed farm or ranch.
  (2) Tour of a logging operation and pulpmill or sawmill.
  (3) Tour of an integrated wood-using plant.
  (4) Visit to a mine or oil field.
  (5) Visit to a fish wharf, fish market, or fish cannery. (If possible, include a fishing cruise.)
  (6) National Park tour conducted by a park naturalist.
  (7) Visit to a nature area, wildlife refuge, or wilderness.
  (8) Visit to a "hydro" development for power, irrigation, flood prevention, and so forth.
  (9) Visit to a sanitary landfill.
  (10) Tour of a sewage-treatment plant.
  (11) Visit to a fish hatchery or game farm.
  (12) Visit to a public park for a cook-out. (A unique opportunity for teaching fire discipline and landscape sanitation by the direct, informal method.)
  (13) Visit to a USDA experiment station or other experimental establishment involving natural resources.
  (14) Visit to a forest tree nursery.
  (15) Visit to a metal-concentration plant or ore smelter.
  (16) Visit to any of the public or private agencies named in this appendix.
  (17) Visit to a wood-preserving plant.

d. Student investigations and reports:

Student contributions to a conservation course, either as individuals or in committee, may run the whole gamut of resource problems from local water supply or land economy to state law and national policy.

The class should have a voice in the selection of problems for special study, and, as far as possible, each student should be allowed a choice of research topics. Findings should be delivered orally for class discussion, the better to benefit both the investigator and his classmates. The possible choice of topics is almost unlimited. The number assigned should be gauged carefully against available class time to avoid the frustration caused by omitting a report after it has been readied for presentation.

e. Collection of literature and teaching materials:

The instructor of in-service and prospective teachers may elect to assemble for each a file of free and inexpensive conservation literature for school use. The author knows from experience that a very considerable collection can be acquired during a twelve-week course. (A wooden apple box serves well as a file.) Also on the basis of experience, the author would caution against the waste of useful materials occasioned by delivering them to students who fail to use them.

Many of the agencies and organizations named in this appendix are sources of material, but perhaps only a few selected ones should be contracted during any term or semester course. Any type or item of information desired should be requested by one letter in sufficient copies for the entire class, thereby saving secretarial time and shipping expense. Never should the instructor permit several students to address individual inquiries to the same source.

f. Course or program planning for teachers:

In a teacher-training institution that offers only one course in conservation, that course should include some work in materials and methods. Actual preparation for conservation teaching may be facilitated by dividing the class into groups according to the grade level at which the class members teach or intend to teach and by requiring each group to prepare a definite plan or guide for future use. Such group planning can be a most profitable experience. When combined with the collection activity (Section e above), including evaluation and graduation of the collected materials, it is particularly valuable. (A teacher-training institution, especially if it operates on a term basis, should offer two terms of work in conservation—a preliminary *survey* course which introduces the entire conservation field and a *professional* course dealing with materials and methods in conservation education.)

g. Essay contests and publicity campaigns:

Conservation students should be encouraged to enter essay contests sponsored by various organizations and business firms, with teacher emphasis, of course, on educational values rather than on prize money.

College students might be encouraged and coached to write timely articles for the local press or to speak on conservation topics before local business clubs, church groups, etc. Findings under Section d above might well merit some off-campus dissemination.

2. Projects:

a. School ground or campus improvement:

Object lessons in landscape housekeeping may be learned without leaving the school ground or campus. Students can be taught to deposit waste paper, candy wrappers, paper cups, empty bottles, etc., in proper receptacles. They can be taught to *conserve* the grass by keeping to the walks (even on corners). They can conserve, and, by example, teach their schoolmates to conserve, the beauty of their school environment.

This technique for teaching conservation may be used at any grade level. The author has a standing rule, announced in the first meeting of each conservation class: any member observed littering the campus with trash or cutting across grassed areas automatically fails the course. He allows points toward a final course grade to class members who persuade other students to refrain from spoiling the campus.

Beautification of the school ground by planting trees and shrubs or sowing grass can be an excellent learning experience for children. Bare spots and any eroding areas should be considered invitations for a conservation class to apply suitable soil-conserving measures. Many a barren, dissected school ground has been made whole and beautiful by young children supervised by a competent teacher.

(Discretion must be exercised in any school-ground, or campus, project. Prevention of normal playground wear must not be contemplated, certainly. The teacher must have administrative sanction before any alteration of grounds is commenced. If permission is granted reluctantly, the project itself, if well done, may be the means of getting enthusiastic administrative endorsement of subsequent proposals. By being conspicuous, beautification has certain advantages as the initial endeavor of a conservation teacher.)

b. Roadside sanitation:

Particularly in rural areas, the conservation teacher can achieve excellent training of students in landscape sanitation by assigning the class (or each of several classes) the task of cleaning, and keeping clean, a certain length of roadsides extending from the school.

The act of collecting and burying all the assorted trash found along a stretch of road or highway succeeds better than discussion to convince children that public slovenliness is wasteful of resources. Roadside planting or seeding for erosion control and beautification may be incorporated with sanitation where opportunity affords and official authorization is forthcoming.

The teacher whose class undertakes any kind of roadside improvement should take special precautions against traffic hazards. Arrangements should be made with the police department or the highway patrol to establish a speed zone where the children are working. The passing motorist, stopped by a police officer and ordered to proceed slowly, may observe what is taking place and be embarrassed by his observation. He may depart the scene a better landscape housekeeper than he was on arrival, taught by child conservators.

To help combat roadside littering, do the following if you see any sort of litter thrown from an automobile moving on a highway:

(1) Write down the license number of the vehicle, the time, date, and place of the violation.

(2) Call the nearest office that has a record of vehicle registrations (write the state office, if necessary). Give the name and address of the person to whom the registration of the vehicle was issued.

(3) Write the registered owner (anonymously, if you wish), telling him that a crime was committed by someone in his vehicle at such and such (date, time, and place). (In case of a commercial vehicle, notify the company management. Corrective measures will almost surely follow, in the interest of public relations).

c. Forestation or reforestation:

The planting of forest seedlings as a school project can be specially recommended both for humid regions (tree plantations) and for dry regions (windbreaks and shelter belts). It is suitable for any age group, from intermediate grades to college. It yields a high educational return for time expended. A class of thirty students can plant an acre of forest in one hour and enjoy themselves while doing the work; they will observe *their* trees with interest year after year and be reminded of conservation concepts symbolized by those trees. Even to many college students, the simple process of planting a small seedling is strangely mysterious until it is demonstrated by the instructor. Its mastery becomes both educational and satisfying to the student.

The conservation teacher desirous of instituting tree planting as a class or school project should make certain arrangements in advance of the spring planting season. Free seedlings can usually be obtained from public or industrial nurseries. Requests may be made through the county agent or other official, specifying number and species desired. If the request is honored, the seedlings will be delivered when season and weather are deemed suitable. Land to be planted must be selected, and approval of the owner secured. Protection against fire and domestic animals should be considered in land selection. The teacher would be well advised to consult the local representative of the U.S. Forest Service or Soil Conservation Service for assistance with project planning.

d. Range seeding or reseeding:

In range regions grass sowing can be a good alternative or complement to tree planting. ("Johnny Grass Seed" serves cooperatively or independently in a "Keep Green" program.) The teacher who contemplates a range-seeding project should contact a representative of the Bureau of Land Management or the Soil Conservation Service for help with choice of site, seed, time of sowing, etc.

e. Preservation of a nature area:

A preservation project involves continuous follow-up demanding sponsorship by a reliable organization. The teacher may organize a sponsoring club, if necessary. Maintenance is infinitely more critical than initial establishment.

Item 7 in Section G will be helpful. Specific instructions may also be obtained from organizations (Sections E, F) and agencies (Section D, 1) identified with nature areas, sanctuaries, refuges, or wilderness.

f. Establishment of a school or community forest:

This is an ambitious undertaking, requiring careful planning and adequate organizational sponsorship. It can be correlated with the nature project suggested in Section e above. The teacher should obtain the advisement of a U.S. Forest Service representative or the state forester. The support of local civic organizations should be solicited.

g. Wildlife habitat improvement:

Planting of living fences is only one among many possible projects in this category. Sponsorship by a sportsmen's club might be most helpful. Of course, no planting should be done on private property without the owner's permission. One successful demonstration should be the first objective. The demonstration should, preferably, be observable from a well-traveled highway. Opportunities for wildlife-habitat improvement are present almost everywhere, ranging in scope from the protection of a bird's nest to the establishment of a nature sanctuary as suggested in e above.

h. Scrap metal salvage drive:

The collection of discarded metal objects can be both instructive and profitable. Definite arrangements for purchase of the objects by a reliable dealer should be made before the drive is launched. Planned use of proceeds for some good purpose might be publicized before collection is commenced. Care should be taken to organize carefully and operate the project systematically. The students should be afforded the opportunity to observe how the salvaged materials are sorted and prepared for shipment. Time and distance permitting, the drive might be climaxed with a visit to a steel plant to see the importance of scrap in steel production.

i. Community improvement:

The conservation teacher may find an excellent opportunity for class, club, or school participation in a community project or program launched by another group or agency. Cooperative effort identifies the genuine conservator.

j. Miscellaneous:

Other possibilities for applied conservation by a group of students are legion, including:

(1) Fire prevention.

(2) School garden.

(3) House-to-house inspection and repair of leaky water faucets.

(4) Building and erection of bird houses.

(5) Building a compost pile with leaves.

The well-trained and inspired conservation teacher will have no difficulty discovering good conservation projects. Selection of one or two best suited to locale and students poses the greater problem.

Notes

CHAPTER 3   **Water on the Land**

1. Philip Henry Kuenen, *Realms of Water,* trans. May Hollander (New York: John Wiley & Sons, Inc., 1955).

2. Kuenen, *Realms of Water,* pp. 14, 20, 302.

3. "Report of the Water Planning Committee," *National Resources Board Report,* Part III (Washington, D.C., 1934), p. 312.

4. "Flood Control Begins at the Top of the Hill," *Tractor Farming,* XXXV, No. 1 (January-February 1952).

5. Oscar Edward Meinzer, "The Occurrence of Ground Water in the United States," *Water Supply Paper 489,* U.S. Geological Survey (Washington, D.C., 1923), p. 42.

6. M. M. Ellis, B. A. Westfall, and Marion D. Ellis, "Determination of Water Quality," *Research Report 9,* Fish and Wildlife Service (Washington, D.C., 1948).

7. Kenneth A. MacKichan and J. C. Kammerer, "Estimated Use of Water in the United States, 1960," *Circular 456,* U.S. Geological Survey (Washington, D.C., 1961), p. 8.

8. Jack R. Barnes, "Water for United States Industry," *A Report to the President,* V: *Selected Reports to the Commission, Report 9,* Materials Policy Commission (Washington, D.C., 1952).

9. Arthur H. Carhart, *Water—Or Your Life* (Philadelphia: J. B. Lippincott Company, 1951), p. 84.

10. Glenn E. McLaughlin, "Water," *Industrial Location and National Resources,* National Resources Planning Board (Washington, D.C., 1942), chap. 8.

11. Senate Committee on Interior and Insular Affairs, *Basic Data Relating to Energy Resources,* Senate Document No. 8, 82nd Cong., 1st sess. (Washington, D.C., 1951), map facing p. 59.

12. *Forty-first Annual Report of the Federal Power Commission, Fiscal Year Ended June 30, 1961* (Washington, D.C., 1961), p. 26.

13. *Forty-first Annual Report of the Federal Power Commission,* p. 43.

14. *Forty-first Annual Report of the Federal Power Commission,* p. 28.

15. Harold A. Hoffmeister, "Alkali Problem of Western United States," *Economic Geography,* XXIII, No. 1 (January 1947).

16. F. E. Staebner, "Supplemental Irrigation," *Farmers' Bulletin 1846,* U.S. Department of Agriculture (Washington, D.C., 1940).

17. "Irrigation Agriculture in the West," *Miscellaneous Publication 670,* U.S. Department of Agriculture (Washington, D.C., 1948).

18. *Land and Water Resources—A Policy Guide,* U.S. Department of Agriculture (Washington, D.C., 1962), p. 29.

19. *Seventy-fifth Annual Report of the Interstate Commerce Commission, Fiscal Year Ended June 30, 1961* (Washington, D.C., 1961), pp. 15, 19.

20. Water-borne Commerce Branch, Statistical Division, Board of Engineers for Rivers and Harbors, Corps of Engineers, U.S. Army.

21. Hearings before the Committee on Interstate and Foreign Commerce, *Domestic Land and Water Transportation,* U.S. Senate on bills relative to domestic land and water transportation, 82nd Cong., 2nd sess. (Washington, D.C., 1952), pp. 1516-1524.

22. Eugene Kafka, Senior Mechanical Engineer, Heating, Refrigeration, and Sewage Disposal Section, Southeast Pentagon Building; personal communication dated August 12, 1952.

23. Robert T. MacMillan, "Water," *Mineral Facts and Problems,* Bureau of Mines (Washington, D.C., 1960), p. 6.

24. U.S. Public Health Service estimates.

25. MacMillan, "Water," *Mineral Facts and Problems,* p. 1.

CHAPTER 4   Water Conservation

1. C. W. Thornthwaite, "Climate and Moisture Conservation," *Annals of the Association of American Geographers,* XXXVII, No. 2 (June 1947), 87-100.

2. "Effect of 15 Years of Forest Cover Improvement upon Hydrologic Characteristics of White Hollow Watershed," *Report No. 0-5163,* Tennessee Valley Authority, Division of Water Control Planning, Hydraulic Data Branch (Knoxville, Tenn., 1951).

3. Harold E. Thomas, *The Conservation of Ground Water* (New York: McGraw-Hill Book Company, Inc., 1951), p. 47.

4. W. D. Potter, "Rainfall and Topographic Factors That Affect Runoff," *Transactions American Geophysical Union,* XXXIV, No. 1 (February 1953), 67-73.

5. "Water Resources," *Proceedings of the United Nations Scientific Conference on the Conservation and Utilization of Resources, 1949,* IV (8 vols.; New York, 1951), p. 99.

6. E. W. Bennison, *Ground-Water—Its Development, Uses, and Conservation* (St. Paul, Minn.: Edward E. Johnson, Inc., 1947), chap. 9.

7. Thomas, *The Conservation of Ground Water,* p. 46.

8. C. L. McGuinness, "Water Law with Special Reference to Ground Water," *Circular 117,* U.S. Geological Survey (Washington, D.C., 1951).

9. Thomas, *The Conservation of Ground Water,* pp. 188-191.

10. George W. Craddock and Charles R. Hursh, "Watersheds and How to Care for Them," *Trees: Yearbook of Agriculture, 1949,* U.S. Department of Agriculture (Washington, D.C., 1949), pp. 603-609.

11. "Effect of 15 Years of Forest Cover Improvement upon Hydrologic Characteristics of White Hollow Watershed," *Report No. 0-5163.*

12. Verne Alexander, "The Greatest Flood of History," *Weatherwise,* IV, No. 5 (October 1951), 110-111.

13. Stuart Chase, *Rich Land, Poor Land* (New York: McGraw-Hill Book Company, Inc., 1936), pp. 169-170.

14. Select Committee on National Water Resources, *Report,* U.S. Senate, 87th Cong., 1st sess. (Washington, D.C.: Government Printing Office, 1961), pp. 13-14.

15. C. P. Vetter, "Sediment Problems in Lake Mead and Downstream on the Colorado River," *Transactions American Geophysical Union,* XXXIV, No. 2 (April 1953), 249-256.

16. Carl B. Brown, "Sediment Steals Water Storage," *Journal of Soil and Water Conservation,* VI, No. 2 (April 1951).

17. Select Committee on National Water Resources, *Report,* Committee Print No. 14, pp. 5-7. (Hereafter "Committee Print" will be abbreviated C.P.)

18. Select Committee on National Water Resources, *Report,* C.P. No. 30, pp. 12, 15.

19. Select Committee on National Water Resources, *Report,* C.P. No. 1, pp. 30, 31.

20. Select Committee on National Water Resources, *Report,* C.P. No. 21, Part I.

21. Select Committee on National Water Resources, *Report,* C.P. No. 21, p. 91.

22. Select Committee on National Water Resources, *Report,* C.P. No. 21, p. 6.

23. Public Health Service, "Clean Water—A Chart Book of America's Water Needs 1900-1980," Superintendent of Documents (Washington, D.C., 1960), pp. 8, 9.

24. Select Committee on National Water Resources, *Report,* C.P. No. 9, p. 18.

25. *Proceedings of the National Conference on Water Pollution, December 12-14, 1960,* Public Health Service (Washington, D.C., 1961), p. 40.

26. "Protecting Our Water Resources," *The Federal Water Pollution Control Program,* Public Health Service (Washington, D.C., 1962), p. 12.

27. *Water Newsletter,* Water Information Center, Inc. (Port Washington, Long Island, New York), November 20, 1961; February 6, 1962.

28. Select Committee on National Water Resources, *Report,* C.P. No. 30, p. 24.

29. Thomas D. Best and Robert C. Smith, "Water in Area Industrial Development," *Battelle Technical Review* (November 1957).

30. *Water Newsletter,* December 6, 1961.

31. Select Committee on National Water Resources, *Report,* C.P. No. 30, p. 8.

32. Select Committee on National Water Resources, *Report,* C.P. No. 30, pp. 8-9.

33. Select Committee on National Water Resources, *Report,* C.P. No. 30, p. 10.

34. Select Committee on National Water Resources, *Report,* C.P. No. 30, p. 15.

35. Select Committee on National Water Resources, *Report,* C.P. No. 30, p. 15.

36. *Saline Water Conversion Report, 1960,* Office of Saline Water (January 1961).

37. "Water"—special report, *Chemical Week,* LXXXIX, No. 14 (October 1961), 49-77.

38. *Water Newsletter,* March 7, 1962.

39. Select Committee on National Water Resources, *Report,* C.P. No. 30, p. 25.

40. C. E. Busby, "Regulation and Economic Expansion," *Water: Yearbook of Agriculture, 1955* (Washington, D.C., 1955), p. 666.

CHAPTER 6   **Soil Conservation**

1. C. B. Shear and H. L. Crane, "Nutrient-Element Balance," *Science in Farming: Yearbook of Agriculture, 1943-1947* (Washington, D.C., 1947), pp. 592-601.

2. F. L. Duley and J. C. Russel, "Stubble-Mulch Farming to Hold Soil and Water," *Farmers' Bulletin 1997,* U.S. Department of Agriculture (Washington, D.C., 1948). Wendell C. Johnson, "Stubble-Mulch Farming on Wheatlands of the Southern High Plains," *Circular No. 860,* U.S. Department of Agriculture (Washington, D.C., 1950).

3. Sydney Franklin, "Mulching to Establish Vegetation on Eroded Areas," *Leaflet 190,* U.S. Department of Agriculture (Washington, D.C., 1940).

4. Harold E. Tower and Harry H. Gardner, "Strip Cropping for Conservation and Production," *Farmers' Bulletin 1981,* U.S. Department of Agriculture (Washington, D.C., 1946).

5. C. L. Hamilton, "Terracing for Soil and Water Conservation," *Farmers' Bulletin 1789,* U.S. Department of Agriculture (Washington, D.C., 1943).

6. Harry H. Gardner and Edwin Freyburger, "Grass Waterways," *Leaflet 257,* U.S. Department of Agriculture (Washington, D.C., 1949). C. L. Hamilton, "Terrace Outlets and Farm Drainageways," *Farmers' Bulletin 1814,* U.S. Department of Agriculture (rev. ed.; Washington, D.C., 1946).

7. Jerry Eastin, "An Old Practice and a New Idea," *What's New in Crops and Soils,* V, No. 3 (December 1952), 14-15.

8. Hans G. Jepson, "Prevention and Control of Gullies," *Farmers' Bulletin 1813,* U.S. Department of Agriculture (Washington, D.C., 1944).

9. Michael Peech and Hans Platenius, "Tests of Plants and Soils," *Science in Farming,* pp. 583-591.

10. Clyde E. Leighty, "Crop Rotation," *Soils and Men: Yearbook of Agriculture, 1938* (Washington, D.C., 1938), pp. 406-430.

11. R. Y. Bailey and W. M. Nixon, "Rotations for Problem Fields," *Grass: Yearbook of Agriculture, 1948* (Washington, D.C., 1948), pp. 195-199.

12. R. E. Uhland, "Grass and the Yields of Cash Crops," *Grass,* pp. 191-194.

13. A. J. Pieters, "Legumes in Soil Conservation Practices," *Leaflet 163,* U.S. Department of Agriculture (Washington, D.C., 1949).

14. Walter V. Kell and Roland McKee, "Cover Crops for Soil Conservation," *Farmers' Bulletin 1758,* U.S. Department of Agriculture (Washington, D.C., 1942).

15. J. H. Stallings, "Continuous Plant Cover—The Key to Soil and Water Conservation," *Journal of Soil and Water Conservation*, VIII, No. 2 (March 1953), 63-68.

16. A. J. Pieters and Roland McKee, "The Use of Cover and Green-Manure Crops," *Soils and Men*, pp. 431-444.

17. Myron S. Anderson, "Wastes That Improve Soil," *Crops in Peace and War: Yearbook of Agriculture, 1950-1951* (Washington, D.C., 1951) pp. 877-882.

18. S. I. Aronousky, L. E. Schniepp, and Elbert C. Lathrop, "Using Residues to Conserve Resources," *Crops in Peace and War*, pp. 829-842.

19. Louis M. Thompson, *Soils and Soil Fertility* (2nd ed.; New York: McGraw-Hill Book Company, Inc., 1957), p. 318.

20. Colin W. Whittaker, Bailey E. Brown, and J. Richard Adams, "Ammonium Nitrate for Crop Production," *Circular No. 771*, U.S. Department of Agriculture (Washington, D.C., 1948). E. N. Paulson and L. R. Swarner, "What's in the Soil?" *The Reclamation Era*, XXXVIII, No. 1 (January 1952), p. 8.

21. F. W. Parker, "Use of Nitrogen Fertilizers," *Science in Farming*, pp. 561-565. W. H. Pierre, "Phosphate Fertilizers," *Science in Farming*, pp. 554-560.

22. T. R. Horning, "Stubble Mulching in the Northwest," *Agricultural Information Bulletin 253*, Agricultural Research Service, U.S. Department of Agriculture (Washington, D.C., 1962). *Applied Mulches and Mulching*, Agricultural Research Service, U.S. Department of Agriculture (Washington, D.C., 1961).

23. D. B. Krimgold, "Managing Surface Runoff," *Science in Farming*, pp. 537-540.

24. H. E. Hayward, "The Control of Salinity," *Science in Farming*, pp. 547-553.

25. Emil Truog, "The Liming of Soils," *Science in Farming*, pp. 566-576.

26. Lionel James Picton, *Nutrition and the Soil* (New York: Devin-Adair Company, 1949).

27. Matthew Drosdoff, "The Use of Minor Elements," *Science in Farming*, pp. 577-582.

28. Report of the Secretary of Agriculture, 1961, p. 22.

29. Report of the Secretary of Agriculture on the 1961 Soil Bank Conservation Reserve Program (to the Congress), March 1962, p. 1.

30. Report of the Secretary of Agriculture on the 1961 Soil Bank Conservation Reserve Program (to the Congress), March 1962, p. 1.

31. Report of the Secretary of Agriculture on the 1961 Soil Bank Conservation Reserve Program (to the Congress), March 1962, p. 1.

CHAPTER 7   **Spoliation and Restoration of Our Dry Grasslands**

1. H. L. Shantz, "Natural Vegetation," *Atlas of American Agriculture*, Part I, Section E, U.S. Department of Agriculture (Washington, D.C., 1924).

2. *The Western Range*, Senate Document No. 199, 74th Cong., 2nd sess., 1936, p. 71.

3. F. W. Albertson, *Man's Disorder of Nature's Design in the Great Plains* (Washington, D.C.: Smithsonian Institution, 1950).

4. Noel E. Runyon, "The Effect of Season of Growth and Clipping on the Chemical Composition of Blue Grama (*Bouteloua Gracilis*) at Hays, Kansas," *Transactions, Kansas Academy of Science*, XLVI (1943), 116-121. Harold H. Hopkins, F. W. Albertson, and D. A. Riegel, "Ecology of Grassland Utilization in a Mixed Prairie," *Transactions, Kansas Academy of Science*, LV, No. 4 (1952), 404.

5. *The Western Range*, p. 130.

6. John C. Hout, "Droughts of 1930-34," *Water Supply Paper 680*, U.S. Geological Survey (Washington, D.C., 1936).

7. "The Dust Farmer Goes West," *Land Policy Review*, Bureau of Agricultural Economics, I, No. 1 (May-June 1938).

8. *The Western Range*, pp. 19-25.

9. John R. Killough, "Managing Our Rangeland Resources," *Our Public Lands*, XI, No. 4 (April 1962). Annual Report of the Secretary of the Interior, 1962.

10. *Program for the Public Lands and Resources*, Bureau of Land Management (Washington, D.C., May 1962), p. 27.

11. Annual Report of the Secretary of the Interior, 1962, p. 24.

12. Killough, "Managing Our Rangeland Resources," *Our Public Lands,* p. 15.

13. *Land: Yearbook of Agriculture, 1958* (Washington, D.C., 1958), pp. 161-166.

14. *Trees That Temper the Western Winds,* Prairie States Forestry Project, Forest Service (Washington, D.C., 1938).

15. Ernest J. George, "Tree and Shrub Species for the Northern Great Plains," *Circular No. 912,* U.S. Department of Agriculture (Washington, D.C., 1953). "Windbreaks and Shelterbelts for the Plains States," *Leaflet No. 276,* Extension Service, Forest Service, and Soil Conservation Service, U.S. Department of Agriculture (Washington, D.C., 1950).

16. "Facts about Wind Erosion and Dust Storms on the Great Plains," *Leaflet No. 394,* Soil Conservation Service, U.S. Department of Agriculture (Washington, D.C., 1961), p. 4.

17. C. Kenneth Pearse, A. Perry Plummer, and D. A. Savage, "Restoring the Range by Reseeding," *Grass: Yearbook of Agriculture, 1948* (Washington, D.C., 1948), pp. 227-233.

18. Arthur W. Sampson, *Range Management, Principles and Practices* (New York: John Wiley & Sons, Inc., 1952).

19. B. W. Allred, "Drought Damage on Southwestern Ranges," *Soil Conservation,* XIX, No. 11 (June 1954).

20. Cyril Luker, Assistant to the Administrator, Great Plains Conservation Program, Soil Conservation Service; personal communication dated March 28, 1963.

21. Report of the Secretary of Agriculture, 1961, p. 63.

22. Report of the Secretary of Agriculture, 1961, pp. 241-244.

23. B. W. Allred, *Practical Grassland Management,* Sheep and Goat Raiser Magazine (San Angelo, Texas, 1949), pp. 288-295. Sampson, *Range Management, Principles and Practices,* pp. 268-274.

24. Allred, *Practical Grassland Management,* p. 456.

25. Sampson, *Range Management, Principles and Practices,* p. 493.

26. *The Western Range,* p. 507. Sampson, *Range Management, Principles and Practices,* chap. 17.

27. *Program for the Public Lands and Resources,* pp. 27, 28.

CHAPTER 8   **Our Forests and Their Exploitation**

1. Bernard Frank, "Deep Go the Roots," *Nature Magazine,* XLV, No. 9 (November 1952).

2. Samuel Trask Dana, *Forest and Range Policy* (New York: McGraw-Hill Book Company, Inc., 1956), chap. 1.

3. Commercial American woods have become classified approximately as grouped below.

Hardwoods. Dicotyledonous trees of commercial species (usually broadleaved and deciduous).

Softwoods. Coniferous trees of commercial species (evergreen, except larches [Northern] and bald cypress [Southern]).

Eastern softwoods. Longleaf and slash pines, spruce and balsam fir, shortleaf and loblolly pines, white and red pines, other Southern yellow pines, jack pine, cypress, larch (tamarack) and hemlock.

Eastern hard hardwoods. White oaks, red oaks, hickory, yellow birch, sugar maple, beech, black walnut, and ash.

Eastern soft hardwoods. Soft maple, cottonwood and aspen, sweetgum, basswood, tupelo and blackgum, and yellow poplar.

Western softwoods. Douglas fir, Sitka spruce, Ponderosa and Jeffrey pines, Engelmann and other spruces, true firs, Western larch, Western hemlock, Western red cedar, sugar pine, California incense cedar, Western white pine, lodgepole pine, and redwood.

Western hardwoods. Aspen and red alder.

IDENTIFICATION MAP: SECTIONS AND REGIONS

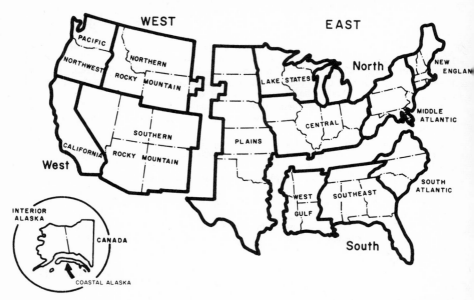

As identified here the Eastern and Western sections are separated by the mid-continent grassland plains. The Eastern section is further divided into North and South as shown on the accompanying map. The three gross divisions—North, South, and West—include twelve regions, as named, to which must be added two in Alaska—coastal and interior. The Pacific Northwest region is subdivisible into a Douglas-fir area (Western mountains) and a pine area (Interior).

Adapted from "Timber Resources for America's Future," *Forest Resource Report No. 14*, Forest Service, U.S. Department of Agriculture (Washington, D.C., 1958), pp. 635-636.

4. Ovid Butler, Lilian Cromelin, and Erle Kauffman, eds., *American Forests Anniversary Number*, XLI, No. 9 (September 1935), 439.

5. Butler, Cromelin, and Kauffman, eds., *American Forests Anniversary Number*, 438.

6. By definition, saw-timber trees are trees of commercial species that contain at least one merchantable saw log and have the following minimum diameters outside the bark at breast height (dbh, 4.5 feet above the ground):

Eastern regions: Softwoods—9.0 inches.
                     hardwoods—11.0 inches.

Western regions: All species 11.0 inches.

Poletimber trees are of commercial species, meet regional specifications of soundness and form, and have the following dbh:

Eastern regions: Softwoods 5.0 to 9.0 inches.
                     hardwoods 5.0 to 11.0 inches.

Western regions: All species 5.0 to 11.0 inches.

Source: "Timber Resources for America's Future," *Forest Resource Report No. 14*, Forest Service, U.S. Department of Agriculture (Washington, D.C., 1958), pp. 636-637.

7. William A. Dayton, "Geography of Commercially Important United States Trees," *Journal of Forestry*, LI, No. 4 (April 1953), 276-279.

8. Report of the Chief of the Forest Service, 1951.

9. *Industrial Forestry in the United States*, American Forest Products Industries, Inc. (Washington, D.C., 1960).

10. "Timber Resources for America's Future," *Forest Resource Report No. 14*, Forest Service, U.S. Department of Agriculture (Washington, D.C., 1958).

11. "Timber Resources for America's Future," *Forest Resource Report No. 14*, p. 23.

12. "Timber Resources for America's Future," *Forest Resource Report No. 14*, p. 29.

13. *Industrial Forestry in the United States*, p. 45.

14. "Timber Resources for America's Future," *Forest Resource Report No. 14*, pp. 452-461.

15. F. J. Champion, "Products of American Forests," *Miscellaneous Publication No. 861*, Forest Service (Washington, D.C., 1961), p. 1.

16. *Progress in Private Forestry in the United States—1961*, American Forest Products Industries, Inc. (Washington, D.C., 1961), p. 44.

17. *Industrial Forestry in the United States*, p. 8.

18. "Timber Resources for America's Future," *Forest Resource Report No. 14*, p. 291.

19. "Timber Resources for America's Future," *Forest Resource Report No. 14*, p. 292.

20. "Timber Resources for America's Future," *Forest Resource Report No. 14*, p. 293.

21. John R. McGuire, "Our Vital Private Forest Lands," *Land: Yearbook of Agriculture, 1958* (Washington, D.C., 1958), p. 389.

CHAPTER 9   **Forest Conservation**

1. "Timber Resources for America's Future," *Forest Resource Report No. 14*, Forest Service, U.S. Department of Agriculture (Washington, D.C., 1958), p. 104.

2. "Timber Resources for America's Future," *Forest Resource Report No. 14*, p. 104.

3. "Timber Resources for America's Future," *Forest Resource Report No. 14*, pp. 102-109.

4. Robert K. Winters, ed., *Fifty Years of Forestry in the U.S.A.*, Society of American Foresters (Washington, D.C., 1950), p. 2.

5. William B. Greeley, *Forests and Men* (Garden City, New York: Doubleday and Company, Inc., 1951).

6. "Development Program for the National Forests," *Miscellaneous Publication No. 896*, Forest Service, U.S. Department of Agriculture (Washington, D.C., 1961), p. 1.

7. "Development Program for the National Forests," *Miscellaneous Publication No. 896*, p. 5.

8. "Development Program for the National Forests," *Miscellaneous Publication No. 896*, p. 6.

9. "Development Program for the National Forests," *Miscellaneous Publication No. 896*, p. 1.

10. "Highlights in the History of Forest Conservation," *Agriculture Information Bulletin No. 83*, Forest Service (Washington, D.C., 1961), p. 23.

11. "Highlights in the History of Forest Conservation," *Agriculture Information Bulletin No. 83*, pp. 10, 12.

12. "Development Program for the National Forests," *Miscellaneous Publication No. 896*, p. 6.

13. "Development Program for the National Forests," *Miscellaneous Publication No. 896*, pp. 19, 20.

14. "Development Program for the National Forests," *Miscellaneous Publication No. 896*, p. 4.

15. "Development Program for the National Forests," *Miscellaneous Publication No. 896*, p. 2.

16. Erle Kauffman, *The Conservation Yearbook 1962*, 6th ed. (Washington, D.C.) pp. 142-146.

17. Kauffman, *The Conservation Yearbook 1962*, p. 140.

18. *Natural Enemies of Timber Abundance*, Report of the Chief of the Forest Service, 1951.

19. "Timber Resources for America's Future," *Forest Resource Report No. 14*, pp. 88, 104.

20. "Timber Resources for America's Future," *Forest Resource Report No. 14*, pp. 106-107.

21. "Development Program for the National Forests," *Miscellaneous Publication No. 896*, p. 23. "Forest Industry Opportunities in Rural Development," *Agriculture Information Bulletin No. 222*, Forest Service (Washington, D.C., 1960), p. 7.

22. R. D. McCulley, "Management of Natural Slash Pine Stands in the Flatwoods of South Georgia and North Florida," *Circular No. 845*, U.S. Department of Agriculture (Washington, D.C., 1950).

23. "Timber Resources for America's Future," *Forest Resource Report No. 14*, pp. 86, 88.

24. Kauffman, *The Conservation Yearbook 1962*, p. 117.

25. *Natural Enemies of Timber Abundance*, p. 4.

26. Kauffman, *The Conservation Yearbook 1962*, pp. 124, 125.

27. "A Reappraisal of the Forest Situation," *Wood Waste in the United States, Forest Resource Report No. 4*, Forest Service (Washington, D.C., 1947).

28. "Timber Resources for America's Future," *Forest Resource Report No. 14*, pp. 52-54.

29. Ralph W. Marquis, "Forest Yield Taxes," *Circular No. 899*, U.S. Department of Agriculture (Washington, D.C., 1952).

30. Kauffman, *The Conservation Yearbook 1962*, pp. 126-128.

31. D. B. King, H. B. Wagner, and G. H. Goldsborough, "The Outlook for Naval Stores," Forest Service, U.S. Department of Agriculture (Washington, D.C., 1962), p. 7.

32. King, Wagner, and Goldsborough, "The Outlook for Naval Stores," *Report*, p. 6.

33. King, Wagner, and Goldsborough, "The Outlook for Naval Stores," *Report*, pp. 24-27.

34. King, Wagner, and Goldsborough, "The Outlook for Naval Stores," *Report*, p. 6.

35. King, Wagner, and Goldsborough, "The Outlook for Naval Stores," *Report*, p. 22.

36. King, Wagner, and Goldsborough, "The Outlook for Naval Stores," *Report*, pp. 3, 7, 13.

37. Irvine T. Haig, Kenneth P. Davis, and Robert H. Weidman, "Natural Regeneration in the Western White Pine Type," *Bulletin (Technical) No. 767*, U.S. Department of Agriculture (Washington, D.C., 1941).

38. Gordon D. Merrick, *Wood Preservation Statistics 1961*, Forest Service and American Wood Preservers Association (Reprinted from 1962 volume of A.W.P.A. Proceedings, p. 4.

39. Merrick, *Wood Preservation Statistics 1961*.

CHAPTER 10   **Conservation Patterns on the Land**

1. "Soil Survey Manual," *Agriculture Handbook No. 18*, Soil Survey Staff, U.S. Department of Agriculture (Washington, D.C., 1951).

2. U.S. Census of Population 1960, United States Summary, Number of Inhabitants, Bureau of the Census, pp. 1-4.

3. U.S. Census of Agriculture 1959, A Graphic Summary of Land Utilization.

4. "Agricultural Land Resources—Capabilities—Uses—Conservation Needs," *Agriculture Information Bulletin 263*, U.S. Department of Agriculture (Washington, D.C., 1962), p. 12.

5. Based on a sampling inventory of land capability conducted by the SCS, the total agricultural area of the country is 2 per cent Class I, 2 per cent Class VIII, 3 per cent Class V, 12 per cent Class IV, 19 per cent Class VI, 20 per cent Class II, 20 per cent Class VII, and 22 per cent Class III (4).

6. J. G. Steele, "The Measure of Our Land," *Pamphlet 128*, Soil Conservation Service (Washington, D.C., 1951).

7. F. G. Renner and B. W. Allred, "Classifying Rangeland for Conservation Planning," *Agriculture Handbook No. 235*, Soil Conservation Service (Washington, D.C., 1962), p. 8.

8. Marion Clawson and Burnell Held, *The Federal Lands: Their Use and Management*, Resources for the Future, Inc. (Baltimore, Md.: The Johns Hopkins Press, 1957), p. 31.

9. U.S. Census of Agriculture 1959.

10. "Improving Agricultural Resources," *Report of the President's Materials Policy Commission*, I (Washington, D.C., 1952), chap. 9. "United States Fertilizer Resources," *Report of the President's Materials Policy Commission, V: Selected Reports of the Commission, Report 8* (Washington, D.C., 1952).

11. H. H. Wooten and Margaret R. Purcell, "Farm Land Development; Present and Future, by Clearing, Drainage, and Irrigation," *Circular No. 825*, U.S. Department of Agriculture (Washington, D.C., 1949).

12. "Improving Agricultural Resources," *Report of the President's Materials Policy Commission*, I, chap. 9.

13. "Ten Rivers in America's Future," *Report of the President's Water Resources Policy Commission*, II (Washington, D.C., 1950), pp. 765-770.

14. Annual Report of the Tennessee Valley Authority, 1961, p. 25.

15. Annual Report of the Tennessee Valley Authority, 1961, p. 28.

16. Annual Report of the Tennessee Valley Authority, 1961, p. 31.

17. "Proposed Practices for Economic Analysis of River Basin Projects," *Report of the Subcommittee on Benefits and Costs*, Federal Inter-agency River Basin Committee (Washington, D.C., 1950).

18. *Proceedings of the National Conference on Water Pollution, December 12-14, 1960*, Public Health Service (Washington, D.C., 1960), pp. 145-148.

19. Annual Report of the Tennessee Valley Authority, 1961, p. 43.

20. Report of the Secretary of Agriculture, 1961, p. 24.

21. Report of the Eighth National Watershed Congress, Tucson, Arizona, April 17-19, 1961, p. 17.

22. Public Land Statistics, 1962, Bureau of Land Management, pp. 69-79.

CHAPTER 11   Wildlife: Functions and Abuses

1. V. E. Shelford, "Conservation of Wildlife," A. E. Parkins and J. R. Whitaker, eds., *Our Natural Resources and Their Conservation* (New York: John Wiley & Sons, Inc., 1936), chap. 19.

2. "The Status of Wildlife in the United States," *Senate Report No. 1203*, 76th Cong., 3rd sess., 1940, p. 1.

3. "History and Significance of American Wildlife," *Wildlife Leaflet 282*, Fish and Wildlife Service (Chicago, Ill., 1946), pp. 2-3.

4. Leonard W. Wing, *Practice of Wildlife Conservation* (New York: John Wiley & Sons, Inc., 1951), p. 6.

5. Wing, *Practice of Wildlife Conservation*, p. 7.

6. "History and Significance of American Wildlife," *Wildlife Leaflet 282*, p. 8.

7. "History and Significance of American Wildlife," *Wildlife Leaflet 282*, p. 6.

8. "History and Significance of American Wildlife," *Wildlife Leaflet 282*, p. 5.

9. Wallace B. Grange and W. L. McAtee, "Improving the Farm Environment for Wild Life," *Farmers' Bulletin No. 1719*, U.S. Department of Agriculture (Washington, D.C., 1934), p. 46.

10. "Food Habits of Common Hawks," *Circular No. 370*, U.S. Department of Agriculture (Washington, D.C., 1935).

11. National Audubon Society, data as of June 1962.

12. National Audubon Society, data as of June 1962.

13. Robert M. Debevec, "The Bounty Bonanza," *Sports Afield*, Vol. CXLII, No. 1 (July 1959).

14. Ira N. Gabrielson, *Wildlife Conservation* (New York: The Macmillan Company, 1941), chap. xiv.

15. Ellsworth D. Lumley, "Save Our Hawks: We Need Them," undated leaflet (New York: National Council of State Garden Clubs, Inc.).

16. *Resources for Tomorrow,* Annual Report of the Secretary of the Interior, 1961, pp. 424-427.

17. Gabrielson, *Wildlife Conservation,* pp. 170-171.

18. Gabrielson, *Wildlife Conservation,* p. 171.

19. F. E. L. Beal, "Some Common Birds Useful to the Farmer," *Conservation Bulletin 18,* Fish and Wildlife Service (Washington, D.C., 1948).

20. J. P. Linduska, "Wildlife in a Chemical World," *Audubon Magazine,* LIV, Nos. 3, 4 (May-June, July-August 1952).

CHAPTER 12   Wildlife Conservation

1. Durward L. Allen, "Wildlife History and the Soil," *Soil Conservation,* XVIII, No. 6 (January 1953).

2. Edward H. Graham, *The Land and Wildlife* (New York: Oxford University Press, 1947), pp. 42-47.

3. Charles A. Dambach, "Conservation of Wildlife," Guy-Harold Smith, ed., *Conservation of Natural Resources* (New York: John Wiley & Sons, Inc., 1950), pp. 400, 401.

4. Graham, *The Land and Wildlife,* p. 210.

5. William R. Van Dersal, "Native Woody Plants of the United States, Their Erosion Control and Wildlife Values," *Miscellaneous Publication 303,* U.S. Department of Agriculture (Washington, D.C., 1938).

6. W. L. McAtee, "Plants Useful in Upland Wildlife Management," *Conservation Bulletin No. 7,* Fish and Wildlife Service (Washington, D.C., 1941), p. 4.

7. Dean A. Murphy and Thomas S. Baskett, "Bobwhite Mobility in Central Missouri," *Journal of Wildlife Management,* XVI, No. 4 (October 1952), 498-510.

8. Dambach, "Conservation of Wildlife," *Conservation of Natural Resources,* p. 401.

9. Allen, "Wildlife History and the Soil," *Soil Conservation.*

10. *Conservation News,* XXVII, No. 11 (June 1962), 8-9, quoting a letter from Assistant Secretary of the Interior Frank P. Briggs to Rep. Hubert C. Bonner, Chairman of the House Merchant Marine and Fisheries Committee, May 7, 1962.

11. *Transactions of the Twenty-fifth North American Wildlife and Natural Resources Conference,* Wildlife Management Institute (Washington, D.C., 1960), pp. 250, 265.

12. "Big Game Inventory for 1961," *Wildlife Leaflet 446,* Fish and Wildlife Service (Washington, D.C., 1962).

13. William Hagen and Joseph P. O'Connor, "Public Fish Culture in the United States, 1958," *Circular 58,* Fish and Wildlife Service (Washington, D.C., 1959).

14. Frederick C. Lincoln, "Migration of Birds," *Circular 16,* Fish and Wildlife Service (Washington, D.C., 1950).

15. Rachel L. Carson, "Guarding Our Wildlife Resouces," *Conservation in Action No. 5,* Fish and Wildlife Service (Washington, D.C., 1948).

16. Lincoln, "Migration of Birds," *Circular 16,* p. 60.

17. Carson, "Guarding Our Wildlife Resources," *Conservation in Action No. 5,* p. 23.

18. Wallace L. Anderson, "Making Land Produce Useful Wildlife," *Farmers' Bulletin No. 2035,* Soil Conservation Service, U.S. Department of Agriculture (Washington, D.C., 1951).

19. Van Dersal, "Native Woody Plants of the United States, Their Erosion Control and Wildlife Values," *Miscellaneous Publication 303.*

20. Wendell H. Harmon, "Hedgerows," *American Forests,* LIV, No. 10 (October, 1948).

21. Anderson, "Making Land Produce Useful Wildlife," *Farmers' Bulletin No. 2035.*

22. R. H. Westfield and Ralph H. Peck, *Forestry in Farm Management* (2nd ed. rev.; New York: John Wiley & Sons, Inc., 1951), chap. 12.

CHAPTER 13   **Resources for Recreation, Inspiration, and Instruction**

1. "Outdoor Recreation for America," *A Report to the President and the Congress,* Outdoor Recreation Resources Review Commission (Washington, D.C., 1962).

2. "Outdoor Recreation for America," *A Report to the President and the Congress,* Study Report 2, pp. 1-4. (Hereafter "Study Report" will be abbreviated S.R.)

3. "Outdoor Recreation for America," *A Report to the President and the Congress,* S.R. 1, p. 139.

4. "Outdoor Recreation for America," *A Report to the President and the Congress,* S.R. 1, p. 17.

5. *Areas Administered by the National Park Service* (Washington, D.C., 1962).

6. Devereux Butcher, *Exploring Our National Parks and Monuments* (Boston: National Parks Association and Houghton Mifflin Company, 1951), p. 7.

7. Butcher, *Exploring Our National Parks and Monuments,* p. 266.

8. Joseph S. Dixon, *Wildlife Portfolio of the Western National Parks,* National Park Service (Washington, D.C., 1942).

9. *State Parks: Statistics—1960,* National Park Service (Washington, D.C., 1961), p. 22.

10. *Proceedings of the National Conference on Planning,* American Society of Planning Officials (Minneapolis, Minn., 1938), p. 75.

11. "Outdoor Recreation for America," *A Report to the President and the Congress,* S.R. 1, p. 17.

12. James C. McClellan, *Recreation on Forest Industry Lands,* American Forest Products Industries, Inc. (Washington, D.C., 1962).

13. C. Frank Keyser, *The Preservation of Wilderness Areas (An Analysis of Opinion on the Problem),* Legislative Reference Service, Library of Congress (Washington, D.C., 1949), p. 46.

14. Aldo Leopold, "Wilderness As a Land Laboratory," *The Living Wilderness,* VI, No. 6 (July 1941).

15. Keyser, *The Preservation of Wilderness Areas,* p. 25.

16. Keyser, *The Preservation of Wilderness Areas,* p. 18.

17. *A Guide to Mississippi Flyway Waterfowl Management,* Mississippi Flyway Council (March 1958).

18. *A Guide to Mississippi Flyway Waterfowl Management.*

19. "Outdoor Recreation for America," *A Report to the President and the Congress,* p. 79.

20. "1960 National Survey of Fishing and Hunting," *Circular 120,* Bureau of Sport Fisheries and Wildlife (Washington, D.C., 1961).

21. Richard H. Stroud and Robert M. Jenkins, *Fish Conservation Highlights, 1957-1959,* Sport Fishing Institute (Washington, D.C., 1960), p. 7.

22. Clifton W. Enfield, *Control of Outdoor Advertising—Federal Law and Standards,* Bureau of Public Roads (Washington, D.C.), undated pamphlet.

23. Enfield, *Control of Outdoor Advertising.*

CHAPTER 14   **Resources of Our Bordering Seas**

1. Milner B. Schaefer and Roger Revelle, "Marine Resources," Martin R. Huberty and Warren L. Flock, eds., *Natural Resources* (New York: McGraw-Hill Book Company, Inc., 1959), chap. 4, p. 89.

2. Schaefer and Revelle, "Marine Resources," *Natural Resources,* p. 87.

3. Horace H. Selby, "Agar, Agaroids, and the American Agar Industry," *Fishery Leaflet 118,* Fish and Wildlife Service (Washington, D.C., 1948).

    4. Victor B. Scheffer, "The Commercial Importance of Seaweed Gums in the U.S.,"
Fishery Leaflet 156, Fish and Wildlife Service (Chicago, Ill., 1945).
    5. Schaefer and Revelle, "Marine Resources," *Natural Resources*, p. 87.
    6. *Fishery Resources of the United States*, Senate Document No. 51, 79th Cong.,
1st sess., 1945, p. 45.
    7. E. A. Power, "Fishery Statistics of the United States, 1960," *Statistical Digest No.
53*, Bureau of Commercial Fisheries (Washington, D.C., 1962), p. 22.
    8. Power, "Fishery Statistics of the United States, 1960," *Statistical Digest No. 53*,
p. 7.
    9. Jennie E. Harris, "Sponge Fishermen of Tarpon Springs," *National Geographic
Magazine*, XCI, No. 1 (January 1947), 133.
    10. Francis Riley, "Fur Seal Industry of the Pribilof Islands: 1786-1960," *Fishery
Leaflet 516*, Bureau of Commercial Fisheries (Washington, D.C., 1961).
    11. Riley, "Fur Seal Industry of the Pribilof Islands: 1786-1960," *Fishery Leaflet 516*.
    12. Riley, "Fur Seal Industry of the Pribilof Islands: 1786-1960," *Fishery Leaflet 516*,
p. 3.
    13. Power, "Fishery Statistics of the United States, 1960," *Statistical Digest No. 53*,
pp. 52, 53.
    14. *Fishery Resources of the United States*, p. 45.
    15. Power, "Fishery Statistics of the United States, 1960," *Statistical Digest No. 53*,
p. 4.
    16. Power, "Fishery Statistics of the United States, 1960," *Statistical Digest No. 53*,
pp. 8, 463-465.
    17. *Commercial Fisheries Review*, Bureau of Commercial Fisheries, XXIV, No. 11,
cover. (November 1962.)
    18. Rachel L. Carson, "Fish and Shellfish of the Middle Atlantic Coast," *Conserva-
tion Bulletin No. 38*, Department of the Interior (Washington, D.C., 1945), p. 30.
    19. Joel W. Hedgpeth, "The Passing of the Salmon," *The Scientific Monthly*, LIX,
No. 5 (November 1944), 370-378.
    20. Hedgpeth, "The Passing of the Salmon," *The Scientific Monthly*, 370-378.
    21. *Fishery Resources of the United States*, pp. 67, 68.
    22. *Fishery Resources of the United States*, p. 10.
    23. Clarence P. Idyll, "A Concept of Conservation in Marine Fisheries and Its Im-
plications in Fishery Management," *Transactions of the Seventeenth North American
Wildlife Conference*, Wildlife Management Institute (Washington, D.C., 1952), p. 367.
    24. Carson, "Fish and Shellfish of the Middle Atlantic Coast," *Conservation Bulletin
No. 38*, p. 17.
    25. *Fishery Resources of the United States*, pp. 21, 22, 131.
    26. Power, "Fishery Statistics of the United States, 1960," *Statistical Digest No. 53*,
p. 7.
    27. Vernon C. Applegate, "The Sea Lamprey in the Great Lakes," *Fishery Leaflet
384*, Fish and Wildlife Service (Washington, D.C., 1950).
    28. Power, "Fishery Statistics of the United States, 1960," *Statistical Digest No. 53*,
pp. 373, 374.
    29. "Wildlife and Fish Resources," *Proceedings of the United Nations Scientific
Conference on the Conservation and Utilization of Resources, 1949*, VII, United Nations Department of Economic Affairs (New York, 1951), pp. 28-41.
    30. *Fishery Resources of the United States*, p. 9.
    31. *Fishery Resources of the United States*, p. 26.
    32. *Commercial Fisheries Review*, Bureau of Commercial Fisheries, XV, No. 2 (Feb-
ruary 1953), 36.
    33. *Fishery Resources of the United States*, pp. 41, 42.
    34. *Fishery Resources of the United States*, p. 23.
    35. *Fishery Resources of the United States*, pp. 99, 102.
    36. "Wildlife and Fish Resources," *Proceedings of the United Nations Scientific
Conference on the Conservation and Utilization of Resources, 1949*, pp. 51-60.
    37. "The United States Fish and Wildlife Service, Its Responsibilities and Func-
tions," *Circular 97*, Fish and Wildlife Service (Washington, D.C., 1960), p. 5.

38. "The United States Fish and Wildlife Service," *Circular 97,* p. 11.

39. "Fisheries of the United States, 1961," *Current Fishery Statistics No. 2900,* Bureau of Commercial Fisheries (Washington, D.C., 1962), p. 29.

40. Power, "Fishery Statistics of the United States, 1960," *Statistical Digest No. 53,* p. 4.

41. "Imports and Exports of Fishery Products, 1957-1961," *Current Fishery Statistics No. 2892, Annual Summary,* Bureau of Commercial Fisheries (Washington, D.C., 1962).

42. *Commercial Fisheries Review,* Bureau of Commercial Fisheries, XXII, No. 1 (January 1960), 35.

43. Lionel A. Walford, *Living Resources of the Sea* (New York: The Ronald Press Company, 1958), pp. 294, 295.

CHAPTER 15   Mineral Fuels and Major Metals

1. T. S. Lovering, *Minerals in World Affairs* (Englewood Cliffs, N.J.: Prentice-Hall, Inc., 1943), chaps. 3, 4.

2. Senate Committee on Public Lands, *Mineral Position of the United States,* Bureau of Mines and Geological Survey, Hearings before a Subcommittee on Investigation of the Factors Affecting Fuels, Forestry, and Reclamation Projects, 80th Cong., 1st sess., 1947, p. 176.

3. Alan M. Bateman, *Economic Mineral Deposits* (2nd ed.; New York: John Wiley & Sons, Inc., 1950), p. 561.

4. Bateman, *Economic Mineral Deposits,* p. 564.

5. Senate Committee on Interior and Insular Affairs, *An Assessment of Available Information on Energy in the United States,* National Fuels and Energy Group, Senate Document No. 159, 87th Cong., 2nd sess., 1962, p. 274.

6. Senate Committee on Interior and Insular Affairs, *An Assessment of Available Information on Energy in the United States,* p. 20.

7. Senate Committee on Interior and Insular Affairs, *An Assessment of Available Information on Energy in the United States,* p. 40.

8. Senate Committee on Interior and Insular Affairs, *An Assessment of Available Information on Energy in the United States,* p. 22.

9. "Fuels," *1960 Minerals Yearbook,* II, Bureau of Mines (Washington, D.C., 1961), pp. 154-155.

10. "Fuels," *1960 Minerals Yearbook,* p. 139.

11. W. H. Young, R. L. Anderson, and E. M. Hall, "Coal—Bituminous and Lignite," *Minerals Yearbook 1961,* Bureau of Mines (Washington, D.C., 1962), p. 9.

12. *Statistics,* Bureau of Mines.

13. Young, Anderson, and Hall, "Coal—Bituminous and Lignite," *Minerals Yearbook 1961,* p. 25.

14. Young, Anderson, and Hall, "Coal—Bituminous and Lignite," *Minerals Yearbook 1961,* p. 7.

15. Young, Anderson, and Hall, "Coal—Bituminous and Lignite," *Minerals Yearbook, 1961,* p. 24.

16. Paul Averitt, "Coal Reserves of the United States—A Progress Report, January 1, 1960," *Bulletin 1136,* U.S. Geological Survey (Washington, D.C., 1961), p. 23.

17. "Mineral Facts and Problems," *Bulletin 556,* Bureau of Mines (Washington, D.C., 1956), p. 636.

18. Senate Committee on Interior and Insular Affairs, *An Assessment of Available Information on Energy in the United States,* p. 71.

19. A. D. Zapp, "Future Petroleum Producing Capacity of the United States," *Bulletin 1142-H,* U.S. Geological Survey (Washington, D.C., 1962), p. H-23.

20. *Petroleum Facts and Figures,* American Petroleum Institute (New York, 1961), p. 24.

21. Zapp, "Future Petroleum Producing Capacity of the United States," *Bulletin 1142-H,* pp. H-23, 24.

22. *Petroleum Facts and Figures,* pp. 19, 20.

23. *Petroleum Facts and Figures,* p. 30.

24. "Mineral Facts and Problems," *Bulletin 556,* pp. 662-664.

25. "Fuels," *1960 Minerals Yearbook,* p. 378.

26. "Fuels," *1960 Minerals Yearbook,* p. 416.

27. Senate Committee on Interior and Insular Affairs, *An Assessment of Available Information on Energy in the United States,* p. 159.

28. *1962 Gas Facts, A Statistical Record of the Gas Utility Industry—1961,* American Gas Association (New York, 1962), pp. 2, 3.

29. "Fuels," *1960 Minerals Yearbook,* p. 306.

30. "Fuels," *1960 Minerals Yearbook,* p. 310.

31. "Mineral Facts and Problems," *Bulletin 556,* p. 608.

32. Annual Report of the Federal Power Commission, 1962, pp. 36, 37.

33. Annual Report of the Federal Power Commission, 1962, p. 61.

34. Select Committee on National Water Resources, *Floods and Flood Control,* C.P. No. 15, 86th Cong., 2nd sess., July 1960, p. 31.

35. Annual Report of the Federal Power Commission, 1962, p. 55.

36. Senate Committee on Interior and Insular Affairs, *An Assessment of Available Information on Energy in the United States,* p. 315.

37. Annual Report of the Federal Power Commission, 1962, p. 46.

38. Annual Report of the Federal Power Commission, 1962, p. 45.

39. Senate Committee on Interior and Insular Affairs, *An Assessment of Available Information on Energy in the United States,* p. 293.

40. *1962 Gas Facts,* p. 1.

41. Senate Committee on Interior and Insular Affairs, *An Assessment of Available Information on Energy in the United States,* p. 161.

42. "Mineral Facts and Problems," *Bulletin 556,* p. 644.

43. *1962 Gas Facts,* p. 72.

44. Senate Committee on Interior and Insular Affairs, *An Assessment of Available Information on Energy in the United States,* p. 164.

45. *Bituminous Coal Facts 1962,* National Coal Association (1962), p. 94.

46. Annual Report of the Federal Power Commission, 1962, p. 55.

47. Senate Committee on Interior and Insular Affairs, *An Assessment of Available Information on Energy in the United States,* p. 198.

48. Senate Committee on Interior and Insular Affairs, *An Assessment of Available Information on Energy in the United States,* p. 199.

49. Senate Committee on Interior and Insular Affairs, *An Assessment of Available Information on Energy in the United States;* p. 198.

50. Hubert E. Risser, "Illinois-Missouri Mineral Resource Complex—A Base for Industrial Development," *Circular 337,* Illinois State Geological Survey (Urbana, Ill., 1962), p. 14.

51. An ore is "material from which the contained raw material or mineral can be extracted profitably at any given time. . . . Material that cannot be worked under present economic and technological circumstances is termed potential ore." Bruce C. Netschert and Hans H. Landsberg, *The Future Supply of the Major Metals (A Reconnaissance Survey),* Resources for the Future, Inc. (Washington, D.C., 1961), pp. 2, 4.

52. "Mineral Facts and Problems," *Bulletin 556,* p. 373.

53. "Metals and Minerals (Except Fuels)," *1960 Minerals Yearbook,* I, Bureau of Mines (Washington, D.C., 1961), p. 569.

54. "Metals and Minerals (Except Fuels)," *1960 Minerals Yearbook,* p. 579.

55. "Metals and Minerals (Except Fuels)," *1960 Minerals Yearbook,* p. 573.

56. "Metals and Minerals (Except Fuels)," *1960 Minerals Yearbook,* pp. 582-583.

57. Netschert and Landsberg, *The Future Supply of the Major Metals,* pp. 15-17.

58. Netschert and Landsberg, *The Future Supply of the Major Metals,* p. 18.

59. Netschert and Landsberg, *The Future Supply of the Major Metals,* p. 7.

60. "Mineral Facts and Problems," *1960 Minerals Yearbook,* p. 219.

61. "Mineral Facts and Problems," *1960 Minerals Yearbook,* p. 438.

62. "Mineral Facts and Problems," *1960 Minerals Yearbook,* p. 23.

63. Netschert and Landsberg, *The Future Supply of the Major Metals,* p. 33.

CHAPTER 16   **Mineral Conservation**

1. W. H. Voskuil, "Fundamentals of Mineral Conservation," *Journal of Geography*, LIV, No. 1 (January 1955), 39.

2. Adolph Knopf, "Strategic Mineral Supplies," *Scientific Monthly*, LXII, No. 1 (January 1946).

3. "The Outlook for Energy Resources," *A Report of the President's Materials Policy Commission*, III (Washington, D.C., 1952), p. 20.

4. Alan M. Bateman, *Economic Mineral Deposits* (2nd ed.; New York: John Wiley & Sons, Inc., 1950), pp. 270-273.

5. "The Outlook for Energy Resources," *A Report of the President's Materials Policy Commission*, III, p. 6.

6. Erich W. Zimmermann, *Conservation in the Production of Petroleum* (New Haven, Conn.: Yale University Press, 1957), p. 339.

7. A. D. Zapp, "Future Petroleum Producing Capacity of the United States," *Bulletin 1142-H*, U.S. Geological Survey (Washington, D.C., 1962), p. H-6.

8. "Secondary Recovery Is Still Growing," *Oil and Gas Journal*, LX, No. 25 (June 1962), 65-66.

9. "Waterflooding," *Petroleum Engineer*, XXXIV, No. 4 (April 1962), 68-70.

10. "The Promise of Technology," *A Report of the President's Materials Policy Commission*, IV (Washington, D.C., 1952), p. 5.

11. Bateman, *Economic Mineral Deposits*, p. 203.

12. W. H. Young, R. L. Anderson, and E. M. Hall, "Coal—Bituminous and Lignite," *Minerals Yearbook 1961*, Bureau of Mines (Washington, D.C., 1962), p. 105.

13. "Mineral Facts and Problems," *Bulletin 585*, Bureau of Mines (Washington, D.C., 1960), pp. 118, 119.

14. "Horizontal Drilling," *Fortune*, XXXVI, No. 3 (September 1947).

15. Thomas B. Nolan, Director, U.S. Geological Survey, personal communication dated January 16, 1963.

16. Nolan, personal communication dated January 16, 1963.

17. Annual Report of the Secretary of the Interior, 1962, p. 73.

18. Annual Report of the Secretary of the Interior, 1962, p. 76.

19. "The Promise of Technology," *A Report of the President's Materials Policy Commission*, IV, p. 27.

20. "The Promise of Technology," *A Report of the President's Materials Policy Commission*, IV, p. 29.

21. "Metals and Minerals (Except Fuels)," *Minerals Yearbook 1961*, Bureau of Mines (Washington, D.C., 1962), pp. 9, 848.

22. "The Outlook for Key Commodities," *A Report of the President's Materials Policy Commission*, II (Washington, D.C., 1952), p. 35.

23. *Steel Facts*, No. 170, American Iron and Steel Institute (New York, 1962), pp. 6, 7.

24. *Steel Facts*, p. 6.

25. "The Outlook for Key Commodities," *A Report of the President's Materials Policy Commission*, II, p. 138.

26. Bateman, *Economic Mineral Deposits*, p. 206.

27. "The Promise of Technology," *A Report of the President's Materials Policy Commission*, IV, pp. 32, 33.

28. *1962 Yearbook*, Institute of Scrap Iron and Steel, Inc. (Washington, D.C., 1962), p. 3.

29. *Nonferrous Scrap Metal Guidebook*, National Association of Secondary Material Industries (New York, 1960), appendix.

30. *1962 Yearbook*, Institute of Scrap Iron and Steel, Inc., pp. 4, 10.

31. "The Promise of Technology," *A Report of the President's Materials Policy Commission*, IV, p. 7.

32. "Foundations for Growth and Security," *A Report of the President's Materials Policy Commission*, I (Washington, D.C., 1952), p. 136.

33. "Oil from Coal," *Synthetic Liquid Fuels,* Annual Report of the Secretary of the Interior, 1951, Part I (Washington, D.C., 1952).

34. "The Outlook for Key Commodities," *A Report of the President's Materials Policy Commission,* II, p. 66.

35. "The Outlook for Key Commodities," *A Report of the President's Materials Policy Commission,* II, p. 76.

36. "The Outlook for Key Commodities," *A Report of the President's Materials Policy Commission,* II, p. 78.

37. "The Outlook for Key Commodities," *A Report of the President's Materials Policy Commission,* II, p. 59.

38. "Oil from Oil Shale," *Synthetic Liquid Fuels,* Annual Report of the Secretary of the Interior, 1951, Part II (Washington, D.C., 1952), p. 1.

39. "Foundations for Growth and Security," *A Report of the President's Materials Policy Commission,* I, p. 109.

40. "Foundations for Growth and Security," *A Report of the President's Materials Policy Commission,* I, p. 78.

41. Annual Report of the Federal Power Commission, 1962, p. 40.

42. "Foundations for Growth and Security," *A Report of the President's Materials Policy Commission,* I, p. 112.

43. "The Promise of Technology," *A Report of the President's Materials Policy Commission,* IV, p. 3.

44. "The Outlook for Key Commodities," *A Report of the President's Materials Policy Commission,* II, p. 157.

45. Bateman, *Economic Mineral Deposits,* pp. 283-284.

46. A. F. Grandt and A. L. Lang, "Reclaiming Illinois Strip Coal Land with Legumes and Grasses," *Bulletin 628,* University of Illinois, Agricultural Experiment Station (Urbana, Ill.; 1958). G. A. Limstrom, "Forestation of Strip-Mined Land in the Central States," *Agriculture Handbook No. 166,* U.S. Department of Agriculture (Washington, D.C., 1960).

47. Lee Guernsey, "The Reclamation of Strip Mined Lands," *Journal of Geography,* LIX, No. 1 (January 1960), 5.

Index

Acadia National Park, Maine, 332
Adirondack Forest Preserves, 199, 334
Advertising, and beauty conservation, 347, 349
Aerial prospecting, for minerals, 438
Agar, 354
Agricultural Act (1956), 149
Agricultural Adjustment Act (1933), 147, 149
Agricultural Conservation Program, 217, 223
Agricultural Stabilization and Conservation Service (ASCS), 146, 149, 160-161
Air conditioning, 48, 78
Air pollution, 444, 463-464
Alaska, 188-189, 196, 198, 273, 323, 359-360, 391, 438
Alfalfa, 66, 137
Algin, 354
Alluvium, 97
Aluminum, 425, 447, 448
American Forest Products Industries, Inc., 204, 206
American Indians, 273, 275, 276-277
American Tree Farm System, 204

Anadromous fish, 372
Anchovies, 387, 391
Animal feeds, fish by-products, 361-362
Animal cycle, 23
Animals and plants, 18-22, 23
Antarctic Ocean, whaling in, 357
Anthracite coal, 402
Antiquities Act (1906), 324
Appalachian coal fields, 403-404
Aquifers, 37, 78; see also Water
Arctic walrus, 279
Arizona elk, 279
Astor, John Jacob, 275
"Athletic-aesthetic" resources, and human well-being, 318-319
Atomic energy, 463
Auger mining, of coal, 433, 436
Automobiles, 453-454
Automobile tires, 408

Badlands, 236; see also Land
Bahamas, sponge propagation, 359
Bald eagle, 279
Bankhead-Jones Farm Tenant Act (1937), 161

Barbed wire, 156
Bar Harbor, Maine, forest fire, 206
Barium, 449
Basin, *term*, 260
Bauxite, 425, 442
Beaches; *see* Shores and beaches
Beauty conservation, 345-351
Beaver, repatriation, 300
Bemidji, Minnesota, 181
Beryllium, 448
Big game, repatriation, 300
Big-plains wolf, extinction, 279
Billboard advertising, 347, 349
Biological Survey, merger with Bureau of
    Fisheries, 471
Birds, 287-290, 299-300, 303, 305, 339-342;
    see also Waterfowl
Birds Not Protected by Federal Law
    (*list*), 288
Bison, 276-277
Bituminous coal, 402-404
Black-footed ferret, 279
Bobwhite quail, 299-300
Border environment, 312-314
Boron, 449
Boundary Waters Catoe Area, Minnesota,
    335
Bounties, 283, 284-285
Bountiful, Utah, water spreading at, 78
Buckeye, Ariz., water supply, 82
Bugs, 290
Burrowers, 287

Calcium, 449
California:
    commercial fisheries, 391
    first salmon fishery, 375
    kelp forests, 354, 355
    Nature Sanctuaries, 337
California condor, 279
Camping, for classes, 486-487
Canada:
    fishery products imported from, 392
    Migratory Bird Treaties, 299, 303, 340
    waterfowl production, 341
Canals, 45-46, 47
Cape Hatteras dunes, Cape Cod, 332
Cape Sable sparrow, 279
Carageenin, 354
Carbon black, 407-408
Carolina paroquet, 277, 279
Cats, 284
Catskill Forest Preserve, 199
Census of Manufactures (1958), 192
Channel Islands, 332, 356
Chemurgy, *term*, 465-466
Chernozem soils, 94
China:
    fishing industry, 391

pheasants from, 293
Civilian Conservation Corps, 162
Clarke-McNary Law (1924), 197, 211
Climate, 15, 22, 29-31, 91, 94
"Closed seasons," 302
Cloud seeding, 464
Coal, 397, 398-400, 401-404, 413-415, 444,
    448, 451-452
    auger mining, 433, 436
    low-grade, 449
    in mineral substitution, 448
    pipe lines, 414-415
    retreat-longwall mining, 436
    waste of, 433, 436
Coalinga, Cal., water supply, 80-82
Coke, 403-404, 444
Colorado River, 265
Commissioners of Fish and Fisheries, 389
Community improvement, as teaching
    project, 491-492
Connecticut, wildlife legislation, 284
Conservation, concept of, 1-13
Conservation education, 473-475
Conservationists, *term*, 2
Conservators, *term*, 2
Consumer spending, outdoor recreation,
    343
Contour tillage, 128-131
"Control" of nature, 25-26
Cooper's hawk, 283-284
Copper, 423, 439
Copper Hill, Tennessee, smog, 463
Cottontail rabbit, 281
Cover, wildlife, 293-296
Coyote, 283
Creosote, 232
Crocodile, 279
Cryolite, 442
Cultural advances, 318
Cultural landscape, beauty of, 350

Dakota bighorn sheep, 279
Dams, 60-63, 261-262, 263, 267, 374, 375-
    376
Death Valley, 15, 326, 449
Deer, 297, 300
Delaware Bay, oyster disease, 385
Delaware River, 264
Demersal fishes, 372
Denver, Col., 77, 265
Deposition, 16
Dermocystidium, 385
Dingell-Johnson Act (1950), 342
District of Columbia, wildlife preserve,
    307
Diversification, of resources, 467-468
Dogs, 284
Donora, Pennsylvania, smog, 463

Drainage systems, 260-261
Drake well, Titusville, Penn., 405
Dredges, 379
Duck stamps, 340
Ducks, population maintenance, 298, 339-342
Dust Bowl, 157, 251, 253
Dust storms (1930's), 157

Eastern puma, 279
"Economic" waste, 5-6
Edge, marginal, 312-314
Edge, and water recreation, 331
Educational Film Guide, 479
EHV transmission, 415-416
Electric power, 409, 411, 415-416, 451-452
Elks, 279
Engineering projects, and fishery resources, 373-375
English sparrows, 293
Environment and resources, 14-26
Erosion, 16, 115-116, 166
Erosion cycles, 22
Everglade kite, 279
Everglades, Florida, 332
Expendable materials, exhaustion of, 465-466
Extinction, restrictions, wildlife, 301-302
Extractive exploitation, 465

Farms:
    conservation plans, 467
    wildlife, 308-314
    woodlands, 202-206
Fauna, U.S., 273
Federal Agencies, as teaching aid sources, 480-481
Federal Aid Highway Act (1956), 347
Federal Aid in Fish Restoration, 342
Federal Aid in Wildlife Restoration (Pittman-Robertson Act, 1937), 342
Federal Geological Survey, 57
Federal Naval Stores Conservation Program, 223
Federal Power Commission, 269, 411-412, 416
Federal resource management, organization of, 470-471
Federal-state coordination, 342-343, 470-471
Federal Water Pollution Control Act, 71, 72
Federal Wildlife Refuge system, 306-307, 329, 335
Feed Grains Program, 149
Fences, 310-312
Ferroalloys, 426-427

Fertilizers, 141-142, 361, 454-455
Field-mouse population, 287
Fires, in forests, 206-213
Fish and fishing; *see also* Food fish; Seas
    artificial propagation, 279-280
    control of numbers, 298
    food; *see* Food fish
    gear and techniques, 367, 379-382
    habitats, 300-301, 388
    import-export, 392
    killing of, 277
    national recreation income, 343-344
    overfishing, 376-377
    restoration projects, 342-343
Fish and Wildlife Act (1956), 390
Fisheries, international agreements on, 382-383
Fisheries, regulation standardization, 383
Fishery Research Board, Canada, 360
Fish flour, 390
Fish-liver oil, 360
Fish-meal industry, 391
Flaring, of natural gas, 429-431
Floods, 59-60, 261, 262, 263, 265, 267, 332
Florida:
    Key deer, 279
    manatee, 279
    sponging grounds, 358, 359
    wild turkey, 300
Flotation, 442
Fly ash, 444
Flyway Councils, 340
Flyways, 305
Food and Agriculture Act (1962), 322
Food fish; *see also* Fish
    fisheries, 364-367
    packaging and transportation, 367, 370
    species variety, 364-367
    underutilization, 387
Food supply, and Malthusian theory, 459
Forestation, as teaching project, 490, 491
Forest industry lands, outdoor recreation, 330-331
Forest Pest Control Act (1947), 227
Forest Products Laboratory, 232
Forests:
    American Indians, 199
    conservation of, 195-233
    crown fires, 207-208
    farm woodlands, 202-206
    fire lanes and breaks, 209-210
    fires, 206-213
    grazing, 219, 221
    green storage, 176
    ground fires, 207
    industrial ownership, 201
    insects and diseases, 224-227
    "Keep Green" program, 206
    legislation, 197, 198, 199, 211, 217

Forests *(Cont.)*
   lumbering, 179-192, 201-202, 213-218
   natural reproduction, 228
   naval stores, 221-224
   pests, 224-227
   preserves, 199
   private ownership, 201, 330-331
   protective forests, 176
   publicly owned, 199-200, 329-331
   pulpwood, 188, 204
   recreational resources, 329-331
   reserves, 196-197
   sawmills, 187-188
   seed blocks, 228
   selective cutting, 214, 216, 217
   settlement, 177, 179
   silviculture, 230
   Smoky Bear campaign, 206
   soil fires, 208
   Southern pine, 211-212, 221-224
   sowing and planting, 227-230
   state forestry, 199-200
   submarginal land, 200
   surface fires, 207
   sustained-yield management, 214
   taxation, 219
   tree farming, 230, 232
   turpentining, 221-224
   uses of, 176-177
   waste, 218
   water supply, 57-59
   wildlife, 176; *see also* Wildlife
   windbreaks, 202
   wood consumption, 192
   wood preserving, 232
   woodworking plants, 202
Forty-ninth Parallel boundary, 275
Fossil fuels, 463
Foxes, 284, 285
Fuels, 393-427; *see also* Minerals
"Fugitive" resources, 3
Fulmer Act (1935), 199
Fur seals, 359-360
Fur trade, 274-275, 281

Game:
   birds, 299-300, 339-342; *see also* Birds;
      Wildfowl
   fish, 279-280
   lands, commercialization, 339-344
   propagation, 297, 298, 300-301
   refuges, state parks, 327
   species, 273, 297-298
Gelidium, 354
General Land Office, 159, 197
General Mining Law (1872), 270
Geographic consolidation, 469-470
Geologic maps, 436, 438

Golden eagle, 284
Government, role of, 6, 73, 82-84
Gracilaria, 354
Grasslands, 150-173
   adjustment, 172-173
   alternate grazing, 168-169
   barbed wire, 156
   deferred grazing, 168
   deferred-rotation, 168
   dust storms (1930's), 157
   grazing, 168-172
   rain, 151
   range conservation, 164
   range management, 167-172
   rotation grazing, 168
   settling of, 152-155
   shelter belts, 162-163
   stock raising, 167-173
   tall and short grass regions, 152-154
   windbreak, North Dakota-Texas, 162
   World War I, 156-157
   World War II, 163
Grazing Service, 159
Great horned owl, 283
Great Lake fisheries, 376, 377, 383, 385-
      387
Great Lakes-St. Lawrence system, 267
Great Plains Conservation Program, 166
Greenland, 442
Grizzly bears, 279
Ground water, 35, 54-58; *see also* Water
Gull Island meadow mouse, 279

Halibut, International Commission con-
      trol, 382-383
Hawaii, 45, 65, 94, 188, 255, 273, 323
Hawks, 283-284
"Heat pumps," 48
Heath hens, 277
Hinckley, Minn., forest fire, 206
Homestead Act of 1862, 152, 251, 253
Homestead Act of 1911, 155
Homestead Act of 1916, 155
Honduras, sponge propagation, 359
Hoover Dam, 62
Horicon Marsh, Wisconsin, 340
Hudson River, shad fishery, 382
Humus, 54, 94; *see also* Soil
Hungary, partridges from, 293
Hunting:
   duck stamp revenue, 339-340
   national recreation income, 343-344
   and wildlife population control, 298-300
Hydraulic mining, 41-42
Hydroelectric power, 42-43, 60-61, 261, 263,
      265-266, 409, 411, 463; *see also* Elec-
      tric power

Hydrologic cycle, 23, 28; *see also* Water
Hyetal maps, 31

Ice, use of, 47-48
India, water in, 38-39
Industry, water use, 67
Insects, 290
Insects and diseases, in forests, 224-227
Intermontane Basins and Plateaus, 150
International agreements, on fisheries, 382-383
International competition, world resources, 459
International Conference for the Regulation of Whaling (1937), 357
Interstate Commerce Commission, 413
Interstate fishery commissions, 383
Interstate Oil Compact Commission, 431
Intracoastal Waterway, 46
Irish Moss, 354
Iron, 396-397, 417-423, 439, 441
Irrigation, 43-45, 64-67, 83, 261, 332
Ivory-billed woodpecker, 279

Jackson Hole, Wyoming, 279
Japan:
    fishery products imported from, 392
    fishing industry, 391
    seaweed industry, 355

Karst, 37
"Keep Green" program, American Forest Products Industries, 206, 491
Kelp, 354, 355
Kit-fox, 279

Labrador ducks, 277
Lake Mead, 62
Lamprey depredations, 376, 385-386
Land:
    badlands, 236
    basins and valleys, 260
    capability ratings, 247
    classification system, 247
    comparative quality, 251
    conservation patterns, 234-270
    crop-pasture-forest ratio, 238
    crops, 236
    cultural uses, 240
    dams, 261-262, 263, 267; *see also* Dams; Flood control
    drainage systems, 260-261
    Dust Bowl, 251-253
    extensive use, 246
    flood control; *see* Flood control

Land (*Cont.*)
    forest, 236; *see also* Forests
    Homestead Act, 152, 251, 253
    intensive use, 246, 250, 257-258
    irrigation; *see* Irrigation
    legislation, 251, 253, 255, 257, 261, 267
    marginal land, 250
    morbidity, 458-459
    muck, 236
    mucklands, 235
    multiple-use concept, 268-269, 308
    organic soils, 236
    pasture, 236
    peat, 236
    population increase, 258-259
    primary land uses, 236-238, 240
    public ownership, 255, 257
    rangelands, 247, 250
    recreational resources, 257, 319-351
    regional interest, 238
    resource status, 236
    rock land, 236
    sand areas, 235, 236
    soilless areas, 235-236
    stony, 236
    submarginal land, 250-251, 253, 255
    TVA, 261-266
    timber crops, 258
    Timber and Stone Act, 255
    undifferentiated sands and gravels, 236
    use apportionment, 234-270, 466-467
    water as fundamental resource, 260-269; *see also* Water
    watersheds, 260-269
    wildlife; *see* Wildlife
Landscape housekeeping, 345-351, 489-490
Landscapes, 20
Laterites, 94
Laterization, 94
Latosols, 94
Latozation, 94
Lea Act (1940), 227
Lead, 423-424
Legumes, 137, 139
Lignite, 402
Linville Gorge Wild Area, 335
Literature and teaching materials, collection of, 488
Living fences, 310-312, 491
Llano Estacado, N. M. and Texas, 65
Locks, on waterways, 64
Long Island, water spreading at, 78
Louisiana, 281, 299-300
Louisville, Ky., water supply, 78
Lumbering, 179-192

Madison, Wisc., Forest Products Laboratory at, 232

Magnesium, 439, 447
Maine, liability laws, 331
Maine mink, 279
Mallard ducks, 341
Malthus, 459
Mammals, control of numbers, 298
Mammals, repatriation, 300
Manganese, 425-426
Manufacturing, water use in, 40-42
Maps, 436, 438
Marginal edge, 312-314
Marginal land, 250
Marine vegetation, 354-356
Market shooting, 277
Martin, 279
"Material" waste, 5-6
Menhaden, 361-362
Mesabi Range, 419, 421
Mesophytes, 99
Metals, 393-427; *see also* Minerals
Metal salvage, 444-447
Metropolitan areas, recreational space, 329
Mexico, Migratory Bird Treaties, 299, 303
Michigan, deer overpopulation, 297
Migratory Bird Conservation Act (1929), 340
Migratory Bird Hunting Stamp Act, 340
Migratory Bird Treaties, 299, 303, 340
Migratory Bird Treaty Act (1918), 340
Migratory waterfowl, habitats, 339-342
Minerals:
    aerial prospecting, 438
    air pollution, 444
    aluminum, 425, 447, 448
    anthracite, 402
    Appalachian coal fields, 403-404
    automobiles, 453-454
    barium, 449
    bauxite, 425, 442
    beryllium, 448
    bituminous coal, 402-404
    boron, 449
    by-products, 444
    calcium, 449
    carbon black, 407-408
    catalytic cracking, 442
    classifications, 395-396
    coke, 403-404, 444
    conservation, 428-457
    conservation and soil fertility, 466
    copper, 423, 439
    cryolite, 442
    EHV transmission of electricity, 415-416
    electric power, 409, 411, 415-416, 451-452
    energy materials, 454
    energy mix, 454
    exhaustion of, 465
    ferroalloys, 426-427

Minerals *(Cont.)*
    fertilizers, 454-455
    flotation, 442
    fly ash, 444
    foreign trade, 451
    gas-oil ratio, 404
    importation, 451
    iron, 396-397, 417-423, 439, 441
    lead, 423-424
    legislation, 411-412, 413, 431-432, 456
    lignite, 402
    low-grade deposits, 439, 449
    magnesium, 439, 447
    manganese, 425-426
    maps, 436, 438
    Mesabi Range, 419, 421
    metal salvage, 444-447
    natural gas, 397-400, 404-405, 407, 411-412, 452-453
        flaring, 429-431
        liquids, 404-405
        underground storage, 412
    new metals, 448
    oil pipe lines, 413
    oil refinery products, 405
    oil wells, 405; *see also* Petroleum
    petrochemicals, 408
    petroleum, 397-400, 404-405, 412-413
    phosphorus, 455
    photogeology, 438
    photogrammetry, 438
    pipe lines, 412-413
    potash, 455
    public lands, 270, 337, 338
    reclamation laws, 456
    recycling, 444
    reserves, 409
    retreat-longwall coal mining, 436
    salt, 394
    salvage, 444-447
    scrap metal, 444-447
    sea, 353-354
    secondary recovery, of oil, 430-433
    shale, 449
    silicon, 449
    sintering, 441
    strip mining, 456
    substitution of abundant for scarce, 447-448
    taconite, 439, 441
    tires, 408
    titanium, 448
    transportation of fuels, 411, 415-416
    transportation of iron, 420-422
    waste, 428-457
    zinc, 424-425
    zirconium, 448
Minnesota:
    fish hatcheries, 301

Minnesota *(Cont.)*
  iron deposits in, 419, 420
  peat bogs, 91
Mississippi flyway, 305
Moles, 286, 287
Mt. McKinley, 326
Mourning dove, 298-299
Movie films, 478-479
MSX, 385
Mucklands, 235
Multiple Surface Use Act (1955), 269-270
Multiple Use-Sustained Yield Act (1960), 197, 198
Muskingum County, Ohio, 116
Muskrat, 281

National Advisory Board Council, 160
National Forests, 196, 197, 198-201, 221, 255, 320, 329-331, 335
National Grasslands, 198, 199
National Land Reserve, 165
National Nature Monuments, 307, 324, 335
National Parks, 255, 307, 316, 324-327, 330, 335; *see also* Parks; State parks
  educational value, 327
  and pressure group threat, 337-338
  scientific values, 325-327
  wildernesses, 333-337
  wildlife sanctuaries, 325-326
National Park Service, 324-325, 327, 331, 332
National Power Survey, 416
National Primeval Parks, 325-327
National Resources Board, 7
National Seashore Parks, 332
National System of Interstate and Defense Highways, 347
Natural Bridge, Va., 257
Natural gas, 397-400, 404-405, 407, 411-412, 452-453
  flaring, 429-431
  liquids, 404-405
  underground storage, 412
Natural Gas Act (1958), 412
Natural resources, 14-26
Nature, "control of," 25-26
Nature Sanctuaries, 335, 337
Naval stores, 221-224
Nene goose, 279
New England:
  fishing industry, 356, 389-390, 391
  Irish Moss harvest, 354
  whaling, 356
New England Banks, overfishing, 376
New Hampshire, liability laws, 331
New Jersey, recreational space, 329
New Mexico, water supply, 65
New York:
  liability laws, 331

New York *(Cont.)*
  recreational space, 329
New York Times, 212
Norris Act (1933), 261
Norris Dam, 262
Norris-Doxey Act (1937), 217
North Dakota-Texas windbreak, 162
North Pacific Fur Seal Convention (1911), 359-360
Nutria, 281

Ohio River, 70, 264, 267
Oil; *see* Petroleum
Oil-shale formations, 449
Opossum, 281
Oregon and California Railroad, 199
Orkney Islands, 356
Outdoor advertising, 347, 349
Outdoor Recreation Resources Review Commission (1958), 257, 319
Outdoor recreational resources; *see* Recreation resources
Overfishing, 375-385
Overpopulation, wildlife, 297-298
Owls, 283-284
Oysters, 385, 388

Pacific Coast region, forests in, 196
Pacific flyway, 305
Pacific halibut, International Commission control, 382-383
Padres Island, Texas, 332
Panama Canal, 182
Parks, 319-320, 328; *see also* National Parks
Partridges, importation of, 293
Passenger pigeons, 277
Peanuts, 137
Pearls, 359
Pelagic fish, 372
Pelagic sealing, 360
Pennsylvania:
  liability laws, 331
  wild turkey, 300
Pentachlorophenol, 232
Peregrine, 284
Periodicals, resources and conservation organizations, 484-486
"Perpetual" resources, 3
Peru, fishing industry, 391
Peshtigo, Wisc., forest fire, 206
Pests, 224-227
Petrochemicals, 408
Petroleum, 357, 397-400, 404-405, 412-413
  pipe lines, 412-413
  secondary recovery of, 430-433
  waste of, 430-433
pH factor, soil, 99-100

Phosphorus, 455
Photogeology, 438
Photogrammetry, 438
Phreatophytes, 66
Picnic areas, 323-324
Pilchard, 387
Pipe lines, in oil transportation, 412-413
Plankton, 354
Plant indicators, 18
Plants and animals, 18-22, 23
Plastics industry, 466
Podzol soils, 89
Point Reyes, California, 332
Polar bear, 279
Pollution, atmospheric, 444, 463-464
Pollution, water, 68-76, 332, 372-373
Pond-fish culture, 388-389
Population, and land resources, 258-259
Population increase, and Malthusian theory, 459
Potash, 455
Potomac River, 70
Power, reservoir construction, 332
Power sources, 463
Prairie chicken, 279
Prairie Pothole Region, 341
Prairie States Forestry Project, 163
Predators, 277, 283, 284, 285
Predators, fishing grounds, 385-386
Preservation, *term*, 4
Pribilof Islands, 359
Private lands subsidization, recreational use, 322
Program planning, for teachers, 488
Public forests, 199-200, 329-331; *see also* Forests
Public Health Service, 73, 373
Public-land acquisition, recreational use, 322-324
Public Land Range Appraisal, 165
Public lands, pressure group threat, 337-338
Public laws:
  P.L. 448, on saline water, 79
  P.L. 540, on land reserve, 149
  P.L. 566, on watersheds, 267, 268, 269
  P.L. 660, on water pollution, 71, 72
  P.L. 1021, on wind erosion, 166
  P.L. 85-470, on outdoor recreation, 257
  P.L. 85-883, on saline water, 79
  P.L. 86-517, on forests, 197, 198
Public ownership and maintenance, natural resources, 320-323
Public wetland acquisition, 340-341
Publicity campaigns, conservation students, 488
Puerto Rico, 94
Purse seines, 379

Rainfall, 29-32, 50, 91, 94, 151
Rain making, 79, 464
Range conservation, 164
Rangeland classification, 247, 250
Range seeding, as teaching project, 490-491
Reclamation Act (1902), 45
Reclamation Service, 332
Recreation resources, 316-351
  beauty conservation, 345-351
  commercial development, 338-339
  consumer spending, 343-344
  forest industry lands, 330-331
  forests, 329-331
  game lands, 339-344
  landscape housekeeping, 345-351
  National Forests, 329-331
  National Parks, 324-327
  parks, 319-320
  picnic areas, 323-324
  private lands subsidization, 322
  privately owned forests, 330-331
  public forests, 329-331
  public-land acquisition, 322-324
  public ownership and maintenance, 320-323
  shores and beaches, 331-333
  space allocation, 319-321
  special land uses, 328
  state park systems, 327-328
  tourism, 344-345
  vandalism, 338-339
  water pollution, 332
  water recreation, 48-49, 331-333
  waterfowl conservation, 339-342
  wetlands acquisition, 340-341
  wildernesses, 333-337
Recycling, principle of, 444
Reforestation, as teaching project, 490
Refrigeration, 47-48
Refuge system, wildlife, 306-308, 327, 329, 335
Regional diversification, 467-468
Regional economic geography, 467-468, 469-470
Regionalism, handicaps of, 461-462
Renewable resources, 465-466
Reseeding, as teaching project, 490-491
Reserve lands, 149
Reservoir construction, 332
Ring-necked pheasants, importation of, 293
Rivers, 59, 70
Roadside advertising, 347, 349
Roadside littering, 490
Roadside sanitation, 489-490
Rock structures, 15-16
Rodents, 281, 283, 284, 285, 286, 287
Run-off; *see* Water

St. Lawrence Seaway, 47, 267, 421, 422
St. Louis, 275
Saline Water Act (1952), 79
Salmon, 374, 375-376, 388
Salt, 394
Saltcedars, 66
Saltonstall-Kennedy Act (1954), 390
Salvage, of minerals, 444-447
Sand areas, 235, 236
Santa Rosa Live Oak Timber Reserve, Pensacola Bay, Florida, 196
Sardines, 387
Scavengers, 285
School ground improvement, 488-489
Scrap metal, 444-447
Seas:
   agar, 354
   algin, 354
   anadromous fish, 372
   anchovies, 387, 391
   animal feeds, 361-362
   animal life, 356
   demersal fishes, 372
   fertilizer, 361
   fish flour, 390
   fishing; *see* Fish and fishing
   fish-liver oil, 360
   fish-meal industry, 391
   fur seals, 359-360
   Gelidium, 354
   Gracilaria, 354
   import-export, fishery products, 392
   international agreements on fisheries, 382-383
   interstate fishery commissions, 383
   Irish Moss, 354
   kelp, 354, 355
   lamprey depredations, 376, 385-386
   legislation, 357, 359-360, 380, 382-383, 389-390
   magnesium from, 439
   menhaden, 361-362
   New England fishing industry, 389-390
   overfishing, 375-385
   oysters, 385, 388
   Pacific halibut fishery, 382-383
   pearls, 359
   pelagic fish, 372
   pelagic sealing, 360
   pilchard, 387
   plankton, 354
   pond-fish culture, 388-389
   preservation of fish foods, 367, 370
   relations to land, 372-375
   resources, 352-392
   salmon, 374, 375-376, 388
   sardines, 387
   seaweed, 354, 355-356

Seas *(Cont.)*
   shad, 376
   sharks, 360-361
   spawning season, 378-379
   sponges, 358-359
   stream pollution, 372-373
   "trash fish," 377
   U.S. commercial fisheries, 390-391
   vegetable contents, 354-356
   whaling, 356-358, 361
Seaweed industry, 354-356
Secondary recovery, of oil, 430-433
Sewage, 49-50, 70-71, 76
Shad, 376, 382
Shale, 449
Sharks, 360-361
Shelter belts, 162-163
Shores and beaches:
   commercialization, 333, 339
   pollution of, 332
   recreational resources, 331-333
Silicon, 449
Silviculture, 230
Sintering, 441
Skunks, 281
Smog, 463
Smoky Bear campaign, Forest Service, 206
Snakes, 285, 286
Soil:
   acidity and alkalinity, 99-100, 144-145
   aging, 89, 91
   alfalfa, 137
   animal industry, 135, 141
   basic slag, 145
   calcification, 94
   catch crops, 139
   catena, 95
   chemical ailments, 134-145
   claypan, 87
   climate, 91, 94, 118-119
   color, 88
   conservation, 121-149
   conservation districts, 146
   contour tillage, 128-131
   cover crops, 139
   crop residues, 140
   crop rotation, 103, 135-137
   depletion, 102-104
   depreciation, 85-120
   development, 87
   erosion, 102, 105-120
   erosion preventives, 127-134
   feel of, 89
   fertility, 85-120, 466
   fertilizers, 139-142
   forests; *see* Forests
   formation, 22-23, 89
   friability, 101

Soil (*Cont.*)
  grasses, 137
  gullying, 113-115
  hardpan, 87
  horizons, 87-88
  humus, 104, 125-126, 142-144
  idleness, 137-139
  individual, 94-96
  land-use planning, 123-124
  legislation, 146
  legumes, 137, 139
  limestone, 144-145
  loss, 91
  management, 124-125
  mass movement erosion, 115-116
  Minnesota, peat bogs, 91
  mulch, 143
  as natural resource, 16
  organic wastes, 139-141
  parent material, 88
  peanuts, 137
  pedalfers, 91
  pedocals, 91
  pedons, 95
  pH factor, 99-100
  physical ailments, 126-134
  podzolization, 94
  productivity factors, 98-99
  reserve lands, 149
  rill erosion, 111-113
  sheet wash, 111
  sierozen, 91
  slope, 116-117
  slope channeling, 111-113
  slope soils, 97
  soil bank, 149
  soil fires, 208
  solum, 87-88
  stabilization, 127, 134
  strip cropping, 129
  structure, 88
  subtillage, 143
  surpluses, 147
  tenure, continuity of, 124-125
  terracing, 131-134
  tests, 98-99
  texture, 88
  tilth, 101
  time, 123
  topography, 96-97
  trace elements, 99, 145
  water erosion, 105, 110-115, 117
  water in, 99
  water-spreading, 143-144
  water storage, 54, 104, 127
  weeds, 138
  wind erosion, 105, 109
  yard manure, 140-141
  zone of enrichment, 87

Soil (*Cont.*)
  zone of impoverishment, 87
Soil Bank, 149, 166-167, 230
Soil Conservation and Domestic Allotment
    Act (1936), 146
Soil Conservation Service, 124, 146, 160-161,
    163, 247, 267, 268, 468, 490
Solar distillation, of saline water, 80
Solar energy, 463
Space allocation, recreation resources, 319-
    321
Sponges, 358-359
Starlings, 293
Starvation, and Malthusian theory, 459
State agencies, as teaching aid sources, 480-
    481
State Nature Sanctuaries, 335, 337
State park systems, recreational resources,
    327-328
State resource management, organization
    of, 470-471
Steel industry, 418-422; *see also* Iron; Min-
    erals
Strip mining, 456
Student investigations and reports, 487-488
Submarginal land, 250-251, 253, 255
Susquehanna River, 264
Synthetics and substitutes, 464-466

Taconite, 439, 441
Tarpon Springs, Fla., sponging grounds,
    358
Taylor Grazing Control Act (1934), 155,
    159
Teacher-conservators, 473-475
Teachers and teaching aids:
  activities for classes, 486-488
  camping, for classes, 486-487
  class work suggestions, 486-492
  community cooperation, 481
  community improvement, 491-492
  Federal Agencies, 480-481
  forestation or reforestation, 490
  landscape housekeeping, 488-489
  literature and teaching materials, 488
  movie films, 478-479
  organizations, as report sources, 482-483
  periodicals, 484-486
  preservation project, 491
  program planning, 488
  projects, 488-492
  public source agencies, 480-481
  range-seeding project, 491
  roadside sanitation, 489-490
  school ground improvement, 488-489
  scrap metal salvage drive, 491
  state agencies, 481

Teachers and teaching aids (*Cont.*)
  student investigations and reports, 487-488
  suggestions to, 477-478
  visits and tours for classes, 487
  vocabulary building, 479-480
  wildlife habitat improvement, 491
Tennessee River system 261-266
Texas, water in, 65
Tillamook, Oreg., forest fire, 206
Timber and Stone Act (1878), 255
Timber crops, 258; *see also* Forests; Lumbering
Tires, 408
Titanium, 448
Titusville, Pennsylvania, petroleum discovery, 357
Topographic maps, 436, 438
Topography, 16-18
Tourism, 344-345
Tours and visits, for classes, 487
Trace elements, 99
Transportation, by water, 45-47
"Trash fish," 377
Trawls, 379
Tree farming, 230, 232
Trumpeter swan, 279
Turkey buzzards, 285
Turpentining, 221-224
TVA, 261-266, 470

Ungulata, 275-276
United States, 8-12
  commercial fisheries, 390-391
  consumption of energy in, 398
  fauna, 273
  land use and population, 258-259
United States Government:
  Army Corps of Engineers, 260-261
  Bureau of Biological Survey (Department of Agriculture), 389
  Bureau of the Census, 460
  Bureau of Commercial Fisheries, 388, 389, 390
  Bureau of Fisheries, merger with Biological Survey, 471
  Bureau of Land Management, 159-160, 164-165, 173, 189, 199, 270, 471
  Bureau of Mines, 423, 426, 449
  Bureau of Outdoor Recreation, 319
  Bureau of Public Roads, 347
  Bureau of Reclamation, 261
  Bureau of Sport Fisheries and Wildlife, 301, 340, 389
  Fish and Wildlife Service, 287, 315, 389, 471
  Forest Service, 165, 196, 198-199, 227, 329-331, 335, 490

United States Government (*Cont.*)
  Office of Coal Research, 414
  Office of Minerals Exploration, 423
  Office of Saline Water, 79
U.S.S.R., fishing industry, 391

Valley, *term*, 260
Vandalism, recreational resources, 338-339
Vegetation, 18
Vegetation climax, 23
Vegetation, marine, 354-356
Venus (trawler), 390

Wabash watershed, 265
War:
  costs, 67
  effect on conservation, 7-8
Waste, material *vs* economic, 5-6
Waste removal, by water, 49-50
Waste treatment, 71
Water:
  air-conditioning, 48, 78
  alfalfa, 66
  aquifers, 37, 78
  artesian water, 37
  "beneficial use" doctrine, 83
  brackish, use of, 79-82
  canals, 45-46, 47
  cone of depression, *term*, 55
  conservation, 51-84
  consumption in U.S., 40
  consumptive use, 64
  dams and reservoirs, 60-63; *see also* Dams
  demineralization, 79-82
  desalinization, 79-82
  draw-down, *term*, 55
  on earth, 27-50
  floods, 59-60
  forests, 57-59, 62
  as fundamental resource, 260-269
  governments, 73, 82-84
  gravel beds, 53-54
  ground water, 35, 54-58
  ground-water flow, *term*, 55
  ground-water replenishment, 77-78
  "heat pumps," 48
  humus, 54
  hydraulic mining, 41-42
  hydroelectric power; *see* Hydroelectric power
  hydrologic cycle, 23, 28
  hyetal maps, 31
  ice, 47-48
  India, 38-39
  industrial pollution, 73
  industrial use, 40-42, 67
  irrigation, 43-45, 64-67, 83

Water *(Cont.)*
  karst, 37
  on land, 27-50
  legislation, 71, 73, 79, 82-84
  levees, 60
  littering, 350
  locks, 64
  manufacturing use, 40-42
  as medium of infection, 37
  meteoric, 29
  municipal systems, 71
  in natural environment, 16
  nonconsumptive use, 64
  nonwithdrawal uses, 64
  overdevelopment, 56-57
  perched water table, 37
  phreatophytes, 66
  pollution, 68-76, 332, 372-373
  power, 42-43; *see also* Electric power;
      Hydroelectric power
  prior appropriation doctrine, 82-83
  public use, 67
  quality control, 264
  quality of, 39
  rain making, 79, 464
  rainfall, 29-32, 50, 91, 94, 151
  "reasonable use" doctrine, 83
  recharge wells, 78
  recreation, 48-49, 331-333
  refrigeration, 47-48
  reserves, desalted sea water, 353
  re-use, 76
  riparian rights, 82
  rivers, 59, 70
  rule of capture, 83
  running, 32
  run-off, 31-32
  saltcedars, 66
  sewage, 49-50, 70-71, 76
  siltation, 62-63
  snow, 29
  soil water, storage of, 54, 104, 127
  solar distillation, 80
  "splash" erosion, 29
  standing, 32
  storage, 51-54, 76-77, 287
  streams, 32, 34
  surface storage, 76-77
  "thermal pollution," 48
  in transportation, 45-47
  underground storage, 77
  "useful," 27-28
  vadose, 29
  waste removal, 49-50, 71
  water spreading, 77-78
  water table, 35-37
  and wildlife, 48, 287, 296-297
  withdrawal uses, 64
Waterfowl, 298, 305-307, 339-342

Water Pollution Control Boards, 73
Watershed, *term,* 260
Watershed Protection and Flood Preven-
      tion Act, 267
Water table, 35-37; *see also* Water
Weeks Law (1911), 197, 211, 261
Westfield River, Mass., 59
Wetlands acquisition, 340
Whaling, 356-358, 361
Whooping crane, 279
Wildernesses, 333-337
Wildlife:
  big game repatriation, 300
  birds, 287-290
  bison, 276-277
  border environment, 312-314
  bounties, 283, 284-285
  burrowers, 287
  "closed seasons," 302
  concealment, 295
  connecting cover, 295
  conservation, 291-315
  cover, 293-296
  destruction of, 274-291
  ducks, 339-342
  escape cover, 295
  extinction restrictions, 301-302
  farms, 308-314
  fauna in U.S., 273
  fences, 310-312
  fish; *see* Fish and fishing
  flyways, 305
  food supply, 295-296, 297, 298
  foraging radius, 296
  functions and abuses, 271-290
  fur bearers, 274-275, 281
  "game," 273
  game propagation, 297, 298, 300-301
  habitat, 149, 293-298, 331, 491
  hunting and population control, 298-300
  importations of, 293
  insects, 290
  legislation, 284, 301-302, 315, 340
  mammals, 279, 300
  management, 292
  marginal edges, 313-314
  market shooting, 277
  migratory, 302-303, 305
  migratory waterfowl, 298, 305-307, 339-
      342
  Mississippi flyway, 305
  multiple function, 293
  overpopulation, 297-298
  Pacific flyway, 305
  predators, 277, 283, 284, 285
  private lands subsidization, 322
  protective coloration, 295
  refuge system, 306-308, 329, 335
  resident, 302-303

Wildlife *(Cont.)*
  restoration projects, 342-343
  sanctuaries, 325-326
  scavengers, 285
  size and habits, 293
  sportsmen's cooperation, 314-315
  state parks system, 327
  term, 271
  ungulata, 275-276
  vegetation, 295-296
  and water, 48, 287, 296-297
  waterfowl, 298, 305-307, 339-342
  wildfowl, 277
Wild turkey, 300
Willow Slough, Indiana, 340
Windbreaks, 162-163, 202

Wind erosion, 166
Wolverine, 279
Wood, preservation of, 232
World War I, 156-157, 182, 354
World War II, 163, 354

Yellowstone Park, 255, 324
Yellowstone Park Timberland Reserve, 197, 255

Zinc, 424-425
Zirconium, 448
Zoar gas field, Buffalo, New York, 412